Theory of Seismic Diffractions

By Kamill Klem-Musatov

Edited by Franta Hron
and Larry Lines

Society of Exploration Geophysicists
Post Office Box 702740/Tulsa, Oklahoma 74170-2740

ISBN 1-56080-030-5 (Series)
ISBN 1-56080-074-7 (Volume)
Society of Exploration Geophysicists
P. O. Box 702740
Tulsa, OK 74170-2740

Published 1994

Printed in the United States of America

Table of Contents

ACKNOWLEDGMENTS

The edge diffraction is undoubtedly the main factor limiting the framework of the elementary theory of wave propagation in the realistic models of media. The search for a simple, general description of this phenomenon was the aim of my study at the Institute of Geology and Geophysics (Novosibirsk, Russia). I express my appreciation to the following individuals who were helpful in the beginning of this work. Professor N. N. Puzirev invited me to start the study; G. L. Kovalevsky as head of the Siberian Geophysical Expedition made significant contributions in the developments of methods of interpretation of diffraction phenomena; and V. G. Chernyakov and E. I. Landa, graduates of Novosibirsk State University, contributed to the search for ways of applying theoretical results. A. M. Aizenberg contributed recent new developments of the theory and its computation methods. Galina A. Klem-Musatova, my wife, authored most of the computation programs and carried out the technical work for preparation of the Russian version of the manuscript.

Preparation of the English version of the book was encouraged by Larry R. Lines (Memorial University-Newfoundland, Canada) and Professor Franta Hron (University of Alberta, Canada) who spent their time editing this updated English version. Theoretical seismograms used in the book were presented by H. B. Helle, J. Pajchel, and L. A. Frøland of Norsk Hydro A/S Research Center in Bergen (Norway).

I sincerely thank all of these individuals who contributed so meaningfully to the preparation of this volume.

Kamill Klem-Musatov
Novosibirsk, Russia
1994

INTRODUCTION

1. Purpose

This book is devoted to one important aspect of development of physical foundations of the seismic method — the theory of edge diffraction phenomena. These phenomena occur when conditions of the regular wave reflection/transmission change sharply. Though these phenomena drew the attention of many scientists for many decades, their real influence on the resolution ability of the seismic method was truly understood rather recently due to interpretation of seismic data in block structures. Clearly, to develop seismic method for investigation of such structures without developing the theory of edge diffraction phenomena is impossible. The latter is the aim of this book.

The seismic method is based on the fundamental laws of continuum mechanics. These laws describe the behavior of wavefields on the microscopic level, i.e., in the form of differential equations of motion. Integrating these equations under some initial conditions or boundary conditions, makes possible acquisition of all necessary information on the wavefield in the given situation. However, the working base of the seismic method consists of not only the differential equations of motion themselves but of some general and simple enough consequences of their solutions, which are formulated in the form of physical principles and laws. The latter include the concepts of wave, Fermat's principle, the law of conservation of the energy flux, and the reflection/transmission laws. Essentially these laws and principles must form a system of concepts sufficient for the solution of some class of typical interpretation problems. In fact, these principles and laws form the physical foundation of the seismic method.

The physical foundations of the seismic method also include the concept of media. In elastodynamics, the medium properties are reflected in the framework of the continuum model describing their continuous changing in space. The surfaces of sharp change of medium properties correspond to the surfaces of conjugation of different solutions of equations of motion. In the seismic method it leads to the notion of the *block structure model* which consists of the regions and interfaces. The media properties within the regions are described by the continuous and smooth functions of space coordinates. At the interfaces they change sharply. The geometrical properties of the interfaces are described by rather arbitrary functions. For example, the interfaces can have the line of discontinuity, the lines of discontinuity of the tangents, and the lines of discontinuity of curvatures. This discontinuity leads to a concept of a diffracting edge — the line of the sharp change of the geometrical properties of the interface. The common line of three or more interfaces, bounding different blocks, is also an edge. Therefore, the edge is the line of the sharp change of the reflecting/transmitting properties of the interface.

The seismic method aim is to find the model of the medium under investigation by interpreting observed data. However, such a problem can be solved only partly in the framework of some simplified models, because of the natural limitations of the resolving ability of the seismic method. Interpretation consists of finding the chosen model parameters under condition of the best coincidence of theoretical and observed wavefields. However, the possibility of choosing between different types of models is restricted by the existing level of knowledge of the wave propagation laws, which can be used for the theoretical prognosis. So, the physical aspect of developing the seismic method includes further development of the system of physical concepts and principles. This allows us to improve the types of interpretation models, and in particular, allows for the consideration of the block structure models with diffracting edges. To discuss the relevant problems, we have to review the general concepts of propagation and diffraction of waves.

2. Book Contents and Organization

The main problem with the systematic theory of edge diffraction consists of finding uniform formulas for the edge-diffracted waves in inhomogeneous media with transparent interfaces. In this book we try to find such uniform formulas with the relative asymptotic error of the order $O(\omega^{-1})$. In principle, such description can serve as a leading term in the expansion of the edge-diffracted waves in asymptotic series. However, we do not consider such series.

The key point of the mathematical description of edge waves is the statement and solution of the canonical problem of the geometrical theory of diffraction. The first part of this book deals with the simplest canonical problem — the problem of diffraction of a plane wave on a system of wedge-shaped regions with the common edge. The mathematical theory of diffraction currently has no means to solve such problems analytically, which is why we have to look for a statement that will allow us to obtain the necessary information on the edge wave without the knowledge of its exact solution. The corresponding statement of the problem can be found on the basis of development of the Sommerfeld method (see Frank and Mises, 1935). The most advanced results in this direction were obtained in (Malyuzhinetz, 1951, 1955, 1958), where the formula for inversion of the Sommerfeld integral was derived and the above-mentioned diffraction problem was strictly formulated. It seems that the diffraction problem, formulated by G. D. Malyuzhinetz, cannot be solved analytically (so far no one has found a solution of the Malyuzhinetz functional equation system in the general case). However, the modification of Malyuzhinetz's approach allows us to find the statement of the problem in the form we are looking for.

Such statement of the problem is considered in Chapter II for the acoustic case and is based on the representation of the sought wavefield in the form of superposition of plane waves [equations I.(43-44)] with the integration along the Sommerfeld's contour. The mentioned expressions comply with wave equations I.(45) automatically. The original 3-D problem is reduced to a 2-D problem in space of polar coordinates (r, θ). That is why in the first part of the book we can restrict ourselves to the consideration of only the 2-D problem. By substituting equation I.(44) into boundary conditions I. (47) and using the specific properties of the Sommerfeld integral from Malyuzhinetz (1951, 1955, 1958), we can reduce the problem under consideration to the special functional equations relative to unknown functions $\Phi_m(\alpha)$. This technique is generalized on the case of diffraction of vector waves as well.

It seems the system of functional equations obtained cannot be solved analytically in the closed form in the general case. In some particular cases, considered in Chapter III, this system leads to the known exact solutions. However, in the general case, the system of functional equations admits the transformation in accordance with the method of simple interaction, i.e., the "formal solution" by the successive approximation method. We talk of the "formal solution" since in the general case there is no mathematical proof of the convergence of the successive approximations to the exact solution. The interaction formulas admit a simple physical interpretation — they are isomorphic to the formulas of multifold reflections/transmissions on a system of nonparallel plane interfaces (Chapter IV). The reason for the interaction process is that all necessary information on the edge waves can be obtained by a high-frequency asymptotic analysis of the integrals from individual terms of the successive approximations series. The corresponding technique for the acoustic case is demonstrated in Chapter V. The information obtained is sufficient to continue the edge waves from the neighborhood of the edge by the geometrical theory of diffraction (Section VII.1). We do not discuss the possibilities of the successive approximations method for finding the exact solution of the canonical problem, because it has nothing to do with the theory of edge-diffracted waves.

Our next problem is to find the formulas of edge waves that are valid simultaneously in domains of geometrical theory of diffraction and in the boundary layers. The description of edge waves in the boundary layers is considered in Chapter VI for the acoustic case. Two ways of deriving these formulas are discussed. The first approach, recently published (Klem-Musatov and Aizenberg, 1989) shows that the wave equation with $\omega \to \infty$ has two linearly independent solutions. The first coincides with the zero-order ray theory solution, the second is the edge-diffracted wave in the boundary layer. Thus, this approach leads directly to the sought description of the edge wave in the boundary layer in the form of the second linearly independent solution of the wave equation. However, this form of the solution is rather inconvenient for deriving the uniform formula that is also valid outside the boundary layer in the 3-D case.

The second approach is based on using Fock's parabolic equation. The edge wave is found as a solution of the special boundary problem of smoothing a discontinuity of the reflected/transmitted wave at its shadow boundary. In this case, the edge wave is described by an integral from the corresponding reflected/transmitted wave. However, such a description is convenient for finding the uniform formula in 3-D space. The uniform formulas are derived in Chapter VII.

The next important aspect of the edge diffraction is the consideration of the effects caused by the unsmoothness of edges, i.e., the explicit description of the vertex diffracted waves. So far, obtaining the description of these waves throughout the whole domain of their existence is not possible because of absence of the solution of the correspondent canonical problem. However, it is possible to describe these waves in the boundary layer approximation, which is sufficient for many practical applications. The description can be obtained by the method of analytical continuation, which is based on the consideration of analytical properties of reflected/transmitted waves and has nothing to do with equations of motion. First we introduce this method for the description of the edge waves in the boundary layers (Chapter VIII) and then generalize it for the case of the vertex diffracted waves (Chapter IX). The obtained formulas for the edge waves coincide with the previously mentioned second linearly independent solution of the wave equation. By supplementing the field of reflected/transmitted waves with the edge and vertex diffracted waves, we obtain a modification of the ray method that is valid in the block structured media.

Organization

To assist the reader in locating referenced material within the text, and explanation of the organization of the material follows. The book is divided first into Parts One and Two, next into Chapters I through IX, with Sections and Subsections as required by the subject.

Chapters are numbered with Roman numerals. A reference to a Section would be a three-part number: e.g., II.3.2, which indicates Chapter II, Section 3, Subsection 2. If the reference is to an equation, the number of the equation would follow the Section number: e.g., II.3.(30), which indicates Chapter II, Section 3, equation (30).

The numerous equations required in the presentation of the material are numbered beginning with (1) in each Section and consecutively through that section. Equations referenced within the Chapter where they are first presented will be referenced by the Section number and the equation number only: I.(13). The reader will note that the equation numbers are always enclosed in parentheses.

A section which is being referenced within the same Chapter will not require the Chapter number but will read Section 2. A subsection within the same Chapter and section will require only the section number and the subsection number or Section 2.3.

A running reference head is provided at the outside edge of each page of the text. The head identifies the Chapter and beginning Section found on that page.

All figures are numbered consecutively throughout the book.

PART ONE

DIFFRACTION IN WEDGE-SHAPED REGIONS

Chapter I

BASIC CONCEPTS

I. Waves

A space-time perturbation of any physical field that can be described by expressions (1) and (2) is called a *nonstationary wave*

$$f^* (t, M) = 0 \qquad \text{when } t < \tau(M), \tag{1}$$

$$f^* (t, M) = f^* [t - \tau(M), M], \qquad \text{when } t \geq \tau(M),$$

$$| \nabla \tau (M) |^2 = 1 / c^2(M), \tag{2}$$

where t is time, and $c(M)$ is a parameter (wave velocity) depending on the arbitrary point M of space. The surface $t = \tau(M)$ is called a *wave front.*

Now consider the so-called stationary waves, changing in time as the harmonic functions. The nonstationary and stationary waves are connected under the time-frequency Fourier transform:

$$f^* (t, M) = \text{Re} \int_{-\infty}^{\infty} f(\omega, M) \exp(-i \omega t) \, d\omega \tag{3}$$

$$f(\omega, M) = \Phi(\omega, M) \exp[i \omega \tau(M)], \tag{4}$$

$$f(\omega, M) = (2\pi)^{-1} \int_{0}^{\infty} f^* (t, M) \exp(i \omega t) \, dt \tag{5}$$

where f, Φ, and ω are the stationary wave, its complex amplitude, and the circular frequency, respectively. The numerical examples show the nonstationary wavefields using this transformation.

The wave motions correspond to some components of the more general form of motion described by equations of dynamics. That is why the substantiation of wave propagation theory can be obtained as the consequences of these exact equations. The main consequences are Fermat's principle, the law of energy flux conservation, and the reflection/transmission law. These laws are valid at the wave fronts only. However, they can give the initial approximation for different methods of perturbation theory or asymptotic expansions in the neighborhood of wave fronts (or for the high-frequency asymptotic description with $\omega \to \infty$ in the stationary case). Of great importance for development of the asymptotic theory of diffraction is the leading term of the ray method (Babich and Alekseyev, 1958; Karal and Keller, 1959; Červený et al., 1977). For brevity I refer to this type of approximation as the *ray method*. In the English literature this type of ray approximation is also known as the zero-order approximation of the asymptotic ray theory or the geometric ray theory.

2. Ray method

The basic principles of the ray method are as follows. The model of the medium is considered as a combination of domains and interfaces. The functions, describing physical properties within the domains, are continuous and slowly changing. A surface, formed by points of discontinuity of any of these functions, is call an *interface*. A point of the interface is considered as regular if the surface is continuous together with its first and second tangentional derivatives. A part of the interface is considered as regular if its points are all regular. The ray method allows us to describe only those components of the wavefield that are connected with reflections/transmissions at the regular parts of interfaces. The description has the form of superposition of the single waves

$$f = \sum_m f_m \tag{6}$$

The main definitions related to a single wave f_m follow.

The *ray* is a space curve, the tangential unit vector e_m of which complies with the differential equation:

$$d(e_m / c_m) / ds = \nabla (1 / c_m), \tag{7}$$

where *ds* is the differential of the arc length and c_m is the wave velocity. Equation (7) determines the ray uniquely if its initial direction is given, and if a connection between the directions of incident and reflected/transmitted rays at the points of the interfaces is also given. The latter is expressed by *Snell's law*.

A set of rays $\boldsymbol{e}_m$, which is a two-parameter set of space curves, is called a *congruence*. A single wave

$$f_m = \Phi_m \exp(i \omega \tau_m) \tag{8}$$

is connected with a congruence of the rays $\boldsymbol{e}_m$. Its eikonal τ_m complies with the differential equation:

$$\nabla \tau_m = \boldsymbol{e}_m / c_m . \tag{9}$$

Equation (8) may represent a scalar wave (optics, acoustics) or a vector wave (elastodynamics, electrodynamics). In the first case, the amplitude Φ_m is a scalar one. In the second case,

$$\Phi_m = \boldsymbol{p}_m \phi_m , \tag{10}$$

where $\boldsymbol{p}_m$ is a unit vector of polarization, and ϕ_m is a scalar. In an isotropic medium and in our approximation (equivalent to the zero-order approximation of asymptotic ray theory) the vector $\boldsymbol{p}_m$ coincides with the vector $\boldsymbol{e}_m$ (a longitudinal wave) or is perpendicular to $\boldsymbol{e}_m$ (a transverse wave).

The scalar amplitude Φ_m or (ϕ_m) complies with the so-called transport equation

$$2 \nabla \tau_m \bullet \nabla \Phi_m + B_m \tau_m = 0 , \tag{11}$$

where the coefficient B_m depends on the type of original accurate equations of optics, acoustics, or elastodynamics and electrodynamics. The solution of equation (11) is well known:

$$\Phi_m = X_m (J_m / c_m^2)^{-1/2}, \quad J_m / c_m^2 = \exp \left[\int_0^{\tau_m} c_m^2 B_m \, d\tau_m \right], \tag{12}$$

where integration must be performed along the ray. Choice of the constant X_m must comply with the boundary conditions. In fact, X_m is the product of reflection/transmission coefficients of plane waves.

The ray method holds true, when the wave motion can be reduced to the transportation of the energy flux along ray tubes (a thin pencil of rays close in direction). It is possible only in those regions, which can be filled continuously and without intersecting, with the ray tubes of the wave under consideration. If a region cannot be filled by the ray tubes continuously (the case of a shadow boundary) or if there is an intersection of the ray tubes (a case of the caustic), the wave motion includes also diffusion of the energy across the ray tubes (Fock, 1965; Malyuzhinetz, 1959). This kind of deviation from the law of the energy flux conservation is called diffraction. Diffraction phenomena in neighborhoods of caustics can be taken into account by the generalized versions of ray method reviewed in Ben-Menahem and Beydoun (1985).

This book deals with only one kind of diffraction phenomena – the *edge diffraction*, which occurs due to deviations from the reflection/transmission laws at interfaces with discontinuous curvatures. That is why it is convenient to introduce the correspondent concept by analyzing the mentioned laws. The classic statement of the reflection/transmission problem with slight changes in its traditional formulation is recalled. We will characterize the position of the interface at the reflection/transmission point by the position of its tangent plane instead of the normal to the interface. The notion of the edge diffraction is then introduced within the framework of the elementary theory.

3. Reflection/transmission

To introduce the concept of diffracted waves, a case is considered when the reflection/transmission problem cannot be set unambiguously. Because this kind of analysis does not depend on the physical type of waves, the acoustic case is taken as the simplest one. The reflected/transmitted wave amplitude at an arbitrary point M on a given ray can be expressed through its value at the reflection/transmission point S by the formula

$$\Phi_m(M) = \Phi_m(S)/L_m; \quad L_m = \left[\frac{c_m^2(S)\,J_m(M)}{c_m^2(M)\,J_m(S)} \right]^{1/2} \tag{13}$$

So, the problem is to find $\Phi_m(S)$.

In a narrow vicinity of the point of incidence when studying the partitioning of seismic energy, it is possible to neglect the inhomogeneity of media, as well as the curvatures of wave fronts and interfaces. Then the problem can be reduced to the reflection/transmission of plane waves at the plane interface, separating homogeneous media.

Let us define the tangential plane to an interface by a pair of the straight lines L and L' , intersecting at the point of incidence S. Let (x_1, x_2, x_3) be Cartesian coordinates with the plane $x_3 = 0$, coinciding with the tangent plane (L, L'), and with the origin at the point of incidence.

When $x_1^2 + x_2^2 + x_3^2 \ll 1$ we can fix the wave amplitudes in equation (8) at the point of incidence

$$\Phi_m(x_1, x_2, x_3) \simeq \Phi_m(0, 0, 0) \tag{14}$$

and approximate the eikonal by the linear part of its Taylor expansion

$$\tau_m(x_1, x_2, x_3) \simeq \tau_m(0, 0, 0) + \sum_{k=1}^{3} x_k (\partial \tau_m / \partial x_k)_{x_1 = x_2 = x_3 = 0} \,. \tag{15}$$

Let us use the known formula for a directional derivative

$$\partial \tau_m / \partial \lambda = |\nabla \tau_m| \cos(\nabla \tau_m, \boldsymbol{i}_\lambda) = (\cos q)/c_m, \tag{16}$$

where $\boldsymbol{i}_\lambda$ is the unit vector in the direction of derivation and q is the angle between $\nabla \tau_m$ and $\boldsymbol{i}_\lambda$.

Then

$$(\partial \tau_m / \partial x_k)_{x_1 = x_2 = x_3 = 0} = (\cos q_{km})/c_m, \tag{17}$$

where q_{km} is the angle between the vector $\nabla\tau_m$ and the axis x_k .

Let f_0, f_1, and f_2 be the incident, reflected, and transmitted waves, respectively. By substituting equations (14) - (17) into equation (8) we get the local approximation of the incident and reflected/transmitted waves

$$f_m = f_0(S) F_m, \tag{18}$$

$$F_m = K_m \exp[i(k_{1m} x_1 + k_{2m} x_2 + k_{3m} x_3)], \; K_0 = 1, \tag{19}$$

$$k_{km} = k_m \cos q_{km}, \; (k = 1, 2, 3), \; k_m = \omega / c_m, \tag{20}$$

$$\cos^2 q_{1m} + \cos^2 q_{2m} + \cos^2 q_{3m} = 1, \tag{21}$$

where q_{km} is the angle between the wave vector $\boldsymbol{k}_m\,(k_{1m}, k_{2m}, k_{3m})$ and the axis x_k, K_m is an unknown reflection/transmission coefficient.

Then the reflection/transmission problem involves the integration of two Helm-

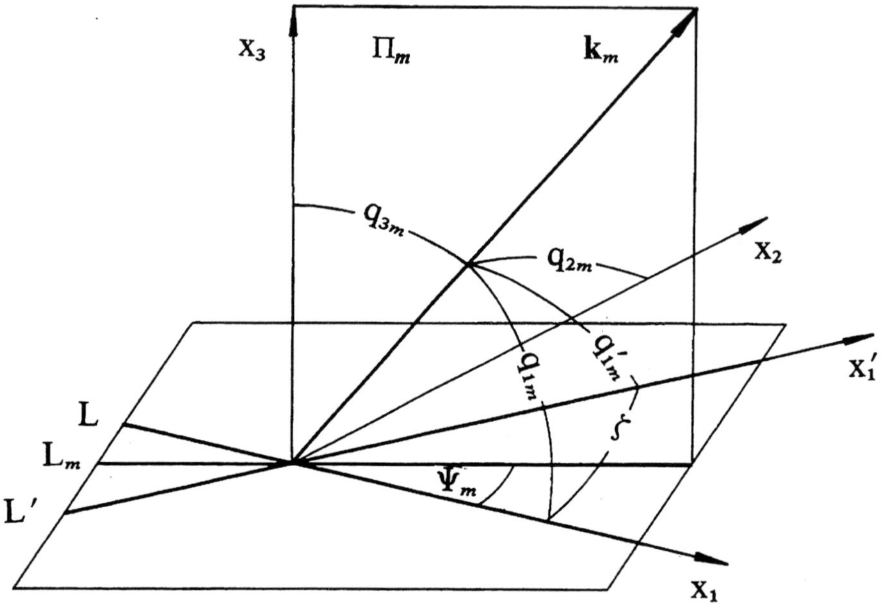

Figure 1. Angles defining the wave vector.

holtz's equations:

$$(\nabla^2 + k_m^2)\,F_m = 0,\ (m = 1, 2) \tag{22}$$

with the boundary conditions involving continuity of sound pressure and the normal component of particle velocity at a boundary

$$F_0 + F_1 = F_2,\quad \rho_1^{-1}\partial\,(F_0 + F_1)\,/\partial x_3 = \rho_2^{-1}\partial F_2\,/\partial x_3 \text{ with } x_3 = 0, \tag{23}$$

where F_m is the incident $(m = 0)$, reflected $(m = 1)$ or transmitted $(m = 2)$ wave and ρ_m is the volume mass density in the m-*th* wave domain. Equations (22) are satisfied, because F_m is the plane wave. We can find the reflection/transmission coefficients K_1 and K_2 with $(K_0 = 1)$ and angles q_{km} with $m = 1, 2$ by substituting Equation (19) into Equations (23). Then we get the following equations:

$$(1 + K_1)\,\exp\,(i\ell_1) = K_2\,\exp\,(i\ell_2), \tag{24}$$

$$a_{31}\ (K_1\ -\ 1)\ \exp\ (\ i\ \ell_1\ )\ =\ -\ a_{32}\, K_2\ \exp\ (\ i\ \ell_2\ ),$$

where

$$a_{km}\ =\ (\ c_m\ \rho_m\ )^{-1}\ \cos\ q_{km}\ ,\quad \ell_m\ =\ c_m^{-1}\ \times\ \omega\ (\ x_1\ \cos\ q_{1m}\ +\ x_2\ \cos\ q_{2m}\ )\ . \tag{25}$$

We will formulate conditions which make it possible to resolve this problem.

Let us express the direction of $\boldsymbol{k}_m$ by its angles, formed with the lines L and L'. If the axis x_1 coincides with L, the angle between $\boldsymbol{k}_m$ and L is q_{1m}. Let us turn the coordinate system around the axis x_3 so that the axis x_1 coincides with L'. Let $\acute{q}_{1m}$ be the angle between $\boldsymbol{k}_m$ and L'. Then

$$\cos\ \acute{q}_{1m}\ =\ \cos\ q_{1m}\ \cos\ \zeta\ +\ \cos\ q_{2m}\ \sin\ \zeta, \tag{26}$$

where ζ is the angle between L and L' (Figure 1). From equation (26) we have

$$\cos\ q_{2m}\ =\ (\ \cos\ \acute{q}_{1m}\ -\ \cos\ q_{1m}\ \cos\ \zeta\ )\ /\ \sin\ \zeta \tag{27}$$

We can always choose the direction of the axis x_1 so that $q_{1m}\ \leq\ \pi/2\ ,\ \ \acute{q}_{1m}\ \leq\ \pi/2$.

Then from equations (21) and (27) we have

$$\cos q_{3m}\ =\ [\ \sin^2 q_{1m} - (\ \cos\ \acute{q}_{1m} - \cos\ q_{1m}\ \cos\ \zeta\ )^2 /\ \sin^2\ \zeta\ ]^{1/2} \tag{28}$$

Equations (27) - (28) express the components of the vector $\boldsymbol{k}_m$ by the angles q_{1m} and $\acute{q}_{1m}$

The reflection/transmission coefficients can be found under the following conditions:

$$(\ \cos\ q_{1m}\ )\ /\ c_m\ =\ (\ \cos\ q_{10}\ )\ /\ c_0\ , \tag{29}$$

$$(\ \cos\ \acute{q}_{1m}\ )\ /\ c_m\ =\ (\ \cos\ \acute{q}_{10}\ )\ /\ c_0\ . \tag{30}$$

Indeed, by substituting equations (29) - (30) into equation (27) we have

$$\cos\, q_{2m} = (c_m / c_0) \cos\, q_{20}\,. \tag{31}$$

Then equations (24) turn into algebraic equations

$$K_1 - K_2 = -1, \quad a_{31} K_1 + a_{32} K_2 = a_{31,}\,, \tag{32}$$

and we get the well-known expressions

$$K_1 = (a_{31} - a_{32})/(a_{31} + a_{32}), \quad K_2 = 2a_{31}/(a_{31} + a_{32})\,. \tag{33}$$

4. Reflected/transmitted rays

Let us show that equations (29) - (30) define directions of reflected/transmitted rays. Equation (29) puts the restriction on the possible directions of the wave vector $\boldsymbol{k}_m$. All allowable directions form a cone with its vertex at the point of incidence. Its axis is the line L. Its apex angle is $2q_{1m}$. The condition (30) produces the second cone of the allowable directions with the axis L'. Because both conditions (29) - (30) must be satisfied, the vector $\boldsymbol{k}_m$ belongs to both cones (Figure 2) and also belongs to the line of intersection of these cones. Thus, the incident $(m = 0)$, reflected $(m = 1)$ and transmitted $(m = 2)$ rays are defined by the angles q_{1m} and $\acute{q}_{1m}$.

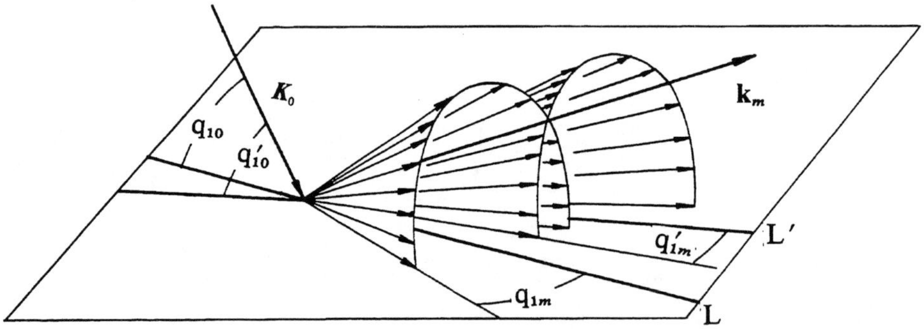

Figure 2. Interpretation of Snell's law.

All this can be rewritten as Snell's law. The wave vector $\boldsymbol{k}_m$ belongs to the plane Π_m, which contains the normal x_3 to the interface. Let us find the dihedral angle ψ_m between the planes Π_m and $x_2 = 0$ (Figure 1). Let L_m be the line of intersection of the planes Π_m and $x_3 = 0$. The cosine of the angle between $\boldsymbol{k}_m$ and L_m is

$$\cos\ (\pi/2 - q_{3m}) = \cos\ q_{1m}\ \cos\ \psi_m + \cos\ q_{2m}\ \sin\ \psi_m\ . \tag{34}$$

From equation (28) we have

$$\sin\ q_{3m} = [\ \cos^2 q_{1m} + (\ \cos\ \acute{q}_{1m} - \cos\ q_{1m}\ \cos\ \zeta)^2 / \sin^2 \zeta\ ]^{1/2}\ . \tag{35}$$

By substituting equations (29) - (30) into equation (35) we have

$$\sin\ q_{3m} = (\ c_m / c_0)\ \sin\ q_{30}\, . \tag{36}$$

By substituting equations (31) and (36) into equation (34) we have

$$\sin\ q_{30} = \cos\ q_{10}\ \cos\ \psi_m + \cos\ q_{20}\ \sin\ \psi_m\ . \tag{37}$$

From equation (37) we have

$$\psi_m = \psi_0 \quad \text{with } m = 1, 2\, . \tag{38}$$

Equations (36) and (38) express Snell's law.

5. Edge

The reflection/transmission problem has been solved under conditions (29) - (30). The latter have meaning only at the regular point of the interface where position of the tangent plane can be determined uniquely. However, the surfaces of the realistic interfaces have the lines formed by the irregular points. For example, if we cut the regular surface in two parts and shift them relative to each other, the obtained compound surface will be discontinuous at the brims of the cut. In such a case position of the tangent plane cannot be determined uniquely at the brims of the cut. The edges of a curvilinear polyhedron give another example of the lines of irregularity where the first tangential derivatives to the surface of the polyhedron are discontinuous. In this case it is also impossible to determine uniquely the position of the tangent plane at the mentioned lines.

In both examples we deal with the space curves that are formed by the points of discontinuity of the surface or by the points of discontinuity of the first tangential derivatives of the surface. A space curve of such type is called the "*edge*" of the surface, or the edge of the interface. We will consider the edges of simple geometric properties without points of break or termination. We call a point of the edge "*regular,*" if the edge and its first tangential derivative are continuous at this point. We call the edge "*smooth,*" if its points are all regular. We will consider here a case when the incident ray strikes a point of the smooth edge.

In a narrow vicinity of any point of a smooth edge we can neglect its curvature and approximate the interface by two half-planes, touching at the edge (Figure 3). Then reflected/transmitted wavefields must comply with the boundary conditions at both half-planes. By using cylindrical coordinates (r, θ, z), where axis z coincides with the edge, we can write the boundary conditions as follows:

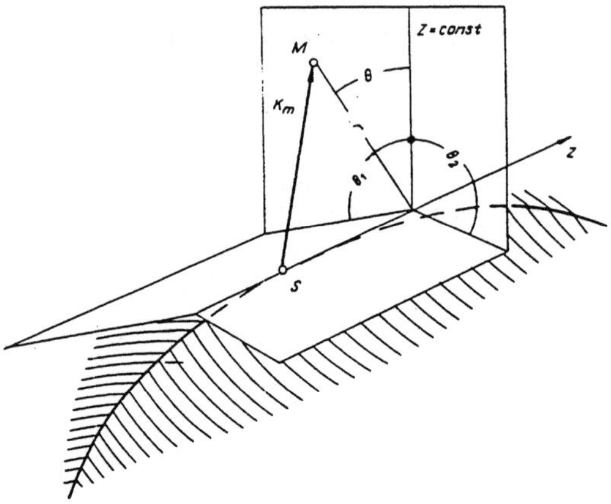

Figure 3. Cylindrical coordinates at the edge.

$$F_0 + F_1 = F_2, \quad \rho_1^{-1}\, \partial(F_0 + F_1)/\partial\theta = \rho_2^{-1}\, \partial F_2/\partial\theta$$

$$\text{with } \theta = \theta_\ell \quad (\ell = 1, 2), \tag{39}$$

where θ_ℓ is the coordinate of the ℓ *–th* half-plane. Then the reflection/transmission problem turns to the integration of equation (22) under conditions (39).

Let us also rewrite equation (19) in cylindrical coordinates. Let the points $x_1 = x_2 = x_3 = 0$ and $r = z = 0$ coincide, the axes x_1 and z coincide, and the planes $x_2 = 0$ and $\theta = 0$ coincide. Then

$$x_1 = z, \quad x_2 = r \sin\theta, \quad x_3 = r\cos\theta,$$

$$k_{2m} = k_m^r \sin\alpha_m, \quad k_{3m} = k_m^r \cos\alpha_m, \quad k_m^r = k_m \sin q_{1m}, \tag{40}$$

where k_m^r is the projection of $\boldsymbol{k}_m$ to the plane $z = \text{const}$, and α_m is the angular cylindrical coordinate of this projection. By substituting equation (40) into equation (19) we have

$$F_m = K_m \exp\left\{ ik_m \left[z\cos q_{1m} + r\sin q_{1m}\cos(\theta - \alpha_m) \right] \right\}. \tag{41}$$

Unlike the reflection/transmission at a regular point of the interface, we cannot use equation (41) to find the unknown quantities K_m directly from the boundary conditions (39). Indeed, by substituting equation (41) into equation (39), using the condition (29) and the conditions

$$[\sin q_{1m} \cos(\theta_\ell - \alpha_m)]/c_m = [\sin q_{10} \cos(\theta_\ell - \alpha_0)]/c_0$$
$$\text{with } \ell = 1, 2 \tag{42}$$

we can get algebraic equations for K_m with coefficients, independent of coordinates. However, they are incompatible – four equations for two unknown quantities.

To extend the reflection/transmission laws to the neighborhood of the edge, we have to look for the solution of equation (22) in the form of a superposition of plane waves, equation (41),

$$F_m = f_m(r, \theta) \exp(ik_m z \cos q_{1m}), \tag{43}$$

$$f_m(r, \theta) = \int_\Gamma \Phi_m(\alpha_n) \exp(ik_m r \sin q_{1m} \cos(\theta - \alpha_n)] \, d\alpha_n, \tag{44}$$

where Γ is some contour, allowing the existence of the integral. By substituting equation (43) into equation (22) we get 2-D Helmholtz's equations

$$\partial^2 f_m/\partial r^2 + r^{-1} \partial f_m/\partial r + r^{-2} \partial^2 f_m/\partial \theta^2 + k_{1m}{}^2 f_m = 0, \text{ and} \tag{45}$$

$$k_{1m} = k_m \sin q_{1m} . \tag{46}$$

By substituting equation (43) into equation (39) and using equation (29) we get 2-D boundary conditions

$$f_0 + f_1 = f_2, \quad \rho_1{}^{-1} \partial(f_0 + f_1)/\partial\theta = \rho_2{}^{-1} \partial f_2/\partial\theta$$
$$\text{with } \theta = \theta_\ell \ (\ell = 1, 2). \tag{47}$$

Thus, in the neighborhood of the edge, the reflection/transmission problem turns to the integration of equations (45) under conditions (47). Note, the representation of the sought field in equation (43) reduces the original 3-D problem to a 2-D problem in the space of polar coordinates (r, θ). This technique is well known in the classic diffraction theory (Born and Wolf, 1968). Equations (45) and (47) describe the wave motion in plane $z = \text{const}$. The true wave velocities c_m are replaced by the apparent velocities

$c_m / \sin\ q_{1m}$, which are the velocities of propagation of the wavefront traces in plane $z = \text{const}$. Because the sought solution is represented by the superposition of plane waves (44), equations (45) are satisfied automatically. Relationships (42) correspond to Snell's law in 2-D space (r, θ) with the apparent wave velocities $c_m / \sin\ q_{1m}$.

6. Diffracted rays

Unlike when the reflection/transmission is at the regular point of the interface, we cannot determine the tangent plane at the edge unambiguously. Indeed, we can make the line L coincide with the tangent to the edge, because the latter is the common element of both half-planes approximating the interface. However, there is not any other line L' that can be the common element of the same half-planes. That is why there is only one limitation, equation (29), on the directions of reflected/transmitted rays. All rays complying with equation (29) are allowable. Such rays are called diffracted.

This fact is known as the law of edge diffraction (Keller, 1962) which reads as follows: Let an incident ray make an acute angle q_{10} with the tangent to an edge. The set of secondary rays form a cone with its vertex at the point of incidence. Its apex angle is $2\,q_{1m}$, where q_{1m} and q_{10} are connected under equation (29). The incident ray and the mentioned cone lie on opposite sides of the plane normal to the edge at the point of incidence. Obviously, this law holds true within a small neighborhood of the point of incidence, in which it is possible to neglect the curvature of the rays.

The diffracted rays can be continued outside the neighborhood of the edge according to equation (7). A set of such rays forms a congruence with parameters (θ, q_{1m}) in such a way that every pair of fixed values $\theta(S) = \text{const}$ and $q_{1m}(S) = \text{const}$ singles out an individual ray emitted by point S of the edge (Figure 4).

7. Edge waves

To reduce the reflection/transmission problem to equations (45) - (47), we have to look for solution in the form of waves propagating along diffracted rays. It is easy to show that the existence of such waves follows from equations (43) - (44) when $\omega \to \infty$.

Equation (44), depending on parameter ω with $\omega \to \infty$, represents an integral from the rapidly oscillating function. The asymptotic value of such integral can be described by the well-known formula of the saddle-point method (Felsen and Marcuvitz, 1973)

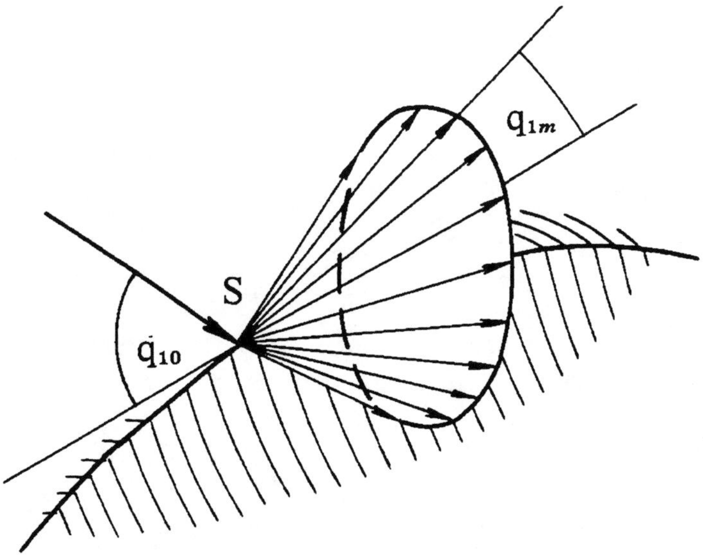

Figure 4. Cone of diffracted rays.

$$\int_{\Gamma} \Phi(\alpha) \exp\,[ip \cos(\alpha - \theta)]\,d\alpha \sim (2\pi/p)^{1/2}\,\Phi(\theta) \exp\,[i(p+\psi)]$$
$$\text{with } p \to \infty, \tag{48}$$

where ψ depends on the form of contour Γ.

Using equation (48), we obtain the following asymptotic value of integral (43) - (44):

$$F_m = \Phi'_m \exp\,(i\omega\tau_m),\ \Phi'_m = \chi'_m\,(J_m/c_m^2)^{-1/2}$$
$$\text{with } k_m\, r \sin q_{1m} \to \infty, \tag{49}$$

$$\chi'_m = (2\pi/k_m)^{1/2}\,\Phi_m(\theta) \exp\,(i\psi),\ \text{and} \tag{50}$$

$$J_m = c_m^2\, r \sin q_{1m},\ \tau_m = (r \sin q_{1m} + z \cos q_{1m})/c_m\,. \tag{51}$$

It is easy to see that quantity τ_m from equation (51) corresponds to the eikonal of a wave propagating along diffracted rays. Quantity Φ'_m complies with the transport equation of the type (11) with $B_m = \Delta\tau_m$, i.e., it corresponds to the amplitude of a propagating wave. Thus, the reflecting/transmission phenomenon at the edge yields the new type of waves propagating along diffracted rays. Such waves are called edge-diffracted waves.

We can see that the concept of edge diffracted waves appears quite naturally in the elementary analysis of the statement of the reflection/transmission problem of plane waves at the wedge-shaped, interface. This concept can be easily extended to a more general case. Indeed, equation (49) holds true outside the neighborhood of the edge, if functions J_m / c_m^2 and τ_m are analytically continued as solutions of equations (11) and (9), respectively. The existence of edge-diffracted waves in the simple enough situations was proved by the analysis of the exact solutions of some problems of the mathematical theory of diffraction. The corresponding references can be found in the basic monographs on the theory of diffraction (Born and Wolf, 1968; Hönl et al., 1961; Felsen and Marcuitz, 1973). In more complicated situations the notion of edge-diffracted waves appears as a result of the high-frequency analysis of the Kirchhoff integral (Trorey, 1970, 1977; Berryhill, 1977; Hilterman, 1982; Frazer and Sen, 1985; Frazer, 1987; Zhu, 1988) and the new integral generalization of ray theory (Hanyga, 1989). There is considerable experience of observing edge waves by means of numerical seismic modeling (Mikhailenko, 1988) and physical modeling (Hilterman, 1970; Kovalevsky et al., 1971; Kozak and Wanieck, 1975; Grad, 1979). The information on more or less successful attempts of observing edge-diffracted waves in seismic prospecting can be found in Starobinetz (1988).

8. Theory of diffraction

The concept of the edge-diffracted wave was introduced in the classic paper by Young (1802). Since then a great number of theoretical studies have been devoted to the waves diffracted by edges. The bibliography of those works can be traced in the previously mentioned monographs on the theory of diffraction. However, the way of the systematical description of edge effects as the waves emitted by the edges has been formulated so far within the framework of the geometrical theory of diffraction (Keller, 1962). Generally speaking, the mentioned theory is designed for finding the asymptotic expansions of diffracted waves in the form of ray series with $\omega \to \infty$. However, here and in the following we do not consider the asymptotic series. We restrict ourselves to the consideration of the high-frequency asymptotic description of edge waves with the relative error of order $O(\omega^{-1})$. The geometrical theory of diffraction describes such a value as follows.

A stationary edge wave is determined in accordance with equations (8) - (9)

$$F_m = \Phi'_m \exp(i \omega \tau_m), \quad \nabla \tau_m = e_m / c_m, \tag{52}$$

where e_m is the unit vector of the tangent to the diffracted ray. The congruence of diffracted rays can be obtained by using the law of edge diffraction. Therefore, the problem of the mathematical description of the edge waves can be reduced to finding their amplitudes.

Let the edge wave at an arbitrary point M of some diffracted ray be determined by equation (52) where Φ'_m complies with the transport equation

$$2\nabla\tau_m \nabla\Phi'_m + \Phi'_m \Delta\tau_m = 0. \tag{53}$$

Let S be a point on the same diffracted ray in a small vicinity of the edge. Solutions of equation (53) at points M and S are related by

$$\Phi'_m(M) = \Phi'_m(S)/L_m, \tag{54}$$

where L_m is determined in equation (13).

On the other hand, quantity $\Phi'_m(S)$ in a small vicinity of the edge can be described by the second expression of equation (49), where $\boldsymbol{x}_m'$ and $\boldsymbol{J}_m$ are determined by equations (50) - (51). We can see that it is necessary to know the function $\Phi_m(\theta)$ and parameter ψ to find the amplitude (54). To find the mentioned quantities, we have to obtain the solution of equations (45) - (47) in the form (44).

Thus, the edge wave within the framework of the geometrical theory of diffraction can be found by its continuation from the neighborhood of the edge in accordance with ray method expression (54). Its amplitude in the neighborhood of the edge has to be obtained from solution of some *canonical problem* of the mathematical theory of diffraction. The solution of such problem must locally approximate the sought edge wave in the neighborhood of the edge. The simplest canonical problem of edge diffraction is a problem of diffraction of the plane wave on a system of wedge-shaped regions with the common edge. However, the analytic solution of this problem is still unknown. This does not allow us to use the geometric theory of diffraction for the direct description of edge waves in general situations.

The geometrical theory of diffraction is valid in those regions of space where the edge-wave amplitude complies with transport equation (53). However, the latter fails in the neighborhoods of shadow boundaries of the reflected/transmitted waves (as well as in the neighborhoods of caustics) where the wave mechanism has a character of transverse diffusion (Malyuzhinetz, 1959). When approaching a shadow boundary, function $\Phi_m(\theta)$ in equation (50) tends to infinity and the second expression in (49) has no meaning. Therefore, expression (54) fails. The domains, where equation (54) is invalid, are called the *boundary layers.*

Equation (50) shows that the edge-wave amplitude is $\omega^{1/2}$ times less than the ordinary reflected/transmitted wave amplitude. So, it is possible to neglect the edge wave comparing with the reflected/transmitted wave when $\omega \to \infty$. However, as we see later, the edge-wave amplitude in the boundary layer is comparable with the reflected/transmitted wave amplitude when $\omega \to \infty$. So, consideration of edge waves in the boundary layers is of importance for applications.

A differential equation, valid for description of the edge-wave amplitude in the boundary layer, can be obtained by the local high-frequency approximation of the original equations of motion. In the asymptotic theory of diffraction (Babich and Buldyrev, 1972), Fock's parabolic equation (Fock, 1965) is used for this purpose. In the particular case of diffraction of acoustic waves on an ideal wedge, the equation allows us to find formulas of the uniform geometrical theory of diffraction, which can be used simultaneously as in regions of validity of equation (54) so in the boundary layers (Ufimtsev, 1965). Formulas of the uniform geometrical theory of diffraction for elastic and electromagnetic edge waves were obtained, as well, by analysis of exact solutions of corresponding canonical problems in the cases of diffraction on ideal boundaries (Fertig and Muller, 1979; Achenbach et al., 1980; Kouyoumjian et al., 1980). However, there are no such formulas for more general situations.

The other important theoretical aspect of edge diffraction concerns diffraction effects on edges with points of termination. The interfaces of 3-D block structure media are represented by surfaces of curvilinear polyhedrons. The edges of such interfaces have points of termination corresponding to the vertices of polyhedrons. Diffraction on such points yields the new type of waves spreading from vertices – *vertex* or *tip-diffracted waves.* The systematic way of description of such waves is postulated by the geometrical theory of diffraction (Keller, 1962; Borovikov and Kinber, 1978; Kouyoumjian et al., 1980) and again reduced to the equations of type (52) – (54), where $\boldsymbol{e}_m$ is the unit vector of the tangent to the vertex diffracted ray. However, this approach cannot be realized so far in the general situation because of the absence of solutions of corresponding canonical problems. There are no papers on the vertex-diffracted waves in the boundary layers. In the case of diffraction of electromagnetic waves by the corner of a perfectly conducting surface, a heuristic approach for description of the vertex effect was proposed in Kouyoumjian et al. (1980).

Chapter II

PROBLEM OF FORCED OSCILLATIONS

The problem of diffraction of a plane wave on a system of wedge-shaped regions with the common edge is the key problem of the mathematical theory of diffraction. Its solution helps us understand the physical mechanism of edge diffraction and can be used for the description of edge-diffracted waves by the method of the geometrical theory of diffraction. Section 1 of this chapter considers a special formulation of this problem aimed at obtaining formulas for the edge waves only. We begin with the simplest case—diffraction of an acoustic wave on a system of wedge-shaped regions with conditions of rigid contact at the interfaces. The statement of this problem is based on the development of the Sommerfeld-Malyuzhinetz method (Malyuzhinetz, 1951), which is considered briefly in Section 1. A modification of this approach is considered in Section 2. Using the modified approach, we state the diffraction problem in Section 3 as a problem of forced oscillations. In Section 4 we generalize the approach on a case of diffraction of the vector waves of any physical nature on a system of wedge-shaped regions with the arbitrary linear conditions of contact at the interfaces.

1. Malyuzhinetz's method

1. Initial equations—Let us formulate the problem of diffraction of a plane wave on a system of wedge-shaped regions with a common edge. A two-dimensional space, where a polar coordinate system $r \geq 0, -\pi \leq \theta \leq \pi$ is introduced, is separated by boundaries $\theta = \theta_\nu$ ($\nu = 1, 2, \ldots, N$) into regions $\theta_\nu \leq \theta \leq \theta_{\nu+1}$. The numbers of these boundaries ν increase in a counterclockwise direction, the boundary $\theta = \theta_{N+1}$ coinciding with boundary $\theta = \theta_1$ (Figure 5). Therefore, it is possible to change indices as follows:

$$\nu - 1 \rightarrow N, \quad \text{when } \nu = 1, \quad \nu \rightarrow 1, \quad \text{when } \nu = N + 1. \tag{1}$$

Henceforth we will also use the following designation for the angular coordinates of the boundaries $\theta_\nu = \theta_\nu^+$, $\theta_{\nu+1} = \theta_\nu^-$. Then the νth region can be defined as $\theta_\nu^+ \leq \theta$, $\theta \leq \theta_\nu^-$. We denote c_ν and ρ_ν as the wave velocity and the medium density of the νth region, respectively.

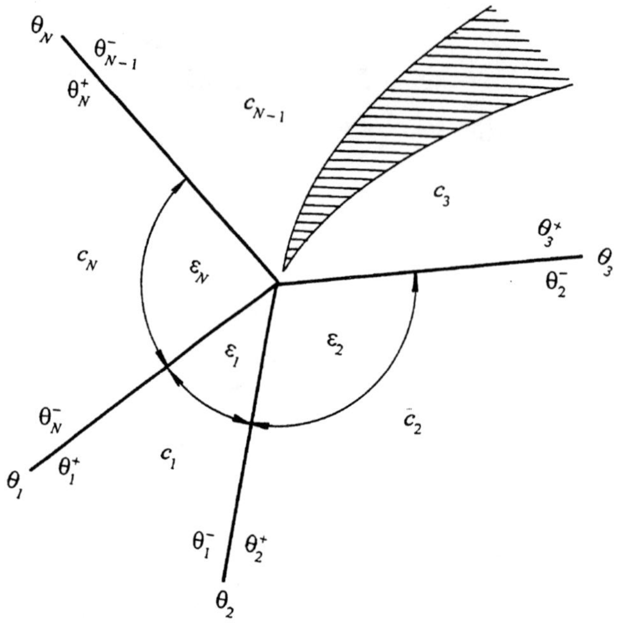

Figure 5. System of wedge-shaped regions.

We are going to look for the wavefield, caused by an incident plane wave

$$f_0 = \exp\left[ik_\nu r \cos(\theta - \theta_0)\right], \quad \text{with } \nu = k, \tag{2}$$

where $k_\nu = \omega / c_\nu$ is the wave number, and θ_0 is the direction of incidence.

Let equation (2) describe an acoustic wave. Then additional acoustic fields of the same frequency ω arise in all regions. The total acoustic field in every region must comply with Helmholtz's equation

$$(\Delta + k_\nu^2) f_\nu = 0, \quad k_\nu = \omega / c_\nu \text{ with } \nu = 1, 2, \ldots N. \tag{3}$$

We suppose that the acoustic pressure fields and the corresponding velocities of oscillations are continuous at the boundaries, such that

$$(f_\nu)_{\theta = \theta_\nu^+} = (f_{\nu-1})_{\theta = \theta_{\nu-1}^-}, \tag{4}$$

$$\rho_\nu^{-1} \, (\partial f_\nu / \partial n)_{\theta = \theta_\nu^+} = \rho_{\nu-1}^{-1} \, (\partial f_{\nu-1} / \partial n)_{\theta = \theta_{\nu-1}^-} \quad \text{with } \nu = 1, 2, \ldots N,$$

where $\partial / \partial n$ is the normal directional derivative.

To find the total fields f_v under the previously mentioned conditions it is necessary to formulate a special mathematical problem, called *the problem of forced oscillations*. The formulation can be based on the idea of the plane waves superposition, equation I.5(44), expressed by Sommerfeld integrals. The corresponding approach was developed in Malyuzhinetz's doctoral thesis (1951) and in two additional papers (1955, 1958). Because his thesis is practically unavailable, we begin with a brief review of his method.

2. *Sommerfeld-Malyuzhinetz integral*—Take $[F_v(r)]$ and $[S_v(\alpha)]$ to be two sets of functions whose elements comply with the following conditions:

$$F_v(r) = O\,[(r^{-1+a} \exp(br)],\ \text{when } r \to \infty, \tag{5}$$

$$S_v(\alpha) = O\,\{\exp[(1-a)\ |\ \mathrm{Im}\,\alpha\ |]\},\ \text{when } |\ \mathrm{Im}\,\alpha\ | \to \infty,$$

where a and b are positive numbers. *Malyuzhinetz transform* expresses an unambiguous correspondence between these functions

$$S_v(\alpha) = ik_v \sin\alpha \int_0^\infty F_v(r) \exp(ik_v r \cos\alpha)\, dr/2, \tag{6}$$

$$F_v(r) = (1/2\pi i) \int_{\Gamma_0} S_v(\alpha) \exp(-ik_v r \cos\alpha)\, d\alpha,$$

where the contour of integration (Figure 6) is placed within domains of regularity of function $S_v(\alpha)/\sin\alpha$. If function $F_v(r)$ is limited in the interval $0 \le r < \infty$, then the function $S_v(\alpha)$ is regular, when $|\ \mathrm{Im}\,\alpha\ | \to \infty$.

Under the mentioned conditions Sommerfeld-Malyuzhinetz integral has the following properties:

(a) the integral

$$F_v(r,\theta) = (1/2\pi i) \int_{\Gamma_0} S_v(\alpha) \exp[-ik_v r \cos(\alpha - \theta)]\, d\alpha \tag{7}$$

complies with Helmholtz equation with the wave number k_v;

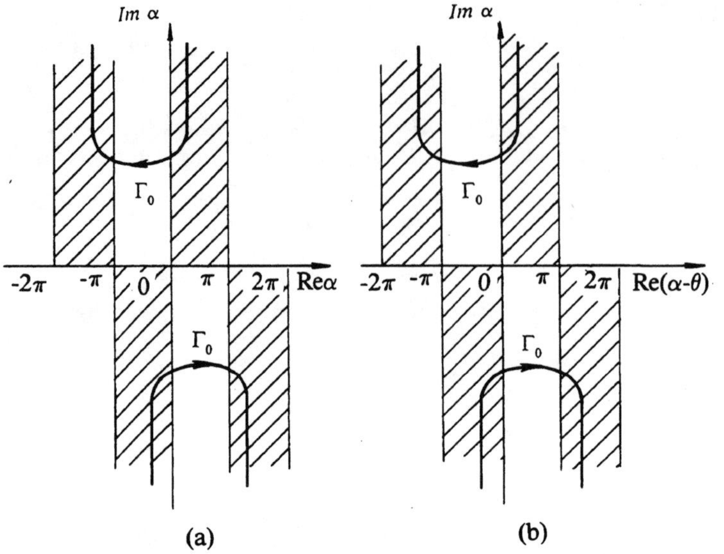

Figure 6. Contours of integration: (a) equations II.1(6) and II.1(17), (b) equation II.1(18). The allowable domains are shaded.

(b) there are relations

$$\int_{\Gamma_0} S_v(\alpha)\exp[-ik_v r\cos(\alpha-\theta)]\,d\alpha$$

$$\equiv \int_{\Gamma_0} S_v(\alpha+\theta)\exp[(-ik_v r\cos\alpha)]\,d\alpha, \tag{8}$$

$$\int_{\Gamma_0} S_v(\alpha+\theta)\exp(-ik_k r\cos\alpha)\,d\alpha)$$

$$\equiv \int_{\Gamma_0} \tau_{kv}(\alpha)S_v[\varphi_{kv}(\alpha)+\theta]\exp(-ik_v r\cos\alpha)\,d\alpha, \tag{9}$$

$$\varphi_{kv}(\alpha) = \arccos[(c_k/c_v)\cos\alpha], \tag{10}$$

$$\tau_{kv}(\alpha) = d\varphi_{kv}/d\alpha = (\sin\alpha)[(c_v/c_k)^2 - \cos^2\alpha]^{-1/2}, \tag{11}$$

where a branch of the function (10) is fixed by the following conditions:

$$\varphi_{kv}(\alpha)=\alpha,\ \tau_{kv}(\alpha)=1,\ \text{when } c_k=c_v;\ \varphi_{kv}(\alpha\pm\pi)=\varphi_{kv}(\alpha)\pm\pi, \tag{12}$$

$$\tau_{kv}(\alpha\pm\pi)=\tau_{kv}(\alpha);\ \varphi_{kv}(-\alpha)=-\varphi_{kv}(\alpha),\ \tau_{kv}(-\alpha)=\tau_{kv}(\alpha);$$

every couple of branch points

$$\alpha = \pm \arccos(c_v/c_k) + n\pi(n = 0, 1, 2, \dots) \tag{13}$$

of function (10) is connected by the cut in the complex plane of α;

(c) the value of integral (7) is finite at the point $r = 0$ and does not depend on the direction of the approach to this point

$$F_v(0, \theta) = 2iS_v(i\infty) = -2iS_v(-i\infty); \tag{14}$$

(d) in order to satisfy the following equation

$$\int_{\Gamma_0} S_v(\alpha) \exp[-ik_v r \cos(\alpha - \theta)] d\alpha \equiv 0 \tag{15}$$

it is necessary and sufficient to satisfy the equation

$$S_v(\alpha + \theta) = S_v(-\alpha + \theta). \tag{16}$$

3. Malyuzhinetz equation system—The Helmholtz equation (3) can be satisfied by the integrals

$$f_v = (1/2\pi i) \int_{\Gamma_0} \tilde{S}_v(\alpha + \theta) \exp(-ik_v r \cos\alpha) d\alpha \tag{17}$$

or

$$f_v = (1/2\pi i) \int_{\Gamma_0} \tilde{S}_v(\alpha) \exp[-ik_v r \cos(\alpha - \theta)] d\alpha. \tag{18}$$

The contour of integration must pass to infinity in those domains of the complex plane of α, where the real parts of the functions, placed under exponents, are negative. Because these functions are periodic, it is sufficient to write the mentioned condition for a single band $|\mathrm{Re}\ \alpha - 2k\pi|$ with any integer k

$$\mathrm{sign}(\mathrm{Re}\ \alpha - 2k\pi) = \mathrm{sign}\ \mathrm{Im}\ \alpha, \tag{19}$$

$$\mathrm{sign}(\mathrm{Re}\ \alpha - \theta - 2k\pi) = \mathrm{sign}\ \mathrm{Im}\ \alpha, \tag{20}$$

where the first line corresponds to equation (17) and the second to equation (18). The domains satisfying these conditions are called *allowable domains*. The domains where these conditions do not hold true are called *prohibited domains*.

Thus, the contour of integration must pass to the infinity within allowable domains. The integrand must not have any singular points in these domains with $k = 0$ and on the right side of the contour of integration. The function $\widetilde{S}_\nu(\alpha)$ is called *a transformant* and the exponent factor *a kernel* of the integral transform (6).

Because the integrals (17) and (18) comply with the Helmholtz equation, the problem can be reduced, in principle, to finding the transformants under the boundary conditions in equation (4). This procedure involves great difficulties because the kernels of the integrals do not coincide in different wedge-shaped regions. Malyuzhinetz's method, by means of the unification of the kernels, overcomes the difficulty, reads as follows.

Upon substituting the integrals (17) into the boundary conditions in equation (4) and performing the differentiation, we have to change the variable of integration by using relations (8) - (9) in such a way that the kernels of all integrals would match. The latter operation, call the *unification of the kernels*, does not change the contour of integration. The function equation (10), is called the *unification function*.

Upon unification, the boundary conditions turn into the following $2N$ relations:

$$\int_{\Gamma_0} Q_{n\nu}(\alpha)\exp(-ik_k r\cos\alpha)\,d\alpha = 0\,;\; n = 1,2\,;\; \nu = 1,2,\ldots N\,; \tag{21}$$

where

$$Q_{1\nu}(\alpha) = L^+_{\nu k}(\alpha) - L^-_{(\nu-1)k}(\alpha),$$

$$Q_{2\nu}(\alpha) = \beta_{\nu k}(\alpha)L^+_{\nu k}(\alpha) - \beta_{(\nu-1)k}(\alpha)L^-_{(\nu-1)k}(\alpha), \tag{22}$$

$$L^\pm_{\nu k}(\alpha) = \tau_{\nu k}(\alpha)\,\widetilde{S}_\nu\,[\varphi_{\nu k}(\alpha) + \theta^\pm_\nu],$$

and $\beta_{\nu k}(\alpha) = (c_\nu\rho_\nu)^{-1}\sin\varphi_{\nu k}(\alpha)$.

To satisfy these conditions, it is sufficient to satisfy the following $2N$ relations:

$$Q_{n\nu}(\alpha) = 0 \quad \text{with } n = 1, 2; \ \ \nu = 1, 2, \dots N. \tag{23}$$

However, these equations cannot be used directly for finding the unknown functions $\tilde{S}_\nu(\alpha)$, because they are not compatible ($2N$ linear equations for N unknown functions). To obtain compatible equations, using the property of equations (15) - (16) of the integral (21) is sufficient:

$$Q_{n\nu}(\alpha) = Q_{n\nu}(-\alpha) \quad \text{with } n = 1, 2; \ \ \nu = 1, 2, \dots N. \tag{24}$$

These relations are called the *Malyuzhinetz functional equation system*. If the function $\tilde{S}_\nu(\alpha)$ with $\nu = k$ has a simple pole at the point $\alpha = \theta_0$, this system guarantees one, and only one, solution of the problem in equations (2) - (4).

However, the complexity of the system equation (24), does not allow us to find its solution, except for some of the simplest cases like $c_1 = c_2 = \dots c_N$. The Malyuzhinetz method is based on two essential points: the unification of the integral kernel and using the condition of even functions of equations (15) - (16). Generally speaking, the value of each of these facts is not equal for stating the problem. The unification of the kernel leads to the separating of variables, which is of great importance for stating any problem of mathematical physics. However, using the condition of even functions of equations represents only one of many possible ways of getting the functional equations compatible. For example, it is possible to make the functional equations compatible by doubling the number of unknown functions. This is the means we will use to modernize the discussed method.

2. Modified equation system

1. Form of solution—Let us look for a solution of equation 1(3) in the form

$$f_\nu = F_\nu^+ + F_\nu^- + F_\nu, \tag{1}$$

$$F_\nu^\pm = (1/2\pi i) \int_{\Gamma_0} S_\nu^\pm(\alpha) \exp[-ik_\nu r \cos(\alpha - \gamma_\nu^\pm)]\, d\alpha, \tag{2}$$

where functions $S_\nu^\pm(\alpha)$ are unknown.

The angles

$$\gamma_\nu^{\pm} = \pm(\theta - \theta_\nu^{\pm}) \tag{3}$$

are taken from the interface $\theta = \theta_\nu^{\pm}$ by the ray $\theta = \text{const}$ as is shown in Figure 7. The allowable domains are given in equation 1(20) where θ must be replaced by $\gamma_\nu^{\pm}$, i.e.,

$$\text{sign}\,(\text{Re}\,\alpha - \gamma_\nu^{\pm} - 2k\pi) = \text{sign Im}\,\alpha\,. \tag{4}$$

The term F_ν represents some *perturbation* including the incident wave, equation 1(2). However, we do not give the explicit expression for this term, so far. We just suppose that it can be represented by the following combination of the integrals

$$F_\nu = \delta_\nu^{+}(\theta)\,F_{0\nu}^{+} + \delta_\nu^{-}(\theta)\,F_{0\nu}^{-}, \tag{5}$$

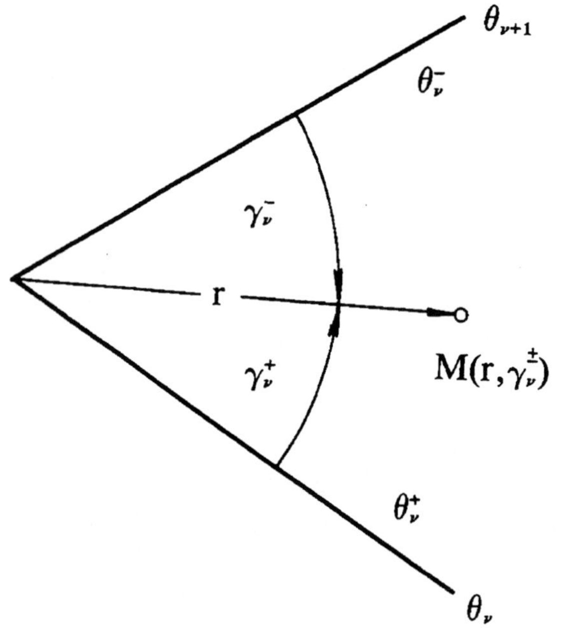

Figure 7. Angles $\gamma_\nu^{\pm}$ in equation II.2(2).

$$F_{0\nu}^{\pm} = (1/2\pi i)\int_{\Gamma_0} D_\nu^{\pm}(\alpha)\,\exp\,[-ik_\nu r\,\cos(\alpha - \gamma_\nu^{\pm})]\,d\alpha\,, \tag{6}$$

where $D_\nu^{\pm}(\alpha)$ are some given functions. Here we use the unit functions

$$\delta_\nu^\pm(\theta) \equiv 0 \text{ or } \delta_\nu^\pm(\theta) \equiv 1, \text{ when } \theta_\nu^+ \le \theta,\ \theta \le \theta_\nu^- . \tag{7}$$

The choice of possible combinations of the functions in equation (5) is discussed later.

Let us show that equation (1) can be rewritten in the form of equation 1(18). To do this we change the variable of integration in equations (2) and (6) as follows: $\alpha = \pm\alpha' \mp \theta_\nu^\pm$.

By taking into consideration the evenness of the function

$$\cos(\alpha - \gamma_\nu^\pm) = \cos(\pm\alpha' \mp \theta_\nu^\pm - \gamma_\nu^\pm) = \cos(\pm\alpha' \mp \theta) = \cos(\alpha' - \theta), \tag{8}$$

the relation 1(8), and the mirror transformation of the contour of integration with replacement α by $-\alpha'$, we get

$$F_\nu^\pm = (1/2\pi i) \int_{\Gamma_0} S_\nu^\pm(\pm\alpha \mp \theta_\nu^\pm) \exp[-ik_\nu r \cos(\alpha - \theta)]\, d\alpha, \text{ and}$$

$$F_{0\nu}^\pm = \pm(1/2\pi i) \int_{\Gamma_0} D_\nu(\pm\alpha \mp \theta_\nu^\pm) \exp[-ik_\nu r \cos(\alpha - \theta)]\, d\alpha, \tag{9}$$

where the new variable of integration is denoted again as α . By substituting these expressions into equation (1), we get equation 1(18), where

$$\tilde{S}_\nu(\alpha) = S_\nu(\alpha) + S_\nu^0(\alpha), \tag{10}$$

$$S_\nu(\alpha) = S_\nu^+(\alpha - \theta_\nu^+) - S_\nu^-(-\alpha + \theta_\nu^-), \text{ and}$$

$$S_\nu^0(\alpha) = \delta_\nu^+(\theta)\, D_\nu^+(\alpha - \theta_\nu^+) - \delta_\nu^-(\theta)\, D_\nu^-(-\alpha + \theta_\nu^-).$$

2. *Boundary conditions*—By substituting equation (1) into boundary conditions equation 1(4), we can write the result in the following compact form:

$$[a_{q\nu}(F_\nu^+ + F_\nu^- + F_\nu)]_{\theta = \theta_\nu^+} =$$

$$= [\, a_{q(\nu-1)} \, (F_{\nu-1}^{+} + F_{\nu-1}^{-} + F_{\nu-1}) \,]_{\theta = \theta_{\nu-1}^{-}} \tag{11}$$

$$a_{1\nu} = 1 , \; a_{2\nu} = \rho_\nu^{\;-1} \partial / \partial n \text{ with } q = 1,2 ; \; \nu = 1, 2, \ldots N .$$

There are three ways to introduce different combinations of integrals (6) in the boundary conditions

$$F_\nu = F_{0\nu}^{+} + F_{0\nu}^{-}, \; F_{\nu-1} = F_{0(\nu-1)}^{+} + F_{0(\nu-1)}^{-}, \tag{12}$$

$$F_\nu = F_{0\nu}^{+}, \; F_{\nu-1} = F_{0(\nu-1)}^{-}, \tag{13}$$

$$F_\nu = F_{0\nu}^{-}, \; F_{\nu-1} = F_{0(\nu-1)}^{+}. \tag{14}$$

They correspond to three combinations of the unit functions (7)

$$\delta_\nu^{\pm} (\theta_\nu^{+}) = \delta_{\nu-1}^{\pm} (\theta_\nu^{-}) = 1 , \tag{15}$$

$$\delta_\nu^{+} (\theta_\nu^{+}) = \delta_{\nu-1}^{-} (\theta_{\nu-1}^{-}) = 1 , \quad \delta_\nu^{-} (\theta_\nu^{+}) = \delta_{\nu-1}^{+} (\theta_{\nu-1}^{-}) = 0 , \tag{16}$$

$$\delta_\nu^{+} (\theta_\nu^{+}) = \delta_{\nu-1}^{-} (\theta_{\nu-1}^{-}) = 0 , \quad \delta_\nu^{-} (\theta_\nu^{+}) = \delta_{\nu-1}^{+} (\theta_{\nu-1}^{-}) = 1 , \tag{17}$$

respectively. The possibility of using these combinations for stating the problem of forced oscillations is discussed later.

3. Functional equations—Let us write equations (2) and (6) in the form

$$F_\nu^{\pm} = (1 / 2 \pi i) \int_{\Gamma_0} S_\nu^{\pm} (\alpha) \exp (- i k_\nu \eta_\nu^{\pm}) \, d \alpha , \tag{18}$$

$$F_{0\nu}^{\pm} = (1 / 2 \pi i) \int_{\Gamma_0} D_\nu^{\pm} (\alpha) \exp (- i k_\nu \eta_\nu^{\pm}) \, d \alpha , \text{ and} \tag{19}$$

$$\eta_\nu^{\pm} = r \cos (\alpha - \gamma_\nu^{\pm}) . \tag{20}$$

Then we connect every interface with its own Cartesian coordinate system (Figure 8)

$$x = r \cos \gamma_\nu^{+} = r \cos \gamma_{\nu-1}^{-}, \; y = r \sin \gamma_\nu^{+} = - r \sin \gamma_{\nu-1}^{-} . \tag{21}$$

Then

$$\eta_\nu^+ = x\cos\alpha + y\sin\alpha,\quad \eta_\nu^- = x\cos(\alpha-\varepsilon_\nu) - y\sin(\alpha-\varepsilon_\nu), \tag{22}$$

$$\eta_{\nu-1}^+ = x\cos(\alpha-\varepsilon_{\nu-1}) + y\sin(\alpha-\varepsilon_{\nu-1}),\quad \eta_{\nu-1}^- = x\cos a - y\sin\alpha,$$

$$\varepsilon_n = \theta_\nu^- - \theta_\nu^+ \quad \text{with } n = \nu-1,\ \nu.$$

Let us substitute equations (18), (5), and (19) into equations (11), perform the operations $\partial/\partial n = \partial/\partial y$ of the integrands, and take $y = 0$. Then let us change α by $\alpha+\varepsilon_\nu$ in the integrals F_ν^- and $F_{0\nu}^-$, and α by $\alpha+\varepsilon_{\nu-1}$ in the integrals $F_{\nu-1}^+$ and $F_{0(\nu-1)}^+$. Then, taking into account equation 1(8), we can write equations (11) in the form

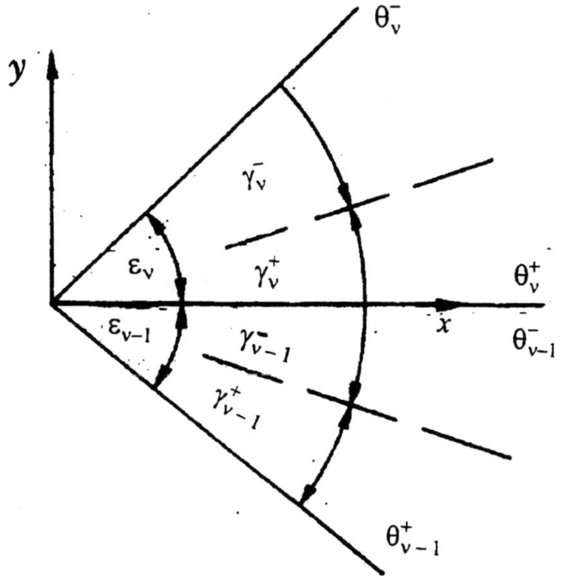

Figure 8. Cartesian coordinates in equations II.2(21).

$$\int_{\Gamma_0} [u_\nu^+(\alpha,\theta_\nu^+) + u_\nu^-(\alpha+\varepsilon_\nu,\theta_\nu^+)]\exp(-ik_\nu x\cos\alpha)\,d\alpha =$$

$$= \int_{\Gamma_0} [u_{\nu-1}^+(\alpha+\varepsilon_{\nu-1},\theta_{\nu-1}^-) + u_{\nu-1}^-(\alpha,\theta_{\nu-1}^-)]\exp(-ik_{\nu-1}x\cos\alpha)\,d\alpha, \tag{23}$$

$$\int_{\Gamma_0} (\rho_\nu c_\nu)^{-1} \sin\alpha \times [u^+_{\nu-1}(\alpha, \theta^+_\nu) - u^-_\nu(\alpha + \varepsilon_\nu, \theta^+_\nu)]$$

$$\exp(-ik_\nu x \cos\alpha)\, d\alpha =$$

$$= \int_{\Gamma_0} (\rho_{\nu-1} c_{\nu-1})^{-1} \sin\alpha \times [u^+_{\nu-1}(\alpha + \varepsilon_{\nu-1}, \theta^-_{\nu-1}) - u^-_{\nu-1}(\alpha, \theta^-_{\nu-1})]$$

$$\exp(-ik_{\nu-1} x \cos\alpha)\, d\alpha,$$

where $\nu = 1, 2, \ldots N$ and

$$u^\pm_\nu(\alpha, \theta) = S^\pm_\nu(\alpha) + \delta^\pm_\nu(\theta) D^\pm_\nu(\alpha). \tag{24}$$

Let us transform these equations to a more convenient form. Replacing α with $\varphi_{(\nu-1)\nu}(\alpha)$ in the integrals with parameter $k_{\nu-1}$ and taking into consideration equation 1(9), we get equations (23) in the form

$$\int_{\Gamma_0} A_q(\alpha) \exp(-ik_\nu x \cos\alpha)\, d\alpha = 0 \quad \text{with } q = 1, 2, \tag{25}$$

$$A_1(\alpha) = u^+_\nu(\alpha, \theta^+_\nu) + u^-_\nu(\alpha + \varepsilon_\nu, \theta^+_\nu) -$$

$$- \tau_{(\nu-1)\nu}(\alpha) \left\{ u^+_{\nu-1}\left[\varphi_{(\nu-1)\nu}(\alpha) + \varepsilon_{\nu-1}, \theta^-_{\nu-1}\right] + u^-_{\nu-1}\left[\varphi_{(\nu-1)\nu}(\alpha), \theta^-_{\nu-1}\right] \right\},$$

$$A_2(\alpha) = (\rho_\nu c_\nu)^{-1} \sin\alpha \left[u^+_\nu(\alpha, \theta^+_\nu) - u^-_\nu(\alpha + \varepsilon_\nu, \theta^+_\nu) \right] -$$

$$- (\rho_{\nu-1} c_{\nu-1})^{-1} \tau_{(\nu-1)\nu}(\alpha) \sin\varphi_{(\nu-1)\nu}(\alpha) \times \left\{ u^+_{\nu-1}\left[\varphi_{(\nu-1)\nu}(\alpha) + \varepsilon_{\nu-1}, \theta^-_{\nu-1}\right] - \right.$$

$$\left. - u^-_{\nu-1}\left[\varphi_{(\nu-1)\nu}(\alpha), \theta^-_{\nu-1}\right] \right\}.$$

By changing α by $\varphi_{\nu(\nu-1)}(\alpha)$ in the integrals of equation (23) with parameter k_ν and taking into consideration equation 1(9), we get

$$\int_{\Gamma_0} B_q(\alpha)\, \exp(-ik_{\nu-1}\, x\cos\alpha)\, d\alpha = 0 \text{ with } q = 1, 2, \tag{26}$$

$$B_1(\alpha) = \tau_{\nu(\nu-1)}(\alpha) \left\{ u_\nu^+ \left[\varphi_{\nu(\nu-1)}(\alpha),\, \theta_\nu^+ \right] + u_\nu^- \left[\varphi_{\nu(\nu-1)}(\alpha) + \varepsilon_\nu,\, \theta_\nu^+ \right] \right\} -$$

$$- \left[u_{\nu-1}^+ (\alpha + \varepsilon_{\nu-1},\, \theta_{\nu-1}^-) + u_{\nu-1}^- (\alpha, \theta_{\nu-1}^- \right],$$

$$B_2(\alpha) = (\rho_\nu c_\nu)^{-1}\, \tau_{\nu(\nu-1)}(\alpha)\, \sin\varphi_{\nu(\nu-1)}(\alpha) \left\{ u_\nu^+ \left[\varphi_{\nu(\nu-1)}(\alpha), \theta_\nu^+ \right] - \right.$$

$$\left. - u_\nu^- \left[\varphi_{\nu(\nu-1)}(\alpha) + \varepsilon_\nu, \theta_\nu^+ \right] \right\} -$$

$$- (\rho_{\nu-1} c_{\nu-1})^{-1} \sin\alpha \left[u_{\nu-1}^+ (\alpha + \varepsilon_{\nu-1}, \theta_{\nu-1}^-) - u_{\nu-1}^- (\alpha, \theta_{\nu-1}^-) \right].$$

To satisfy equations (25) and (26) requires satisfying the following equations:

$$A_1(\alpha) \equiv 0, \quad A_2(\alpha) \equiv 0, \tag{27}$$

$$B_1(\alpha) \equiv 0, \quad B_2(\alpha) \equiv 0. \tag{28}$$

These equations cannot be used directly for finding the unknown functions $S_\nu^\pm(\alpha)$, because they are not compatible ($4N$ linear equations for $2N$ unknown functions). To get the compatible equations, we have to form $2N$ new combinations.

By excluding the function $u_{\nu-1}^-$ from equation (27), and the function u_ν^+, from equation (28), we get

$$u_\nu^+(a, \theta_\nu^+) = K_{\nu\nu}(\alpha)\, u_\nu^-(\alpha + \varepsilon_\nu) +$$

$$+ \tau_{(\nu-1)\nu}(\alpha)\, K_{(\nu-1)\nu}(\alpha)\, u_{\nu-1}^+ \left[\varphi_{(\nu-1)\nu}(\alpha) + \varepsilon_{\nu-1},\, \theta_{\nu-1}^- \right], \tag{29}$$

$$u^-_{\nu-1}(\alpha,\ \theta^-_{\nu-1}) = K_{(\nu-1)(\nu-1)}(\alpha)\, u^+_{\nu-1}\ (\alpha + \varepsilon_{\nu-1},\ \theta^-_{\nu-1}) +$$

$$+\ \tau_{\nu(\nu-1)}\ (\alpha)\, K_{\nu(\nu-1)}\ (\alpha)\, u^-_\nu \left[\ \varphi_{\nu(\nu-1)}\ (\alpha) + \varepsilon_\nu,\ \theta^+_\nu\right],$$

where

$$K_{u\nu}\ (\alpha) = 2\rho_\nu c_\nu \sin^{-1}\alpha \times \left[\rho_u c_u \sin^{-1}\varphi_{u\nu}\ (\alpha) + \rho_\nu c_\nu \sin^{-1}\alpha\ \right]^{-1},$$

$$K_{uu}\ (\alpha) = 1 - K_{u\nu}\ (\alpha). \tag{30}$$

Note, the terms $K_{u\nu}(\alpha)$ and $K_{uu}(\alpha)$ coincide, respectively, with the reflection/transmission coefficients, equations I.3(33), at the interface between domains with parameters (c_u, ρ_u) and (c_ν, ρ_ν). Here the incident wave has to be given in the domain with the index u. The variable α corresponds to the difference between the right angle and the angle of reflection/transmission.

Let us introduce the operator transforming an arbitrary function as follows:

$$\kappa_{u\nu} f(\alpha) = \tau_{u\nu}\ (\alpha) K_{u\nu}(\alpha) f\left[\ \varphi_{u\nu}(\alpha) + \varepsilon_u\right] \tag{31}$$

Then equations (29)-(30) can be rewritten in the form

$$u^+_\nu\ (\alpha\ \theta^+_\nu) = \kappa_{\nu\nu}\, u^-_\nu(\alpha, \theta^+_\nu) + \kappa_{(\nu-1)\nu}\ u^+_{\nu-1}\ (\alpha,\ \theta^-_{\nu-1}), \tag{32}$$

$$u^-_{\nu-1}\ (\alpha, \theta^-_{\nu-1}) = \kappa_{(\nu-1)(\nu-1)}\, u^+_{\nu-1}(\alpha,\ \theta^-_{\nu-1}) + \kappa_{\nu(\nu-1)}\, u^-_\nu\ (\alpha, \theta^+_\nu)$$

These relations with $\nu = 1, 2, \ldots N$ represent the system of functional equations for unknown functions $S^\pm_\nu(\alpha)$.

4. Matrices—Let us regroup $2N$ equations (32) in the following pairs:

$$u^+_\nu(\alpha,\ \theta^+_\nu) = \kappa_{(\nu-1)\nu}\, u^+_{\nu-1}(\alpha, \theta^-_{\nu-1}) + \kappa_{\nu\nu}\, u^-_\nu(\alpha, \theta^+_\nu),$$

$$u^-_\nu(\alpha, \theta^-_\nu) = \kappa_{\nu\nu}\, u^+_\nu(\alpha, \theta^-_\nu) + \kappa_{(\nu+1)\nu}\, u^-_{\nu+1}(\alpha, \theta^+_{\nu+1}) \tag{33}$$

and introduce the matrix-columns

$$X_\nu = \begin{Bmatrix} S_\nu^+(\alpha) \\ S_\nu^-(\alpha) \end{Bmatrix}, \qquad D_\nu = \begin{Bmatrix} D_\nu^+(\alpha) \\ D_\nu^-(\alpha) \end{Bmatrix}. \tag{34}$$

Let us introduce the operator transforming an arbitrary function as

$$m_\nu^\pm f(\alpha) = \pm f(\pm\alpha \mp \theta_\nu^\pm), \tag{35}$$

and the matrix-row operator as

$$M_\nu = (m_\nu^+, m_\nu^-). \tag{36}$$

Then the first item in equation (10) can be written in the matrix product form

$$S_\nu(\alpha) = M_\nu X_\nu. \tag{37}$$

Let us introduce the square matrices

$$\Delta_\nu^\pm = \begin{pmatrix} \delta_\nu^+(\theta_\nu^\pm) & 0 \\ 0 & \delta_\nu^-(\theta_\nu^\mp) \end{pmatrix} \tag{38}$$

and the square matrix operators

$$\chi_{(\nu-1)\nu} = \begin{pmatrix} \kappa_{(\nu-1)\nu} & 0 \\ 0 & 0 \end{pmatrix}, \quad \chi_{\nu\nu} = \begin{pmatrix} 0 & \kappa_{\nu\nu} \\ \kappa_{\nu\nu} & 0 \end{pmatrix}, \quad \chi_{(\nu+1)\nu} = \begin{pmatrix} 0 & 0 \\ 0 & \kappa_{(\nu+1)\nu} \end{pmatrix}. \tag{39}$$

Then the pair of equations (33) can be written as the single-matrix equation

$$X_\nu + \Delta_\nu^+ D_\nu = \chi_{(\nu-1)\nu}(X_{\nu-1} + \Delta_{\nu-1}^- D_{\nu-1}) +$$

$$+ \chi_{\nu\nu}(X_\nu + \Delta_\nu^- D_\nu) + \chi_{(\nu+1)\nu}(X_{\nu+1} + \Delta_{\nu+1}^- D_{\nu+1}). \tag{40}$$

Now the system of functional equations can be represented by N matrix equations (40) with $\nu = 1, 2, \dots N$.

Let us introduce the block column-matrices of the Nth order

$$\boldsymbol{X} = \begin{Bmatrix} X_1 \\ \cdot \\ \cdot \\ \cdot \\ X_N \end{Bmatrix}, \quad \boldsymbol{D} = \begin{Bmatrix} D_1 \\ \cdot \\ \cdot \\ \cdot \\ D_N \end{Bmatrix}, \quad \boldsymbol{S} = \begin{Bmatrix} S_1(\alpha) \\ \cdot \\ \cdot \\ \cdot \\ S_N(\alpha) \end{Bmatrix} \tag{41}$$

and the block diagonal-matrix of the N^{-th} order

$$\boldsymbol{M} = (m_{uv}), \tag{42}$$

$$m_{uv} = M_v, \text{ when } u = v; \; m_{uv} = (0, 0), \text{ when } u \neq v.$$

Then

$$\boldsymbol{S} = \boldsymbol{MX}. \tag{43}$$

Let us introduce the block diagonal-matrix of the N^{-th} order

$$\Delta^{\pm} = (\Delta^{\pm}_{uv}) \text{ with } u = 1, 2, \dots N, \quad v = 1, 2, \; N, \tag{44}$$

$$\Delta^{\pm}_{uv} = 0 \text{ with } u \neq v, \; \Delta^{\pm}_{uv} = \Delta^{\pm}_{v} \text{ with } u = v, \tag{45}$$

and the block square-matrix operator of the N^{-th} order

$$\boldsymbol{T} = (T_{uv}), \tag{46}$$

$$T_{1v} = \delta_{v1}\,\chi_{11} + \delta_{v2}\,\chi_{21} + \delta_{vN}\,\chi_{N2},$$

$$T_{uv} = \delta_{(u+1)v}\;\chi_{(v-1)v} + \delta_{uv}\;\chi_{vv} + \delta_{(u-1)v}\,\chi_{(v+1)v}, \quad 1 < v < N,$$

$$T_{Nv} = \delta_{v1}\,\chi_{1N} + \delta_{v(N-1)}\;\chi_{(N-1)N} + \delta_{vN}\;\chi_{NN},$$

where 0 is zero-matrix and δ_{uv} is the Kronecker δ. The structure of this matrix is shown in Figure 9 where the first bottom index corresponds to the column number and the second to the row number.

Now equation (40) can be considered as the v^{-th} row of the following matrix relation

$$\boldsymbol{X} + \Delta^{+}\,\boldsymbol{D} = \boldsymbol{T}\,(\boldsymbol{X} + \Delta^{-}\boldsymbol{D}). \tag{47}$$

$$\begin{pmatrix} B & C & & & & & \\ A & B & C & & & & \\ & A & B & C & & & \\ & & A & B & C & & \\ & & & \cdots & & & \\ & & & & A & B & C \\ & & & & & A & B \end{pmatrix}$$

Figure 9. Structure of the operator matrix. $A - T_{(\nu-1)\nu}$, $B - T_{\nu\nu}$, $C - T_{(\nu+1)\nu}$

This expression represents the system of functional equations in the form of the single-matrix equation.

3. Scalar problem

1. Perturbation—We are going to consider the case of the perturbation in the region with $\nu = k$, i.e.,

$$F_\nu \equiv 0\,, \text{ when } \nu \neq k\,. \tag{1}$$

Then the elements of the block matrices Δ and D comply with relations

$$D_\nu = 0\,, \text{ when } \nu \neq k\,, \tag{2}$$

$$\Delta^{\pm}_{u\nu} = \delta_{uk}\,\Delta^{\pm}_{k}\,,$$

$$\delta^{\pm}_{\nu}(\theta) = 0\,, \text{ when } \nu \neq k\,,$$

where 0 is zero-matrix and δ_{uk} the Kronecker symbol δ.

In this case we can get the possible combinations of perturbations from equations 2(12) - 2(14) with $\nu = k$ and $\nu = k+1$

$$F_k = F^{+}_{0k} + F^{-}_{0k} \quad \text{with } \theta = \theta^{\pm}_{k} \tag{3}$$

$$F_k = F^{+}_{0k} \text{ with } \theta = \theta^{+}_{k}\,, \quad F_k = F^{-}_{0k} \quad \text{with } \theta = \theta^{-}_{k}\,, \tag{4}$$

$$F_k = F_{0k}^- \text{ with } \theta = \theta_k^+, \quad F_k = F_{0k}^+ \quad \text{with } \theta = \theta_k^- . \tag{5}$$

The corresponding combinations of the unit functions we get from equations 2(15) - 2(17) with $\nu = k, \ \nu = k + 1$

$$\delta_k^\pm(\theta_k^+) = \delta_k^\pm(\theta_k^-) = 1 , \tag{6}$$

$$\delta_k^\pm(\theta_k^\pm) = 1, \quad \delta_k^\pm(\theta_k^\mp) = 0, \tag{7}$$

$$\delta_k^\pm(\theta_k^\pm) = 0, \quad \delta_k^\pm(\theta_k^\mp) = 1 . \tag{8}$$

2. *Variants of the problem formulation*—Let us consider each of the above given combinations of the perturbations separately.

In the case of equation (6) we get from equations 2(38) and 2(44)

$$\Delta_k^+ = \Delta_k^- = \begin{pmatrix} 1 & 0 \\ 0 & 1 \end{pmatrix}, \quad \Delta^\pm \boldsymbol{D} = \boldsymbol{D} . \tag{9}$$

Then equation 2(47) can be written as

$$\boldsymbol{X} + \boldsymbol{D} = \boldsymbol{T}(\boldsymbol{X} + \boldsymbol{D}) \tag{10}$$

and will have the evident solution

$$\boldsymbol{X} = -\boldsymbol{D} , \tag{11}$$

which is

$$S_\nu^\pm(\alpha) = 0 , \text{ when } \nu \neq k, \quad S_k^\pm(\alpha) = -D_k^\pm(\alpha) . \tag{12}$$

Then from equations 2(2), 2(5) and 2(6) we have

$$F_\nu^\pm = - F_{0\nu}^\pm , \tag{13}$$

and the desired solution is the trivial one

$$f_\nu = 0 . \tag{14}$$

Thus, this variant does not lead to the solution of the problem of forced oscillations, because it does not depend on the perturbation.

Let us take the combination in equation (7). Then from equations 2(38) and 2(44) we have

$$\Delta_k^+ = \begin{pmatrix} 1 & 0 \\ 0 & 1 \end{pmatrix}, \quad \Delta_k^- = \begin{pmatrix} 0 & 0 \\ 0 & 0 \end{pmatrix}, \quad \Delta^+ \boldsymbol{D} = \boldsymbol{D}, \quad \Delta^- D = 0 \tag{15}$$

and equation 2(47) can be written as

$$\boldsymbol{X} + \boldsymbol{D} = \boldsymbol{TX}. \tag{16}$$

In the case of equation (8) from equations 2(38) and 2(44) we have

$$\Delta_k^+ = \begin{pmatrix} 0 & 0 \\ 0 & 0 \end{pmatrix}, \quad \Delta_k^- = \begin{pmatrix} 1 & 0 \\ 0 & 1 \end{pmatrix}, \quad \Delta^+ \boldsymbol{D} = \boldsymbol{0}, \quad \Delta^- \boldsymbol{D} = \boldsymbol{D} \tag{17}$$

and equation 2(47) can be written as

$$\boldsymbol{X} = \boldsymbol{T}(\boldsymbol{X} + \boldsymbol{D}). \tag{18}$$

We will show that the solution of equation (18) can be expressed through the solution of equation (16). Let $\boldsymbol{X}'$ satisfy equation (16), i.e.,

$$\boldsymbol{X}' + \boldsymbol{D} = \boldsymbol{TX}'. \tag{19}$$

Let us apply the operator $\boldsymbol{T}$ to this equation

$$\boldsymbol{TX}' + \boldsymbol{TD} = \boldsymbol{T}(\boldsymbol{TX}'). \tag{20}$$

By denoting

$$\boldsymbol{X}'' = -\boldsymbol{TX}' \tag{21}$$

we can write equation (20) in the form

$$\boldsymbol{X}'' = \boldsymbol{T}(\boldsymbol{X}'' + \boldsymbol{D}). \tag{22}$$

Now we can see that $\boldsymbol{X}''$ complies with equation (18). Thus, the solution $\boldsymbol{X}''$ of equation (18) can be expressed through the solution $\boldsymbol{X}'$ of equation (16) by relation (21).

The summation of equations (19) and (22) shows that the sum $\boldsymbol{X}' + \boldsymbol{X}''$ complies with equation (10). Then from equation (11) we have

$$\boldsymbol{X}' + \boldsymbol{X}'' = -\boldsymbol{D}. \tag{23}$$

Thus, we can use any of the two possible combinations from equations (7) or (8) to state the problem of forced oscillations. The corresponding solutions are connected by relations (21) and (23). In the following we express the perturbation by equation (5).

3. Condition of correctness—The mathematical substantiation of the statement of the problem implies the demonstration of the existence and uniqueness of its solution, as well as its continuous dependence on the initial data. Here we explain how this is related to the problem under consideration.

It is well-known that the solution of the inhomogeneous equation

$$\boldsymbol{X} - \boldsymbol{TX} = \boldsymbol{F}, \quad \boldsymbol{F} = \boldsymbol{TD} \tag{24}$$

is unique if the corresponding homogeneous equation

$$\boldsymbol{X} - \boldsymbol{TX} = \boldsymbol{O} \tag{25}$$

has only the trivial solution $\boldsymbol{X} = \boldsymbol{O}$. This means that the statement of the problem must prevent the possibility of *free oscillations*. Such types of oscillations are possible, in principle, if the right part of the equation is linearly dependent on the solution

$$\boldsymbol{F} = (1 - \lambda)\boldsymbol{X}, \tag{26}$$

where λ is some constant. Then equation (24) can be reduced to the form

$$\lambda\boldsymbol{X} - \boldsymbol{TX} = \boldsymbol{O}. \tag{27}$$

In principle, such an equation can have the nontrivial solution $\boldsymbol{X} \neq \boldsymbol{O}$, corresponding to some values of λ, called *eigenvalues*. Thus, equation (24) has only one solution if λ is not the eigenvalue of equation (27).

All this puts some limitations on the parameters of the operator $\boldsymbol{T}$. However, we cannot find these limitations so far, because the theory of this type of functional equations is still undeveloped. Only in the particular case of $c_\nu = c_k$ $(\nu = 1, 2)$ can we demonstrate the uniqueness of solution (see Chapter III).

Now let us rewrite equation (24) in the form

$$LX = F, \quad L = I - T, \tag{28}$$

where I is the operator of identical transformation $IX = X$. The linear operator L acts from some domain M of the linear metric space of matrices X into some domain N of the linear metric space of matrices LX The solution of equation (28) exists if the matrices F are the elements of the domain N. Only in this case is there an inverse operator L^{-1}. The latter puts in correspondence the element X from M to any element F from N, i.e., $X = L^{-1}F$. It is essential that this condition put some limitation on the choice of F.

The solution continuously has to depend on initial data. When choosing the matrix F, we may understand it in the following way. Let $X(n)$ be some sequence of solutions of the equation $LX(n) = F(n)$ with $n = 1, 2, \ldots$. Let us suppose the existence of some limit $F(n) \to F$ with $n \to \infty$. Then there has to exist the same kind of limit $X(n) \to X$ with $n \to \infty$, where $LX = F$.

4. Reduced equation—It is impossible, so far, to formulate conditions of correctness of equation (28) in the form of restrictions for parameters of the problem because of the very complicated form of the functional operator. However, the information necessary for the edge wave theory can be obtained directly from equation (24) without studying the mentioned conditions. We give the form of equation (28) which allows us to obtain the necessary information. By introducing the operator

$$AX = TX + TD \tag{29}$$

we can rewrite equation (24) as

$$X = AX. \tag{30}$$

By successively using this operator we have

$$AX = TX + TD,$$

$$A(AX) = A^2 X = T^2 X + T^2 D + TD$$

$$A^n X = T^n X + \sum_{p=1}^{n} T^p D, \tag{31}$$

where A^n and T^n denote the n-fold use of the corresponding operators. From equations (30) and (31) we have

$$X = AX = A^2X = A^n X. \tag{32}$$

These relations for any integer $n \geq 1$ can be rewritten in the form

$$X = T^nX + X^n, \tag{33}$$

where

$$X^n = AX^{n-1} \tag{34}$$

or, stated another way,

$$X^n = \sum_{p=1}^{n} X^{(p)}, \quad X^{(p)} = TX^{(p-1)} = T^p D. \tag{35}$$

Substituting equation (33) into equation 2(43) gives

$$S = MT^n X + \sum_{p=1}^{n} MT^pD. \tag{36}$$

5. *The method of successive approximations*—Because equation (36) holds true for any $n \geq 1$, we can try to take it to the limit with $n \to \infty$. If there is the limit

$$T^n X = O, \quad \text{when } n \to \infty, \tag{37}$$

equation (36) gives the sought solution

$$S = \sum_{p=1}^{\infty} MT^p D. \tag{38}$$

Then equations (34) and (35) would be used as the recursion formulas of the successive approximations method.

6. *Consideration of the incident wave*—Let us introduce a perturbation in such a way that it would take into consideration the incident wave. Let $\alpha_k^{\pm}$ be the angle between the interface $\theta = \theta_k^{\pm}$ and the direction, opposite to the incident wave vector (Figure 10). Then the incident wave equation 1(2), can be rewritten in the form

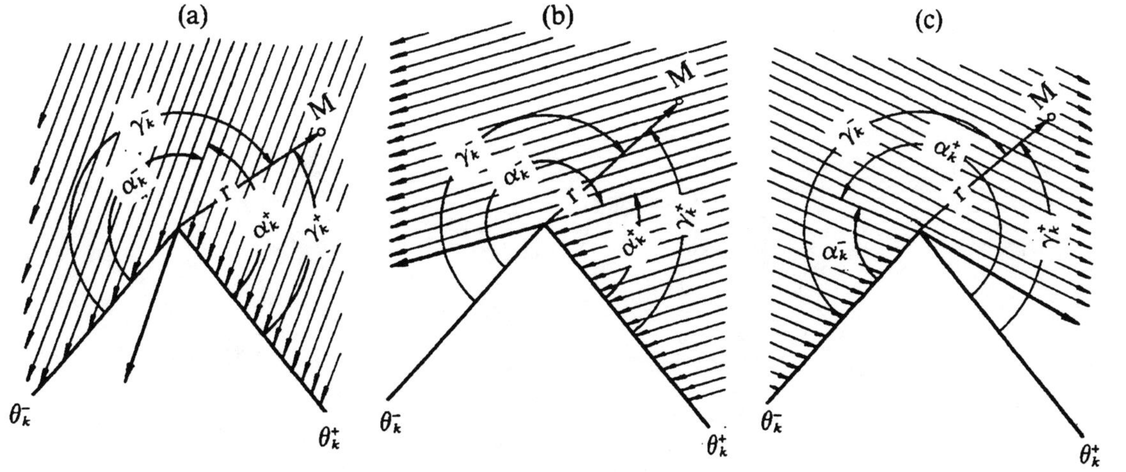

Figure 10. Angles $\alpha_k^{\pm}$ ***in equation II.3(39). (a) the shadow zone is absent. (b) the shadow zone:*** $\gamma_k^+ - \alpha_k^+ > \pi, \gamma_k^- - \alpha_k^- < -\pi$. ***(c) the shadow zone:*** $\gamma_k^+ - \alpha_k^+ < -\pi, \gamma_k^- - \alpha_k^- > \pi$

$$f_0 = \exp\,[\,-ik_k r\,\cos\,(\,\gamma_k^{\pm} - \alpha_k^{\pm}\,)\,]\,. \tag{39}$$

Let us write the function $D_k^{\pm}(\,\alpha\,)$ from equation 2(6) as follows:

$$D_k^{\pm}(\,\alpha\,) = (\,\alpha - \alpha_k^{\pm}\,)^{-1}\,A_k^{\pm}(\,\alpha - \alpha_k^{\pm}\,)\,, \tag{40}$$

where $A_k^{\pm}(\,\alpha\,)$ is some function, regular at $\alpha = 0$, and

$$A_k^{\pm}(\,0\,) = 1\,. \tag{41}$$

We will show that the integral 2(6) takes into account the incident wave (39).

Let us substitute equation (40) into equation 2(6) with $\nu = k$. If the point $\alpha = \alpha_k^{\pm}$ belongs to the interval

$$-\,\pi < \alpha - \gamma_k^{\pm} < \pi\,, \tag{42}$$

the integral has the simple pole at $\alpha = \alpha_k^{\pm}$. By substituting this value into equation (42) we can rewrite the latter in the form

$$-\pi < \gamma_k^{\pm} - \alpha_k^{\pm} < \pi \, . \tag{43}$$

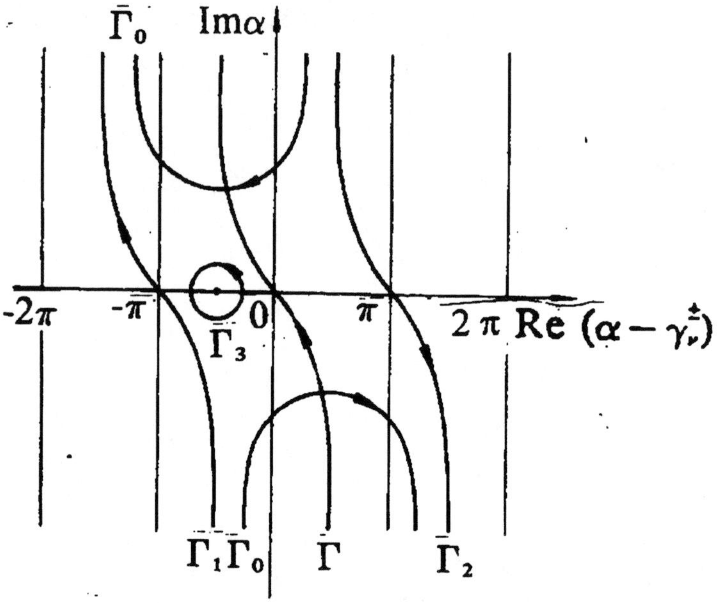

Figure 11. Transformation of the contour of integration.

Let us transform the contour of integration into two contours Γ_1 and Γ_2 (Figure 11). If condition (43) holds true, we have to add the closed contour Γ_3, going counterclockwise around the pole $\alpha = \alpha_k^{\pm}$. Then

$$F_{0k}^{\pm} = f_{0k}^{\pm} + F_{1k}^{\pm} + F_{2k}^{\pm}, \quad \text{when } -\pi < \gamma_k^{\pm} - \alpha_k^{\pm} < \pi ,$$
$$\tag{44}$$
$$F_{0k}^{\pm} = F_{1k}^{\pm} + F_{2k}^{\pm}, \quad \text{when } \gamma_k^{\pm} - \alpha_k^{\pm} < -\pi \quad \text{or } \gamma_k^{\pm} - \alpha_k^{\pm} < \pi ,$$

where

$$f_{0k}^{\pm} = f_0 , \tag{45}$$

$$F_{nk}^{\pm} = (1/2\pi i) \int_{\Gamma_n} (\alpha - \alpha_k^{\pm})^{-1} A_k^{\pm}(\alpha - \alpha_k^{\pm}) \exp\left[-i k_k r \cos(\alpha - \gamma_k^{\pm})\right] d\alpha \, . \tag{46}$$

Here the term equation (45), corresponds to the residue at the above-mentioned pole.

Equations (44) have a clear physical interpretation. On one hand, they take into account the incident wave, equation (39), within the domain, where its existence is admitted by the geometrical acoustics (Figure 10). The domain, where condition (43) is not satisfied, is the shadow zone of the incident wave. In the framework of geometrical acoustics such a situation would lead to the discontinuity of the wavefield at the shadow boundary. On the other hand, equations (44) describe the continuous field complying with the Helmholtz equation within the entire domain $\theta_k^+ \leq \theta \leq \theta_k^-$. This is provided by the terms $F_{1k}^{\pm}$ and $F_{2k}^{\pm}$. Thus, the incident wave happens to be only a part of the whole perturbation.

We cannot find the whole set of functions $A_k^{\pm}(\alpha)$, guaranteeing the existence of solution of the problem. However, we can try some particular functions. We take

$$A_k^{\pm}(\alpha - \alpha_k^{\pm}) = \exp\left[-\zeta_0(\alpha - \alpha_k^{\pm})\right] \quad \text{with } \zeta_0 > 0, \tag{47}$$

where ζ_0 is some arbitrary parameter. By substituting equations (40) and (47) into equation 2(6) and introducing a new variable of integration $\alpha' = \alpha - \alpha_k^{\pm}$ we have

$$F_{0k}^{\pm} = (1/2\pi i) \int_{\Gamma_0} (\alpha')^{-1} \exp\left[(-\zeta_0 \alpha') - ik_k r \cos(\alpha' - \xi_k^{\pm})\right] d\alpha', \quad \xi_k^{\pm} = \gamma_k^{\pm} - \alpha_k^{\pm}. \tag{48}$$

Because these functions comply with the following conditions:

$$F_{0k}^{+} = F_{0k}^{-}, \; \partial^n F_{0k}^{+}/(\partial\xi_k^{+})^n = \partial^n F_{0k}^{-}/(\partial\xi_k^{-})^n \text{ with } n = 1, 2, \ldots, \; \textit{when} \; \xi_k^{\pm} = 0,$$

we can describe the perturbation as

$$F_k = \delta^*(\xi_k^+) F_{0k}^+ + \delta^*(\xi_k^-) F_{0k}^-, \tag{49}$$

$$\delta^*(\xi) = 0, \text{ when } \xi < 0, \quad \delta^*(\xi) = 1, \text{ when } \xi > 0.$$

It is the continuous analytic function of θ within the region $\theta_k^+ \leq \theta$, $\theta \leq \theta_k^-$. Of special interest is the case of the plane-wave diffraction which appears as a result of taking the solution to the limit with $\zeta_0 \to 0$. We have only managed to study this limit in the simplest case of $c_\nu = c_k\, (\nu = 1, 2)$ (see Chapter III). When $\zeta_0 \to 0$, the solution gets unlimited, and the limit [equation (37)] does not exist. However, the limit [equation (38)] does exist and coincides with the closed form of solution of the problem with $\zeta_0 = 0$.

7. Complex poles—Because function (40) has a pole, the elements of matrix ***TD*** in equation (18) have poles also. The integrals 1(18) exist if the singular points of the integrands belong to the allowable domains [equation 1(20)] i.e.,

$$\text{sign}\ (\text{Re}\,\alpha - \gamma_v^{\pm} - 2k\pi) = \text{sign Im}\ \alpha \quad \text{with } k = -1,\ 0,\ 1\,. \tag{50}$$

Here we consider how this condition can be satisfied for the above-mentioned poles.

The elements of matrix *TD* have the form

$$\kappa_{uv} D_u^{\pm}(\alpha) = [\varphi_{uv}(\alpha) + \varepsilon_u - \alpha_u^{\pm}]^{-1} \left\{ \tau_{uv}(\alpha) K_{uv}(\alpha) A_u^{\pm} [\varphi_{uv}(\alpha) + \varepsilon_u] \right\} \tag{51}$$

with $u = k,\ v = k$ or $v = k - 1$, *or* $v = k + 1$. The pole of this function can be found from the equation

$$\varphi_{uv}(\alpha) = -a, \quad a = \varepsilon_u - \alpha_u^{\pm} \geq 0 \tag{52}$$

which has the following solution:

$$\alpha^* = -\varphi_{vu}(a) = -\text{arc cos}\ [(c_v/c_u)\ \cos\ a]\,. \tag{53}$$

Equations (B-14) - (B-17) of Appendix B show that this formula defines the pole uniquely under the following condition:

$$\cos\ a \leq c_u/c_v\,. \tag{54}$$

If this is not so, then function (53) transforms the real value a into the pair of complex-conjugate values

$$\alpha^* = \text{Re}\ \alpha^* \pm i\ \text{Im}\ \alpha^*, \tag{55}$$

where

$$\text{Re}\ \alpha^* = -k\pi,\ \text{if } k\pi \leq a < k\pi + \text{arccos}\ (c_v/c_u),$$

$$\text{Re}\ \alpha^* = -(k+1)\pi,\ \text{if } (k+1)\pi - \text{arc cos}\ (c_v/c_u) < a \leq (k+1)\pi,$$

$$\text{Im}\ \alpha^* = \text{arsh}\ \{[(c_v/c_u)\ \cos\ a]^2 - 1\}^{1/2}$$

with $k = 0$ or $k = 1$.

The uncertainty of the choice of the signs in equation (55) can be solved by taking into acount condition (50). The sign "plus" breaks this condition, when $\gamma_\nu^\pm < \pi$. The sign "minus" satisfies the condition with $0 \le \gamma_\nu^\pm \le 2\pi$. So we have to take the "minus." Then the position of the pole in the complex plane of α complies with the following unequalities:

$$\mathrm{Re}\ \alpha^* \le 0\,, \quad \mathrm{Im}\ \alpha^* \le 0\,. \tag{56}$$

Section V.1.2. shows that these inequalities guarantee the unique description of that part of the solution, which corresponds to edge waves.

4. General case

1. Vector diffraction problem—The above approach can be expanded to the case of vector waves (elastodynamics, electrodynamics), because their scalar potentials comply with Helmholtz equation.

Let us return to the system of wedge-shaped regions shown in Figure 5. Let $c_{\nu 1}$ and $c_{\nu 2}$ be two possible wave velocities in the region $\theta_\nu^+ \le \theta$, $\theta \le \theta_\nu^-$. For example, in the elastodynamics case they are the longitudinal and transverse wave velocities, respectively. Let the incident wave be given by the expression

$$F_{kg}^0 = \exp\left[\, ik_{kg}\, r\ \cos\left(\theta - \theta_{kg}\right)\right], \quad k_{\nu g} = \omega / c_{\nu g} \ \text{ with } \nu = k\,;\ g = 1 \text{ or } g = 2\,, \tag{1}$$

where θ_{kg} is the direction of incidence.

The incident wave causes in each region additional wavefields of the same frequency ω. The total wavefields $f_{\nu 1}$ and $f_{\nu 2}$ in each region must comply with the Helmholtz equations

$$\left(\Delta + k_{\nu\ell}^2\right) f_{\nu\ell} = 0 \quad \text{with } \ell = 1, 2\,. \tag{2}$$

For example, in the elastodynamics case they are the fields of the longitudinal ($\ell = 1$) and transverse ($\ell = 2$) potentials.

We consider the case of the general linear-boundary conditions at the interfaces

$$\sum_{t\ell} D^{\nu}_{qt\ell} f_{t\ell} = 0 \text{ with } \theta = \theta^{+}_{\nu} = \theta^{-}_{\nu-1} \tag{3}$$

$$t = \nu,\ \nu - 1;\ \ell = 1, 2;\ q = 1, 2, 3, 4,\ \nu = 1, 2, \ldots N;$$

$$D^{\nu}_{qt\ell} \sum_{m_{q\ell} + n_{q\ell} = 0}^{M_{q\ell}} C^{\nu}_{m_{q\ell} n_{q\ell} t\ell}\ \partial^{m_{q\ell} + n_{q\ell}} / \partial x^{m_{q\ell}}\ \partial y^{n_{q\ell}}$$

$$x = r \cos(\theta - \theta^{+}_{\nu}),\ y = r \sin(\theta^{+}_{\nu}),$$

where $C^{\nu}_{m_{q\ell} n_{q\ell} t\ell}$ and $M_{q\ell}$ are some given constants. The summation must be carried over indices $t\ell$ of all functions $f_{t\ell}$, whose domains border on the interface $\theta^{+}_{\nu} = \theta^{-}_{\nu-1}$. The different types of boundary conditions can be written in this form by choosing the above-mentioned constants. One can be an ideal contact between elastic media or the visco-elastic contact, etc. These conditions include the case, when in the separate λ^{th} region (or several regions) exist not two but the one wave velocity $c_{\nu 1}$ (for example, the contact between the elastic and fluid media). In that case $C_{m_{q\ell}}\ n^{\nu}_{q\ell}\ t\ell = 0$, when $t = \lambda,\ \ell = 2$.

We suppose that the choice of the constants in boundary conditions does not contradict the existence of a solution. Then the problem of forced oscillations can be reduced to finding the solution of equations (2) subject to conditions (3).

2. *Representation of scalar potentials*—Let us look for the solution in the form

$$f_{\nu\ell} = \delta_{k\nu}\, \delta_{\ell g} F_{0kg} + F^{+}_{\nu\ell} + F^{-}_{\nu\ell}, \tag{4}$$

$$F_{0kg} = \delta^{*}(\gamma^{+}_{\nu} - \alpha^{+}_{kg}) F^{+}_{0kg} + \delta^{*}(\gamma^{-}_{\nu} - \alpha^{-}_{kg}) F^{-}_{0kg}$$

$$F^{\pm}_{0kg} = (1/2\pi i) \int_{\Gamma_o} D^{\pm}_{kg}(\alpha) \exp(-ik_{kg}\ \eta^{\pm}_{k})\, d\alpha,$$

$$F^{\pm}_{\nu\ell} = (1/2\pi i) \int_{\Gamma_o} S^{\pm}_{\nu\ell}(\alpha) \exp(-ik_{\nu\ell}\eta^{\pm}_{\nu})\, d\alpha,$$

$$D^{\pm}_{kg}(\alpha) = (\alpha - \alpha^{\pm}_{kg})^{-1} A^{\pm}_{kg}(\alpha - \alpha^{\pm}_{kg}), \; A^{\pm}_{kg}(\alpha) = \exp\left[-\zeta_0(\alpha - \alpha^{\pm}_{kg})\right],$$

where $\alpha^{\pm}_{kg}$ is the angle between the interface $\theta = \theta^{\pm}_k$ and the direction, opposite to the wave vector of the incident wave (1). The term $\eta^{\pm}_{\nu}$ is defined in equation 2(22) and function $\delta^*(\xi)$ in equation 3(49). The term δ_{uv} is the Kronecker symbol δ. The contour of integration is shown in Figure 6. The residues of the integrals $F^{\pm}_{0kg}$ at poles $\alpha = \alpha^{\pm}_{kg}$ give the incident wave in equation (1).

3. Transformation of boundary conditions—Because the perturbation at the interfaces is represented in the form

$$F_{0kg} = F^{-}_{0kg}, \text{ when } \theta = \theta^{+}_k; \quad F_{0kg} = F^{+}_{0kg}, \text{ when } \theta = \theta^{-}_k, \tag{5}$$

the boundary conditions can be rewritten as follows:

$$\sum_{\ell=1}^{2}\left[(D^{\nu}_{q\nu\ell}F^{+}_{\nu\ell})_{\theta=\theta^{+}_{\nu}} + (D^{\nu}_{q(\nu-1)\ell}F^{-}_{q(\nu-1)\ell})_{\theta=\theta^{-}_{\nu-1}}\right] = \tag{6}$$

$$-\sum_{\ell=1}^{2}\left\{\left[D^{\nu}_{q\nu\ell}\,(F^{-}_{\nu\ell} + \delta_{\nu k}\,\delta_{\ell g}\,F^{-}_{0\nu\ell})\right]_{\theta=\theta^{+}_{\nu}} + \right.$$

$$\left.\left[D^{\nu}_{q(\nu-1)\ell}\,(F^{+}_{(\nu-1)\ell} + \delta_{(\nu-1)k}\,\delta_{\ell g}\,F^{+}_{0(\nu-1)\ell})\right]_{\theta=\theta^{-}_{\nu-1}}\right\}$$

with $q = 1, 2, 3, 4; \quad \nu = 1, 2, \ldots N$.

Let us substitute the terms $F^{\pm}_{\nu\ell}$ and $F^{\pm}_{0\nu\ell}$ by the corresponding integrals from equations (4) with terms $\eta^{\pm}_{\nu}$ given by equations 2(22), perform the differentiation, and take $y = 0$. Then we substitute α by $(\alpha + \varepsilon_{\nu})$ in the integrals $F^{-}_{\nu\ell}$ and $F^{-}_{0\nu\ell}$, and α by $(\alpha + \varepsilon_{\nu-1})$ in the integrals $F^{+}_{(\nu-1)\ell}$ and $F^{+}_{0(\nu-1)\ell}$. After taking into account equation 1(8) we can write equations (6) in the form

$$\sum_{\ell=1}^{2} \int_{\Gamma_0} [A^{+}_{qv\ell}(\alpha) S^{+}_{v\ell}(\alpha) \exp(-ik_{v\ell}\, x \cos\alpha) + A^{-}_{q(v-1)\ell}(\alpha) S^{-}_{(v-1)\ell}(\alpha) \,.$$

$$\times \exp(-ik_{(v-1)\ell}\, x \cos\alpha)]\, d\alpha = -\sum_{\ell=1}^{2} \int_{\Gamma_0} [A^{-}_{qv\ell}(\alpha)\, x^{-}_{v\ell}(\alpha+\varepsilon_v)$$

$$\exp(-ik_{v\ell}\, x \cos\alpha) +$$

$$A^{+}_{q(v-1)\ell}(\alpha)\, x^{+}_{q(v-1)\ell}(\alpha+\varepsilon_{v-1}) \exp(-ik_{v-1}\, x \cos\alpha)]\, d\alpha$$

$$\text{with } q = 1,2,3,4; \quad v = 1,2,\ldots N; \tag{7}$$

$$A^{\pm}_{qt\ell}(\alpha) = \sum_{m_{q\ell}+n_{q\ell}=0}^{M_{q\ell}} (-ik_{t\ell})^{m_{q\ell}+n_{q\ell}} \cos^{m_{q\ell}}\alpha\, (\pm\sin\alpha)^{n_{q\ell}}\; C^{v}_{m_{q\ell}\, n_{q\ell}\, t\ell}$$

$$x^{\pm}_{t\ell}(\alpha) = S^{\pm}_{t\ell}(\alpha) + \delta_{tk}\, \delta_{\ell g} D^{\pm}_{t\ell}(\alpha) \tag{8}$$

Let us introduce a temporary notation for the functions and parameters in the left part of equation (7)

$$S^{\pm}_{vn}(\alpha) = x_j(\alpha),\; A^{\pm}_{qvn}(\alpha) = A_{qj}(\alpha),\; k_{vn} = k_j \;\text{ with } j = n + 1 - (\pm 1) \tag{9}$$

and the temporary notation in the right part of the same equation

$$x^{\pm}_{um}(\alpha) = y_h(\alpha),\; A^{\pm}_{qum}(\alpha) = B_{qh}(\alpha),\; k_{um} = k_h,\; \varepsilon_u = \varepsilon_h$$

$$\text{with } h = m + 1 \pm 1. \tag{10}$$

Then we can write equation (7) as

$$\sum_{j=1}^{4} \int_{\Gamma_0} A_{qj}(\alpha)\, x_j(\alpha) \exp(-ik_j x \cos\alpha)\, d\alpha = -\sum_{h=1}^{4} \int_{\Gamma_0} B_{qh}(\alpha)\, y_h(\alpha +$$

$$+\varepsilon_h) \exp(-ik_h x \cos\alpha)\, d\alpha, \;\text{ with } q = 1,2,3,4. \tag{11}$$

Let us substitute α by $\varphi_{jb}(\alpha)$ in all the left integrals and α by $\varphi_{hb}(\alpha)$ in all the right integrals. Then taking into account equation 1(9) we can rewrite equation (11) in the form

$$\int_{\Gamma_0} \left(\sum_{j=1}^{4} U_{qj} X_j + \sum_{h=1}^{4} v_{qh} Y_h \right) \exp(-ik_b \ x \cos \alpha) \, d\alpha = 0 \quad q = 1, 2, 3, 4 ; \tag{12}$$

$$U_{qj} = A_{qj} [\varphi_{jb}(\alpha)], \quad v_{qh} = B_{qh} [\varphi_{hb}(\alpha)],$$

$$X_j = \tau_{jb}(\alpha) x_j [\varphi_{jb}(\alpha)], \quad Y_h = \tau_{hb}(\alpha) y_h [\varphi_{hb}(\alpha) + \varepsilon_h]$$

These equations are satisfied if the factors, placed before exponents, are zero, i.e.,

$$\sum_{j=1}^{4} U_{qj} X_j = - \sum_{h=1}^{4} v_{qh} Y_h \quad \text{with } q = 1, 2, 3, 4 . \tag{13}$$

We can consider these equations as the system of linear equations for X_j.

Because $X_b = x_b(\alpha)$, the solution of this system for the unknown quantity with $j = b$ has the form

$$x_b(\alpha) = \det(V_{qj}) / \det(U_{qj}), \quad V_{qj} = (1 - \delta_{jb}) U_{qj} - \delta_{jb} \sum_{h=1}^{4} v_{qh} Y_h . \tag{14}$$

By using the rule of summation of determinants we have

$$\det(V_{qj}) = \sum_{h=1}^{4} \det(W_{qj}), \quad W_{qj} = (1 - \delta_{jb}) U_{qj} - \delta_{jb} v_{qh} Y_h . \tag{15}$$

Because Y_h does not depend on the row number q, we can factor it out of the determinant

$$\det(W_{qj}) = - Y_h \det(Q_{qj}), \quad Q_{qj} = (1 - \delta_{jb}) U_{qj} + \delta_{jb} v_{qj} . \tag{16}$$

By substituting equations (15) - (16) into equation (14) we obtain

$$x_b(\alpha) = \sum_{h=1}^{4} K_{hb}(\alpha) Y_h, \quad K_{hb}(\alpha) = - \det(Q_{qj}) / \det(U_{qj}) . \tag{17}$$

Let us introduce an operator transforming an arbitrary function as

$$\sigma_{hb} f(\alpha) = \tau_{hb}(\alpha) K_{hb}(\alpha) f(\varphi_{hb}(\alpha) + \varepsilon_h). \tag{18}$$

Then equation (17) can be written in the matrix product form

$$\{x_b(\alpha)\} = (\sigma_{hb})\{y_h(\alpha)\}; \quad \nu = 1, 2, \ldots N, \tag{19}$$

where $\{x_b(\alpha)\}$ and $\{y_h(\alpha)\}$ are column matrices ($b = 1, 2, 3, 4$; $h = 1, 2, 3, 4$), (σ_{hb}) is a square matrix (h is the column number and b is the row number).

Let us introduce a new notation for function $K_{hb}(\alpha)$ and represent the corresponding formula from equations (17) for this function in the form

$$K^{\pm}_{u(m)\nu(n)}(\alpha) = -\det(Q^{\pm}_{qj}) / \det(U_{qj}), \tag{20}$$

$$Q^{\pm}_{qj} = (1 - \delta_{jb\pm}) U_{qj} + \delta_{jb\pm} v_{qj\pm};$$

$$b^{\pm} = n \pm 1 \mp 1; \; j^{\pm} = m + 2(\nu - u) + 1 \mp 1 \quad \text{with } \nu = \nu \text{ or } \nu - 1,$$

$$u = \nu \text{ or } \nu - 1, \tag{21}$$

Here U_{qj} and v_{qj} can be expressed through the functions $A^{\pm} = A^{\pm}_{qtl}[\varphi_{t(l)\nu(n)}(\alpha)]$ as

$$U_{qj} = A^{+}, \; v_{qj} = A^{-}, \; t = \nu, \text{ when } j = 1, 2; \; U_{qj} = A^{-}, \; v_{qj} = A^{+}, \; t = \nu - 1,$$

$$\text{when } j = 3, 4; \; \ell = 1, \text{ when } j = 1, 3; \; \ell = 2, \text{ when } j = 2, 4. \tag{22}$$

If $\nu = 1$, then it is necessary to take $\nu - 1 = -1$, when computing $j^{\pm}$.

4. Matrix equation—Let us introduce operator $\sigma^{\pm}_{u(m)\nu(n)}$ that transforms an arbitrary function $f(\alpha)$ as follows:

$$\sigma^{\pm}_{u(m)\nu(n)} f(\alpha) = \tau_{u(m)\nu(n)}(\alpha) \; K^{\pm}_{u(m)\nu(n)}(\alpha) f[\varphi_{u(m)\nu(n)}(\alpha) + \varepsilon_u], \tag{23}$$

where $\varphi_{u(m)\nu(n)}(\alpha)$ and $\tau_{u(m)\nu(n)}(\alpha)$ are defined by equations 1(10) and 1(11). Then matrix (σ_{hb}) can be represented in the form

$$(\sigma_{hb}) = \begin{pmatrix} \kappa^{+}_{\nu\nu} & \kappa^{+}_{(\nu-1)\nu} \\ \kappa^{-}_{\nu(\nu-1)} & \kappa^{-}_{(\nu-1)(\nu-1)} \end{pmatrix}, \quad \kappa^{\pm}_{uv} = \begin{pmatrix} \sigma^{\pm}_{u(1)v(1)} & \sigma^{\pm}_{u(2)v(1)} \\ \sigma^{\pm}_{u(1)v(2)} & \sigma^{\pm}_{u(2)v(2)} \end{pmatrix}. \tag{24}$$

Let us introduce the column matrices

$$X^{\pm}_{\nu} = \begin{Bmatrix} S^{\pm}_{\nu(1)}(\alpha) \\ S^{\pm}_{\nu(2)}(\alpha) \end{Bmatrix}, \quad D^{\pm}_{\nu} = \begin{Bmatrix} \delta_{k\nu}\,\delta_{1g}\,D^{\pm}_{\nu(1)}(\alpha) \\ \delta_{k\nu}\,\delta_{2g}\,D^{\pm}_{\nu(2)}(\alpha) \end{Bmatrix} \tag{25}$$

Then

$$\{x_b(\alpha)\} = \begin{Bmatrix} X^{+}_{\nu} \\ X^{-}_{\nu-1} \end{Bmatrix}, \quad \{y_h(\alpha)\} = \begin{Bmatrix} X^{-}_{\nu} + D^{-}_{\nu} \\ X^{+}_{\nu-1} + D^{+}_{\nu-1} \end{Bmatrix} \tag{26}$$

By substituting equations (24) and (26) into equation (19) we have

$$\begin{Bmatrix} X^{+}_{\nu} \\ X^{-}_{\nu-1} \end{Bmatrix} = \begin{pmatrix} \kappa^{+}_{\nu\nu} & \kappa^{+}_{(\nu-1)\nu} \\ \kappa^{-}_{\nu(\nu-1)} & \kappa^{-}_{(\nu-1)(\nu-1)} \end{pmatrix} \cdot \begin{Bmatrix} X^{-}_{\nu} + D^{-}_{\nu} \\ X^{+}_{\nu-1} + D^{+}_{\nu-1} \end{Bmatrix} \quad \text{with } \nu = 1, 2, \ldots N \tag{27}$$

By introducing matrices

$$X_{\nu} = \begin{Bmatrix} X^{+}_{\nu} \\ X^{-}_{\nu} \end{Bmatrix}, \quad D_{\nu} = \begin{Bmatrix} D^{+}_{\nu} \\ D^{-}_{\nu} \end{Bmatrix}, \quad T_{uv} = \begin{Bmatrix} \delta^{+}_{uv}\,\kappa^{+}_{uv} & \delta_{uv}\,\kappa^{+}_{uv} \\ \delta^{-}_{uv}\,\kappa^{-}_{uv} & \delta^{-}_{uv}\,\kappa^{-}_{uv} \end{Bmatrix}, \tag{28}$$

$$\delta^{\pm}_{uv} = \delta_{(u+1)v} + \delta_{(u-1)v} \quad \text{with } N = 2,$$

$$\delta^{\pm}_{uv} = \delta_{(u\pm1)v} + \delta^{*}_{\pm}(\delta_{uN}\,\delta_{1v} + \delta_{u1}\,\delta_{Nv}) \quad \text{with } N > 2,$$

$$\delta^{*}_{\pm} = [\,1 + (\pm1)\,(u-v)/\,|\,u - v\,|\,]/2 \quad \text{with } u \neq v, \;\; \delta^{*}_{\pm} = 0 \quad \text{with } u = v,$$

we can rewrite equation (27) in the form

$$\boldsymbol{X} = \boldsymbol{TX} + \boldsymbol{TD}, \tag{29}$$

where $\boldsymbol{X} = \{ X_v \}$ and $\boldsymbol{D} = \{ D_v \}$ are the block matrices of the Nth order and $\boldsymbol{T} = (T_{uv})$ is the square-block matrix of the Nth order (u is the column number, v is the row number).

The structure of matrix $\boldsymbol{T}$ looks like this:

$$
\mathbf{T} = \left[\begin{array}{cc|cc|cc c cc|cc|cc}
0 & \kappa_{11}^{+} & 0 & 0 & 0 & 0 & & 0 & 0 & 0 & 0 & \kappa_{N1}^{+} & 0 \\
\kappa_{11}^{-} & 0 & 0 & \kappa_{21}^{-} & 0 & 0 & & 0 & 0 & 0 & 0 & 0 & 0 \\
\hline
\kappa_{12}^{+} & 0 & 0 & \kappa_{22}^{+} & 0 & 0 & \cdots & 0 & 0 & 0 & 0 & 0 & 0 \\
0 & 0 & \kappa_{22}^{-} & 0 & 0 & \kappa_{32}^{-} & & 0 & 0 & 0 & 0 & 0 & 0 \\
\hline
0 & 0 & \kappa_{23}^{+} & 0 & 0 & \kappa_{33}^{+} & & 0 & 0 & 0 & 0 & 0 & 0 \\
0 & 0 & 0 & 0 & \kappa_{33}^{-} & 0 & & 0 & 0 & 0 & 0 & 0 & 0 \\
\hline
 & & \cdots & & & & & & & \cdots & & & \\
\hline
0 & 0 & 0 & 0 & 0 & 0 & & \bullet & \bullet & \bullet & \bullet & \bullet & \bullet \\
0 & 0 & 0 & 0 & 0 & 0 & & \bullet & \bullet & \bullet & \bullet & \bullet & \bullet \\
\hline
0 & 0 & 0 & 0 & 0 & 0 & \cdots & \bullet & \bullet & \bullet & \bullet & \bullet & \bullet \\
0 & 0 & 0 & 0 & 0 & 0 & & \bullet & \bullet & \bullet & \bullet & \bullet & \bullet \\
\hline
0 & 0 & 0 & 0 & 0 & 0 & & \bullet & \bullet & \bullet & \bullet & 0 & \kappa_{NN}^{+} \\
0 & \kappa_{1N}^{-} & 0 & 0 & 0 & 0 & & \bullet & \bullet & \bullet & \bullet & \kappa_{NN}^{-} & 0
\end{array} \right] \tag{30}
$$

where the separate blocks T_{uv} correspond to the separate cells.

If $N = 2$, this matrix has the form

$$\mathbf{T} = \left[\begin{array}{cc|cc} 0 & \kappa_{11}^{+} & \kappa_{21}^{+} & 0 \\ \kappa_{11}^{-} & 0 & 0 & \kappa_{21}^{-} \\ \hline \kappa_{12}^{+} & 0 & 0 & \kappa_{22}^{+} \\ 0 & \kappa_{12}^{-} & \kappa_{22}^{-} & 0 \end{array}\right] \qquad (31)$$

Let us mention characteristic features of matrix (30) with $N > 2$. The matrix can be represented as the sum of three block matrices: $\boldsymbol{T} = \boldsymbol{T}^{*} + \boldsymbol{T}^{+} + \boldsymbol{T}^{-}$. In matrix $\boldsymbol{T}^{*}$ only those blocks are not zero which coincide with the central diagonal and with two neighboring diagonals. Each of the matrices $\boldsymbol{T}^{+}$ and $\boldsymbol{T}^{-}$ has only one nonzero block T_{N1} and T_{1N}, respectively. In the blocks of the central diagonal only those elements are nonzero which belong to the left bottom and the right top corners. In the blocks of the left diagonal and in T_{N1} the only left top element is nonzero. In the blocks of the right diagonal and in T_{1N} the only right bottom element is nonzero.

Equation (29) expresses the boundary conditions (3) in the form of the system of functional equations for the unknown functions $S_{\nu l}^{\pm}(\alpha)$. It has the form of a single-matrix equation like in the scalar case. Thus, the case of vector waves differs from the scalar case by the structure of matrix blocks and by the reflection / transmission coefficients. That is why in the following we may limit our analysis to the scalar case.

Chapter III

EXAMPLES OF THE CONVERGENCE OF THE SUCCESSIVE APPROXIMATION METHOD

The solution of the problem of forced oscillations can be reduced to finding a solution to the system of functional equations II.4(29). However, this system is so complicated that there is little hope in finding its solution in the closed form. That is why in diffraction theory it is important to study the successive approximations method for this system in those particular situations where it is possible. In this Chapter we consider the particular case of diffraction on the acoustic wedge, when $c_1 = c_2$, and the incident wave is given in the region $\nu = 1$.

1. Series of successive approximations

1. Representation of matrix elements by series—In the following we have to study every single element of matrix $\boldsymbol{X}$ from equation II.3(18). To introduce the corresponding representation, we denote $(T^p D)^{\pm}_{\nu}$ a single element of matrix $T^p D$ by putting all elements in order in the same way as we did for matrix $\boldsymbol{X}$, i.e., in equation II.3(33) - II.3(35)

$$S^{\pm}_{\nu}(\alpha) = \sum_{p=1}^{n} (T^p D)^{\pm}_{\nu} \quad \text{with } n \to \infty . \tag{1}$$

Every item of this series can be represented by a finite sum. Let us introduce the corresponding notations. By performing the operation $T^p D = TT^{p-1} D$ we have

$$(T^p D)^{\pm}_1 = \kappa_{11}\,(T^{p-1} D)^{\mp}_1 + \kappa_{21}\,(T^{p-1} D)^{\pm}_2 , \tag{2}$$

$$(T^p D)^{\pm}_2 = \kappa_{12}\,(T^{p-1} D)^{\pm}_1 + \kappa_{22}\,(T^{p-1} D)^{\mp}_2 ,$$

where $(T^0 D)^{\mp}_1 = D^{\mp}_1$,, $(T^0 D)^{\pm}_2 = 0$.

By using these relations repeatedly with $p = 1, 2, \ldots$ we have

$$(T^1 D)^{\pm}_1 = \kappa_{11}\, D^{\mp}_1 , \quad (T^1 D)^{\pm}_2 = \kappa_{12}\, D^{\pm}_1 , \tag{3}$$

$$(T^2 D)_1^{\pm} = \kappa_{11}\,\kappa_{11}\,D_1^{\pm} + \kappa_{21}\,\kappa_{12}\,D_1^{\pm},\quad (T^2 D)_2^{\pm} = \kappa_{12}\,\kappa_{11}\,D_1^{\mp} + \kappa_{22}\,\kappa_{12}\,D_1^{\mp},$$

$$(T^3 D)_1^{\pm} = \kappa_{11}\kappa_{11}\kappa_{11}\,D_1^{\mp} + \kappa_{11}\kappa_{21}\kappa_{12}\,D_1^{\mp} + \kappa_{21}\kappa_{12}\kappa_{11}\,D_1^{\mp} + \kappa_{21}\kappa_{22}\kappa_{12}\,D_1^{\mp},$$

$$(T^3 D)_2^{\pm} = \kappa_{12}\kappa_{11}\kappa_{11}\,D_1^{\pm} + \kappa_{12}\kappa_{21}\kappa_{12}\,D_1^{\pm} + \kappa_{22}\kappa_{12}\kappa_{11}\,D_1^{\pm} + \kappa_{22}\kappa_{22}\kappa_{12}\,D_1^{\pm},$$

etc. This process can be continued infinitely. However, the structure of arising expressions can be guessed by the induction.

The corresponding expression can be written as

$$(T^p D)_\nu^{\pm} = \sum_{m(p)=1}^{N(p)} X_{m(p)},\quad X_{m(p)} = \kappa_{m(p)} D_{m(p)}(\alpha), \tag{4}$$

$$D_{m(p)}(\alpha) = (\alpha + a_{m(p)}^{\pm})^{-1} \exp\left[-\zeta_0\,(\alpha - \alpha_1^{\pm})\right],$$

$$\alpha_{m(p)}^{\pm} = -\begin{cases} \alpha_1^{\pm} & \text{even} \\ & \text{with } p \\ \alpha_1^{\mp} & \text{odd} \end{cases} \quad \text{for } \nu = 1,$$

$$\alpha_{m(p)}^{\pm} = -\begin{cases} \alpha_1^{\mp} & \text{even} \\ & \text{with } p \\ \alpha_1^{\pm} & \text{odd} \end{cases} \quad \text{for } \nu = 2$$

where $m(p) = 1, 2, \ldots N(p)$ is the number of each term with $N(p) = 2^{p-1}$ being the total number of terms. The term $\kappa_{m(p)}$ represents the product of p operators

$$\kappa_{m(p)} = \kappa_{j\nu}\,\kappa_{ej}\,\kappa_{de}\,\kappa_{cd}\,\ldots\,\kappa_{ab}\,\kappa_{1a}\,. \tag{5}$$

Here the sequence of indices depends on the index $m(p)$ of $X_{m(p)}$ and follows the given rules:

(1) indices of any pair of neighboring factors are connected as

$$\ldots\,\kappa_{vw}\,\kappa_{uv}\,\ldots\,; \tag{6}$$

(2) the first index of the first right-hand factor agrees with the index k of the region, where the incident wave is given;

(3) the second index of the first left-hand factor agrees with the index ν of the element $(T^p D)^{\pm}_{\nu}$ of matrix $T^p D$.

The expressions for $a^{\pm}_{m(p)}$ can be written in a more convenient form. By substituting the obvious relation

$$\alpha^{\pm}_1 = \beta \pm \theta^*_0, \quad -\beta = \pm\theta^{\pm}_1, \tag{7}$$

where θ^*_0 is the direction contrary to the direction of incidence, into formulas for $a^{\pm}_{m(p)}$ from equations (4) we have

$$a^{\pm}_{m(p)} = \begin{cases} -\beta \mp \theta^*_0 & \text{even} \\ & \text{with } p \qquad \text{for } \nu = 1, \\ -\beta \pm \theta^*_0 & \text{odd} \end{cases}$$

$$a^{\pm}_{m(p)} = \begin{cases} -\beta \pm \theta^*_0 & \text{even} \\ & \text{with } p \qquad \text{for } \nu = 2. \\ -\beta \mp \theta^*_0 & \text{odd} \end{cases} \tag{8}$$

It is easy to see that these expressions can be written in the following compact form:

$$a^{\pm}_{m(p)} = -\beta \pm \Omega_{\nu p}, \quad \Omega_{\nu p} = (-1)^{\nu+p}\,\theta^*_0. \tag{9}$$

Every term of equation (4) can be written in the form showing the repeated use of operator (5). To do so, we introduce the following notation:

$$U_{uv}(\alpha) = \tau_{uv}(\alpha) K_{uv}(\alpha), \quad f_{uv}(\alpha) = \varphi_{uv}(\alpha) + \varepsilon_u, \tag{10}$$

$$\alpha_{kv}(\alpha) = f_{ku}\Big(f_{uv}\,\big\{f_{vn}\,\cdots\,f_{wm}\,[f_{mv}(\alpha)]\,\dots\big\}\Big),$$

where $\varphi_{uv}(\alpha)$, $\tau_{uv}(\alpha)$ and $K_{uv}(\alpha)$ are defined by equations II.1(10), II.1(11), and II.2(30), respectively. Then the result of applying the operator II.2(31) to an arbitrary function $f(\alpha)$ can be written as

$$\kappa_{uv} f(\alpha) = U_{uv}(\alpha) f[f_{uv}(\alpha)]. \tag{11}$$

By using this operation repeatedly we obtain

$$\kappa_{1a} D_{m(p)} = U_{1a}(\alpha) D_{m(p)} [f_{1a}(\alpha)],$$

$$\kappa_{ab} \kappa_{1a} D_{m(p)} = U_{ab}(\alpha) U_{1a} [f_{ab}(\alpha)] D_{m(p)} \{f_{1a} [f_{ab}(\alpha)]\}. \tag{12}$$

We can write by induction

$$X_{m(p)} = U_{fv}(\alpha) U_{ef}\left[f_{fv}(\alpha)\right] U_{de}\left\{f_{ef}\left[f_{fv}(\alpha)\right]\right\} U_{cd}\left(f_{de}\left\{f_{ef}\left[f_{fv}(\alpha)\right]\right\}\right) \dots$$

$$\dots U_{1a}\left[f_{ab} \dots f_{cd}\left(f_{de}\left\{f_{ef}\left[f_{fv}(\alpha)\right]\right\}\right)\right] \times \tag{13}$$

$$\times D_{m(p)}\left\{f_{1a}\left[f_{ab} \dots f_{cd}\left(f_{de}\left\{f_{ef}\left[f_{fv}(\alpha)\right]\right\}\right)\right]\right\}$$

or

$$X_{m(p)} = U_{fv}(\alpha) U_{ef}(\alpha_{fv}) U_{de}(\alpha_{ev}) U_{cd}(\alpha_{dv}) \dots$$

$$\dots U_{1a}(\alpha_{av}) D_{m(p)}(\alpha_{1v}). \tag{14}$$

A set of terms $X_{m(p)}$ in equation (4) can be arranged according to a graph which is similar to the ray scheme of multifold reflections/transmissions in multilayered media. An example of such a graph is shown in Figure 12. There, every arc within the region with index ν corresponds to a proper item of the sum (4) with the same index ν. The arcs, directed counterclockwise, correspond to items $(T\,{}^{P}D)^{+}_{\nu}$ and clockwise to $(T\,{}^{P}D)^{-}_{\nu}$. The inscriptions at the arcs correspond to the expressions for $X_{m(p)}$. The elements of matrix D are shown by dash-dotted lines, $(T\,{}^{1}D)^{\pm}_{\nu}$ by dash lines, $(T\,{}^{2}D)^{\pm}_{\nu}$ by solid lines.

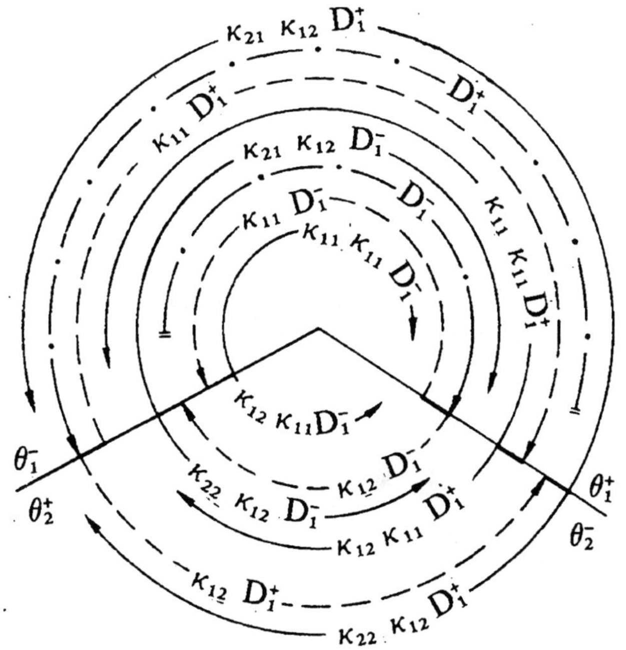

Figure 12. Graph arranging the terms in equation III.1(4).

2. *Formal algorithm*—Let us suppose that (a) the system II.3(18) with $\zeta_0 > 0$ has a solution that admits the representation(1); and (b) the solution allows us to take to the limit with $\zeta_0 \to 0$ every item of the series in equation (1) and after that to perform integration.

Then by substituting equation (4) into equation (1), equation (1) into equation II.2(10), equation II.2(10) into equation II.1(18) we obtain the original Malyuzhinetz's representation of solution in the form

$$f_\nu = (1/2\pi i) \sum_{p=1}^{\infty} \sum_{m(p)=1}^{N(p)} \int_{\Gamma_0} \lim_{\zeta_0 \to 0} [X_{m(p)}(\alpha - \theta_\nu^+) -$$

$$- X_{m(p)}(-\alpha + \theta_\nu^-)] \exp[-ik_\nu r \cos(\alpha - \theta)]\, d\alpha . \tag{15}$$

The mathematical substantiation of this algorithm implies the demonstration of the above-mentioned assumptions. Note, the convergence of successive approximations can be easily demonstrated by some rough estimate, when the parameter ζ_0 is big enough. However, the estimate of such kind is of no importance for the theory of diffraction, because only the case of $\zeta_0 = 0$ has some practical value.

2. Case of equal velocity $c_1 = c_2$

1. Initial relations—The possibility of mathematical substantiation of the above approach, when $c_1 = c_2$ arises due to the following facts.

First, when $c_1 = c_2$, equations II.1(10) - II.1(11) and 1(10) turn to the form

$$\varphi_{uv}(\alpha) = \alpha + \varepsilon_u, \quad \tau_{uv}(\alpha) = 1, \quad U_{uv}(\alpha) = K_{uv}, \text{ and} \tag{1}$$

$$\alpha_{kv} = \alpha + \varepsilon_k + \varepsilon_u + \varepsilon_v + \ldots + \varepsilon_w + \varepsilon_m .$$

Because of this change the items of the series 1(1) and 1(4)

$$S_v^{\pm}(\alpha) = \sum_{p=1}^{\infty} \sum_{m(p)=1}^{N(p)} X_{m(p)}, \quad X_{m(p)} = \kappa_{m(p)} D_{m(p)}(\alpha) \tag{2}$$

have the simplest form

$$X_{m(p)} = K_{m(p)}[\alpha + a_{m(p)}^{\pm} + \varepsilon_{m(p)}]^{-1} \exp[-\zeta_0(\alpha - \alpha_1^{\pm} + \varepsilon_{m(p)})], \tag{3}$$

$$K_{m(p)} = K_{fv} K_{ef} K_{de} K_{cd} \ldots K_{1a},$$

$$\varepsilon_{m(p)} = \varepsilon_1 + \varepsilon_a + \ldots \varepsilon_c + \varepsilon_d + \varepsilon_e + \varepsilon_f,$$

$$\left.\begin{array}{ll} K_{11} = (1-n)/(1+n), & K_{22} = -(1-n)/(1+n), \\ K_{12} = 2/(1+n), & K_{21} = 2n/(1+n), \\ n = \rho_1/\rho_2 & \end{array}\right\} \tag{4}$$

Second, when $c_1 = c_2$, we can reduce the system of functional equations II.3(18) to the system of algebraic equations by using the integral transformation. The solution of such system can be obtained in the closed form. The series (2) turned into the successive approximation series for the algebraic equations. The conditions of convergence for such series can be obtained much easier.

We have managed to demonstrate the convergence of the successive approximations under the following limitations: $\rho_1 < \rho_2$, $\varepsilon_1 < \varepsilon_2$. In this case, when Re $\alpha >$ const,

Im $\alpha = 0$, all finite sums in equation (2) are positive. It is this quality that we use to prove the convergence. That is why we begin with the corresponding representation of the series (2).

2. *Conditions for the terms of the series to be real and positive*----The terms of series (2) are real if

$$\operatorname{Im} X_{m(p)} = 0, \quad \text{when } c_1 = c_2, \ \operatorname{Im} \alpha = 0. \tag{5}$$

Let us find when the mentioned terms are positive under condition (5). According to equations 1(4) the term $a^{\pm}_{m(p)}$ can take one of the two values: α_1^+ or α_1^- . According to equations (3) the quantity $\varepsilon_{m(p)}$ increases, when the interaction number p increases. Hence, for any finite Re α it is always possible to find such finite interaction number p_0 that

$$\operatorname{Re} \alpha + a_{m(p)} + \varepsilon_{m(p)} > 0, \quad \text{when } p > p_0. \tag{6}$$

Under this condition the sign of the quantity $X_{m(p)}$ agrees with the sign of $K_{m(p)}$, i.e.,

$$\operatorname{sign} X_{m(p)} = \operatorname{sign} K_{m(p)} \ \text{with Im } \alpha = 0, \quad p > p_0. \tag{7}$$

Let $n = \rho_1 / \rho_2 > 1$. Then according to equations (4) we have

$$K_{11} < 0, \ K_{22} > 0, \ K_{12} > 0, \ K_{21} > 0,$$

and, therefore,

$$\begin{aligned} &X_{m(p)} < 0, \ \text{if the product } K_{m(p)} \text{ consists of the odd number of factors } K_{11}; \\ &X_{m(p)} > 0, \ \text{in the contrary case} \end{aligned} \tag{8}$$

for Im $\alpha = 0$, $p > p_0$.

Let $n = \rho_1 / \rho_2 < 1$. Then according to equations (4) we have

$$K_{11} > 0, \ K_{22} < 0, \ K_{12} > 0, \ K_{21} > 0,$$

and, therefore, with Im $\alpha = 0, \ p > p_0$

$$\begin{aligned} &X_{m(p)} < 0, \ \text{if the product } K_{m(p)} \text{ consists of the odd number of factors } K_{22}; \\ &X_{m(p)} > 0, \ \text{in the contrary case} \end{aligned} \tag{9}$$

3. Regrouping terms within finite sums—We can replace the terms within the finite sums. The following assertions (with their proofs given in Appendix A) claim that under certain conditions it is possible to get the series with the positive terms only by regrouping and assembling the terms of the initial series.

Assertion 1

Suppose

$$c_1 = c_2 , \quad n = \rho_1 / \rho_2 < 1 , \quad \text{Im } \alpha = 0 . \tag{10}$$

Then for any Re α, complying with condition (6), any negative term $X_{m(p)} < 0$ of equation (2) admits the representation

$$X_{m(p)} = A \, \kappa_{22} \, \kappa_{12} \, BD_{m(p)} < 0 , \tag{11}$$

where A and B are the operator products of equation 1(5) with the total even number of factors κ_{22} .

Assertion 2

Let the conditions of Assertion 1 hold true. Then to any negative term of equation (2) it is possible to relate a positive term $X_{q(p)} > 0$ of the same series. This admits the representation

$$X_{q(p)} = A \, \kappa_{12} \, \kappa_{11} \, BD_{m(p)} > 0 , \tag{12}$$

where A and B are as previously defined.

Assertion 3

Let $\varepsilon_2 > \varepsilon_1$, and conditions of Assertion 1 hold true. Then the sum $[X_{m(p)} + X_{q(p)}]$, with terms that are defined by equations (11) and (12), is positive.

4. Regrouped series—Let us consider equation (2) as the function of the variable α and parameters $\eta = c_1 / c_2$ and ζ_0, i.e.,

$$S_v^{\pm}(\alpha, \eta, \zeta_0) = \sum_{p=1}^{\infty} \sum_{m(p)=1}^{N(p)} X_{m(p)}(\alpha, \eta, \zeta_0). \tag{13}$$

Suppose

$$\rho_1/\rho_2 < 1, \ \eta = 1, \ \varepsilon_2 > \varepsilon_1, \ \text{Im}\,\alpha = 0. \tag{14}$$

Then all terms of series (13) are real. By using equations (11) and (12) we can relate a positive term to any negative term of the finite sum over index $m(p)$. Because every inner sum in equation (13) is finite, we can replace its terms. Hence, by assembling the terms in proper groups we can represent the finite sum as the sum of positive terms (see Assertion 3).

Let Σ_0 be the symbol of summation of those positive and negative terms that are related to one another by equations (11) and (12), and Σ_m be the symbol of summation over indices of other terms, which are obviously positive. Then by regrouping items within the finite sums we have

$$\sum_{m(p)=1}^{N(p)} X_{m(p)}(\text{Re}\,\alpha, 1, \zeta_0) = \Sigma_m X_{m(p)}(\text{Re}\,\alpha, 1, \zeta_0) + \tag{15}$$

$$+ \Sigma_0 [X_{m(p)}(\text{Re}\,\alpha, 1, \zeta_0) + X_{q(p)}(\text{Re}\,\alpha, 1, \zeta_0)],$$

where the terms $X_{m(p)}$ and $X_{q(p)}$ of the sum Σ_0 are related by equations (11) - (12).

Suppose that the series (13) converges under conditions (14). Then it converges absolutely, because its terms are positive. By using the commutative property of the absolutely converging series we can represent the latter in the form

$$S_v^{\pm}(\alpha, 1, \zeta_0) = \boldsymbol{R}(\alpha, 1, \zeta_0) + \boldsymbol{M}(\alpha, 1, \zeta_0), \tag{16}$$

$$\boldsymbol{R}(\alpha, 1, \zeta_0) = \sum_{p=1}^{\infty} \Sigma_m X_{m(p)}(\alpha, 1, \zeta_0),$$

$$\boldsymbol{M}(\alpha, 1, \zeta_0) = \sum_{p=1}^{\infty} \Sigma_0 [X_{m(p)}(\alpha, 1, \zeta_0) + X_{q(p)}(\alpha, 1, \zeta_0)].$$

Here every series converges absolutely, when Im $\alpha = 0$.

Thus, under conditions (14) the series of successive approximations can be written in the form (16). We are going to demonstrate the convergence of this series to the solution of equation II.3(18).

3. Method of integral transformation

1. Closed form solution—Let us represent the function $D_1^{\mp}(\alpha)$ in the form

$$D_1^{\mp}(\alpha) = (\alpha - \alpha_1^{\mp})^{-1} \exp\,[-\zeta_0(\alpha - \alpha_1^{\mp})] = \exp\,(\zeta_0 \alpha_1^{\mp}) \int_0^{\infty} U^{\pm}(\zeta) \exp\,(-\alpha\zeta)\, d\zeta, \tag{1}$$

$$U^{\pm}(\zeta) = \begin{cases} 0, & \text{when } \zeta < \zeta_0, \\ \exp\,[\alpha_1^{\mp}(\zeta - \zeta_0)], & \text{when } \zeta > \zeta_0. \end{cases} \tag{2}$$

The correctness of this formula for Re $\alpha > \alpha_1^{\pm}$ can be proved by the direct integration.

We are looking for the unknown functions $S_\nu^{\pm}(\alpha)$ in the form of the integrals

$$S_\nu^{\mp}(\alpha) = \exp\,(\zeta_0 \alpha_1^{\mp}) \int_0^{\infty} Z_\nu^{\pm}(\zeta) \exp(-\alpha\zeta)\, d\zeta. \tag{3}$$

By substituting equations (1) and (3) into equation II.3(18) we get the system of algebraic equations for $Z_\nu^{\pm}(\zeta)$ that can be written in the matrix form

$$\boldsymbol{Z} = \boldsymbol{RZ} + \boldsymbol{RG}, \tag{4}$$

$$\boldsymbol{Z} = \begin{Bmatrix} Z_1^+ \\ Z_1^- \\ Z_2^+ \\ Z_2^- \end{Bmatrix}, \quad \boldsymbol{G} = \begin{Bmatrix} U^+ \\ U^- \\ 0 \\ 0 \end{Bmatrix}, \quad \boldsymbol{R} = \begin{pmatrix} 0 & R_{11} & R_{21} & 0 \\ R_{11} & 0 & 0 & R_{21} \\ R_{12} & 0 & 0 & R_{22} \\ 0 & R_{12} & R_{22} & 0 \end{pmatrix}, \tag{5}$$

$$R_{uv} = K_{uv} \exp\,(-\zeta \varepsilon_u), \tag{6}$$

where K_{uv} is defined by equations 2(4).

By transferring the sought-after matrix to the left part, we can write the system (4) in the canonical form

$$(\boldsymbol{R} - \boldsymbol{I})\boldsymbol{Z} = -\boldsymbol{R}\boldsymbol{G}, \tag{7}$$

where $\boldsymbol{I}$ is the unit identity matrix $\boldsymbol{IZ} = \boldsymbol{Z}$. We write this system in the expanded form as

$$\begin{pmatrix} -1 & R_{11} & R_{21} & 0 \\ R_{11} & -1 & 0 & R_{21} \\ R_{12} & 0 & -1 & R_{22} \\ 0 & R_{12} & R_{22} & -1 \end{pmatrix} \times \begin{Bmatrix} Z_1^+ \\ Z_1^- \\ Z_2^+ \\ Z_2^- \end{Bmatrix} = - \begin{Bmatrix} R_{11}\,U^- \\ R_{11}\,U^+ \\ R_{12}\,U^+ \\ R_{12}\,U^- \end{Bmatrix}. \tag{8}$$

<u>Assertion 4</u>

For any $\zeta > 0$ system (8) has the only solution (see proof in Appendix A) .

With the help of this Assertion the solution of system (8) can be expressed by the formula

$$Z_\nu^\pm = \Delta_\nu^\pm / \Delta \quad \text{with } \zeta > 0, \tag{9}$$

where Δ is the determinant of the system, and $\Delta_\nu^\pm$ are the corresponding minors, given by the following expressions:

$$\Delta = \det\,(\boldsymbol{R} - \boldsymbol{I}) = 1 - \delta, \tag{10}$$

$$\delta = 2R_{11}R_{12}R_{21}R_{22} - R_{11}^2R_{22}^2 - R_{12}^2R_{21}^2 + R_{11}^2 + R_{22}^2 + 2R_{12}R_{21}, \tag{11}$$

$$\Delta_\nu^\pm = U^\pm(\zeta)A_\nu + U^\mp(\zeta)B_\nu, \tag{12}$$

$$A_1 = R_{11}(R_{11} - R_{11}R_{22}^2 + R_{12}R_{21}R_{22}) + R_{12}R_{21}(1 - R_{12}R_{21} + R_{11}R_{22}),$$

$$B_1 = R_{11}(1 - R_{22}^2 - R_{12}R_{21}) + R_{12}R_{21}(R_{11} + R_{22}),$$

$$A_2 = R_{11}R_{22}(R_{11} + R_{22}) + R_{12}(1 - R_{11}^2 - R_{12}R_{21}),$$

$$B_2 = R_{11} R_{12} (1 + R_{11} R_{22} - R_{12} R_{21}) + R_{12} (R_{22} - R_{11}^2 R_{22} + R_{11} R_{12} R_{21}).$$

The determinant has no roots when $\zeta > 0$. The functions $\Delta_v^{\pm}(\zeta)$ are limited and tend exponentially to zero when $\zeta \to \infty$. Therefore, the function $Z_v^{\pm}(\zeta)$ is limited when $\zeta > 0$, and tends to zero when $\zeta \to \infty$.

Note. Let us consider the integral

$$S_v^{\pm}(\alpha) = \exp(\zeta_0 \alpha_1^{\pm}) \int_{\zeta_0}^{\infty} Z_v^{\pm}(\zeta) \exp(-\alpha \zeta) d\zeta, \tag{13}$$

where $Z_v^{\pm}(\zeta)$ is given by equation (9) with

$$U^{\pm}(\zeta) = \exp[\alpha_1^{\pm}(\zeta - \zeta_0)] \quad \text{with} \; -\infty < \zeta < \infty. \tag{14}$$

This function coincides with function (3). Hence, by using this expression we can define the function $U_v^{\pm}(\zeta)$ in equation (12) by formula (14) as demonstrated in the following.

Let us give two auxiliary assertions which we have to use further.

Assertion 5

Let the function $Z_v^{\pm}(\zeta)$ be defined by equations (9) and (14). Then in the neighborhood of the point $\zeta = 0$ the following representation holds true:

$$Z_v^{\pm}(\zeta) = \Delta_v^{\pm} / \Delta \cong A(\zeta_0)/B\zeta \quad \text{with} \; \zeta \to 0, \tag{15}$$

$$A(\zeta_0) = -\varepsilon_1 [k_v \exp(-\alpha_1^{\pm} \zeta_0) + m_v \exp(-\alpha_1^{\mp} \zeta_0)]$$

$$- \varepsilon_2 [l_v \exp(-\alpha_1^{\pm} \zeta_0) + n_v \exp(-\alpha_1^{\mp} \zeta_0)],$$

$$B = 4\pi^2 - (\varepsilon_1 - \varepsilon_2)^2 (1 - n)^2/(1 + n)^2,$$

$$k_1 = 2K_{11} (K_{11} - K_{11} K_{22}^2 + K_{12} K_{21} K_{22}) +$$

$$+ K_{12} K_{21} (1 - 2K_{12} K_{21} + 2K_{11} K_{22}),$$

$$l_1 = K_{11}(-2K_{11}K_{22}^2 + 2K_{12}K_{21}K_{22}) +$$

$$+ K_{12}K_{21}(1 - 2K_{12}K_{21} + 2K_{11}K_{22}),$$

$$m_1 = K_{11}(1 - K_{22}^2 - 2K_{12}K_{21}) + K_{12}K_{21}(2K_{11} + K_{22}),$$

$$n_1 = K_{11}(-2K_{22}^2 - K_{12}K_{21}) + K_{12}K_{21}(K_{11} + 2K_{22}),$$

$$k_2 = K_{11}K_{12}(3K_{11} + 2K_{22}) + K_{12}(1 - 3K_{11}^2 - 2K_{12}K_{21}),$$

$$l_2 = K_{11}K_{12}K_{22} - K_{12}^2K_{21},$$

$$m_2 = K_{11}K_{12}(2 + 3K_{11}K_{22} - 3K_{12}K_{21}) +$$

$$+ K_{12}(K_{22} - 3K_{11}^2K_{22} + 2K_{11}K_{12}K_{21}),$$

$$n_2 = K_{11}K_{12}(K_{11}K_{22} - K_{12}K_{21}) + K_{12}(K_{22} - K_{11}^2K_{22} + K_{11}K_{12}K_{21}).$$

The proof of Assertion 5 is given in Appendix A.

<u>Assertion 6</u>

When $c_1 = c_2$ the homogeneous system of functional equations

$$\boldsymbol{X} = \boldsymbol{TX} \tag{16}$$

has only the one solution $\boldsymbol{X} = \boldsymbol{0}$, where $\boldsymbol{0}$ is zero-matrix.

Really, due to Assertion 4 the system of equations (4) has only the one solution, when $\boldsymbol{G} = \boldsymbol{0}$. But then the integrals in equation (3), which are the solutions of system (16) with $c_1 = c_2$, are equal to zero identically. This proves the assertion.

2. *Successive approximations*—Let us consider the solution of system (7) by the successive approximation method and find the condition of convergence of approximations. To do this we rewrite system (7) in the form (4) and look for the solution by the method of simple interaction

$$\boldsymbol{Z}^p = \boldsymbol{R}\boldsymbol{Z}^{p-1} + \boldsymbol{R}\boldsymbol{G} \quad \text{with } \boldsymbol{Z}^0 = \boldsymbol{O}, \; p = 1, 2, \dots, \tag{17}$$

where $\boldsymbol{O}$ is zero-matrix. If the successive approximations converge, the solution can be represented in the form

$$\boldsymbol{Z} = \sum_{p=1}^{\infty} \boldsymbol{R}^p \, \boldsymbol{G} \, . \tag{18}$$

Assertion 7

Let us introduce notations

$$\varepsilon_{\min} = \min\,(\varepsilon_1, \varepsilon_2), \quad \rho_{\max} = \max(\rho_1, \rho_2), \quad \rho_{\min} = (\rho_1, \rho_2) \; . \tag{19}$$

Then the sufficient condition for the uniqueness of solution of system (4) and the convergence of the successive approximations (17) to this solution can be written as

$$\zeta > M = (1/\varepsilon_{\min}) \, \ln[(3-\mu)/(1+\mu)], \; \mu = \rho_{\min}/\rho_{\max} . \tag{20}$$

The proof of this assertion is given in Appendix A. It is easy to see from equation (20) that the closer M is to zero the closer μ is to the unity. So, the less different the properties of media in contact, the less the limitation on the parameter ζ.

3. *Convergence of series with positive terms*—Condition (20) guarantees the convergence of successive approximations. However, this condition is not necessary. It is possible to imagine that the successive approximations also converge for some values of parameter $\zeta < M$. However, to prove this assumption it is necessary to use some functional properties of series (18). Here we are going to study these properties.

By using the analogy with equations 1(4) and 2(3) we can write the element of matrix (18) in the form

$$Z_\nu^\pm = \sum_{p=1}^{\infty} (\boldsymbol{R}^p \boldsymbol{G})_\nu^\pm , \tag{21}$$

$$(\boldsymbol{R}^p\ \boldsymbol{G})_v^{\pm} = \sum_{m(p)=1}^{N(p)} Y_{m(p)},\quad Y_{m(p)} = K_{m(p)}\ \exp\left[\ a_{m(p)}^{\pm}\ \zeta_0 - \zeta\left(\varepsilon_{m(p)} + a_{m(p)}^{\pm}\right)\right],\tag{22}$$

using the same notations as equations 1(4) and 2(3).

When $\rho_1/\rho_2 < 1$, we have $K_{11} > 0$, $K_{22} < 0$. Then any negative item of the sum (22) can be written in the form

$$Y_{q(p)} = A'\ R_{22}\, R_{12}\, B' < 0,\tag{23}$$

where A' and B' are the positive factors. Now we can relate any negative term (23) of the sum (22) to the positive term $Y_{t(p)} > 0$ of the same sum

$$Y_{t(p)} = A'\ R_{12}\, R_{11}\, B' > 0\tag{24}$$

with the same A' and B'. Then

$$Y_{q(p)} + Y_{t(p)} > 0,\tag{25}$$

if the terms are defined by equations (23) and (24). The Assertions (23), (24), and (25) can be proven in the same way as Assertions 1, 2, and 3.

Let us relate every negative term (23) of the finite sum (22) to a positive term (24) of the same sum. Because every sum (22) is finite, we can replace its terms. Hence, by assembling terms of the finite sum (22) in the proper groups we can represent the sum in the form

$$(\boldsymbol{R}^p\ \boldsymbol{G})_v^{\pm} = \sum_{s(p)=1}^{A(p)} Y_{s(p)} + \sum_{t(p)=1}^{B(p)} Y_{t(p)} + \sum_{q(p)=1}^{B(p)} Y_{q(p)},\tag{26}$$

$$Y_{s(p)} > 0,\ Y_{t(p)} > 0,\ Y_{q(p)} < 0,\ A(p) + 2B(p) = N(p),$$

where the correspondence between the terms $Y_{t(p)}$ and $Y_{q(p)}$ of the two last sums is set up by equations (23) - (25).

By taking into account relations (23) - (25) we have

$$\sum_{t(p)=1}^{B(p)} Y_{t(p)} + \sum_{q(p)=1}^{B(p)} Y_{q(p)} = \sum_{k(p)=1}^{B(p)} L_{k(p)}\ R_{12}\left(R_{11} + R_{22}\right),\ L_{k(p)} = A'\,B'.\tag{27}$$

By substituting R_{uv} into equation (27) and taking into account the relation $K_{22} = -K_{11}$, we have

$$\sum_{t(p)=1}^{B(p)} Y_{t(p)} + \sum_{q(p)=1}^{B(p)} Y_{q(p)} = [\exp(-\zeta\varepsilon_1) - \exp(-\zeta\varepsilon_2)] \sum_{k(p)=1}^{B(p)} T_{k(p)}, \tag{28}$$

$$T_{k(p)} = K_{11} K_{12} A' B' \exp(-\zeta\varepsilon_1).$$

Now equation (26) can be written as

$$(\boldsymbol{R}^p \boldsymbol{G})_v^{\pm} = \sum_{s(p)=1}^{A(p)} Y_{s(p)} + [\exp(-\zeta\varepsilon_1) - \exp(-\zeta\varepsilon_2)] \sum_{k(p)=1}^{B(p)} T_{k(p)}, \tag{29}$$

where all items are positive because of the inequality $\varepsilon_2 > \varepsilon_1$.

Because of the positiveness of all terms of the finite sums (29), the convergence of series (21) results in its absolute convergence, as well as in the absolute convergence of the series, obtained by opening the brackets in equation (21),

$$Z_v^{\pm} = \sum_{p=1}^{\infty} \left[\sum_{s(p)=1}^{A(p)} Y_{s(p)} + [\exp(-\zeta\varepsilon_1) - \exp(-\zeta\varepsilon_2)] \sum_{k(p)=1}^{B(p)} T_{k(p)}, \right] =$$

$$z_1 + [\exp(-\zeta\varepsilon_1) - \exp(-\zeta\varepsilon_2)]\, z_2, \tag{30}$$

$$z_1 = \sum_{p=1}^{\infty} \sum_{s(p)=1}^{A(p)} Y_{s(p)}, \quad z_2 = \sum_{p=1}^{\infty} \sum_{k(p)=1}^{B(p)} T_{k(p)}. \tag{31}$$

Thus, the problem of convergence of series (21) results in the problem of convergence of series (31) with the positive terms. Let us write the latter in a more convenient form. Taking into consideration the commutative property of the series with positive terms, we can rearrange the terms of series (31) by many ways. For example,

$$z_1(\zeta) = \sum_{n=1}^{\infty} f_n^{(1)}(\zeta), \quad z_2(\zeta) = \sum_{n=1}^{\infty} f_n^{(2)}(\zeta), \tag{32}$$

where n is some arbitrary index.

It follows from the positiveness and monotony of the functions $Y_{s(p)}(\zeta)$ and $T_{k(p)}(\zeta)$ that the terms of the series (32) are the positive functions of ζ and that they monotonously increase, when ζ decreases. Therefore, the following assertion holds true (see proof in Appendix A).

Assertion 8

Every series (32) and their sum (30) converge inside the open interval $0 < \zeta < \infty$. The series (30) converges uniformly for any $\zeta > C$ with any $C > 0$.

Thus, the only solution of the system (4) can be found by the successive approximation method for any $\zeta > 0$.

4. Inner integrals—According to equation (2), the function $U^{\pm}(\zeta)$ is no zero, if only $\zeta > \zeta_0$. Hence, the functions $Z_{\nu}^{\pm}(\zeta)$ in equation (9) are not zero, when $\zeta > \zeta_0$.

That is why the integral (3) can be rewritten as

$$S_{\nu}^{\pm}(\alpha) = \exp(\zeta_0 \alpha_1^{\pm}) \int_{\zeta_0}^{\infty} Z_{\nu}^{\pm}(\zeta) \exp(-\alpha\zeta) d\zeta. \tag{33}$$

When $\zeta_0 > 0$, the function $Z_{\nu}^{\pm}(\zeta)$ can be found by the successive approximation method, i.e.,

$$S_{\nu}^{\pm}(\alpha) = \exp(\zeta_0 \alpha_1^{\pm}) \int_{\zeta_0}^{\infty} \sum_{p=1}^{\infty} (\boldsymbol{R}^p \boldsymbol{G})_{\nu}^{\pm} \exp(-\alpha\zeta) d\zeta. \tag{34}$$

According to Assertion 8, the series (21) converges uniformly for any $\zeta > C$ with any $C > 0$. It is a well-known fact of the theory of the functional series that the multiplication of the series by the finite function does not change its uniform convergence. That is why the series in the integral (34), multiplied by $\exp(-\alpha\zeta)$, can be integrated term by term. The sum of the integrals is equal to the integral of the series. To carry out the mentioned integration, we use the following representation:

$$(\boldsymbol{R}^p \boldsymbol{G})_{\nu}^{\pm} = \sum_{m(p)=1}^{N(p)} K_{m(p)} \exp[-a_{m(p)}^{\pm}(\zeta - \zeta_0) - \varepsilon_{m(p)}\zeta], \tag{35}$$

where all notations are taken from equations 1(4) and 2(3). Then

$$\int_{\zeta_0}^{\infty} \sum_{p=1}^{\infty} (\boldsymbol{R}^p\ \boldsymbol{G})_{\mathrm{v}}^{\pm} \exp(-\alpha\zeta)\, d\zeta = \sum_{p=1}^{\infty} \sum_{m(p)=1}^{N(p)} K_{m(p)} \exp(a_{m(p)}^{\pm}\zeta_0) \times \int_{\zeta_0}^{\infty} \exp[-(\alpha + a_{m(p)}^{\pm} + \varepsilon_{m(p)})\zeta]\, d\zeta\,,$$

where the integrals exist in the half -plane

$$\operatorname{Re}\alpha > -(a_{m(p)}^{\pm} + \varepsilon_{m(p)}) \quad \text{with } 1 \le m(p) \le N(p)\,. \tag{36}$$

By taking these integrals and substituting the results into equation (34) we obtain

$$S_{\mathrm{v}}^{\pm}(\alpha) = \sum_{p=1}^{\infty} \sum_{m(p)=1}^{N(p)} X_{m(p)}(\alpha) \quad \text{and} \tag{37}$$

$$X_{m(p)}(\alpha) = \exp(\zeta_0\,\alpha_1^{\pm})\, K_{m(p)}(\alpha + a_{m(p)}^{\pm} + \varepsilon_{m(p)})^{-1} \exp[-(\alpha + \varepsilon_{m(p)})\zeta_0]\,. \tag{38}$$

The domains of existence of the above integrals as the functions of the complex parameter α are defined by the inequalities (36) However, the functional series (37) converges in the half-plane Re $\alpha > -C$ for any positive C. To prove this assertion, we write the mentioned series in the form

$$S_{\mathrm{v}}^{\pm}(\alpha) = f(\alpha) + \psi(\alpha)\,, \tag{39}$$

$$f(\alpha) = \sum_{p=1}^{p_o-1} \sum_{m(p)=1}^{N(p)} X_{m(p)}(\alpha)\,, \quad \psi(\alpha) = \sum_{p=p_o}^{\infty} \sum_{m(p)=1}^{N(p)} X_{m(p)}(\alpha)$$

with $p_o \ge 2$.

The finite sum $f(\alpha)$ is formed by the functions $X_{m(p)}(\alpha)$ that are analytic in the complex plane Re $\alpha > -\infty$ except for the simple poles on the real axis

$$\operatorname{Re}\alpha = -(a_{m(p)}^{\pm} + \varepsilon_{m(p)})\,, \quad \operatorname{Im}\alpha = 0\,. \tag{40}$$

The number p_o can always be chosen so that the above integrals with $p > p_o$ exist in the half-plane Re $\alpha > -C$ for any positive C except for the finite number of points (40), where the function $\psi(\alpha)$ has simple poles. Indeed, by taking into account the expression for $\varepsilon_{m(p)}$ equation from 2(3) and using the notation $\varepsilon_{\min}$ from equation (19) we have the inequality $\varepsilon_{m(p)} \geq p\,\varepsilon_{\min}$. Then condition (36) can be replaced by the sufficient condition

$$\mathrm{Re}\ \alpha > -\,(a^{\pm}_{m(p)} + p\ \varepsilon_{\min})\,. \tag{41}$$

If this condition holds true, then condition (36) is also satisfied.

The obvious assertion follows from condition (41): for any positive C we can always take such number

$$p_o = (C - a^{\pm}_{m(p)})/\varepsilon_{\min} \tag{42}$$

that the above integrals with $p > p_o$ exist in the half-plane Re $\alpha > -\,C$ except for the finite number of points (40). Thus, equation (39) defines the function of the complex variable α in any half-plane Re $\alpha > -\,C$.

We have reached the following results:

Assertion 9

The successive approximations 1(1) converge to the only solution of the system II.3(18) with any $\zeta_0 > 0$, when $c_1 = c_2$, $\rho_1/\rho_2 < 1$, $\varepsilon_2 > \varepsilon_1$, Re $\alpha > -\,C$ with any positive C.

4. Passage to the limit with $\zeta_0 \to 0$

1. Existence of the solution within a class of the odd functions—The integrals 3(33) exist only if $\zeta_0 > 0$. If $\zeta_0 = 0$ the integrals diverge, because the functions $Z^{\pm}_{\nu}(\zeta) = \Delta^{\pm}_{\nu}/\Delta$ have the singularity of the type $1/\zeta$ at the point $\zeta = 0$. Then because of the uniqueness of the solution of system 3(7) the successive approximations also diverge. However, because of relations II.1(15) - II.1(16) it is sufficient to find only the odd parts of the sought-after functions $S^{\pm}_{\nu}(\alpha)$. Here we show that the odd parts of functions 3(33) exist, when $\zeta_0 = 0$.

Let $A^{\pm}_{\nu}(\alpha)$ and $B^{\pm}_{\nu}(\alpha)$ be the even and odd parts of the functions

$$S^{\pm}_{\nu}(\alpha) = A^{\pm}_{\nu}(\alpha) + B^{\pm}_{\nu}(\alpha),\ A^{\pm}_{\nu}(\alpha) = A^{\pm}_{\nu}(-\alpha),\ B^{\pm}_{\nu}(\alpha) = -\,B^{\pm}_{\nu}(-\alpha), \tag{1}$$

$$A_\nu^\pm = [S_\nu^\pm(\alpha) + S_\nu^\pm(-\alpha)]/2, \quad B_\nu^\pm(\alpha) = [S_\nu^\pm(\alpha) - S_\nu^\pm(-\alpha)]/2 \,. \tag{2}$$

The integrals 3(33) can be written in the form

$$S_\nu^\pm(\alpha) = S_\nu^\pm(\alpha, \zeta_0, M) + S_\nu^\pm(\alpha, M, \infty), \tag{3}$$

$$S_\nu^\pm(\alpha, a, b) = \exp\,(\zeta_0 \alpha_1^\pm) \int_a^b Z_\nu^\pm(\zeta)\, \exp\,(-\alpha\zeta)\, d\zeta,$$

where $M > \zeta_0$ is any finite number. By substituting this expression into equation (2) we have

$$A_\nu^\pm(\alpha) = \exp\,(\zeta_0 \alpha_1^\pm) \int_{\zeta_0}^{M} Z_\nu^\pm(\zeta)\ \mathrm{ch}\ \alpha\zeta\ d\zeta + Q,$$

$$B_\nu^\pm(\alpha) = -\ \exp\,(\zeta_0 \alpha_1^\pm) \int_{\zeta_0}^{M} Z_\nu^\pm(\zeta)\ \mathrm{sh}\ \alpha\zeta\ d\zeta + P, \tag{4}$$

$$Q = [S_\nu^\pm(\alpha,\, M,\, \infty) + S_\nu^\pm(-\alpha,\, M,\, \infty)]/2, \text{ and}$$

$$P = [S_\nu^\pm(\alpha,\, M,\, \infty) - S_\nu^\pm(-\alpha,\, M,\, \infty)]/2 \,.$$

We have shown that $S_\nu^\pm(\alpha,\, M,\, \infty)$ are the fractional analytic functions in any domain of the complex plane of α. Hence, the items $Q(\alpha)$ and $P(\alpha)$ are the fractional analytic functions with $|\alpha| < \infty$. The functions $A_\nu^\pm(\alpha)$ and $B_\nu^\pm(\alpha)$ depend on the parameter ζ_0 in equations (4) only by means of the integral terms. If $\zeta_0 > 0$, the mentioned integrals exist for any $|\alpha| < \infty$. If $\zeta_0 = 0$, the integral in the expression for $A_\nu^\pm(\alpha)$ diverges because of the singularity 3(15) at the point $\zeta = 0$. So the function $A_\nu^\pm(\alpha)$ does not exist when $\zeta_0 = 0$. However, the integral in the expression for $B_\nu^\pm(\alpha)$ has no singularity at $\zeta = 0$ when $\zeta_0 = 0$. Indeed, taking into consideration equation 3(15) we have

$$\lim_{\zeta \to 0} [Z_\nu^\pm(\zeta)\, \mathrm{sh}\, \alpha\zeta] = \lim_{\zeta \to 0} [A(\zeta)(\mathrm{sh}\, \alpha\zeta)/B\zeta] = \alpha A(0)/B. \tag{5}$$

That is why the odd part $B_\nu^\pm(\alpha)$ of the function $S_\nu^\pm(\alpha)$ exists when $\zeta_0 = 0$.

When performing successive approximations, it is rather cumbersome to pick out the odd part of the mentioned function. We show below that it is possible to avoid this by using the expression for $S_v(\alpha)$ from equations II.2(10). To do so, we have to show that the passage to the limit with $\zeta_0 \to 0$ is possible directly in equations II.2(10).

2. *Definition*—Let $S_v(\alpha) = S_v(\alpha, \zeta_0)$ denote the corresponding function from equations II.2(10) with its dependence on ζ_0. Then the result of passage to the limit in the mentioned equation can be written in the form

$$S_v(\alpha, 0) = \lim_{\zeta_0 \to 0} [S_v^+(\alpha - \theta_v^+) - S_v^-(-\alpha + \theta_v^-)]. \tag{6}$$

This limit exists, if for any given $\varepsilon > 0$ there is such a number $\zeta^* > 0$ that

$$\begin{aligned} &|\operatorname{Re} S_v(\alpha, 0) - \operatorname{Re} S_v(\alpha, \zeta_0)| \le \varepsilon, \\ &|\operatorname{Im} S_v(\alpha, 0) - \operatorname{Im} S_v(\alpha, \zeta_0)| \le \varepsilon, \end{aligned} \quad \text{when } \zeta_0 < \zeta^*. \tag{7}$$

Let us show that these conditions hold true in any finite domain of the complex plane of α.

3. *Passage to the limit in the closed solution*—Let us consider the function of the two variables

$$S_v^*(\alpha, \zeta_0) = S_v(\alpha, 0) - S_v(\alpha, \zeta_0). \tag{8}$$

By using equations (6), 2.2(10), and 3(33) we have

$$\begin{aligned} S_v^*(\alpha, \zeta_0) = {} & e^+ \int_0^\infty Z_v^+(\zeta, 0) \exp[-(\alpha - \theta_v^+)\zeta]\, d\zeta - e^- \int_0^\infty Z_v(\zeta, 0) \times \\ & \exp[-(-\alpha + \theta_v^-)\zeta]\, d\zeta - \\ & - e^+ \int_{\zeta_0}^\infty Z_v^+(\zeta, \zeta_0) \exp[-(\alpha - \theta_v^+)\zeta]\, d\zeta + e^- \int_{\zeta_0}^\infty Z_v^-(\zeta, \zeta_0) \times \\ & \exp[-(-\alpha + \theta_v^+)\zeta]\, d\zeta, \end{aligned} \tag{9}$$

$$e^\pm = \exp(\zeta_0\, \alpha_1^\mp),$$

where $Z_v^{\pm}(\zeta, \zeta_0)$ denotes the function $Z_v^{\pm}(\zeta)$ with its dependence on parameter ζ_0. Here $Z_v^{\pm}(\zeta, \zeta_0)$ is defined by equations 3(9) and 3(14). Generally speaking, the form (9) of equation (8) is not correct, because the first and the second integrals do not exist separately. The first line of the right part of equation (9) should be written as a single integral which exists in a sense of its principle value. In fact, we proceed in the following way, keeping the form (9) just for brevity.

Let us decompose equation 3(14) as the function of ζ_0 in the neighborhood of the point $\zeta_0 = 0$ into power series, considering the two first terms only,

$$U_v^{\pm}(\zeta) \approx \exp(\alpha_1^{\pm}\zeta) \cdot (1 - \alpha_1^{\pm}\zeta_0). \tag{10}$$

Then we have from equation 3(9)

$$Z_v^{\pm}(\zeta, \zeta_0) = (1 - \beta\zeta_0)\, Z_v^{\pm}(\zeta, 0) \mp \Omega\,\zeta_0\, V_v^{\pm}(\zeta, 0), \tag{11}$$

$$V_v^{\pm}(\zeta, 0) = [\exp(\alpha_1^{\pm}\zeta) \cdot A_v - \exp(\alpha_1^{\mp}\zeta) \cdot B_v]/\Delta,$$

$$\beta = \mp\,\theta_1^{\pm}, \quad \Omega = -\,\theta_0.$$

By substituting this expression into equation (9) we have

$$S_v^*(\alpha, \zeta_0) = I[0, \zeta_0] + \beta\zeta_0\, I[\zeta_0, \infty] + \Omega\zeta_0\, V[\zeta_0, \infty], \tag{12}$$

$$I[a, b] = e^+ \int_a^b Z_v^+(\zeta, 0)\exp[-(\alpha - \theta_v^+)\zeta]\, d\zeta -$$

$$e^- \int_a^b Z_v^-(\zeta, 0)\exp[-(-\alpha + \theta_v^-)\zeta]\, d\zeta,$$

$$V[a, b] = e^+ \int_a^b V_v^+(\zeta, 0)\exp[-(\alpha - \theta_v^+)\zeta]\, d\zeta +$$

$$e^- \int_a^b V_v^-(\zeta, 0)\exp[-(-\alpha + \theta_v^-)\zeta]\, d\zeta.$$

The integrals $I[\zeta_0, \infty]$ and $V[\zeta_0, \infty]$ exist, when $\zeta_0 > 0$. If the integrals $I[0, \zeta_0]$ and $V[0, \zeta_0]$ exist, the sums

$$I[0, \infty] = I[0, \zeta_0] + I[\zeta_0, \infty], \; V[0, \infty] = V[0, \zeta_0] + V[\zeta_0, \infty]$$

exist also. Then equation (12) can be written as

$$S_v^*(\alpha, \zeta_0) = (1 - \beta\zeta_0)\, I[0, \zeta_0] - \Omega\zeta_0\, V[0, \zeta_0] + \\ + \zeta_0 \{ \beta I[0, \infty] + \Omega V[0, \infty] \} \tag{13}$$

where the factor in the braces does not depend on ζ_0. Hence, the limit with $\zeta_0 \to 0$ exists, if the integrals $I[0, \zeta_0]$ and $V[0, \zeta_0]$ exist. We will demonstrate the existence only of the first integral by representing $Z_v^{\pm}(\zeta, 0)$ in the form 3(15). By the same approach as in the proof of Assertion 5 the similar representation can be obtained even for the second integral. In this way proof of the existence of the integral $V[0, \zeta_0]$ would be the same as for $I[0, \zeta_0]$ and we will skip that demonstration.

We have

$$I[0, \zeta_0] = e^+ \int_0^{\zeta_0} Z_v^+(\zeta, 0) \exp[-(\alpha - \theta_v^+)\zeta]\, d\zeta - \\ e^- \int_{-\zeta_0}^{0} Z_v^-(-\zeta, 0) \exp[-(\alpha - \theta_v^-)\zeta]\, d\zeta. \tag{14}$$

Let ζ_0 be so small that $\exp(\theta_v^{\pm}\zeta) \approx e^{\pm} \approx 1$ with $|\zeta| \le \zeta_0$, and the approximation 3(15) holds true

$$Z_v^{\pm}(\pm\zeta, 0) \approx A(0)/B\zeta.$$

By substituting these expressions into equation (14) we obtain

$$I[0, \zeta_0] = [A(0)/B] \int_{-\zeta_0}^{\zeta_0} \zeta^{-1} \exp(-\alpha\zeta)\, d\zeta. \tag{15}$$

This integral exists in a sense of its principle value, when Re $\alpha > -\infty$.

Let us estimate the integral (15) asymptotically with $\zeta_0 \to 0$. In any finite domain of the complex plane of α the exponent can be represented by the series

$$\exp(-\alpha\zeta) = 1 + \sum_{n=1}^{\infty} (1/n!)(-\alpha\zeta)^n. \tag{16}$$

If ζ_0 is small enough, for any finite α from this expression we have $\exp(-\alpha\zeta) \approx 1 - \alpha\zeta$. By substituting the latter into equation (15) we obtain

$$I[0,\zeta_0] = [A(0)/B] \lim_{\mu\to 0} \left(\int_{-\zeta_0}^{-\mu} d\zeta/\zeta + \int_{\mu}^{\zeta_0} d\zeta/\zeta - \alpha \int_{-\zeta_0}^{\zeta_0} d\zeta \right)$$

$$= -2\alpha\zeta_0 A(0)/B. \tag{17}$$

It is easy to obtain the similar approximation

$$V[0,\zeta_0] = \alpha\zeta_0 C, \tag{18}$$

where C does not depend on ζ_0 and α. By substituting equations (17) and (18) into (13) and neglecting the terms with ζ_0^2 we obtain

$$S_v^*(\alpha,\zeta_0) = D\zeta_0, \tag{19}$$

$$D = -2\alpha A(0)/B + \beta I[0,\infty] + \Omega V[0,\infty].$$

In inequalities (7) we can take $\zeta^* = \varepsilon / |D|$. By substituting this expression and equation (18) into equation (7) we obtain the obvious inequalities

$$|\operatorname{Re}\alpha| \le |\alpha|, \quad |\operatorname{Im}\alpha| \le |\alpha|, \tag{20}$$

which hold true in the whole complex plane of α. Thus, conditions (7) can always be satisfied for any finite α. This proves the existence of the limit (6).

4. *Term-by-term passage to the limit*—Here we show that in equation II.2(10), where $S_v^{\pm}(\alpha)$ are represented by the infinite series I(1), it is possible to pass to the limit with $\zeta_0 \to 0$ term by term. We have

$$S_v^{\pm}(\pm\alpha\mp\theta_v^{\pm}) = \sum_{p=1}^{\infty} \sum_{m(p)=1}^{N(p)} X_{m(p)}(\pm\alpha\mp\theta_v^{\pm}, a_{m(p)}^{\pm}) \tag{21}$$

where $X_{m(p)}(\alpha, a^{\pm}_{m(p)})$ are the terms of finite sums 1(4), considered as the functions of α and $\alpha^{\pm}_{m(p)}$. By substituting $a^{\pm}_{m(p)}$ from equations 1(9) into 2(3) we have

$$X_{m(p)}(\pm\alpha\mp\theta^{\pm}_{\nu}, a^{\pm}_{m(p)}) = K_{m(p)}(\pm\alpha\mp\theta^{\pm}_{\nu}-\beta\pm\Omega_{\nu p} + \varepsilon_{m(p)})^{-1} \times$$

$$\times \exp[-\zeta_{0}(\pm\alpha\mp\theta^{\pm}_{\nu} + \varepsilon_{m(p)} - \alpha^{\pm}_{1})]. \tag{22}$$

By denoting

$$v_{m(p)} = \theta^{-}_{\nu} - \beta + \varepsilon_{m(p)}, \quad w_{m(p)} = (\theta^{-}_{\nu} + \varepsilon_{m(p)})\,\zeta_{0} \tag{23}$$

and taking into account the relation $\mp\theta^{\pm}_{\nu} = \theta^{-}_{\nu}$, we can write equation (22) in the form

$$X_{m(p)}(\pm\alpha\mp\theta^{\pm}_{\nu}, a^{\pm}_{m(p)}) = \pm K_{m(p)}(\alpha+\Omega_{\nu p}\pm v_{m(p)})^{-1} \times$$

$$\exp\{-[w_{m(p)} + \zeta_{0}(\pm\alpha - \alpha^{\pm}_{1})]\} \tag{24}$$

By substituting this expression into equation (21) we have

$$S^{\pm}_{\nu}(\pm\alpha\mp\theta^{\pm}_{\nu}) = \pm\exp[\zeta_{0}(\mp\alpha+\alpha^{\pm}_{1})]\sum_{p=1}^{\infty}\sum_{m(p)=1}^{N(p)} K_{m(p)}(\alpha+\Omega_{\nu p}\pm v_{m(p)})^{-1} \times$$

$$\exp(-w_{m(p)}). \tag{25}$$

Formula shows that every item has a simple pole at a point

$$\alpha = \alpha^{\pm}_{m(p)}, \quad \alpha^{\pm}_{m(p)} = -\Omega_{\nu p} \mp v_{m(p)}. \tag{26}$$

The substitution of α by $\pm\alpha \mp 0^{\pm}_{\nu}$ leads to the transformation points 3(40) into points (26). Position of the poles do not depend on ζ_{0}. Hence, the function $S_{\nu}(\alpha) = S_{\nu}(\alpha, \zeta_{0})$, obtained as a result of substituting equation (24) into 2(2), has no singularities except for the simple poles (26), when $\zeta_{0} = 0$. The singularities at $\mathrm{Re}\,\alpha \to \infty$ in equation (24), caused by factors $\exp(\mp\alpha\,\zeta_{0})$, disappear, when $\zeta_{0} = 0$. The infinite points $\mathrm{Im}\,\alpha \to \infty$ are not singular either (as is shown in the following section). Thus, the function $S_{\nu}(\alpha, 0)$ is fractional, because all of its singular points are the simple poles.

Let $g^{\pm}_{m(p)}(\alpha)$ be the singular part of the Laurent series of the function $S_v(\alpha, 0)$ at the pole $\alpha = \alpha^{\pm}_{m(p)}$. Then from equation (24) we have

$$g^{\pm}_{m(p)}(\alpha) = \pm K_{m(p)} (\alpha + \Omega_{vp} \pm v_{m(p)})^{-1} \exp(\zeta_0 \alpha^{\pm}_1). \tag{27}$$

In mathematical analysis such functions are called *the simple fractions.* It is a well-known fact that any fractional function, regular at the point $\alpha = 0$, can be expanded into the simple fractions within any finite domain of the complex plane of α. By taking into consideration equations 2(2) and (24) we obtain the corresponding expansion

$$S_v(\alpha, 0) = \sum_{p=1}^{\infty} \sum_{m(p)=1}^{N(p)} [g^{+}_{m(p)}(\alpha) + g^{-}_{m(p)}(\alpha) + h_{m(p)}(\alpha)], \tag{28}$$

where $h_{m(p)}(\alpha)$ are some functions that are regular within any finite domain of the complex plane of α. The latter guarantees the convergence of the series (28).

Let us show that

$$\sum_{p=1}^{\infty} \sum_{m(p)=1}^{N(p)} h_{m(p)}(\alpha) \equiv 0. \tag{29}$$

By substituting equation (25) into II.2(10) and taking into account equation (27) we get

$$S_v(\alpha, \zeta_0) = \sum_{p=1}^{\infty} \sum_{m(p)=1}^{N(p)} \{ g^{+}_{m(p)}(\alpha) \exp[-(w_{m(p)} + \alpha \zeta_0)] + g^{-}_{m(p)}(\alpha) \exp[-(w_{m(p)} - \alpha \zeta_0)] \}. \tag{30}$$

By subtracting equation (30) from equation (28) we have

$$S_v(\alpha, 0) - S_v(\alpha, \zeta_0) = \sum_{p=1}^{\infty} \sum_{m(p)=1}^{N(p)} \{ g^{+}_{m(p)}(\alpha) \{1 - \exp[-(w_{m(p)} + \alpha \zeta_0)]\} + g^{-}_{m(p)}(\alpha) \{1 - \exp[-(w_{m(p)} - \alpha \zeta_0)]\} + h_{m(p)}(\alpha) \}. \tag{31}$$

When $\zeta_0 \to 0$, the factors in braces tend to zero. Then

$$\lim_{\zeta_0 \to 0} [S_v(\alpha, 0) - S_v(\alpha, \zeta_0)] = \sum_{p=1}^{\infty} \sum_{m(p)=1}^{N(p)} h_{m(p)}(\alpha). \tag{32}$$

As shown, the limit of the left part of this relation is zero in any finite domain of the complex plane of α. This proves the relation (29).

Thus, the passage to the limit with $\zeta_0 \rightarrow 0$ gives

$$S_v(\alpha) = \sum_{p=1}^{\infty} \sum_{m(p)=1}^{N(p)} [\, g^{+}_{m(p)}(\alpha) + g^{-}_{m(p)}(\alpha)\,]. \tag{33}$$

This expression coincides with the result of the passage to the limit term by term in the successive approximations method.

5. Dependence on ζ_0 far away from the corner point—The existence of the limit (6) implies a continuous dependence of the solution on the small parameter ζ_0. Here we study this dependence in the case of $k_v\, r >> 1$, i.e., far away from the corner point—$r = 0$.

Let us write equation (8) in the form

$$\tilde{S}_v(\alpha) = S_v(\alpha, 0) = S_v(\alpha, \zeta_0) + S^*_v(\alpha, \zeta_0). \tag{34}$$

$$S_v(\alpha, \zeta_0) = \int_{\zeta_0}^{\infty} \{ e^{+} Z^{+}_v(\zeta) \exp[-(\alpha - \theta^{+}_v)\zeta] - e^{-} Z^{-}_v(\zeta) \exp[(\alpha - \theta^{-}_v)\zeta] \}\, d\zeta, \tag{35}$$

where $S^*_v(\alpha, \zeta_0)$ is given by equation (9).

By substituting equation (34) into II.1(18) we get the solution in the form

$$f_v(0) = f_v(\zeta_0) + F^*_v, \tag{36}$$

$$F^*_v = (1/2\pi i) \int_{\Gamma_o} S^*_v(\alpha, \zeta_0) \exp[-ik_v r \cos(\alpha - \theta)]\, d\alpha, \tag{37}$$

where the notation $f_v(\zeta_0)$ reflects the dependence on parameter ζ_0. The term F^*_v represents the difference between $f_v(0)$ and $f_v(\zeta_0)$, caused by the inequality $\zeta_0 \neq 0$. We are going to study the wave effect corresponding to this term far away from the corner point.

We suppose that parameter ζ_0 is small enough to use the following approximations in equation (9):

$$Z_\nu(\zeta,\zeta_0) \approx Z_\nu(\zeta,0), \ \exp(\zeta_0\alpha_1^\pm) \approx 1 . \tag{38}$$

Besides, we will consider instead of function (9) the function

$$S_\nu^*(\alpha,\zeta_0,b) = \int_b^{\zeta_0} Z_\nu^+(\zeta)\exp[-(\alpha-\theta_\nu^+)\zeta]\,d\zeta - \int_b^{\zeta_0} Z_\nu^-(\zeta)\exp[-(-\alpha+\theta_\nu^-)\zeta]\,d\zeta, \tag{39}$$

depending on a small parameter $0 < b < \zeta_0$. When $b = 0$ this function coincides with the function (9) under approximations (38). Upon taking the corresponding integrals we will pass to the limit with $b \to 0$. Such an approach allows us to change the order of integration.

By substituting equation (39) into equation (37) and changing the order of integration we get

$$F_\nu^* = \int_b^{\zeta_0} Z_\nu^+(\zeta)\exp(\theta_\nu^+\zeta)\cdot I_\nu^-\,d\zeta - \int_b^{\zeta_0} Z_\nu^-(\zeta)\exp(-\theta_\nu^-\zeta)\,.\,I_\nu^+\,d\zeta, \tag{40}$$

and

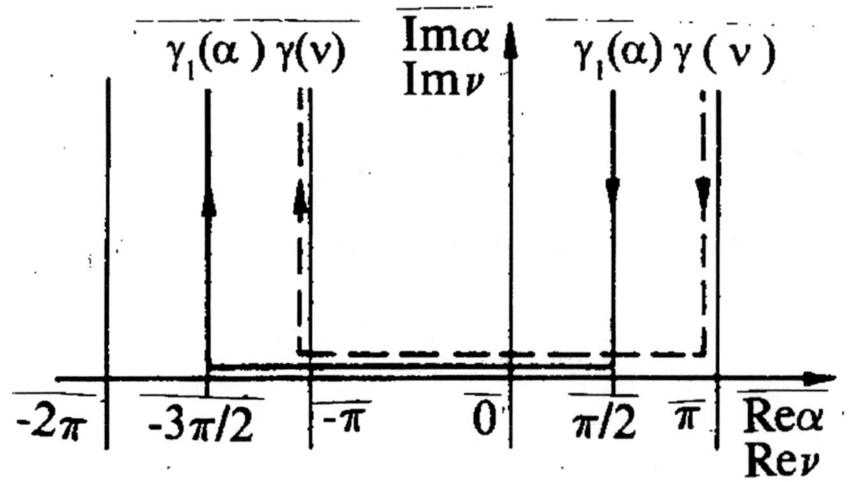

Figure 13. Contours of integration in equations III.4(44) and III.4(45)

$$I_\nu^\pm = (1/2\pi i) \int_{\Gamma_o} \exp\,[\,\pm\alpha\zeta - ik_\nu r \cos(\alpha - \theta)]\,d\alpha. \tag{41}$$

The integral (41) can be expressed through the well-known special functions. By substituting α with $\alpha + \theta$ and taking into consideration equation II.1(8) we have

$$I_\nu^\pm = i^{-1} \exp(\pm\theta\zeta)\cdot I^\pm,\ I^\pm = (1/2\pi) \int_{\Gamma_o} \exp\,[\pm\,\alpha\zeta - i\text{–}z\ \cos\alpha\,]\,d\alpha,$$
$$z = k_\nu r. \tag{42}$$

This integral can be written as the sum of the integrals

$$I^\pm = (1/2\pi)[\int_{\gamma_1} \exp(\pm\alpha\,\zeta - i\ z\ \cos\alpha)\,d\alpha + \int_{\gamma_2} \exp(\pm\alpha\,\zeta - i\ z\ \cos\alpha)\,d\alpha\,] \tag{43}$$

along the loops of the contour $\Gamma_o = \gamma_1 + \gamma_2$ placed in the top (γ_1) and bottom (γ_2) half-planes. By substituting α by $-\alpha$ in the integral along γ_2 we have

$$I^\pm = (1/2\pi)[\int_{\gamma_1} \exp(\pm\alpha\ \zeta - i\,z\ \cos\alpha)\,d\alpha - \int_{\gamma_1} \exp(\mp\alpha\,\zeta - i\,z\ \cos\ \alpha)\,d\alpha\,], \tag{44}$$

where both integrals are taken along the same contour γ_1.

Because the integrand is analytic within the allowable domains, it is possible to choose the contour γ_1 as shown in Figure 13. By substituting α by $v - \pi/2$ we have

$$I^\pm = -\exp(\mp\pi\zeta/2)[(1/2\pi) \int_{-\gamma} \exp(\pm\ \nu\ \zeta - i\ z\ \sin\ \nu)\,d\nu] +$$
$$+ \exp(\pm\pi\zeta/2)\ [(1/2\pi) \int_{-\gamma} \exp(\mp\nu\zeta - i\ z\ \sin\ \nu)\,d\nu\ ]. \tag{45}$$

The new contour of integration is shown in Figure 13.

By using the Bessel function

$$I_\nu(z) = (1/2\pi) \int_{-\gamma} \exp(i\nu\ v - iz\ \sin\ v)\ dv$$

we get

$$I^\pm = -\exp(i\nu\pi/2)\,I_{-\nu}(z) + \exp(-i\nu\pi/2)\ I_\nu(z\,) = -$$
$$\exp(i\nu\pi/2)[I_{-\nu}(\,z\,) - \exp(-i\nu\pi)\ I_\nu(z)],\quad \nu = \pm i\zeta \tag{46}$$

By using the relation between the Hankel and Bessel functions

$$H_{\nu}^{(1)}(z) = (i \sin \nu\pi)^{-1} [I_{-\nu}(z) - \exp(-i\nu\pi) I_{\nu}(z)] \tag{47}$$

we get

$$I^{\pm} = \mp i \exp(\mp\pi\zeta/2) H_{\mp i\zeta}^{(1)}(z) \sin i\zeta\pi . \tag{48}$$

By substituting formula (48) into equation (42) we obtain

$$I_{\nu}^{\pm} = \mp \exp[\pm(\theta - \pi/2)\zeta] . H_{\pm i\zeta}^{(1)}(k_{\nu} r) \sin i\pi\zeta . \tag{49}$$

Equations 3(15) and (49) show that the integrands in equation (40) are finite at $\zeta = 0$. It is possible, therefore, to pass to the limit with $b \to 0$ in the mentioned integrals. Let us substitute equation (49) into (40), take $b = 0$ and substitute ζ by $-\zeta$ in the second integral. Then equation (40) can be written as

$$F_{\nu}^{*} = \int_{-\zeta_0}^{\zeta_0} [Z_{\nu}^{+}(\zeta) \exp(\theta_{\nu}^{+}\zeta) - Z_{\nu}^{-}(-\zeta) \exp(\theta_{\nu}^{-}\zeta)] \times$$

$$\times H_{-i\zeta}^{(1)}(k_{\nu} r) \exp[-(\theta - \pi/2)\zeta] \sin i\pi\zeta d\zeta . \tag{50}$$

When ζ_0 is small enough, we can use approximation 3(15)

$$Z_{\nu}^{+}(\zeta) \exp(\theta_{\nu}^{+}\zeta) - Z_{\nu}^{-}(-\zeta) \exp(\theta_{\nu}^{-}\zeta) \approx Z_{\nu}^{+}(\zeta) - Z_{\nu}^{-}(-\zeta) \approx$$

$$\approx 2A(0)/B\zeta = f_{\nu}(0)/\pi\zeta . \tag{51}$$

The following section will show that $f_{\nu}(0)$ corresponds to the value of the solution at the corner point. We can also use the following approximations:

$$\exp[-(\theta - \pi/2)\zeta] \approx 1, \quad \sin i\pi\zeta \approx i\pi\zeta . \tag{52}$$

When $z = k_{\nu} r >> 1$, the Hankel function can be represented by the well-known asymptotic representation

$$H_{\mu}^{(1)}(z) = (2/\pi z)^{1/2} \exp[i(z - \pi\mu/2 - \pi/4)] \times [1 + O(z^{-1})] \quad (53)$$

with Re $\mu > -1/2$. In our case $z = k_{\nu} r$ and $\mu = -i\zeta$. When ζ_0 is small, we can neglect the factor exp $(-i\pi\mu/2)$. Then

$$H_{-i\zeta}^{(1)}(k_{\nu} r) \sim (2/\pi k_{\nu} r)^{1/2} \exp[i(k_{\nu} r - \pi/4)] \text{ with } k_{\nu} r >> 1, \ \zeta_0 << 1. \quad (54)$$

By substituting equations (51) - (54) into (50) we obtain

$$F_{\nu}^{*} = \zeta_0 C (k_{\nu} r)^{-1/2} \exp(i k_{\nu} r), \ C = f_{\nu}(0) 2\sqrt{2\pi} \exp(i\pi/4). \quad (55)$$

Expression (55) describes a wave, that is spreading from the corner point according to the laws of geometrical acoustics. Its amplitude is proportional to parameter ζ_0. Hence, it is always possible to take such a small ζ_0 that the contribution of this wave in the total wavefield would be less than any given number. All of this allows us to use the small parameter ζ_0 to make the successive approximations convergable.

5. Corner point

1. Infinite point of the plane α—Let us consider the case of the infinite α. The contour Γ_o of Sommerfeld-Malyuzhinetz integrals belongs to the band $-2\pi <$ Re $\alpha < 2\pi$. It is therefore sufficient to consider the case of | Im α | $\to \infty$. Then in equation 4(6) it is necessary to perform two passages to the limits: with $\zeta_0 \to 0$ and with | Im α | $\to \infty$. The question is how to choose the order of the limit passages (first with ζ_0 then with α or in the reverse)? To answer this question, we will find the value of the function 4(8) at Im $\alpha \to \pm\infty$, considering parameter ζ_0 small but nonzero.

Let us consider the integral 4(15), when | Im α | $\to \infty$. In this case the expansion 4(16) holds true only for the factor exp $(-$Re $\alpha\ \zeta)$ which is approximately equal to unity for small enough values of ζ_0. The series 4(16) for exp $(-i$ Im $\alpha)$ diverges, when | Im α | $\to \infty$. Taking into consideration this fact, we represent the integral 4(15) for small ζ_0 in the form

$$I[0, \zeta_0] = [A(0)/B] I, \ I = \int_{-\zeta_0}^{\zeta_0} \zeta^{-1} \exp(-iq\zeta) d\zeta, \ q = \text{Im } \alpha. \quad (1)$$

The integral I can be written as

$$I = I_0 - I_1 - I_2, \quad (2)$$

$$I_0 = \int_{-\infty}^{\infty} \zeta^{-1} \exp(-iq\zeta)\,d\zeta, \quad I_1 = \int_{-\zeta_\infty}^{\infty} \zeta^{-1} \exp(-iq\zeta)\,d\zeta,$$

$$I_2 = \int_{\zeta_0}^{\infty} \zeta^{-1} \exp(-iq\zeta)\,d\zeta.$$

Suppose $q > 0$. By changing in the integrals I_1 and I_2 the variable of integration $q\zeta = x$ we have

$$I_1 = \int_{-\infty}^{-q\zeta_0} x^{-1} \exp(-ix)\,dx, \quad I_2 = \int_{q\zeta_0}^{\infty} x^{-1} \exp(-ix)\,dx. \tag{3}$$

When $q \to \infty$, we have $-q\zeta_0 \to -\infty$, $q\zeta_0 \to \infty$ which shows that $I_1 = I_2 = 0$ when $q \to \infty$. It is easy to see that $I_1 = I_2 = 0$ when $q \to -\infty$.

Thus, when $|q| \to \infty$, the sum (2) has only one non-zero item I_o which is the tabular integral $I_o = -(\operatorname{sign} q)\, i\pi$. Equation (1) then reads

$$I[0, \zeta_0] = \mp i\pi A(0)/B, \tag{4}$$

where $A(0)$ and B do not depend on ζ_0.

It follows from equation (4) that condition 4(7) does not hold true with $|\operatorname{Im} \alpha| \to \infty$, because its left part does not decrease with $\zeta_0 \to 0$ but tends to the non-zero value (4). This means that we cannot pass to the limit [equation 4(6)], when the variable α is fixed at infinity $|\operatorname{Im} \alpha| \to \infty$. The mentioned limit does not exist. This answers the question on the allowable order of the double passage to the limits with $\zeta_0 \to 0$ and $|\operatorname{Im} \alpha| \to \infty$. To find the value $S_v(\pm i\infty, 0)$, we have to use the following order of passing to the limits:

$$S_v(\pm i\infty, 0) = \lim_{\operatorname{Im} \alpha \to \pm\infty} \left\{ \lim_{\zeta_0 \to 0} \left[S_v^+(\alpha - \theta_v^+) - S_v^-(-\alpha + \theta_v^-) \right] \right\} \tag{5}$$

To change this order is not allowed.

Let us trace the connection between the conclusion and the integral representation of function $S_v(\alpha, 0)$. It follows from equation 4(17), obtained for finite values of α, that the second term in equation 4(34) is small when compared with the first one, when ζ_0 is sufficiently small. We can neglect this term and integrate within the interval

$\zeta_0 \leq \zeta < \infty$, i.e., we can approximate the function by equation 4(35). This implies the existence of the limit 4(6).

The situation is different, when $|\,\mathrm{Im}\ \alpha\,| \to \infty$. Using the same approach as for integral (3) it is easy to find by substituting $|\,\mathrm{Im}\ \alpha\,|\ \zeta$ for ζ in equation 4(35) that $S_v(\alpha, \zeta_0)$ tends to zero, when $|\,\mathrm{Im}\ \alpha\,| \to \infty$ for any $\zeta_0 > 0$. At the same time, the integrals 4(9) or (1) tend to the finite non-zero value (4). Hence, when $|\,\mathrm{Im}\ \alpha\,| \to \infty$ and $\zeta_0 > 0$, the principle term of equation 4(34) is the second term $S_v(\alpha, 0) \approx S_v^*(\alpha, \zeta_0)$, which is connected with integration in the interval $|\,\zeta\,| \leq \zeta_0$. Then in equation 4(12) with $\zeta_0 \to 0$ the only non-zero term is the first one. This yields

$$S_v(\pm i\infty, 0) = \lim_{\zeta_0 \to 0}\ \lim_{\mathrm{Im}\,\alpha \to \pm\infty} I\ [0, \zeta_0] = \mp\, i\pi A(0)/B. \tag{6}$$

But in equation 4(6) the second term of the sum 4(34) behaves like a small discrepancy 4(7) disappearing with $\zeta_0 \to 0$. The impossibility to satisfy conditions 4(7), when $|\,\mathrm{Im}\ \alpha\,| \to \infty$, just reflects the situation prohibiting the change of the order the limits in equation (5).

2. *Restriction on the passage to the limit*—The double limit (5) only holds true for the closed form solution, because the term-by-term passage to the limit with $\zeta_0 \to 0$ in the successive approximations is allowed within the finite domains of the complex plane of α (condition of expansion into simple fractions). To pass to the limit with $\mathrm{Im}\ \alpha \to \pm\infty$, it is necessary to run up all successive approximations, i.e., to obtain the closed solution. Any attempt to pass to the limit term-by-term leads to the wrong result $S_v(\pm i\infty) = 0$.

3. *Value of the solution*—According to equation II.1(14) the value of the solution at the corner point $r = 0$ is formed by contributions to the Sommerfeld-Malyuzhinetz integral from the infinite parts of the contour of integration with $|\,\mathrm{Im}\ \alpha\,| \to \infty$. As shown, these contributions result in zero, if $\zeta_0 > 0$. Hence, to find the sought value, we have to use the closed solution with $\zeta_0 = 0$ which can be obtained by using equations II.1(14) and (6).

By substituting equation (6) into equation II.1(14) we get the solution at the corner point

$$f_v(0, \theta) = 2\pi A(0)/B, \tag{7}$$

where $A(\zeta_0)$ and B are defined in equation 3(15). When $\zeta_0 = 0$ we have

$$A(0) = -\varepsilon_1 (k_\nu + m_\nu) - \varepsilon_2 (l_\nu + n_\nu). \tag{8}$$

To find the sums $(k_\nu + m_\nu)$ and $(l_\nu + n_\nu)$, we substitute $K_{u\nu}$ from equation 2(4) into the corresponding expressions from equations 3(15). Upon multiplication and summation we obtain

$$k_\nu + m_\nu = -4n/(1+n)^2, \; l_\nu + n_\nu = -4/(1+n)^2, n = \rho_1/\rho_2, \nu = 1, 2.$$

By substituting these formulas into equations (8) and (7) and taking into account the expression for B from equation 3(15) we get

$$f_\nu(0,\theta) = 8\pi(\varepsilon_1 n + \varepsilon_2)/[4\pi^2(1+n)^2 - (\varepsilon_1 - \varepsilon_2)^2(1-n)^2]. \tag{9}$$

Taking into account relation $\varepsilon_2 = 2\pi - \varepsilon_1$, we can also write this expression in the form

$$f_\nu(0,\theta) = 2\pi[2\pi + \varepsilon_1(n-1)/[\pi^2(1+n)^2 - (\pi - \varepsilon_1)^2(1-n)^2]. \tag{10}$$

The solution must satisfy some obvious conditions at the corner point. In the case of acoustics the pressure $f_\nu(r,\theta)$ is limited at the corner point. In any case it must not depend on the direction of approaching the corner point, i.e., on the coordinate θ. Some theories state other necessary conditions [for example, the quasi-static behavior (Hönl et al., 1961)]. Let us show that the obtained expression satisfies some obvious conditions.

The value, equation (10), is always limited. It does not depend on θ. It does not depend on the region where the incident wave is given nor on the direction of incidence. This indicates quasi-static behavior of the solution, because the incident wave eikonal does not matter.

Formula (10) gives the obvious values of the known solutions for the simplest or trivial cases. Let the interface be plane $\varepsilon_1 = \pi$. Then from equation (10) we have

$$f_\nu(0,\theta) = 2/(1+n) = K_{12} = 1 + K_{11}, \tag{11}$$

i.e., the value of the wavefield is described by the usual reflection/transmission formulas. Let the interface be absent, i.e., $n = 1$. Then from equation (10) we have $f_\nu(0,\theta) = 1$, i.e., there is the incident wave only.

Let the pressure be zero at the interface (the Dirichlet problem). We get this case by taking $\rho_2 = 0$, i.e., when $n \to \infty$. Then from equation (10) we have $f_\nu(0, \theta) = 0$ which suits the initial suggestion. Let the interface be perfectly rigid, i.e., let the normal component of the vibration velocity be zero at the interface (the Neumann problem). We get this case, when $\rho_2 \to 0$, i.e., $n = 0$. Then from equation (10) we have $f_\nu(0, \theta) = 2\pi/\varepsilon_1$ which coincides with the result of the exact solution.

6. Examples

1. Transformation of series—Let us consider the form of the successive approximation series that is useful for understanding "the mechanism of convergence." By using equation 4(25) we can write equation II.2(10) as follows:

$$S_\nu(\alpha) = \exp[\zeta_0(\alpha_1^+ - \alpha)] \sum_{p=1}^{\infty} \sum_{m(p)=1}^{N(p)} K_{m(p)}(u_{m(p)} + v_{m(p)})^{-1} \exp(-w_{m(p)})$$

$$+ \exp[\zeta_0(\alpha_1^- + \alpha)] \sum_{p=1}^{\infty} \sum_{m(p)=1}^{N(p)} K_{m(p)}(u_{m(p)} - v_{m(p)})^{-1} \exp(-w_{m(p)}), \tag{1}$$

$$u_{m(p)} = \alpha + \Omega_{\nu p},\ v_{m(p)} = \theta_\nu^- - \beta + \varepsilon_{m(p)},\ w_{m(p)} = (\theta_\nu^- + \varepsilon_{m(p)})\zeta_0, \tag{2}$$

$$\beta = \varepsilon_1/2.$$

By adding both series term by term we get

$$S_\nu(\alpha) = a_1 \sum_{p=1}^{\infty} \sum_{m(p)=1}^{N(p)} K_{m(p)}\, u_{m(p)}\, (u_{m(p)}^2 - v_{m(p)}^2)^{-1} \exp(-w_{m(p)}) +$$

$$+ a_2 \sum_{p=1}^{\infty} \sum_{m(p)=1}^{N(p)} K_{m(p)}\, v_{m(p)}\, (u_{m(p)}^2 - v_{m(p)}^2)^{-1} \exp(-w_{m(p)}), \tag{3}$$

$$a_1 = \exp[\zeta_0(\alpha_1^+ - \alpha)] + \exp[\zeta_0(\alpha_1^- + \alpha)],$$

$$a_2 = \exp[\zeta_0(\alpha_1^- - \alpha)] - \exp[\zeta_0(\alpha_1^- + \alpha)].$$

Both of the above equations describe the same function. In equation (1) every infinite series corresponds to function $S_\nu^+(\alpha - \theta_\nu^+)$ or $-S_\nu^-(-\alpha + \theta_\nu^-)$, satisfying the system of functional equations II.3(18). However, every infinite series of equation (3) does not correspond to the mentioned functions and, therefore, does not comply with the functional equations. As was shown each of the series in equation (1) diverges with $\zeta_0 \to 0$. However, the sum of these diverging series exists, if every term of the first series is added with the corresponding term of the second series. This results in series (3) that in the case of $\zeta_0 = 0$ turns into

$$S_\nu(\alpha) = 2 \sum_{p=1}^{\infty} \sum_{m(p)=1}^{N(p)} K_{m(p)} u_{m(p)} (u_{m(p)}^2 - v_{m(p)}^2)^{-1} . \tag{4}$$

Thus, we come to an important conclusion. Though the system of functional equations II.3(18) has no solution for $\zeta_0 = 0$ (to be more precise, there is no even part), the method of successive approximations with the term-by-term substitution of approximations into equation II.2.(10) leads to building up the desired transformant of the Sommerfeld-Malyuzhinetz integral II.1(18). Here we demonstrate this fact in the case of the ideal wedge by using a known exact solution.

2. *Neumann problem*—(1) Let $\rho_1 / \rho_2 = 0$. If $\rho_1 \neq 0$, this case arises as a result of the passage to the limit with $\rho_2 \to \infty$. In acoustics it corresponds to the case of a perfectly rigid medium within the domain of index $\nu = 2$. To find the field f_1 in this case it is necessary to formulate the Neumann problem. The latter demands the normal component of the vibration velocity $\partial f_1 / r \partial \theta$ to be zero at the interface.

By denoting

$$\theta_1^{\pm} = \mp \beta, \; \theta_0^* = \pm \alpha_1^{\pm} \mp \beta \text{ or } \theta_0^* = \theta_0 \pm \pi \text{ when } \pm \theta_0 > 0 \tag{5}$$

we can write the known solution of the problem (Malyzhinetz, 1959; Tuzhilin, 1963) in the form

$$f_1 = (1/2\pi i) \int_{\Gamma_o} \tilde{S}_1(\alpha) \exp[-ik_1 r \cos(\alpha - \theta)] d\alpha, \tag{6}$$

$$\tilde{S}_1(\alpha) = (\pi/4\beta) \{ \cot[\pi(\alpha - \theta_0^*)/4\beta] + \cot[\pi(\alpha + \theta_0^* - 2\beta)/4\beta] \},$$

where $\theta = \theta_0$ is the direction of incidence. Here the function $\tilde{S}_1(\alpha)$ corresponds to the total field including the incident wave. This function can be represented in the form II.2(10). When $\zeta_0 = 0$, we will use Malyuzhinetz's representation

$$\widetilde{S}_1(\alpha) = S_1(\alpha) + (\alpha - \theta_0^*)^{-1}, \tag{7}$$

where $S_1(\alpha)$ corresponds to the function (4). We will show that equations (7) and (4) lead to the same formula stated in equation (6). To do so, we build up the series (4) by the method of successive approximations.

—(2) When $\rho_1/\rho_2 = 0$, we have

$$K_{11} = 1, \quad K_{22} = -1, \quad K_{12} = 2, \quad K_{21} = 0. \tag{8}$$

The operator κ_{21} in matrix $\boldsymbol{T}$ turns to zero

$$\kappa_{21} f(\alpha) \equiv 0. \tag{9}$$

By using the well-known matrix product rules, it is easy to see that in this case the elements of the two top lines of matrix

$$\boldsymbol{X} = \sum_{p=1}^{\infty} \boldsymbol{T}^{p} \boldsymbol{D}$$

coincide with the elements of the matrix

$$\begin{Bmatrix} S_1^+(\alpha) \\ S_1^-(\alpha) \end{Bmatrix} = \sum_{p=1}^{\infty} \begin{pmatrix} 0 & \kappa_{11} \\ \kappa_{11} & 0 \end{pmatrix}^p \begin{Bmatrix} D_1^+(\alpha) \\ D_1^-(\alpha) \end{Bmatrix}. \tag{10}$$

Here the function $D_1^{\pm}(\alpha)$ can be written in the notation of equation (5) as

$$D_1^{\pm}(\alpha) = (\alpha - \beta \mp \theta_0^*)^{-1} \exp[\zeta_0(\alpha_1^{\mp} - \alpha)].$$

Matrix products of this type can be developed according to the following rule:

$$\begin{pmatrix} 0 & \kappa \\ \kappa & 0 \end{pmatrix}^p \begin{Bmatrix} A \\ B \end{Bmatrix} = \begin{Bmatrix} \kappa^p [aA + (1-a)B] \\ \kappa^p [(1-a)A + aB] \end{Bmatrix} \quad \text{with } a = [1 + (-1)^p]/2.$$

By using this rule for the matrix equation (10) and taking into account the definition of the operator II.2(31) for the case of $K_{11} = 1$

$$\kappa_{11} f(\alpha) = f(\alpha + 2\beta), \quad \kappa_{11}^p f(\alpha) = f(\alpha + 2p\beta), \quad \beta = \varepsilon_1/2$$

we get

$$S_1^{\mp}(\alpha)=\sum_{p=1}^{\infty}[\alpha-\beta\mp(-1)^p\theta_0^*+2p\beta]^{-1}\exp[\zeta_0(\alpha_1^{\mp}\mp\alpha+\beta+2p\beta)]. \tag{11}$$

By substituting this expression into the second formula of equations II.2(10)

$$S_1(\alpha)=S_1^+(\alpha-\theta_1^+)-S_1^-(-\alpha+\theta_1^-)\quad\text{with}\quad \theta_1^{\pm}=\mp\beta,$$

and passing to the limit with $\zeta_0\to 0$, we get the sum of divergent series

$$S_1(\alpha)=\sum_{p=1}^{\infty}[\alpha-(-1)^p\theta_0^*+2p\beta]^{-1}+\sum_{p=1}^{\infty}[\alpha-(-1)^p\theta_0^*-2p\beta]^{-1}. \tag{12}$$

In the case under consideration the quantities from equations (2) can be written as

$$\Omega_{1p}=-(-1)^p\theta_0^*,\ \theta_1^-=\beta,\ \varepsilon_{m(p)}=p\,\varepsilon_1=2p\beta.$$

When $\zeta_0=0$, we have

$$u_{m(p)}=\alpha-(-1)^p\theta_0^*,\ v_{m(p)}=2p\beta,\ w_{m(p)}=0. \tag{13}$$

By using this notation in equations (12) we get equation (1) with $N(p)=1$, $\zeta_0=0$. Thus, formula (12) describes the result of passage to the limit with $\zeta_0\to 0$ in equation (1). The same formula can be rewritten in the form of the convergent series (4)

$$S_1(\alpha)=2\sum_{p=1}^{\infty}[\alpha-(-1)^p\theta_0^*]\left\{[\alpha-(-1)^p\theta_0^*]^2-(2p\beta)^2\right\}^{-1}. \tag{14}$$

—(3) By substituting equation (14) into equation (7) and assembling the terms with the even ($p=2m$) and the odd ($p=2m+1$) indices of summation in separate groups we get

$$\tilde{S}_1(\alpha)=(\alpha-\theta_0^*)^{-1}+2\sum_{m=1}^{\infty}(\alpha-\theta_0^*)[(\alpha-\theta_0^*)^2-(4m\beta)^2]^{-1}+$$

$$2\sum_{m=0}^{\infty}(\alpha+\theta_0^*)\left\{(\alpha+\theta_0^*)^2-[2(2m+1)\beta]^2\right\}^{-1}. \tag{15}$$

By denoting

$$\alpha - \theta_0^* = 4\beta x, \quad \alpha + \theta_0^* = 2\beta y \tag{16}$$

and substituting index m by $n-1$ in the second sum of equation (15) we get

$$\widetilde{S_1}(\alpha) = (1/4\beta)\left\{1/x + 2x\sum_{m=1}^{\infty}(x^2 - m^2)^{-1} - 4y\sum_{n=1}^{\infty}[(2n-1)^2 - y^2]^{-1}\right\} \tag{17}$$

By using the well-known formulas of expansion of trigonometric functions into simple fractions

$$\pi \cot \pi x = 1/x + 2x\sum_{m=1}^{\infty}(x^2 - m^2)^{-1},$$

$$\pi \tan(\pi y/2) = 4y\sum_{n=1}^{\infty}[(2n-1)^2 - y^2]^{-1} \tag{18}$$

we can find the sum of the infinite series in equation (17)

$$\widetilde{S_1}(\alpha) = (\pi/4\beta)[\cot \pi x - \tan(\pi y/2)]. \tag{19}$$

By using relation

$$\tan(\pi y/2) = -\cot[\pi(y-1)/2] \tag{20}$$

and expressing x and y by means of equations (16) we obtain equation (6). This is what we wanted to demonstrate.

(4) Equations (12) and (14) can be obtained directly from equation (6) by performing the above transformations in the reverse order. By using the notation in (16) we can write equation (6) in the form (19) and expand trigonometric functions into simple fractions (18). This shows the very nature of equations (12) and (14): they are the results of expansions of the fractional analytic function $S_1(\alpha)$ into simple fractions. It is a well-known fact that such an expansion holds true within any finite domain of the complex plane of α. When $|\alpha| \to \infty$, the expansion fails. For example, when $|\operatorname{Im} \alpha| \to \infty$, moduli of the right parts of equations (18) tend to zero, while moduli of the left parts tend to π. So it is impossible to find the function $S_1(\alpha)$ with $|\operatorname{Im} \alpha| \to \infty$, by the successive approximation method and therefore the function $f_1(r, \theta)$ at the corner point $r = 0$ as well.

(5) The above example illustrates the main idea of the approach under consideration. Equation (12) makes no sense, if the items of both series are not summed up in pairs with the equal indices p. This follows from the divergence of each series in the mentioned equation. On the other hand, the successive approximation method with $\zeta_0 = 0$ permits finding the sought function $S_1(\alpha)$ in the form of a convergent series (14), if every corresponding pair of the two divergent series is summed. Thus, when $\zeta_0 = 0$, it is the term-by-term passage to the limit with $\zeta_0 \to 0$ in the process of successive approximations and the term-by-term summation of successive approximations that allow us to build the solution.

3. Numerical example—The convergence of successive approximations has been demonstrated under the conditions: $\rho_1 < \rho_2$, $\varepsilon_1 < \varepsilon_2$. To explain the meaning of these limitations, we have to recall the important concept of the theory of series. A function $F(x)$, which values the greater than the values of the given function $f(x)$ in the considered domain, is called the majorant of function $f(x)$. Take a convergent series that is obtained from the given series by replacing its terms with their absolute values. Such series is called the *major series* of the given series. We introduced the mentioned limitations to apply the one major series for the proof. To remove these limitations, it would be necessary to choose some other way of the proof. Instead we restrict ourselves to a numerical verification of the convergence of successive approximations to a known closed solution (Malyuzhinetz, 1951).

Suppose $\varepsilon_1 = 3\pi/2$, $\varepsilon_2 = \pi/2$. Then the above condition $\varepsilon_1 < \varepsilon_2$ fails. Figure 14 shows results of calculations of the function $\widetilde{S}_1(\alpha)$ at a point Re $\alpha = -\pi/2$, Im $\alpha = 0$ for $\zeta_0 = 0$, $\theta_1 = -5\pi/6$, $\rho_1/\rho_2 = 1/3$ and $\rho_1/\rho_2 = 3$. The number of the successive approximations is shown on the x axis and the result of the calculation on the y axis (the calculated function is real when Im $\alpha = 0$). With increasing p the result of calculations approaches a certain limit, which confirms the convergence of the successive approximations. For the situation under consideration this limit can be established also on the basis of the known exact solution (Malyuzhinetz, 1951),

$$\begin{aligned}\widetilde{S}_1(\alpha) = {} & [2\cos^2(v/2)]^{-1}\{\cos v \cot(\alpha-\alpha^*) + \sin(v/2)\tan(\alpha+\alpha^*) + \\ & + \cos[(\alpha-\alpha^*)v/\pi]/\sin(\alpha-\alpha^*) - \sin[(\alpha+\alpha^*)v/\pi]/\cos(\alpha+\alpha^*) - \\ & - i\cos v + i\sin(v/2)\},\end{aligned} \tag{21}$$

$$v = -2\arcsin[(\rho_2-\rho_1)/2(\rho_2+\rho_1)], \quad \alpha^* = \theta_0 \pm \pi \text{ when } \pm\theta_0 > 0.$$

In Figure 14 the horizontal lines show the values of the solution obtained by the given known formula and the deviation from the known exact solution for various values of p are marked by the vertical lines. We see from these graphs that the successive approximations converge to the known exact solution.

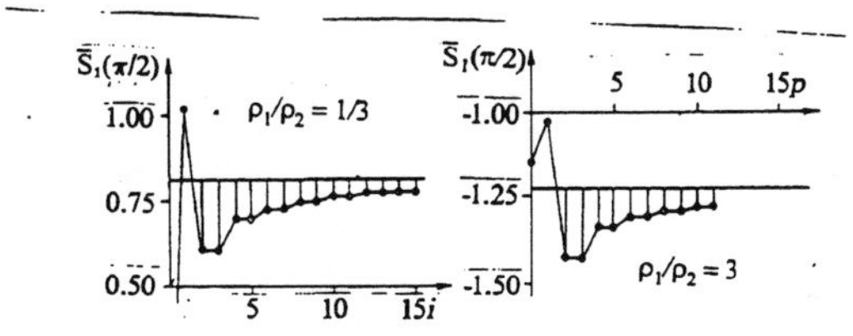

Figure 14. Example of the convergence of the successive approximations to the known exact solution when condition $\varepsilon_1 < \varepsilon_2$ ***fails.***

7. Asymptotic properties of operator κ_{uv} in the case of unequal wave velocities

The existence of solution and the convergence of successive approximations to the solution in a case of $c_1 = c_2$ allow us to substantiate the above approach under certain limitations on the values of parameters ρ_ν and ε_ν ($\nu = 1, 2$) for a more general case of $c_1 \neq c_2$. This will be done in Section 8 for $\zeta_0 > 0$. To do this, we have to use the asymptotic properties of operator κ_{uv} when $|\ \mathrm{Im}\ \alpha\ | \to \infty$. We will formulate these properties in the form of a number of assertions with the proofs in Appendix A. But first we must give some definitions necessary to formulate the mentioned assertions.

1. Principal values of functions $\varphi_{uv}(\alpha)$, $\tau_{uv}(\alpha)$—Because function $\varphi_{uv}(\alpha)$ is transitive and odd, equations II.1(12), its value at any Re α can be expressed through its value in the band $0 \leq \mathrm{Re}\ \alpha < \pi/2$ by the formulas

$$\varphi_{uv}(\alpha) = b\ \varphi_{uv}\ [\ b(\alpha - d)] + d, \tag{1}$$

$$b = 1,\ d = \pi\ E(\mathrm{Re}\,\alpha/\pi)\ \text{ when Re } \alpha/\pi - E(\mathrm{Re}\,\alpha/\pi) < 1/2,$$

$$b = -1,\ d = \pi\ E(\mathrm{Re}\,\alpha/\pi) + \pi\ \text{ when Re } \alpha/\pi - E(\mathrm{Re}\,\alpha/\pi) \geq 1/2,$$

where always $0 \le b(\alpha - d) < \pi/2$, and $E(x)$ denotes the whole part of x. Hence, in the following it is sufficient to study the properties of this function in the band $0 \le \text{Re}\ \alpha < \pi/2$ only. In this band (see Appendix B)

$$\text{Re}\ \varphi_{uv}(\alpha) = \arccos\ [Q - (Q^2 - R^2)^{1/2}]^{1/2}, \tag{2}$$

$$\text{Im}\ \varphi_{uv}(\alpha) = (\text{sign Im}\ \alpha)\ \text{arsh}\ [Q - 1 + (Q^2 - R^2)^{1/2}]^{1/2},$$

$$Q = (1 + R^2 + M^2)/2,$$

$$R = \eta_{uv} \cos \text{Re}\alpha\ \text{ch Im}\ \alpha, \quad M = \eta_{uv} \sin \text{Re}\alpha\ \text{sh Im}\ \alpha, \quad \eta_{uv} = c_u/c_v,$$

where the absolute values of the square roots are taken.

Because function $\tau_{uv}(\alpha)$ is transitive and odd, equations II.1(12), its value at any Re α can be expressed through its value in the band $0 \le \text{Re}\ \alpha < \pi/2$ by the formula

$$\tau_{uv}(\alpha) = \tau_{uv}[b(\alpha - d)], \tag{3}$$

where b and d are defined in equations (1). Hence, it is sufficient to study this function within the mentioned band.

2. *Uniform approach to a limit*—We now consider asymptotic representations of functions from equation II.2(31) for operator κ_{uv}, when $|\text{Im}\ \alpha| \to \infty$. We are looking for the representations valid for any Re α. Such kind of representations can be based on the concept of the uniform convergence to a limit with regard to some parameter. We say that the function of complex variable $f(\alpha)$ with $|\text{Im}\ \alpha| \to \infty$ tends to zero uniformly with regard to Re α inside the interval $-C \le \text{Re}\ \alpha \le C$, where C is some positive number, if for any given $\varepsilon > 0$ there is such positive number $N(\varepsilon)$ that $|f(\alpha)| < \varepsilon$ with $|\text{Im}\ \alpha| > N(\varepsilon)$ for any Re α from the mentioned interval. Note, that this definition is analogous to the definition of the uniform convergence to a limit with regard to a parameter for a function of the real variable. This is clear if we consider the function $f(\alpha) = f(x + iy)$ as the function of the real variable y, while regarding x as a parameter.

<u>Assertion 10</u>

Function $\varphi_{uv}(\alpha)$, defined by equations II.1(10) and II.1(12), can be represented as

$$\varphi_{uv}(\alpha) = \alpha + e_{uv} + \varphi(\alpha), \quad e_{uv} = (\text{sign Im } \alpha)\, i \ln(c_u/c_v), \tag{4}$$

where $\varphi(\alpha)$ is limited for $|\text{Im } \alpha| > 0$ and with $|\text{Im } \alpha| \to \infty$ tends to zero uniformly with regard to Re α for $-\infty < \text{Re } \alpha < \infty$.

Assertion 11

Function $\tau_{uv}(\alpha)$, defined by equations II.1(11) and II.1(12), allows representation

$$\tau_{uv}(\alpha) = 1 + \tau(\alpha), \tag{5}$$

where $\tau(\alpha)$ is limited for

$$|\text{Im } \alpha| > 0 \quad \text{when} \quad c_v < c_u,$$
$$|\text{Im } \alpha| > \text{arch}\,(c_v/c_u) \quad \text{when} \quad c_v > c_u, \tag{6}$$

and with $|\text{Im } \alpha| \to \infty$ tends to zero uniformly with regard to Re α inside interval $-\infty < \text{Re } \alpha < \infty$.

Assertion 12

Functions $K_{uv}(\alpha)$, defined by equations II.2(30), allows the representation

$$K_{uv}(\alpha) = \widetilde{K_{uv}} + K(\alpha), \quad \widetilde{K_{uv}} = [K_{uv}(\alpha)] \text{ with } c_u = c_v, \tag{7}$$

where $K(\alpha)$ with $|\text{Im } \alpha| \to \infty$ tends to zero uniformly with regard to Re α for $-\infty < \text{Re } \alpha < \infty$.

Assertion 13

The result of operation κ_{uv} on an arbitrary function $f(\alpha)$ allows representation

$$\kappa_{uv} f(\alpha) = [1 + \lambda(\alpha)]\, \widetilde{K_{uv}}\, f[\alpha + \varepsilon_u + e_{uv} + \varphi(\alpha)], \tag{8}$$

$$\widetilde{K}_{uv} = [\,K_{uv}(\alpha)\,] \text{ with } c_u = c_v,\; e_{uv} = (\text{sign Im } \alpha)\, i \ln (c_u / c_v),$$

where $\varphi(\alpha)$ and $\lambda(\alpha)$ with $|\text{Im } \alpha| \to \infty$ tend to zero uniformly with regard to $\text{Re } \alpha$ for $-\infty < \text{Re } \alpha < \infty$.

Consequence

Let function $f(\alpha)$ be regular in domain $|\text{Im } \alpha| >$ const. Then there is always such a positive number M that for $|\text{Im } \alpha| > M$ there is the representation

$$\kappa_{uv} f(\alpha) = [\,1 + \lambda(\alpha)\,]\, \widetilde{\kappa}_{uv} f(\alpha), \tag{9}$$

where $\lambda(\alpha)$ with $|\text{Im } \alpha| \to \infty$ tends to zero uniformly with regard to $\text{Re } \alpha$ for $-\infty < \text{Re } \alpha < \infty$. Here $\widetilde{\kappa}_{uv}$ denotes the operator κ_{uv} with $c_u = c_v$.

Indeed, by choosing number M big enough we can make the sum $e_{uv} + \varphi(\alpha)$ in equation (8) as small as we like compared to $|\text{ Im } \alpha\ |$ and drop the small quantity. Then

$$f\,[\,\alpha + \varepsilon_u + e_{uv} + \varphi(\alpha)\,] \approx f(\alpha + e_{uv}).$$

This leads to representation (9).

Assertion 14

The result of the multifold substitutions

$$\alpha_{kv}(\alpha) = f_{ku}\left\{f_{uv}\left[\,f_{vn} \cdots f_{wm}\,[\,f_{mv}(\alpha)\,] \cdots\right]\right\}, \tag{10}$$

where

$$f_{\lambda\mu}(\alpha) = \varphi_{\lambda\mu}(\alpha) + \varepsilon_\lambda,\; \varphi_{\lambda\mu}(\alpha) = \arccos\,[\,(c_\lambda / c_\mu)\cos\alpha\,],$$

allows the representation

$$\alpha_{kv}(\alpha) = \alpha + \varepsilon_k + \varepsilon_u + \varepsilon_v + \ldots + \varepsilon_w + \varepsilon_m +$$

$$+ \Psi_{ku}(f_{uv}) + \Psi_{uv}(f_{vn}) + \Psi_{vn}(\dots) + \dots + \Psi_{wm}(f_{m\nu}) + \Psi_{m\nu}(\alpha), \tag{11}$$

where every composite function with $|\mathrm{Im}\ \alpha| \to \infty$ tends to its limit $\Psi_{\lambda\mu} \to e_{\lambda\mu} = (\mathrm{sign\ Im}\ \alpha)\, i \ln(c_\lambda / c_\mu)$ uniformly with regard to Re α for $-\infty < \mathrm{Re}\ \alpha < \infty$.

A useful relationship follows from Assertion 14. Because

$$\lim_{|\mathrm{Im}\ \alpha| \to \infty} (\Psi_{ku} + \Psi_{uv} + \Psi_{vn} + \dots + \Psi_{wm} + \Psi_{m\nu}) =$$

$$= e_{ku} + e_{uv} + e_{vn} + \dots + e_{wm} + e_{m\nu} = (\mathrm{sign\ Im}\ \alpha)\, i [\ln(c_k/c_u) +$$

$$+ \ln(c_u/c_v) + \ln(c_v/c_n) + \dots + \ln(c_w/c_m) + \ln(c_m/c_\nu)] =$$

$$= (\mathrm{sign\ Im}\ \alpha)\, i \ln(c_k/c_\nu),$$

we have

$$\lim_{|\mathrm{Im}\ \alpha| \to \infty} [\alpha_{k\nu}(\alpha) - \alpha] = \varepsilon_k + \varepsilon_u + \varepsilon_v + \dots + \varepsilon_w + \varepsilon_m +$$

$$+ (\mathrm{sign\ Im}\ \alpha)\, i \ln(c_k/c_\nu). \tag{12}$$

<u>Assertion 15</u>

Let functions $\tau_{uv}(\alpha)$, $K_{uv}(\alpha)$, $\alpha_{kv}(\alpha)$ be defined by equations II.1(11), II.2(30), and (10), respectively. Then there is the representation

$$\tau_{uv}[\alpha_{kv}(\alpha)]\, K_{uv}[\alpha_{kv}(\alpha)] = [1 + \lambda_{uv}(\alpha)]\, \widetilde{K}_{uv}, \tag{13}$$

$$\widetilde{K}_{uv} = [K_{uv}(\alpha)] \quad \text{with } c_u = c_v,$$

where $\lambda_{uv}(\alpha)$ with $|\mathrm{Im}\ \alpha| \to \infty$ tends to zero uniformly with respect to Re α in the interval $-\infty < \mathrm{Re}\ \alpha < \infty$.

Assertion 16

Every item of the equation 1.(4) allows the representation

$$X_{m(p)} = Q_{m(p)} \widetilde{K}_{m(p)} \left(\alpha + a^{\pm}_{m(p)} + \varepsilon_{m(p)} + \Psi_{m(p)} \right)^{-1} \exp \left[-\zeta_0 \left(\alpha - \alpha^{\pm}_{1} + \varepsilon_{m(p)} + \Psi_{m(p)} \right) \right], \tag{14}$$

$$\widetilde{K}_{m(p)} = \widetilde{K}_{fv} \widetilde{K}_{ef} \widetilde{K}_{de} \widetilde{K}_{cd} \ldots \widetilde{K}_{ab} \widetilde{K}_{1a}, \ \widetilde{K}_{uv} = K_{uv} \text{ with } c_u = c_v,$$

$$\varepsilon_{m(p)} = \varepsilon_f + \varepsilon_e + \varepsilon_d + \varepsilon_c + \ldots + \varepsilon_b + \varepsilon_a + \varepsilon_1,$$

$$Q_{m(p)} = (1 + \lambda_{fv})(1 + \lambda_{ef})(1 + \lambda_{de})(1 + \lambda_{cd}) \ldots (1 + \lambda_{ab})(1 + \lambda_{1a}),$$

$$\Psi_{m(p)} = \Psi_{fv} + \Psi_{ef} + \Psi_{de} + \Psi_{cd} + \ldots + \Psi_{ab} + \Psi_{1a},$$

where functions $\lambda_{uv}(\alpha)$, $\Psi_{uv}(\alpha)$ with $|\ \mathrm{Im}\ \alpha\ | \to \infty$ tend to the limits

$$\lambda_{uv}(\alpha) \to 0, \ \Psi_{uv}(\alpha) \to e_{uv} = (\mathrm{sign\ Im}\ \alpha)\ i \ln (c_u/c_v)$$

uniformly with respect to Re α in the interval $-\infty < \mathrm{Re}\ \alpha < \infty$.

8. Convergence of successive approximations with $c_1 \neq c_2$, $\zeta_0 > 0$

We demonstrate the convergence of successive approximations under the same limitations that were used in the case $c_1 = c_2$, i.e.,

$$\rho_1 < \rho_2, \ \varepsilon_1 < \varepsilon_2. \tag{1}$$

Then the successive approximations series 1(1) can be written in the form 2(16)

$$S^{\pm}_{v}(\alpha, \eta, \zeta_0) = \boldsymbol{R}(\alpha, \eta, \zeta_0) + \boldsymbol{M}(\alpha, \eta, \zeta_0), \tag{2}$$

where there is a correspondence between the terms of series (2) and 2(16) by indices $m(p)$. When $\eta = 1$, each term of series (2) turns into a corresponding term of series 2(16).

1. Auxiliary inequalities----The terms of the series (2) comply with some inequalities that can be used to demonstrate the convergence of this series. The existence of the mentioned inequalities is formulated below in the form of two assertions (proofs in Appendix A).

Assertion 17

Let $X_{m(p)} = X_{m(p)}(\alpha, \eta, \zeta_0)$ be any item of the sum 1(4), considered as a function of the complex variable α in the domain $-C < \text{Re}\ \alpha < C$ and parameters $\eta = c_1/c_2$ and ζ_0, where C is any positive number. Then for any given $\delta > 0$ and $\mu > 0$ there are always numbers such as B_m and p_m that for $|\text{Im}\ \alpha| > B_m$ and $p > p_m$ the following inequality holds true:

$$|X_{m(p)}(\alpha, \eta, \zeta_0 + \delta)| \leq \mu |X_{m(p)}(\text{Re}\ \alpha, 1, \zeta_0)|. \tag{3}$$

Assertion 18

Let $X_{m(p)} = X_{m(p)}(\alpha, \eta, \zeta_0)$ and $X_{q(p)} = X_{q(p)}(\alpha, \eta, \zeta_0)$ with $\eta = c_1/c_2$ be any such pair of the terms of the sum 1(4) that can be related to one another by equations 2(11) and 2(12). Then for any given $\delta > 0$ there are numbers B_{mq} and p_{mq} that with $|\text{Im}\ \alpha| > B_{mq}$ and $p > p_{mq}$ for any $-C < \text{Re}\ \alpha < C$ the following inequality holds true:

$$|X_{m(p)}(\alpha, \eta, \zeta_0 + \delta) + X_{q(p)}(\alpha, \eta, \zeta_0 + \delta)| \leq$$

$$|X_{m(p)}(\text{Re}\ \alpha, 1, \zeta_0) + X_{q(p)}(\text{Re}\ \alpha, 1, \zeta_0)|. \tag{4}$$

2. *Convergence of auxiliary series*—Because the terms of the series (2) are positive with $c_1 = c_2$, $\text{Im}\ \alpha = 0$, the existence of inequalities (3) and (4) allows us to use equation (2) as the majorizing series to demonstrate the convergence of the same series when $c_1 \neq c_2$. The following assertions are proved in Appendix A.

Assertion 19

Let each of the series in equation 2(16) under conditions (1) with $\text{Im}\ \alpha = 0$ converge absolutely in the interval

$$-C < \text{Re}\ \alpha < C, \tag{5}$$

where C is any finite positive number. Then for any given $\delta > 0$ there is a positive number B that with $|\text{Im}\ \alpha| > B$ in the same interval (5) the following series converge

$$S_\nu^{\pm}(\alpha,\eta,\zeta_0+\delta) = \boldsymbol{R}(\alpha,\eta,\zeta_0+\delta) + \boldsymbol{M}(\alpha,\eta,\zeta_0+\delta), \tag{6}$$

$$\tilde{S}_\nu^{\pm}(\alpha,\eta,\zeta_0+\delta) = \sum_{p=1}^{\infty} V_p^{\pm},\ V_p^{\pm} = |\,\tilde{V}_p^{\pm}\,|,\ \tilde{V}_p^{\pm} = \sum_{m(p)=1}^{N(p)} X_{m(p)}(\alpha,\eta,\zeta_0+\delta) \tag{7}$$

According to Assertion 9, the conditions of Assertion 19 are satisfied for any $\zeta_0 > 0$. Then the following assertion holds true (proof in Appendix A).

<u>Assertion 20</u>

Let the conditions of Assertion 19 be satisfied. Then for any given $\zeta_0 > 0$ there is a finite number B that with $|\operatorname{Im}\alpha| > B$ the series (6) and (7) converge with $\delta = 0$.

3. *Value of solution with* $|\operatorname{Im}\alpha| \to \infty$—Here we give an assertion concerning the values of function $S_\nu^{\pm}(\alpha)$ at the infinite points (proof in Appendix A).

<u>Assertion 21</u>

The solution of equation II.3(18) with $c_1 \neq c_2$ coincides with the solution of the same equation with $c_1 = c_2$ at the infinite points $\operatorname{Im}\alpha \to \pm\infty$.

4. *Existence of solution with* $\zeta_0 > 0$—On the strength of Assertions 19 and 20 the following series converges for any $\zeta_0 > 0$

$$S_\nu(\alpha) = S_\nu^{+}(\alpha-\theta_\nu^{+}) - S_\nu^{-}(-\alpha+\theta_\nu^{-}) = \sum_{p=1}^{\infty} U_{\nu p},$$

$$U_{\nu p} = \sum_{m(p)=1}^{N(p)} \left[X_{m(p)}(\alpha-\theta_\nu^{+}, a_{m(p)}^{+}) - X_{m(p)}(-\alpha+\theta_\nu^{-}, a_{m(p)}^{-}) \right], \tag{8}$$

because it represents the sum of convergent series $\pm S_\nu^{\pm}(\pm\alpha \mp \theta_\nu^{\pm})$. Simultaneously with equation (8) we can consider the series with the positive terms

$$\sum_{p=1}^{\infty} |\,U_{\nu p}\,|. \tag{9}$$

Assertion 22

Let the series (8) converge in the domains $|\operatorname{Re}\alpha| <$ const, $|\operatorname{Im}\alpha| >$ const, when $\rho_1 < \rho_2$, $\varepsilon_1 < \varepsilon_2$, $\zeta_0 > 0$. Then under the same conditions the series (9) converges in the same domains (proof in Appendix A).

The Sommerfeld-Malyuzhinetz integral II.2(2) will not change its value, if we shift the contour of integration to such a position that the entire contour is placed in the half-planes $|\operatorname{Im}\alpha| > B$, where B is any positive number. But then conditions of Assertions 19 - 21 are satisfied. Thus, we have demonstrated the convergence of the series (8) to the function $S_\nu(\alpha)$ with any $\zeta_0 > 0$.

Let us show that such a solution is stable, i.e., it depends continuously on all parameters. It is well-known that a functional series converges uniformly in some domain, if it can be majorized by the convergent numerical series in the same domain. The functional series (8) is majorized by the numerical series (9) under condition $|\operatorname{Im}\alpha| > B$, where B is sufficiently large. Hence, the series (8) converges uniformly with regard to all parameters. The sum of any uniformly convergent series, with terms that are continuous functions, is continuous. The same is true when all items are multiplied by the factor $\exp[-i k_\nu r \cos(\alpha - \theta)]$. Such a series can be integrated term by term, while the sum of the integrals from its terms is equal to the integral from the sum of the terms. The result of the integration is a continuous function of all parameters.

We have demonstrated the existence of the solution and the convergence of successive approximations to that solution under limitations (1). These limitations have the role of sufficient conditions, because they have been introduced to use the majorizing series for the proof of convergence.

5. Case of $\zeta_0 = 0$—In the situations considered the existence of the solution was guaranteed due to the presence of the small parameter $\zeta_0 \neq 0$. Next, we consider a case of diffraction of the plane wave when $\zeta_0 = 0$ and show that equation II.3(36) can be used also in the case of $\zeta_0 = 0$.

The recurrent formulas of Section II.3(5) suggest two ways of finding the solution of the diffraction problem under consideration. The first way consists of calculating quantities $F_\nu^\pm$ in equation II.2(1), where functions $S_\nu^\pm(\alpha)$ can be found by the *direct summation* of successive approximations according to equation II.3(35). The second way consists of calculating quantity II.1(18), where function $S_\nu(\alpha)$ can be found by the *term-by-term summation* of successive approximations according to equation II.3(36). If the solution of equation II.3(24) exists, and successive approximations converge to this solution, both ways lead to the same result. However, the case of $\zeta_0 = 0$ is singular. Sections 4.4 and 6.2 show that the passage to the limit with $\zeta_0 \to 0$ is possible only with term-by-term summation, i.e., in equation II.3(36), while the series of the direction summation II.3(35) diverges with $\zeta_0 \to 0$. The situation seems paradoxical: the term-by-term summation leads to the solution of the diffraction problem even in the case ($\zeta_0 = 0$) when there is no solution of the operator equation II.3(24) producing the successive approximation formulas. Nevertheless, this situation allows the explanation.

Recurrent formulas II.3(35) leading to the term-by-term summation formula II.3(36) were developed within the framework of one of the possible statements of the diffraction problem, which assumed the possibility of splitting the sought solution in two parts F_ν^+ and F_ν^- in equation II.2(1). The mentioned paradoxical situation can be explained, if the recurrent relationships II.3(35) express the more general concept of description of the sought wavefield, which can be implemented without the splitting of the wavefield in the indicated parts. We now show that such concept can be developed by means of interpretation of the mentioned recurrent formulas.

We begin with some obvious considerations derived from the representation of the solution by the Sommerfeld-Malyuzhinetz integral II.1(18). This integral represents the sought solution in the form of superposition of the infinite set of inhomogeneous plane waves. If the waves of this set comply with the given boundary conditions, the integral gives the solution of the diffraction problem. In a class of the plane waves it is possible to satisfy the boundary conditions by means of the traditional methods of geometric acoustics (the deviation from the well-known formulas of multiple reflections/transmissions in the layered medium appears here because of unparalleled interfaces). The semi-infinity of the interface causes the shadow boundary in the plane wavefield – the latter ceases to comply with wave equation. However, the following integration smoothes the shadow boundaries, and the integral complies with the boundary conditions and wave equation simultaneously. Thus, the form of representation of the solution suggests a possible way of finding a solution: the application of the formal apparatus of geometric acoustics for calculating the multiple reflection/transmission of plane inhomogeneous waves under the sign of the Sommerfeld-Malyuzhinetz integral. We will show that the obtained recurrent formulas can be interpreted within the framework of such concept.

Integral II.1(18) can be considered as a superposition of plane inhomogeneous waves with the complex directions of propagation $\theta = \alpha$ and unknown amplitudes

$S_v(\alpha)\,d\alpha$. It is clear that for finding the amplitudes of all waves it is sufficient to find the directional characteristic $S_v(\alpha)$ of one plane wave as a function of the direction of propagation α. The function $S_v(\alpha)$ has to comply with the given boundary conditions. To describe a wavefield in terms of the elementary reflection/transmission theory, four plane waves must be connected with each individual interface as a minimum, because at each side of the interface there must be the incident and departing waves. So, in each wedge-shaped region there must be a minimum of two waves. Obviously, the model of a wavefield in the form of integral II.1(18) cannot be used directly for description of the reflection/transmission phenomena by the elementary methods, because its integrand corresponds to the single plane wave with the variable direction of propagation $\theta = \alpha$.

To describe these phenomena by the elementary methods, it is necessary to change the representation of the sought solution in such a way that in each wedge-shaped region there would be two plane waves with different variable directions of propagation. This kind of representation is given by equation II.2(1), where each integral II.2(2) represents a superposition of plane inhomogeneous waves with directions of propagation $\gamma_v^{\pm} = \alpha$ and unknown amplitudes $S_v^{\pm}(\alpha)\,d\alpha$. To find the amplitudes of all these waves, it is sufficient to find the directional characteristics $S_v^{+}(\alpha)$ and $S_v^{-}(\alpha)$ of one pair of plane waves as the functions of their directions of propagation α. The problem of finding these functions can be formulated in terms of the elementary reflection/transmission theory and results in the operator equation II.3(24). Indeed, the sought functions in this equation are connected by the classic operations of reflection/transmission at the set of unparalleled interfaces.

Suppose that the amplitudes of given incident waves are described by equations II.3(40) and II.3(47) with $\zeta_0 > 0$, and series II.3(35) converges with $n \to \infty$ to the solution of equation II.3(24). Then the mathematical formalism of the successive approximation method, equation II.3(35), corresponds precisely to the elementary description of the amplitudes of the branching sequence of inhomogeneous plane waves formed as a result of the multiple reflections/transmissions at the set of unparalleled interfaces.

Thus, within the framework of the representation II.2(1) the finding of the sought diffraction wavefield can be reduced to the application of the formal apparatus of geometric acoustics under the sign of the Sommerfeld-Malyuzhinetz integral. To express this process within the framework of representation II.1(18), it is sufficient to change the reference system of directions in accordance with equation II.2(3) or, what is the same, use relationships II.2(10). Then the integrand in equation II.1(18) is described by the corresponding elements of matrix II.3(38) representing the set of inhomogeneous reflected/transmitted plane waves in the new reference system of directions. The given interpretation of the recurrent relationships can be easily expanded on the case of vector waves.

The assumption about a possibility of the splitting of the sought solution in two parts F_v^+ and F_v^- in equation II.2(1) allows us to formulate the concept under consideration in a rather elegant way as a solution of the operator equation II.3(24) by the successive approximation method. However, this assumption is not necessary – the same concept can be formulated directly in terms of the elementary theory of reflection/transmission of plane waves on a system of unparalleled interfaces without consideration of the operator equation II.3(24). If the mentioned assumption holds true, the infinite set of reflected/transmitted plane waves in each wedge-shaped region can be united in two groups F_v^+ and F_v^-. In this case the convergence of series II.3(38) follows from the existence of solution of the operator equation II.3(24). If the mentioned assumption fails, it is impossible to form the indicated groups and necessary to check the convergence of series II.3(36) with $n \to \infty$, for example, by means of a numerical experiment. However, in any case these considerations do not affect the mathematical description of the concept under consideration, i.e., equations II.1(18) and II.3(36). Therefore, we can apply these formulas to the case of $\zeta_0 = 0$, checking the convergence of series II.3(36), if necessary, numerically.

Chapter IV

INTERPRETATION OF SUCCESSIVE APPROXIMATIONS

1. Development of the matrix product

1. Analyzable part of solution—Our goal, to single out the edge-diffracted waves from the total wavefield, can be obtained in principle by solving the *forced oscillations problem*. Because of complexity the system of functional equations seems to be unsolvable in the closed form. Currently we do not know if the total wavefield usually can be obtained with $\zeta_0 = 0$. However, the only possible way to obtain the wanted information on the edge-diffracted waves is from the functional equations and is based on the analysis of the properties of these equations. The problem, as stated in Chapter II, was aimed at making such analysis possible.

We can use the system of functional equations, as stated in equations II.3(33) and II.3(35) in the form

$$\boldsymbol{X} - \boldsymbol{T}^n \boldsymbol{X} = \boldsymbol{F}^{(n)}, \quad \boldsymbol{F}^{(n)} = \sum_{p=1}^{n} \boldsymbol{X}^{(p)}, \tag{1}$$

$$\boldsymbol{X}^{(p)} = \boldsymbol{T} \boldsymbol{X}^{(p-1)} = \boldsymbol{T}^p \boldsymbol{D}, \tag{2}$$

where n is any positive integer and $\boldsymbol{F}^{(n)}$ depends on a choice of n.

The solution of this system can be considered as the sum

$$\boldsymbol{X} = \boldsymbol{F}^{(n)} + \boldsymbol{Y}^{(n)}, \; \boldsymbol{Y}^{(n)} = \boldsymbol{T}^n \boldsymbol{X} \tag{3}$$

of the known $\boldsymbol{F}^{(n)}$ and unknown $\boldsymbol{Y}^{(n)}$ terms. We assume that all information on reflected/transmitted and edge-diffracted waves, required for geophysical applications, is contained in the term $\boldsymbol{F}^{(n)}$ if the number n is large enough. This is trivial in the case of the proven convergence of successive approximations (Chapter III). However, we usually can justify this assumption only by the analysis of obtained asymptotic formulas and numerical experiments. Therefore, we restrict this discussion to the study of the part of the solution corresponding to the right part $\boldsymbol{F}^{(n)}$ of system (1).

The matrix form of the system of functional equations has helped to simplify the statement of the problem. However, in this discussion we have to study every individual element of matrix $\boldsymbol{F}^{(n)}$ and to do so, we revert from the matrix form to the original representation of the solution. Chapter 4 deals with one of many possible ways of representing the result of the multiple matrix product (2) and its interpretation in terms of the plane wave theory.

Let us denote the elements of the column matrices as

$$\boldsymbol{X}^{(p)} = \left\{ \boldsymbol{X}_{\nu}^{(p)} \right\}, \quad \boldsymbol{Y}^{(n)} = \left\{ \boldsymbol{Y}_{\nu} \right\}, \text{ and} \tag{4}$$

$$\boldsymbol{X}_{\nu}^{(p)} = \begin{Bmatrix} S_{\nu p}^{p} \\ S_{\nu p}^{-} \end{Bmatrix}, \quad \boldsymbol{Y}_{\nu} = \begin{Bmatrix} y_{\nu}^{+} \\ y_{\nu}^{-} \end{Bmatrix}.$$

Then equation (3) leads to the following representation of the sought-after functions:

$$S_{\nu}^{\pm}(\alpha) = \sum_{p=1}^{n} S_{\nu p}^{\pm}(\alpha) + y_{\nu}^{\pm}(\alpha), \tag{5}$$

where $S_{\nu p}^{\pm}$ and $y_{\nu}^{\pm}$ are the known and unknown functions, respectively. By substituting equation (5) into equations II.2(1) II.2(2) we get

$$f_{\nu} = F_{\nu}^{(n)} + x, \quad F_{\nu}^{(n)} = \sum_{p=1}^{n} (f_{\nu p}^{+} + f_{\nu p}^{-}) + F_{\nu}, \tag{6}$$

$$f_{\nu p}^{\pm} = (1/2\pi i) \int_{\Gamma_0} S_{\nu p}^{\pm}(\alpha) \exp\left[-i k_{\nu} r \cos\left(\alpha - \gamma_{\nu}^{\pm}\right)\right] d\alpha, \tag{7}$$

where $F_{n}^{(n)}$ and x are the known and unknown parts of the solution, respectively. We are going to study the item $F_{\nu}^{(n)}$.

2. *Matrix product graph*—The functions $S_{\nu p}^{\pm}$ from integrals (7) are the elements of the block matrix $\boldsymbol{X}^{(p)}$. Because this matrix is a result of the p–fold matrix product (2), each element of its individual row can be written in the form of a series

$$S_{vp}^{\pm} = \sum_{m(p)} S_{m(p)}, \tag{8}$$

$$S_{m(p)} = \kappa_{\lambda v} \kappa_{\mu\lambda} \ldots \kappa_{bc} \kappa_{ab} S_{m(o)}, \tag{9}$$

where each term (9) contains p operators κ_{uv} and the double indices $m(p)$ enumerate all possible combinations of indices of operators κ_{uv}. A couple of cofactors $S_{m(o)}$ correspond to the elements of the perturbation matrix [II.3(40)]

$$S_{m(o)} = D_k^+ \text{ or } S_{m(o)} = D_k^- \tag{10}$$

The possible combinations of indices in equations (8) - (9), determined by the formal rules of matrix multiplication, admit a clear physical interpretation that will be given in Section IV.2.5. We now consider a graphic way of putting these indices in order. To simplify the graphic illustrations, we demonstrate this technique by using a wedge ($N=2$), which was briefly discussed in Section III.1.1 (Figure 12). The formal description of this technique in a general case of arbitrary N is given in Appendix C.

In the case of a wedge ($N = 2$) we can write equation (2) as

$$\begin{Bmatrix} S_{1p}^+ \\ S_{1p}^- \\ S_{2p}^+ \\ S_{2p}^- \end{Bmatrix} = \begin{pmatrix} 0 & \kappa_{11} & \kappa_{21} & 0 \\ \kappa_{11} & 0 & 0 & \kappa_{21} \\ \kappa_{12} & 0 & 0 & \kappa_{22} \\ 0 & \kappa_{12} & \kappa_{22} & 0 \end{pmatrix} \times \begin{Bmatrix} S_{1(p-1)}^+ \\ S_{1(p-1)}^- \\ S_{2(p-1)}^+ \\ S_{2(p-1)}^- \end{Bmatrix}. \tag{11}$$

According to the formal rule of matrix multiplication, the elements of matrix T interact with the elements of matrix $X^{(p-1)}$ as illustrated in Figure 15(a) with the bold arrows. The results of these operations are assigned to the rows of matrix $X^{(p)}$, according to a scheme shown with the thin arrows. Therefore, the rule of transformation (11) is illustrated graphically in the form of *an elementary scheme* in Figure 15 (b), where each arrow denotes an operation of transformation of an element of an individual row of matrix $X^{(p-1)}$ into an element of an individual row of matrix $X^{(p)}$, according to the expression $\kappa_{uv} S_{u(p-1)}^{\pm}$. The beginning and the end of an arrow indicate the corresponding elements of matrices. The element of each row of matrix $X^{(p-1)}$ is transformed into the elements of those two rows of matrix $X^{(p)}$ which are marked with arrows. The element of each row of matrix $X^{(p)}$ is formed by the contributions of those two rows of matrix $X^{(p-1)}$, where the corresponding arrows come from.

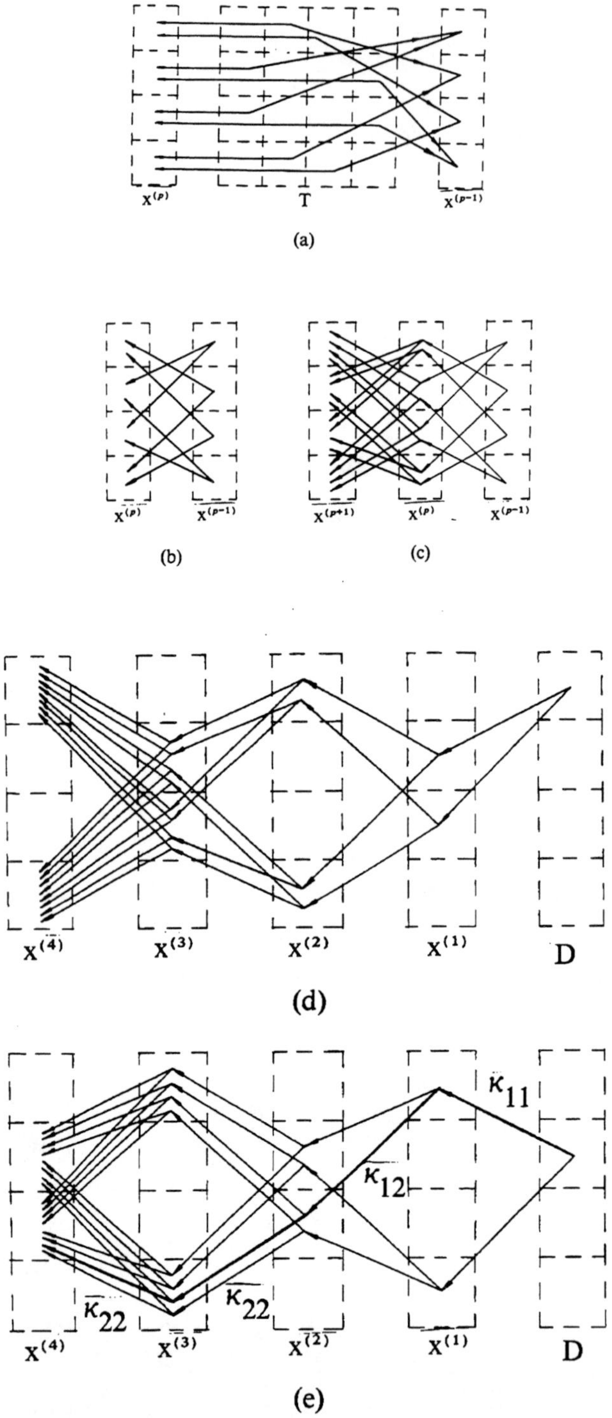

Figure 15. Graphs of the matrix product. (a) interaction between the matrix elements in equation IV.1(11). (b) Connection between the elements of matrices $X^{(p-1)}$ and $X^{(p)}$. (c) interconnection between the matrix elements in the recursion process. Parts of the graph of matrix $X^{(4)}$ connected with the first (d) and the second (e) rows of matrix D.

In recursion formula (2) each row-element of matrix $X^{(p-1)}$ is the sum of 2^{p-1} elements. The transformation of each element can be displayed by this elementary scheme. The matrix $X^{(p)}$ acts at the pth step as a product, while at the following $(p+1)^{th}$ step it acts as a cofactor. Therefore, the elementary schemes of the recursion process are interconnected (Figure 15 (c)). The sequence of interconnected elementary schemes, displaying the recursion algorithm of development of matrix $X^{(p)}$, is called the *graph* of this matrix.

A graph of matrix $X^{(4)}$ is shown in Figure 15 (d, e) where parts of the graph are connected with the elements of the first and second rows of matrix D, but are shown separately for convenience. Parts connected with the third and fourth rows of matrix D are absent because the corresponding elements of matrix D are zeros.

The *element* of the graph is marked by an arrow that connects the rows of neighboring matrices and corresponds to the individual operator κ_{uv}. The beginning and the end of the element are *the nodes* of the graph. A nonbranching succession of transitions from one node to the other, shown by the corresponding succession of the elements, forms *the branch* of the graph [in Figure 15 (e) an individual branch is indicated by a bold line]. The corresponding index, assigned to each node, coincides with the index of the corresponding matrix row: $\nu = 1$ for the first and second rows, $\nu = 2$ for the third and fourth rows. A sequence of indices of corresponding nodes is assigned to each branch [for example, indices 11222 is for the branch shown bold in Figure 15 (e)]. An individual branch corresponds to the product of p operators $\kappa_{\lambda\nu}\ \kappa_{\mu\lambda}\ \ldots\ \kappa_{bc}\ \kappa_{ab}$, where the indices show positions of the nodes of this branch. Thus, each item of the sum (8) has a corresponding branch of the graph.

The graph helps us enumerate all items of the sum (8) and the sequence of indices of each item, and to find element $S_{m(0)}$ of matrix D for each item ($S_{m(0)} = D_1^+$) for the branches shown in Figure 15 (d) and ($S_{m(0)} = D_1^-$) in Figure 15 (e). The double indices $m(p)$ is assigned to each branch, where p is the index of matrix $X^{(p)}$ and m the number of the branch independent of p. Then the expression $X^{(p)} = T^p\ D$ can be written as

$$X^{(p)} = \begin{Bmatrix} S^+_{1p} \\ S^-_{1p} \\ S^+_{2p} \\ S^-_{2p} \end{Bmatrix} = \begin{Bmatrix} \sum\limits_{m(p)} S_{m(p)} \\ \sum\limits_{m(p)} S_{m(p)} \\ \sum\limits_{m(p)} S_{m(p)} \\ \sum\limits_{m(p)} S_{m(p)} \end{Bmatrix} = \begin{pmatrix} 0 & \kappa_{11} & \kappa_{21} & 0 \\ \kappa_{11} & 0 & 0 & \kappa_{21} \\ \kappa_{12} & 0 & 0 & \kappa_{22} \\ 0 & \kappa_{12} & \kappa_{22} & 0 \end{pmatrix}^p \times \begin{Bmatrix} D^+_1 \\ D^-_1 \\ 0 \\ 0 \end{Bmatrix}, \tag{12}$$

where $\sum\limits_{m(p)}$ is the symbol of summation over the branches of the graph. In each row of this matrix the summation is carried out over those branches only, the end-nodes of which belong to this row.

The above technique can be used to draw the graph of matrix (2) for any $N \geq 2$. By using representation (8) we can write the part $F^{(n)}_\nu$ of the solution (6) in the form

$$F^{(n)}_\nu = \sum_{p=0}^{n} \sum_{m(p)} f_{m(p)}\,(\gamma) \quad \text{with } \gamma = \gamma^+_\nu \quad \text{or } \gamma = \gamma^-_\nu\,, \tag{13}$$

$$f_{m(p)}\,(\gamma) = (1/2\pi i) \int_{\Gamma_0} S_{m(p)}\,(\alpha)\, \exp\,[-i k_\nu r \cos\,(\alpha - \gamma)]\, d\alpha\,, \tag{14}$$

where the terms $f_{m(p)}\,(\gamma^+_\nu)$ and $f_{m(p)}\,(\gamma^-_\nu)$ belong to different branches, i.e., they have different indices m. The term with $p = 0$ corresponds to the perturbation II.3(49).

3. Recursion relations—According to equation (9) function $S_{m(p)}\,(\alpha)$ with $p \geq 1$ is the result of p–fold operations II.2(31), i.e.,

$$S_{m(k)}\,(\alpha) = \kappa_{uv}\, S_{m(k-1)}\,(\alpha) = \tau_{uv}\,(\alpha)\; K_{uv}\,(\alpha)\; S_{m(k-1)}\;[\varphi_{uv}\,(\alpha) + \varepsilon_u] \tag{15}$$

with $k = 1, 2, \ldots p$ and $m = \text{const}$. The direct representation of the results of such multiple operation is rather cumberson. Therefore, we write the corresponding relations in a simplified recursion form (for more details, see Appendix C). Here we write the result of the multiple operations (15) in the form

$$S_{m(p)}\,(\alpha) = P'_{m(p)}\,(\alpha)\; H_{m(p)}\,(\alpha)\; S_{m(0)}\,[P_{m(p)}\,(\alpha)]\,, \tag{16}$$

where $P'_{m(p)}$ corresponds to a multiple product of quantities τ_{uv}, $H_{m(p)}$ to the product of quantities K_{uv}, and $P_{m(p)}$ to the result of multiple substitutions of α by $\varphi_{uv}(\alpha) + \varepsilon_u$.

Then from equation (15) we have the following recursion relations:

$$P_{m(p)}(\alpha) = P_{m(p-1)}[\varphi_{uv}(\alpha) + \varepsilon_u], \; P_{m(0)}(\alpha) = \alpha, \tag{17}$$

$$H_{m(p)}(\alpha) = K_{uv}(\alpha)\, H_{m(p-1)}[\varphi_{uv}(\alpha) + \varepsilon_u], \; H_{m(0)}(\alpha) = 1, \tag{18}$$

$$P'_{m(p)}(\alpha) = \tau_{uv}(\alpha)\, P'_{m(p-1)}[\varphi_{uv}(\alpha) + \varepsilon_u], \; P'_{m(0)}(\alpha) = 1, \tag{19}$$

and the relation

$$P'_{m(p)}(\alpha) = dP_{m(p)}/d\alpha. \tag{20}$$

The properties of these functions are given in Appendix C.

4. Account of perturbation—When $p = 0$, we can represent perturbation by formula II.3(49). When $p \geq 1$, by using equations (10) and II.3(40) we introduce the following representation:

$$S_{m(0)}(\alpha) = (\alpha - \alpha_{m(0)})^{-1} A_{m(0)}(\alpha - \alpha_{m(0)}), \tag{21}$$

$$A_{m(0)}(\alpha) = A_k^{\pm}(\alpha), \; \alpha_{m(0)} = \alpha_k^{\pm}. \tag{22}$$

We take here "plus," if the branch under consideration m = const of the matrix $X^{(p)}$ product graph begins at the node D_k^+, and "minus," if it begins at D_k^-.

5. Element of the matrix product—By substituting equation (21) into equation (16) we get the following representation of function $S_{m(p)}(\alpha)$ with $p \geq 1$ in integral (14):

$$S_{m(p)}(\alpha) = H_{m(p)}(\alpha)\, A_{m(o)}[P_{m(p)}(\alpha) - \alpha_{m(0)}] \,/\, V_{m(p)}(\alpha), \tag{23}$$

$$V_{m(p)}(\alpha) = [P_{m(p)}(\alpha) - \alpha_{m(0)}] \,/\, P'_{m(p)}(\alpha). \tag{24}$$

2. Transformation of the system of reference

1. Inverse function—We can consider expression 1(17) as a function transforming the complex plane of a variable α into the complex plane of some new variable z. Then we can introduce function $Q_{m(p)}(z)$, inverted in regard to the function 1(17) according to the following relations:

$$z = P_{m(p)}(\alpha), \quad \alpha = Q_{m(p)}(z), \tag{1}$$

$$P'_{m(p)}(\alpha)\, Q'_{m(p)}(z) = 1, \tag{2}$$

where

$$Q'_{m(p)}(z) = d\,Q_{m(p)}/dz. \tag{3}$$

2. Inverse recursion relations—The recursion relations for the inverse function can be obtained by solving equation 1(17) relative to α. By substituting the first expression from equations (1) into the left part of equation 1(17) we derive

$$z = P_{m(p-1)}[\varphi_{uv}(\alpha) + \varepsilon_u],$$

and solving it relative to α, we get

$$\alpha = \varphi_{vu}[\,Q_{m(p-1)}(z) - \varepsilon_u].$$

By substituting the expression for α from equation (1) into this formula we obtain the desired recursion relation

$$Q_{m(p)}(z) = \varphi_{vu}[\,Q_{m(p-1)}(z) - \varepsilon_u], \quad Q_{m(0)}(z) = z. \tag{4}$$

The real part of function $\varphi_{vu}(z)$ is a monotonous function of Re z (see Appendix B) and, therefore, the following inequality holds true:

$$\text{Re}\ Q_{m(p)}(z) < \text{Re}\ Q_{m(p-1)}(z). \tag{5}$$

Equation (13) of Appendix B leads to the following relation:

$$\text{sign Im}\ Q_{m(p)}(z) = \text{sign Im}\ Q_{m(p-1)}(z). \tag{6}$$

The other properties of the inverse function are given in Appendix C.

3. Integral formula—We introduce a new variable z in integral 1(14) by using the first expression of equations (1). Then we get a new integral representation of the term of sum 1(13):

$$f_{m(p)}(\gamma) = (1/2\pi i) \int_{\Gamma_z} S^*_{m(p)}(z) \exp\left\{-ik_v r \cos\left[Q_{m(p)}(z) - \gamma\right]\right\} dz, \tag{7}$$

$$S^*_{m(p)}(z) = H_{m(p)}\left[Q_{m(p)}(z)\right] S_{m(0)}(z), \tag{8}$$

$$S_{m(0)}(z) = (z - \alpha_{m(0)})^{-1} A_{m(0)}(z - \alpha_{m(0)}). \tag{9}$$

The allowable domains of the complex plane of z are determined by equations II.2(4), where α has to be substituted by $Q_{m(p)}(z)$, i.e.,

$$\text{sign}\left[\text{Re } Q_{m(p)}(z) - \gamma - 2k\pi\right] = \text{sign Im } Q_{m(p)}(z). \tag{10}$$

To find the contour of integration Γ_z, we suppose that the initial contour Γ_0 of the integral 1(14) is placed outside the band $|\text{Im } \alpha| < C$, where C is a sufficiently large number. Then in the domain $|\text{Im } \alpha| > C$ the transformation function from equations (1) can be approximated by its asymptotic representation (see proof of Assertion 14 in Appendix A)

$$P_{m(p)}(\alpha) \sim \alpha + \mu_1 + i\mu_2, \tag{11}$$

$$\mu_1 = \sum_{m(p)} \varepsilon_{m(p)}, \quad \mu_2 = (\text{sign Im } \alpha) \ln(c_k/c_v),$$

where $\varepsilon_{m(p)}$ is a current parameter ε_u in the recursive formula 1(17) marked with the index $m(p)$ of the matrix-product graph. This formula shows that contour Γ_z is the result of the transformation of contour Γ_0 by shifting it without deformation (Figure 16)

$$\text{Re } z = \text{Re } \alpha + \mu_1, \quad \text{Im } z = \text{Im } \alpha + \mu_2. \tag{12}$$

4. Interpretation in terms of geometrical acoustics—We can consider the integral (7) as a superposition of plane waves of amplitudes

$$A(z) = (1/2\pi i)\, S^*_{m(p)}(z)\, dz, \tag{13}$$

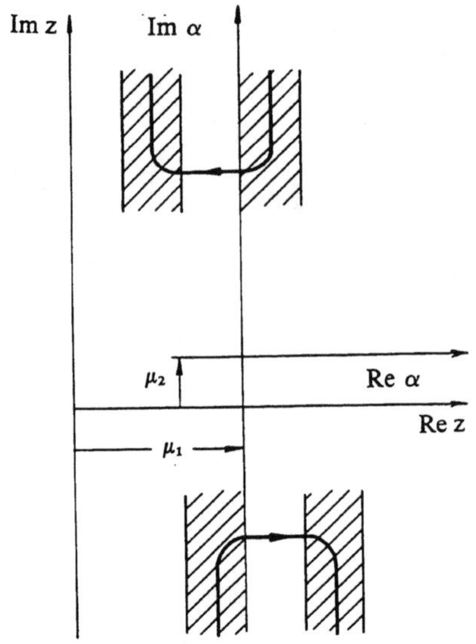

Figure 16. Contour of integration in equation IV.2(7).

and directions of propagation $Q_{m(p)}(z)$. Then the initial step of the recursion process $Q_{m(0)}(z) = z$, $H_{m(0)}[Q_{m(0)}(z)] = 1$ means that the integral $f_{m(0)}(\gamma)$ is formed by the superposition of waves propagating in the direction $\gamma = z$. Their amplitudes (13) with $p = 0$ depend on the direction of propagation.

To find the direction of propagation, when $p \geq 1$, we have to perform the transformation $Q_{m(p)}(z)$. To get the physical interpretation of this transformation, it is sufficient to rewrite equation (4) in the form

$$c_v^{-1} \cos Q_{m(p)}(z) = c_u^{-1} \cos [Q_{m(p-1)}(z) - \varepsilon_u], \tag{14}$$

which is the well-known Snell's law, and connects directions of the incident $Q_{m(p-1)}(z) - \varepsilon_u$ and reflected/transmitted $Q_{m(p)}(z)$ rays (Figure 17). Therefore, function $Q_{m(p)}(z)$ determines the direction of the p–fold reflected/transmitted ray, if the direction z of incidence is given. The inverse function $z = P_{m(p)}(\alpha)$ determines the direction z of incidence, if the direction α of the p–fold reflected/transmitted ray is given.

We find the amplitude (13) of the p–fold reflected/transmitted wave, by taking into account all reflection/transmission coefficients according to equation (8).

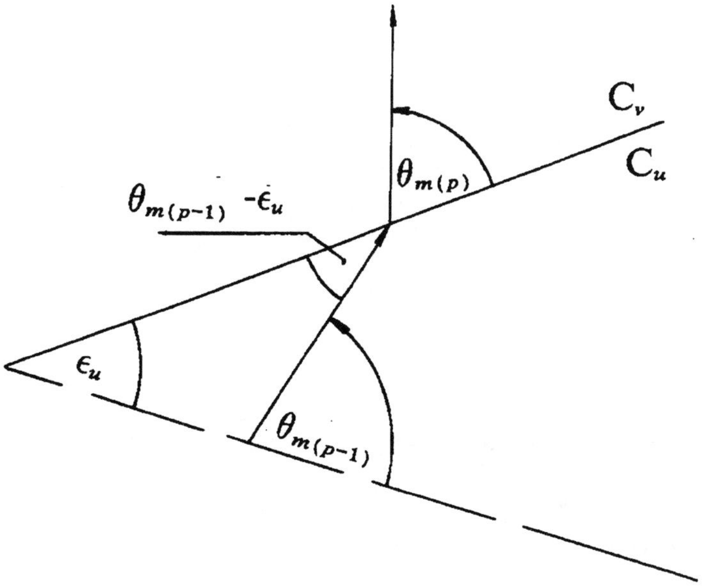

Figure 17. Interpretation of equation IV.2(14).

5. *Reflection/transmission graph*—The succession of reflections/transmissions can be correlated with the matrix-product graph (Figure 15). To make the graph more illustrative, we can match the graph with a model of wedge-shaped regions and derive *the reflection/transmission graph* (or the ray scheme). An explanation of how this can be done follows.

An individual node of the matrix-product graph can be identified with an individual interface or, to be more precise, with the boundary of a domain. Each wedge-shaped domain has two half-plane boundaries, marked with indices (+) and (-) in such a way that the transition from (+) to (-) within the domain is possible in a counterclockwise direction. On the other hand, we mark with the same indices (+) and (-) the column-matrix row that has a fixed index ν. Therefore, the indication of a row in the column matrix, i.e., the node of the graph, can indicate a boundary of the domain. So the transition from one node of the graph to another can be correlated with the transition from one boundary of the wedge-shaped domain to another.

Figure 18 shows an example of the transformation of the matrix-product graph into the reflection/transmission graph. The elements of the matrix-product graph are shown on the right side by bold lines. The result of the elementary operation is placed in the row, to which the arrow is pointing. This result is displayed as well on the left side as an element of the reflection/transmission graph. Its beginning coincides with the boundary

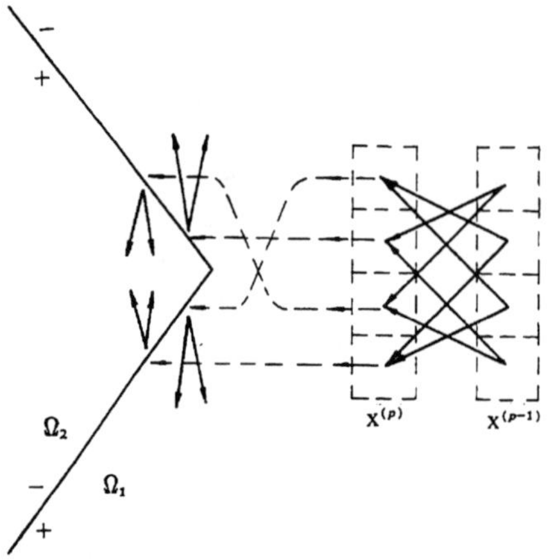

Figure 18. Transformation of the matrix-product graph into the reflection/transmission graph.

that is identified with the corresponding row of the matrix $X^{(p)}$, i.e., with the corresponding node of the matrix-product graph. The correspondence between boundaries and nodes is shown with dashed lines. Note that the element of the matrix product graph denotes an operation, while the element of the reflection/transmission graph denotes the result of the operation.

The reflection/transmission graph gives the so-called ray scheme of multifold reflections/transitions. Figure 19 shows the ray schemes, obtained from the matrix-product graph of Figure 15. Here each direct succession of the elements corresponds to an individual branch of the matrix-product graph [in Figure 19 (b) the bold line corresponds to the bold line of Figure 15 (e)] and to the $m\,(p)^{th}$ wave of the kind (13). The ray scheme on the whole displays the set of waves, enumerated with index $m\,(p)$.

Now we can interpret the terms $f_{m(p)}(\gamma_v^+)$ and $f_{m(p)}(\gamma_v^-)$ in formula 1.(13) in terms of the reflection/transmission graph. The term $f_{m(p)}(\gamma_v^+)$ is formed as a result of the reflection/transmission at the boundary θ_v^+, while $f_{m(p)}(\gamma_v^-)$ is formed at the boundary θ_v^-.

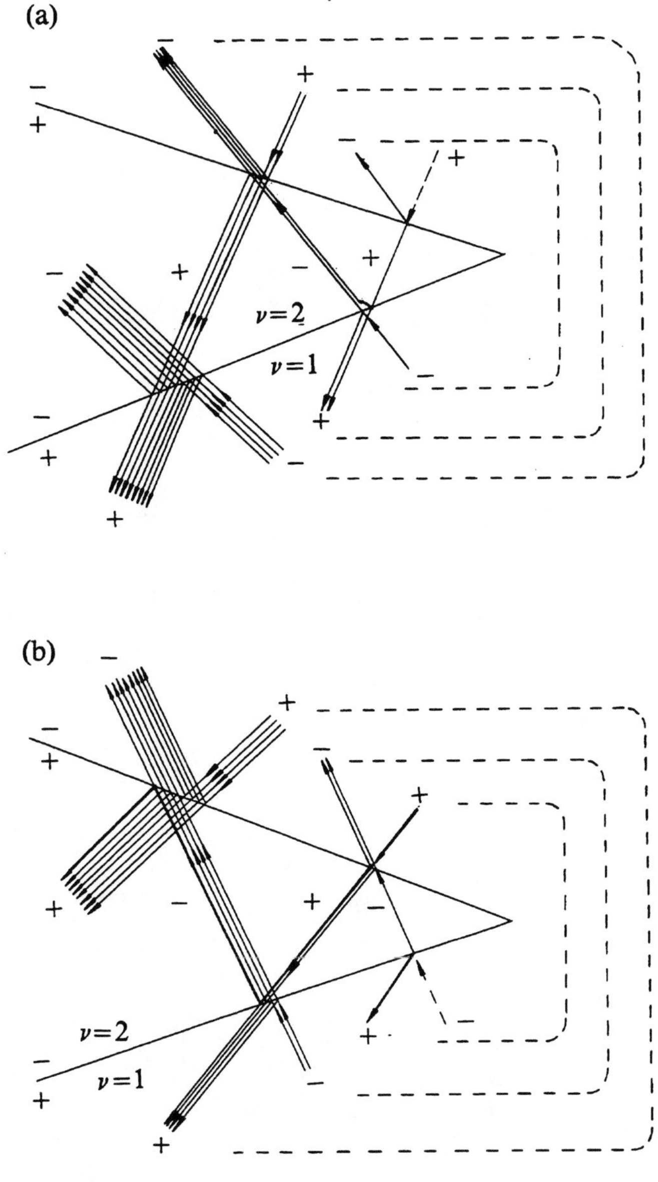

Figure 19. Ray schemes of multifold reflections/transmissions.

Chapter V

HIGH-FREQUENCY ANALYSIS

1. High-frequency analysis

1. Initial integral—Chapter V deals with the information on the edge-diffracted waves that can be obtained by an asymptotic analysis of the integral IV.2(7), i.e.,

$$f_{m(p)}(\gamma) = (1/2\pi i) \int_{\Gamma_z} \Psi(z)\,dz \tag{1}$$

$$\Psi(z) = A_{m(p)}(z)(z-\alpha_{m(0)})^{-1} \exp[-i k_v r\, \xi(z)], \tag{2}$$

$$A_{m(p)}(z) = H_{m(p)}[Q_{m(p)}(z)]\, A_{m(0)}(z-\alpha_{m(0)}), \tag{3}$$

$$\xi(z) = \cos[Q_{m(p)}(z) - \gamma]. \tag{4}$$

We are going to obtain a high-frequency asymptotic representation of this integral with $k_v r \to \infty$ by using a traditional technique for a contour integral of a rapidly oscillating function (Felsen and Marcuvitz, 1973). We will deform the contour of integration to the form that allows us to obtain the asymptotic formulas by integrating over its separate particular parts. Such parts of the contour must pass through the neighborhoods of those points of the complex plane of z, which give the essential contribution in the integral, when $k_v r \to \infty$.

The asymptotic value of the integral (1) with $k_v r \to \infty$ is formed by contributions from the neighborhoods of the singular points, where the integrand loses its analytic character, and *the saddle points*, which are the minimax points of the modulus of the integrand. Let us consider the behavior of the integrand in the neighborhoods of the mentioned points.

2. *Pole*—The integrand has a simple pole at $z = \alpha_{m(0)}$, in the neighborhood of which it can be approximated by the principal term of the Laurent series

$$\Psi(z) \approx \Psi^0(z) \text{ with } z \to \alpha_{m(0)}, \tag{5}$$

$$\Psi^0(z) = F_{m(p)}(\gamma)(z - \alpha_{m(0)})^{-1} \tag{6}$$

with the residue

$$F_{m(p)}(\gamma) = A_{m(p)}(\alpha_{m(0)}) \exp[-i k_v r \, \xi(\alpha_{m(0)})], \tag{7}$$

$$A_{m(p)}(\alpha_{m(0)}) = H_{m(p)}[Q_{m(p)}(\alpha_{m(0)}] A_{m(0)}(0) = H_{m(p)}[Q_{m(p)}(\alpha_{m(0)})]. \tag{8}$$

The residue is limited with $k_v r \to \infty$, if the real part of the exponent is less or equal to zero, i.e., within the allowable domain IV.2(10)

$$\text{sign}[\text{Re } Q_{m(p)}(\alpha_{m(0)}) - \gamma] = \text{sign Im } Q_{m(p)}(\alpha_{m(0)}). \tag{9}$$

Let us show that this condition is always satisfied. If $p = 1$, we have $Q_{m(1)}(\alpha_{m(0)}) = \alpha^*$. Here α^* is determined by equations II.3(53) or II.3(55) and it complies with inequalities II.3(56) which can be rewritten now in the form

$$\text{Re } Q_{m(1)}(\alpha_{m(0)}) \le 0, \text{ Im } Q_{m(1)}(\alpha_{m(0)}) \le 0. \tag{10}$$

Then it follows from equations IV.2(5) - IV.2(6) that

$$\text{Re } Q_{m(p)}(\alpha_{m(0)}) \le 0, \text{ Im } Q_{m(p)}(\alpha_{m(0)}) \le 0 \text{ with } p \ge 1. \tag{11}$$

These inequalities show that condition (9) holds true, when $\gamma \ge 0$.

Because of the second inequality (11) the modulus of the quantity (7) tends to zero exponentially, when $k_v r \to \infty$ with $\text{Im } Q_{m(p)}(\alpha_{m(0)}) \ne 0$. That is why we have to consider the residue when

$$\text{Im } Q_{m(p)}(\alpha_{m(0)}) = 0. \tag{12}$$

On the strength of relations [IV.2(1)] condition (12) can be satisfied only at the points $\alpha_{m(0)}$, which can be transformed to the real axis of the plane of α.

3. Branch points—The first cofactor in equation IV.1(19) turns to infinity at the branch points of the unifying function. Hence, on the strength of equation IV.2(2) the branch points of function $P_{m(p)}(\alpha)$ can be given as the solutions of the equation

$$Q'_{m(p)}(z) = 0 \quad \text{with } z = P_{m(p)}(\alpha), \text{ i.e., } Q'_{m(p)}[P_{m(p)}(\alpha)] = 0, \tag{13}$$

and the branch points of function $Q_{m(p)}(z)$ as the solutions of the equation

$$P'_{m(p)}(\alpha) = 0 \quad \text{with } \alpha = Q_{m(p)}(z), \text{ i.e., } P'_{m(p)}[Q_{m(p)}(z)] = 0. \tag{14}$$

4. Saddle points—Positions of saddle points $z = z_h$ are determined by the following condition

$$d\xi(z)/dz = 0 \quad \text{when } z = z_h, \tag{15}$$

which, upon differentiation, can be written as

$$Q'_{m(p)}(z_h) \sin[Q_{m(p)}(z_h) - \gamma] = 0. \tag{16}$$

First, this equation is satisfied when $Q'_{m(p)}(z_h) = 0$. According to equation (13) the solution to this equation is a branch point of function $P_{m(p)}(\alpha)$. This case, i.e., the coincidence of the saddle and branch points, is out of the line of our consideration.

Second, equation (16) is satisfied, when

$$Q_{m(p)}(z_h) - \gamma = h\pi, \tag{17}$$

where h is an integer including zero. Let us find the solution of this equation by using equations IV.2(1)

$$z_h = P_{m(p)}(\alpha_h), \quad \alpha_h = \gamma + h\pi. \tag{18}$$

We can consider the behavior of the integrand in the neighborhood of a saddle point. The function (4) can be approximated by a part of the power expansion

$$\xi(z) \approx \xi(z_h) + \frac{1}{2}(d^2\xi/dz^2)_{z=z_h}(z - z_h)^2, \tag{19}$$

where, because of condition (15), the term corresponding to the first power is absent. By taking into consideration equation (17) we have

$$\xi(z_h) = \cos h\pi, \ (d^2\xi/dz^2)_{z=z_h} = -[Q'_{m(p)}(z_h)]^2 \cos h\pi. \tag{20}$$

From equations IV.2(2) and (17) we have

$$Q'_{m(p)}(z_h) = 1/P'_{m(p)}(\alpha_h), \ \alpha_h = Q_{m(p)}(z_h) = \gamma + h\pi. \tag{21}$$

By substituting equations (18), (20), and (21) into (19), we obtain the approximate representation of function (4) in the neighborhood of a saddle point

$$\xi(z) = \cos h\pi \cdot [1 - \zeta_h(z - z_h)^2], \tag{22}$$

$$\zeta_h = [\sqrt{2}\ P'_{m(p)}(\alpha_h)]^{-2} \tag{23}$$

It is sufficient to approximate function (3) by its value at a saddle point. Then we get the following approximation of the integrand:

$$\Psi(z) \approx \Psi_h(z) \quad \text{with } z \to z_h, \tag{24}$$

$$\Psi_h(z) = A_{m(p)}(z_h)(z - \alpha_{m(0)})^{-1} \exp\left\{-i k_v r \cos h\pi \times [1 - \zeta_h(z - z_h)^2]\right\}. \tag{25}$$

5. *Approximate integrals*—To get a single-valued branch of the integrand, it is necessary to connect all branch points pairwise by cuts in the complex plane of z. The very existence of branch points and corresponding cuts is the main difficulty with the idea of deforming the contour of integration to a form, convenient for the asymptotic analysis, because a number of branch points (and corresponding cuts) grows rapidly with the number of interaction p increasing. This makes search for the contour, which has to circumvent all cuts without crossing them, very difficult. However, the contributions from the integrals along the cuts to the integral under consideration have nothing to do with the edge-diffracted waves we are interested in. So we can essentially simplify the analysis, if we limit ourselves to the study of the edge-diffracted waves. To do so, we use the local approximations of the integrand in the neighborhoods of poles and saddle points, which eliminate the branch points.

To carry out these approximations, we represent function (2) in the form

$$\Psi(z) = \tilde{\Psi}(z) + \Psi^*(z), \tag{26}$$

$$\tilde{\Psi}(z) = \Psi^0(z) + \sum_h \Psi_h(z), \quad \Psi^*(z) = \Psi(z) - \tilde{\Psi}(z),$$

where the corresponding functions are determined by equations (2), (6), and (25). The summation is carried out over indices h of those saddle points, which can contribute to the integral under consideration. The term $\widetilde{\Psi}(z)$ approximates the integrand in the neighborhoods of the pole $z = \alpha_{m(0)}$ and the saddle points. This term has no singular points except the mentioned pole. The term $\Psi^*(z)$ can be neglected with $k_v r \to \infty$ at $z = \alpha_{m(0)}$ and the saddle points. Its singular points are the branch points, i.e., the roots of equation (14). Thus, expression (26) allows us to separate the contributions of the pole and saddle points (the first term) from the contribution of the branch points (the second term).

We will study the contribution of the pole and saddle points with $k_v r \to \infty$ only. Therefore, we consider the integral

$$f_{m(p)} \approx (1/2\pi i) \int_{\Gamma_z} \widetilde{\Psi}(z)\, dz + \ldots, \tag{27}$$

where the points correspond to the omitted second term of equation (26).

Let us deform the contour of integration Γ_z into a pair of contours Γ_{-1} and Γ_1, passing through the saddle points as is shown in Figure 20. If the initial contour crosses over the pole, we have to go around the pole with the closed contour Γ^* in a counterclockwise direction. Then integral (27) can be written as

$$f_{m(p)}(\gamma) = g_{m(p)}(\gamma) + l_{m(p)}(\gamma - \pi) + l_{m(p)}(\gamma + \pi), \tag{28}$$

$$g_{m(p)}(\gamma) = (1/2\pi i) \int_{\Gamma^*} \Psi^0(z)\, dz, \tag{29}$$

$$l_{m(p)}(\gamma + h\pi) = (1/2\pi i) \int_{\Gamma_h} \Psi_h(z)\, dz, \tag{30}$$

where Ψ^0 and Ψ_h are determined by equations (6) and (25), respectively.

6. *Plane waves*—Let us consider integral (29) under condition (12). In this case the integral under consideration is not zero, if the pole $z = \alpha_{m(0)}$ is located between the real saddle points z_{-1} and z_1 [Figure 20(a)], i.e., under conditions

$$\mathrm{Re}\, z_{-1} < \alpha_{m(0)} < \mathrm{Re}\, z_1 \quad \text{with } \mathrm{Im}\, z_h = 0\,. \tag{31}$$

These conditions can be transformed into the complex plane of α as

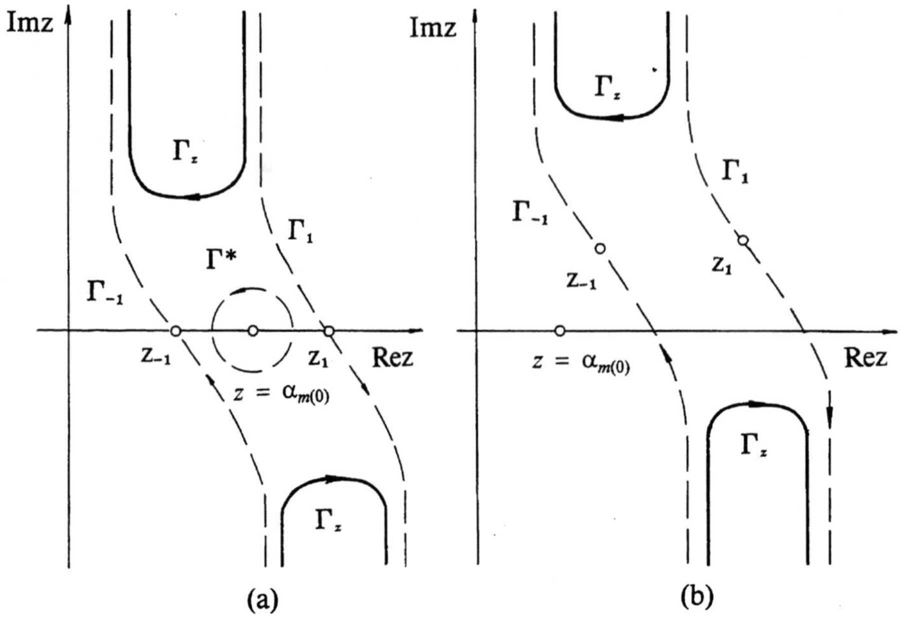

Figure 20. Transformation of contour Γ_z (bold lines) into contours Γ_h (dash lines) when the residue is (a) present and (b) absent.

$$\alpha_{-1} < \operatorname{Re} Q_{m(p)}(\alpha_{m(0)}) < \alpha_1 \quad \text{with} \quad \operatorname{Im} Q_{m(p)}(\alpha_{m(0)}) = 0 . \tag{32}$$

By taking into consideration equation (18) and introducing notation

$$\alpha_{m(p)} = Q_{m(p)}(\alpha_{m(0)}) \tag{33}$$

we can rewrite inequalities (32) in the form

$$\gamma - \pi < \operatorname{Re} \alpha_{m(p)} < \gamma + \pi \quad \text{with} \quad \operatorname{Im} \alpha_{m(p)} = 0 \tag{34}$$

or in the form

$$0 < \xi < 2\pi , \tag{35}$$

where

$$\xi = \gamma + \pi - \operatorname{Re} \alpha_{m(p)} \quad \text{with} \quad \operatorname{Im} \alpha_{m(p)} = 0 . \tag{36}$$

Then taking into consideration equations (6) - (7) we obtain

$$g_{m(p)}(\gamma) = \begin{cases} F_{m(p)}(\xi) & \text{when } 0 < \xi < 2\pi \\ 0 & \text{when } \xi < 0 \text{ or } \xi > 2\pi . \end{cases} \qquad (37') \; (37'')$$

$$F_{m(p)}(\xi) = H_{m(p)}(\alpha_{m(p)}) \exp(i k_\nu r \cos\xi). \qquad (38)$$

Expression (38) describes a plane homogeneous wave of the amplitude $H_{m(p)}(\alpha_{m(p)})$, propagating in the direction $\xi = 0$. Its formation can be described in the framework of an ordinary plane-wave theory, according to the reflection/transmission graph. The wave exists only in the domain (35) and does not exist outside of the domain.

By using inequalities IV.2(5) it is easy to prove the existence of such a number p^* that with $p > p^*$ conditions (34) cannot be satisfied. Hence, it is sufficient to take $n \geq p^*$ in equation IV.1(1) to consider all the possible plane waves.

2. Integration in the neighborhood of a saddle point

1. *Initial representation*—Let us write integral 1(30) in the form

$$l_{m(p)}(\gamma + hx) = A_{m(p)}(z)\, I_h \exp(i k_\nu r), \qquad (1)$$

$$I_h = (1/2\pi i) \int_{\Gamma_h} (z - \alpha_{m(0)})^{-1} \exp[-i k_\nu r\, \zeta_h (z - z_h)^2]\, d\zeta. \qquad (2)$$

By introducing a new variable τ of integration

$$z = \tau (k_\nu r\, \zeta_h)^{-1/2} + \alpha_{m(0)} \qquad (3)$$

we get

$$I_h = (1/2\pi i) \int_{T_h} \tau^{-1} \exp[-i(\tau - \beta_h)^2]\, d\tau, \qquad (4)$$

$$\beta_h = (k_\nu r\, \zeta_h)^{1/2} (z_h - \alpha_{m(0)}). \qquad (5)$$

2. *Property of the odd function*—There are two important properties of integral (4), which we have to use in the following. Substitute the variable τ by $-\tau$ and parameter β_h by $-\beta_h$. As a result of the substitution of the variable of integration, each point of

contour T_h will be transformed into a point symmetrical with respect to $\tau = 0$. As a result of the substitution β_h by $-\beta_h$, the contour of integration will return to its initial position but with the opposite direction of integration. The result of these transformations leads to the following relation:

$$I_h(-\beta_h) = -I_h(\beta_h). \tag{6}$$

Let us represent parameter β_h in the form

$$\beta_h = \text{sign Re } \beta_h \cdot \beta_h^*, \ \beta_h^* = | \text{ Re } \beta_h | + i \text{ sign Re } \beta_h \cdot \text{Im } \beta_h. \tag{7}$$

Then from equation (6) we have the relation

$$I_h(\beta_h) = \text{sign Re } \beta_h \cdot I_h(\beta_h^*). \tag{8}$$

By using this relation in the following discussion we can consider an integral depending on the parameter b_h^* with the positive real part.

3. Discontinuities—Let us consider another property of the integral as a function of parameter β_h. Because $I_h(0) \neq 0$, it follows from equation (6) that function $I_h(\beta_h)$ has a discontinuity at $\beta_h = 0$. Let us find the value of this discontinuity in the case of $\text{Im } \beta_h = 0$. The integral (4) has a pole at $\tau = 0$ and saddle points $\tau = \beta_h$ with $h = -1$ and $h = 1$. Therefore, we have to consider the case, when a real saddle point approaches the pole. To make the directions of integration identical in both cases of $h = -1$ and $h = 1$, we change the direction of integration at the contour T_1 to the opposite and consider the discontinuity of the function $-h \ I_h(\beta_h)$.

Let us deform contour T_h in such a way that with

$$\text{Re } \beta_h \to \pm 0, \ \text{Im } \beta_h = 0 \tag{9}$$

we could go around the pole $\tau = 0$ along a small semicircle (Figure 21). Then for any direction of approach of the saddle point to the pole (9), the integrals along the parts of the contour outside the semicircles coincide, and the value of the discontinuity of function $-h \ I_h(\beta_h)$ corresponds to the integral along the semicircle. Let us consider this integral.

We introduce a new variable of integration φ with the expression $\tau = R \exp(i\varphi)$, where R is the radius of the semicircle. Then

$$\lim_{\substack{\mathrm{Re}\,\beta_h \to \pm 0}} [-h\, I_h(\beta_h)] = (1/2\pi) \lim_{\substack{\mathrm{Re}\,\beta_h \to \pm 0 \\ \mathrm{Im}\,\beta_h = 0}} \int_{-\pi/2}^{-\pi/2\pm\pi} \exp[R \exp(i\varphi) - \beta_h]^2\, d\varphi .$$

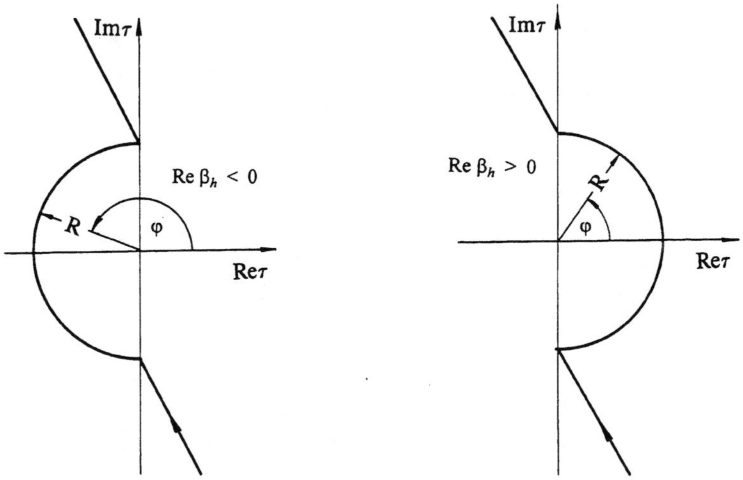

Figure 21. Contour of integration in the neighborhood of the pole.

By taking the previous equation to the limit with $R \to 0$ we obtain the value of the discontinuity

$$\lim_{\substack{\mathrm{Re}\,\beta_h \to \pm 0 \\ \mathrm{Im}\,\beta_h = 0}} [-h\, I_h(\beta_h)] = (1/2\pi) \int_{-\pi/2}^{-\pi/2\pm\pi} d\varphi = \pm 1/2 =$$

$$(1/2)\ \mathrm{sign}\ \mathrm{Re}\ \beta_h . \tag{10}$$

4. Reduction to known special functions—Let us express integral $-\ h\ I_h$, where I_h is determined by equation (4), through the known special functions. We first take the simplest case of

$$\mathrm{Re}\ \beta_h > 0,\ \ \mathrm{Im}\ \beta_h = 0 \tag{11}$$

and deform contour T_h along the imaginary axis Re $\tau = 0$.

Next we introduce a new variable of integration

$$t = -(\tau - \beta_h)^2/\beta_h^2, \tag{12}$$

cutting the complex plane of t along the real semiaxis Re $t > 0$. Then contour T_h is transformed into the contour shown in Figure 22. The variable τ is expressed through t by the formula

$$\tau = \beta_h\,(1 \pm i\sqrt{t}\,), \tag{13}$$

where different signs correspond to the different sides of the cut.

We fix the signs of the square root by the conditions

$$\sqrt{t} < 0 \text{ when } \arg t = 0, \quad \sqrt{t} > 0 \text{ when } \arg t = 2\pi. \tag{14}$$

Then equation (13) can be written

$$\left.\begin{aligned} \tau &= \beta_h(1 - \sqrt{t}\,) \text{ when } \arg t = 0, \\ \tau &= \beta_h(1 + \sqrt{t}\,) \text{ when } \arg t = 2\pi, \end{aligned}\right\}. \tag{15}$$

The integral (4) can be transformed to the form

$$\begin{aligned} -h\,I_h &= -(1/4\pi)\int_{\infty}^{0} t^{-1/2}\,(1 - i\sqrt{t}\,)^{-1}\exp\,(i\beta_h^2\,t)\,dt + \\ &+ (1/4\pi)\int_0^{\infty} t^{-1/2}(1 + i\sqrt{t}\,)^{-1}\exp\,(i\beta_h^2 t)\,dt \\ &= (1/2\pi)\int_0^{\infty} t^{-1/2}(1+t)^{-1}\exp\,(i\beta_h^2\,t\,)\,dt\,. \end{aligned} \tag{16}$$

Figure 22. Mapping the contour of integration in equation V.2(4) onto complex plane t due to transformation V.2(12).

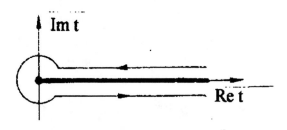

Let us take the well-known representations of a confluent hypergeometric function $\Psi(1/2, 1/2; x)$ and an incomplete gamma function $\Gamma(1/2, x)$, for example from Abramowitz and Stegun (1972)

$$\Psi(1/2, 1/2; x) = \exp(x)\Gamma(1/2, x)$$
$$= \pi^{-1/2} \int_0^\infty t^{-1/2}(1+t)^{-1} \exp(-xt)\,dt, \tag{17}$$

where x is a complex variable. If $x = -i\beta_h^2$, integral (17) can be reduced to the integral (16), i.e.,

$$\begin{aligned} -h\, I_h &= (1/2)\pi^{-1/2}\, \Psi(1/2, 1/2; -i\beta_h^2) \\ &= (1/2)\pi^{-1/2}\exp(-i\beta_h^2)\Gamma(1/2, -i\beta_h^2). \end{aligned} \tag{18}$$

5. Function W (w)—Let us transform the obtained expressions to a more convenient form by introducing a new parameter

$$w_{m(p)} = \beta_h (2/\pi)^{1/2}. \tag{19}$$

By substituting equations (5), 1(18) and 1(23) into equation (19) we introduce the function

$$w_{m(p)}(\alpha) = V_{m(p)}(\alpha)\,(k_v r/\pi)^{1/2}, \quad \text{with } \alpha = \alpha_h = \gamma + h\pi \tag{20}$$

where function $V_{m(p)}(\alpha)$ is determined by equation IV.1(24). Using equation (19), we can express parameter β_h through this function

$$\beta_h = w_{m(p)}(\gamma + h\pi)(\pi/2)^{1/2}. \tag{21}$$

By substituting equation (21) into equation (18) we get the desired expression

$$-\,h\, I_h = W[\,w_{m(p)}(\gamma + h\pi)\,], \tag{22}$$

where the following new function is introduced:

$$W(w) = (1/2)\pi^{-1/2} \exp(-i\pi w^2/2)\,\Gamma(1/2, -i\pi w^2/2). \tag{23}$$

6. Generalization on the complex argument—Formula (22) is derived under conditions (11) and we can generalize formula (22) to the arbitrary complex values of β_h. The integral (16) exists with Im $\beta_h \neq 0$, if Re $(i\beta_h^2) \leq 0$. This condition also can be written in the form

$$\text{sign Re } \beta_h = \text{sign Im } \beta_h, \tag{24}$$

or taking into consideration equations (21) and (20) in the form

$$\text{sign Re } V_{m(p)}(\gamma) = \text{sign Im } V_{m(p)}(\gamma). \tag{25}$$

Formula (22) can be extended to the case Re $\beta_h < 0$ by means of equation (8). Then taking into account equations (21) and (20) we get

$$-h\, I_h = s_{m(p)}(\gamma + h\pi)\, W\,[w_{m(p)}(\gamma + h\pi)], \tag{26}$$

$$s_{m(p)}(\gamma) = \text{sign Re } V_{m(p)}(\gamma), \tag{27}$$

$$w_{m(p)}(\gamma) = [\,|\text{Re } V_{m(p)}(\gamma)| + i\, s_{m(p)}(\gamma) \text{ Im } V_{m(p)}(\gamma)\,](k_v r/\pi)^{1/2}. \tag{28}$$

Because function $V_{m(p)}(\gamma)$ must comply with condition (25), equation (28) can be rewritten as

$$w_{m(p)}(\gamma) = V^*_{m(p)}(\gamma)(k_v r/\pi)^{1/2}, \tag{29}$$

$$V^*_{m(p)}(\gamma) = |\text{Re } V_{m(p)}(\gamma)| + i\,|\text{Im } V_{m(p)}(\gamma)|. \tag{30}$$

Condition (25) means that function $W(w)$ transforms the first or the third quadrant of the complex plane w into the complex plane W. Because in equation (23) a quantity w is risen to the second power, the transformations of the mentioned quadrants in plane W coincide. Therefore, we can always consider Re $w \geq 0$, Im $w \geq 0$. This is what representation (29) implies. The transformation of the first quadrant of the complex plane of w into the plane of W is shown in Figure 23.

7. Approximation of function $V_{m(p)}(\alpha)$—In fact, relation (25) puts no limitations on the functions under consideration. We will show that this relation follows from inequalities 1(11). This can be done by considering the function $V_{m(p)}(\alpha)$ in the neighborhood of the point $\alpha = \alpha_{m(p)}$, where $\alpha_{m(p)}$ is determined by equation 1(33).

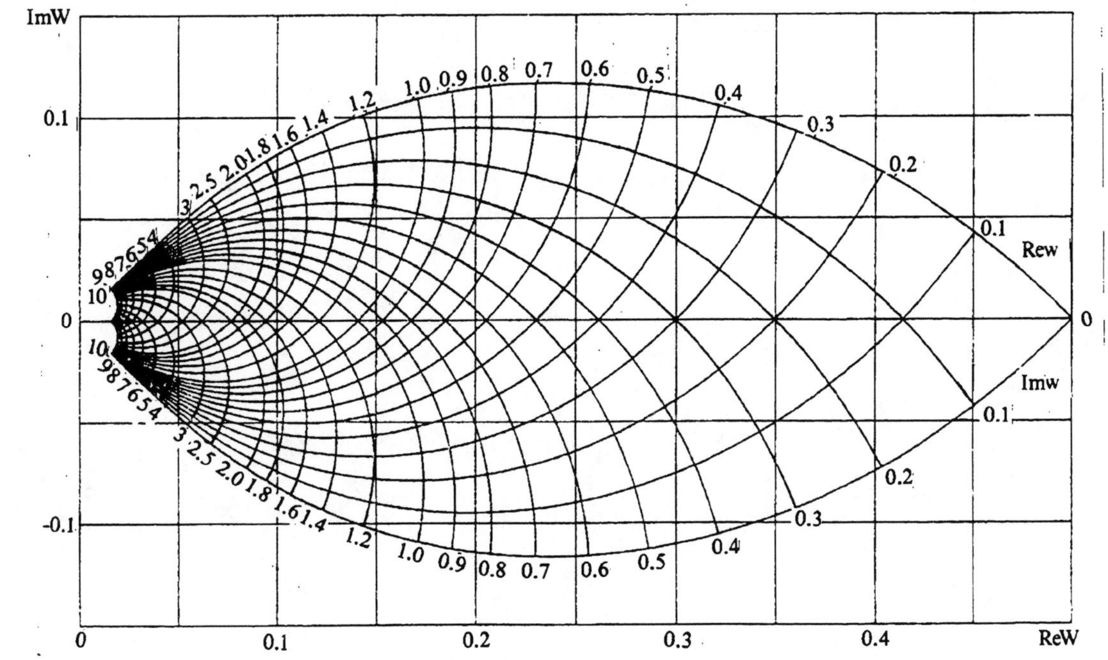

Figure 23. Transformation of the first quadrant of plane w into plane W.

Let us expand the numerator of expression IV.1(24) into a power series in the neighborhood of the mentioned point dropping the second and the following powers

$$P_{m(p)}(\alpha) \approx P_{m(p)}(\alpha_{m(p)}) + P'_{m(p)}(\alpha_{m(p)})(\alpha - \alpha_{m(p)}) \tag{31}$$

and fix the denominator at the same point

$$P'_{m(p)}(\alpha) \approx P'_{m(p)}(\alpha_{m(p)}). \tag{32}$$

From equation 1(33) we have

$$P_{m(p)}(\alpha_{m(p)}) = \alpha_{m(0)}. \tag{33}$$

By substituting equations (31) - (33) into IV.1(24) we get

$$V_{m(p)}(\alpha) \approx \alpha - \alpha_{m(p)} \quad \text{when } \alpha \to \alpha_{m(p)}. \tag{34}$$

By substituting equation (34) into equation (25) with Im $\gamma = 0$ we have

$$\text{sign Re } (\alpha_{m(p)} - \gamma) = \text{sign Im } \alpha_{m(p)} . \tag{35}$$

Using equation 1(33) we can rewrite the relation in the form

$$\text{sign } [\text{ Re } Q_{m(p)} (\alpha_{m(0)}) - \gamma] = \text{sign Im } Q_{m(p)} (\alpha_{m(0)}) . \tag{36}$$

When $\gamma > 0$, this condition follows from equation 1(11), and is what we wanted to show.

8. Final formula—By using equations 1(3) and 1(18) and taking into account the relation, following from equation IV.2(1)

$$Q_{m(p)} [P_{m(p)} (\gamma + h\pi)] = \gamma + h\pi \tag{37}$$

we have

$$A_{m(p)} (z_h) = H_{m(p)} (\gamma + h\pi) \, A_{m(0)} [P_{m(p)} (\gamma + h\pi) - \alpha_{m(0)}] . \tag{38}$$

By substituting equations (26) and (38) into equation (1) we obtain the final formula

$$\begin{aligned} l_{m(p)} (\gamma) = & - h \, s_{m(p)} (\gamma) \, H_{m(p)} (\gamma) \, A_{m(0)} [P_{m(p)} (\gamma) - \alpha_{m(0)}] \\ & \times W [w_{m(p)} (\gamma)] \exp (i k_\nu r) . \end{aligned} \tag{39}$$

3. Physical interpretation

1. Plane and edge-diffracted waves—We formulate the results of the given analysis taking $\zeta_0 = 0$ in equation II.3(47). Then the known part of the solution IV.1(6) can be written as

$$f_\nu \approx F_\nu^0 + F_\nu^D \text{ with } k_\nu r \to \infty . \tag{1}$$

Here the first term corresponds to a set of plane waves (including the incident wave with $\nu = k$) that is formed by the successive reflections/transmissions at the interfaces. This set is put in order by the index $m(p)$ of the reflection/transmission graph and represented by the sum

$$F_\nu^0 = \sum_{p=0}^{p^*} \sum_{m(p)} g_{m(p)} (\gamma) \text{ with } \gamma = \gamma_\nu^+ \text{ and } \gamma = \gamma_\nu^- , \tag{2}$$

$$g_{m(p)}(\gamma) = \begin{cases} F_{m(p)}(\xi) & \text{when } 0 < \xi < 2\pi \quad (3') \\ 0 & \text{when } \xi < 0 \text{ or } \xi > 2\pi\,, \quad (3'') \end{cases}$$

$$F_{m(p)}(\xi) = H_{m(p)}(\alpha_{m(p)}) \exp(i\,k_\nu\, r \cos\xi), \tag{4}$$

$$\xi = \gamma + \pi - \mathrm{Re}\;\alpha_{m(p)}, \tag{5}$$

$$\alpha_{m(p)} = Q_{m(p)}(\alpha_{m(0)}), \tag{6}$$

$$\alpha_{m(0)} = \alpha_k^{\pm} \tag{7}$$

where $\alpha_k^{\pm}$ is determined in Section II.3.6. This description is fair only under the condition

$$\mathrm{Im}\;\alpha_{m(p)} = 0 \tag{8}$$

The top summation index in equation (2) is determined by the following condition:

when $p > p^*$, condition (3') or condition (8) breaks down.

The terms of sum (2) are put in the order over index *m(p)* of reflection/transmission graph. The top index of quantity $\gamma_\nu^{\pm}$ corresponds to the top index of the end node of the mth branch (see Section 1.3 of Appendix C and Section IV.2.5). The term $g_{m(p)}(\gamma_\nu^{+})$ corresponds to a wave, formed at the boundary $\theta = \theta_\nu^{+}$, while $g_{m(p)}(\gamma_\nu^{-})$ at $\theta = \theta_\nu^{-}$. The top index of $\alpha_k^{\pm}$ corresponds to the top index of the first node of the branch under consideration. We take α_k^{+}, when the incident wave strikes the boundary $\theta = \theta_k^{+}$, and α_k^{-} when it strikes the boundary θ_k^{-}. On the formal choice of the top indices in equation (7) see, as well, explanations to equation IV.1(22).

The second term in equation (1) corresponds to an edge-diffracted wave, radiating from point $r = 0$

$$F_\nu^D = \Phi_\nu \exp(ik_\nu r) \tag{9}$$

The amplitude of the edge-diffracted wave is determined as

$$\Phi_{\mathrm{v}} = \sum_{p=0}^{n} \sum_{m(p)} [\, s_{m(p)}(\gamma - \pi)\, \Phi_{m(p)}(\gamma - \pi) - s_{m(p)}(\gamma + \pi)\, \Phi_{m(p)}(\gamma + \pi)\,]$$

$$\text{with } \gamma = \gamma_{\mathrm{v}}^{+} \text{ and } \gamma = \gamma_{\mathrm{v}}^{-}, \tag{10}$$

$$\Phi_{m(p)}(\gamma) = H_{m(p)}(\gamma)\; W[\, w_{m(p)}(\gamma)\,], \tag{11}$$

$$w_{m(p)}(\gamma) = V^{*}_{m(p)}(\gamma)\; (k_{\mathrm{v}} r/\pi)^{1/2}, \tag{12}$$

$$V^{*}_{m(p)} = |\, \mathrm{Re}\; V_{m(p)} \,| + i\, |\, \mathrm{Im}\; V_{m(p)} \,|, \quad V_{m(p)}(\gamma) = [\, P_{m(p)}(\gamma) - \alpha_{m(o)}\,] / P'_{m(p)}(\gamma), \tag{13}$$

$$s_{m(p)}(\gamma) = \mathrm{sign}\; \mathrm{Re}\; V_{m(p)}(\gamma). \tag{14}$$

The top summation index $n > p^{*}$ in equation (10) depends on the accuracy of the result one wants to get. The functions $P_{m(p)}(\alpha)$, $P'_{m(p)}(\alpha)$, $H_{m(p)}(\alpha)$, and $Q_{m(p)}(z)$, are determined by recursion formulas IV.1(17) - IV.1(19) and IV.2(4).

2. *Boundary layer*—Let us consider the following combination of terms in equations (2) - (10)

$$f(\gamma) = g_{m(p)}(\gamma) - s_{m(p)}(\gamma + \pi)\, \Phi_{m(p)}(\gamma + \pi) \exp(\, i\, k_{\mathrm{v}} r\,) \quad \text{with } \xi \to 0. \tag{15}$$

From equation (5) we have

$$\gamma + \pi \to \mathrm{Re}\; \alpha_{m(p)} \text{ with } \mathrm{Im}\; \alpha_{m(p)} = 0. \tag{16}$$

In this case we can take approximately

$$H_{m(p)}(\gamma + \pi) \approx H_{m(p)}(\alpha_{m(p)}) \tag{17}$$

and use approximation 2(34)

$$V_{m(p)}(\gamma + \pi) \approx \gamma + \pi - \alpha_{m(p)} = \xi. \tag{18}$$

Then from equation (18) and (14) we have

$$s_{m(p)}(\gamma + \pi) = \mathrm{sign}\; \xi. \tag{19}$$

By using equations (9), (11), and (17) - (19) we can represent equation (15) as

$$f(\gamma) = \begin{cases} f_0 - f_D & \text{when } \xi > 0 \\ f_D & \text{when } \xi < 0, \end{cases} \tag{20}$$

$$f_0 = \begin{cases} H \exp(i\omega\tau_0) & \text{when } \xi > 0 \\ 0 & \text{when } \xi < 0, \end{cases} \tag{21}$$

$$f_D = H\, W(\tilde{w}) \exp(i\omega\tau_D), \quad \tilde{w} = \xi(k_v r/\pi)^{1/2}, \tag{22}$$

$$H = H_{m(p)}(\alpha_{m(p)}), \quad \tau_0 = (r \cos \xi)/c_v, \quad \tau_D = r/c_v. \tag{23}$$

Equations (20) - (21) illustrate the basic idea of the edge-diffracted wave theory. The domains $\xi > 0$ and $\xi < 0$ can be called *the illuminated and shadow zones,* respectively, of the wave f_0, and the ray $\xi = 0$ *the shadow boundary*. The wave f_D is called *the diffracted wave.*

If $\xi \to 0$ then

$$\tau_D \to \tau_0, \; \tilde{w} \to 0, \; W(\tilde{w}) \to 1/2, \; f_D \to f_0/2, \tag{24}$$

and

$$\left.\begin{aligned} &f(\gamma) \to f_0 - f_0/2 = f_0/2 \quad \text{when } \xi \to 0 \quad \text{with } \xi \geq 0 \\ &f(\gamma) \to f_0/2 \quad \text{when } \xi \to 0 \quad \text{with } \xi \leq 0 \end{aligned}\right\} \tag{25}$$

So the continuity of the wavefield, equation (20), at the shadow boundary is provided by the changing sign of the diffracted wave.

The amplitude of the diffracted wave is proportional to the amplitude of the wave f_0. The coefficient of proportionality is the function $W(w)$. Figure 24 shows the graph of this function when w is real. We can write the quantity w as

$$w = \sqrt{2N}, \; N = l/(\lambda/2), \; l = c_v(\tau_D - \tau_0), \; \lambda = 2\pi c_v/\omega, \tag{26}$$

where N represents the phase difference in the half-period *Fresnel zones*. Figure 25 shows the modulus of $W(w)$ as the function of N. The function changes rapidly when $N < 2$, and slowly when $N > 2$. The domain $N < 2$ is called *the boundary layer.*

Thus, equation (20) describes the interference of two waves. One of them has the shadow boundary. The other smooths this discontinuity. The explanation of this phenomenon is known as *Young's principle* (Young, 1802). Equations (20) - (23) express this principle in a mathematical form.

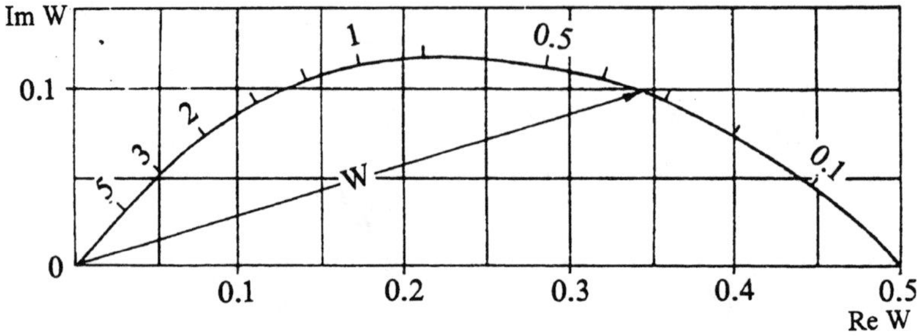

Figure 24. Function $W(w)$ of the real variable.

Equation (20) can be written in the form showing its connection with the Fresnel diffraction theory. By substituting equation (22) into (20) we have

$$f(\gamma) = \begin{cases} f_0 \left\{1 - W(\tilde{w}) \exp\left[i\omega(\tau_D - \tau_0)\right]\right\} & \text{when } \xi > 0 \\ f_0 W(\tilde{w}) \exp\left[i\omega(\tau_D - \tau_0)\right] & \text{when } \xi < 0 . \end{cases} \tag{27}$$

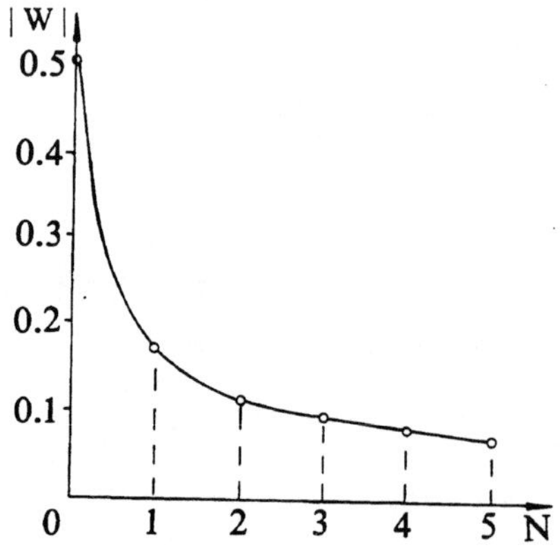

Figure 25. Modulus of W as the function of the number N of the half-period Fresnel zones.

From equation (23) we have

$$i\omega(\tau_D - \tau_0) = i k_v r (1 - \cos\xi) . \tag{28}$$

In the boundary layer $|\xi| \ll 1$ we can use the approximation $\cos\xi \approx 1 - \xi^2/2$. Then

$$i\omega(\tau_D - \tau_0) \approx i k_v r\, \xi^2/2 = i\pi\tilde{w}^2/2\,. \tag{29}$$

By substituting equation (29) into (27) and taking into account equation (D-18) we obtain

$$f(\gamma) = \begin{cases} f_0\, F(+s\tilde{w}\sqrt{\pi/2}) & \text{when } \xi > 0 \\ f_0\, F(-\tilde{w}\sqrt{\pi/2}) & \text{when } \xi < 0\,, \end{cases} \tag{30}$$

where the term $F(z)$ denotes the *Fresnel integral*

$$F(z) = \pi^{-1/2}\exp(-i\pi/4) \times \int_{-\infty}^{z} \exp(i\tau^2)\,d\tau\,. \tag{31}$$

Relations of this kind figure in the classic Fresnel-Kirchoff diffraction theory (Born and Wolf, 1968). Therefore, equations of the boundary layer (20) or (30) also can be called *Fresnel's approximation.*

3. Boundary layer at $\xi \to 2\pi$—Let us consider now the following combination of terms in equations (2) - (10)

$$f(\gamma) = g_{m(p)}(\gamma) + s_{m(p)}(\gamma - \pi)\,\Phi_{m(p)}(\gamma - \pi)\exp(i k_v r) \text{ with } \xi \to 2\pi\,. \tag{32}$$

From equation (5) we have

$$\gamma - \pi \to \mathrm{Re}\,\alpha_{m(p)},\ \mathrm{Im}\,\alpha_{m(p)} = 0\,. \tag{33}$$

By using approximations analogous to equations (17) - (19)

$$H_{m(p)}(\gamma - \pi) \approx H_{m(p)}(\alpha_{m(p)}),$$

$$V_{m(p)}(\gamma - \pi) \approx \gamma - \pi - \alpha_{m(p)} = \xi - 2\pi\,, \tag{34}$$

$$s_{m(p)}(\gamma - \pi) = \mathrm{sign}(\xi - 2\pi)\,,$$

we can write equation (32) as

$$f(\gamma) = \begin{cases} f_0 - f_D & \text{when } \xi < 2\pi \\ f_D & \text{when } \xi > 2\pi , \end{cases} \tag{35}$$

$$f_0 = \begin{cases} H \exp(i\omega\tau_0) & \text{when } \xi < 2\pi \\ 0 & \text{when } \xi > 2\pi , \end{cases} \tag{36}$$

where the quantities at the right-hand side are determined by equations (22) - (23) with

$$\tilde{w} = (\xi - 2\pi)(k_v r/\pi)^{1/2} . \tag{37}$$

Interpretation of these expressions is analogous to that given above for the case of equations (20) - (21). But now the illuminated and shadow zones are determined by inequalities $\xi < 2\pi$ and $\xi > 2\pi$, respectively, and the diffracted wave f_D smooths the discontinuity of the wave f_0 at the shadow boundary $\xi = 2\pi$.

4. Deep shadow zone—Let us consider the case, when the modulus of the quantity (12) tends to infinity

$$w_{m(p)}(\gamma) \to \infty . \tag{38}$$

By replacing function $W(w)$ in equation (11) with its asymptotic representation (D-9) we get

$$\Phi_{m(p)}(\gamma) \approx H_{m(p)}(\gamma)[(2\pi k_v r)^{1/2} V^*_{m(p)}(\gamma)]^{-1} \exp(i\pi/4) . \tag{39}$$

Then the diffracted wave in equations (20) and (35) can be written as

$$f_D \approx (2\pi k_v r)^{-1/2} A \exp(i\omega\tau_D) , \tag{40}$$

$$A = H_{m(p)}(\gamma) \exp(i\pi/4) / V^*_{m(p)}(\gamma) . \tag{41}$$

This formula holds true under condition (38), i.e., outside the boundary layers connected with the shadow boundaries $\xi = 0$ and $\xi = 2\pi$. The domain, where equation (40) holds true, is called *the deep shadow zone*.

By using this representation we can write the amplitude of the edge-diffracted wave (9) in the intersection of the deep shadow zones of all items of the sum (10) as

$$\Phi_\mathrm{v} = A_\mathrm{v}\ (c_\mathrm{v}\ /r)^{1/2}\,, \tag{42}$$

$$A_\mathrm{v} = \psi_\mathrm{v}\,(2\pi\,\omega)^{-1/2}\ \exp\ (i\,\pi/4)\,, \tag{43}$$

$$\psi_\mathrm{v} = \sum_{p=0}^{n}\ \sum_{m(p)} [\,\Lambda_{m(p)}\,(\gamma-\pi) - \Lambda_{m(p)}\,(\gamma+\pi)\,]\ \text{ with }\ \gamma = \gamma_\mathrm{v}^{+}\ \text{ and }\ \gamma = \gamma_\mathrm{v}^{-}\,, \tag{44}$$

$$\Lambda_{m(p)}\,(\gamma) = s_{m(p)}\,(\gamma)\ H_{m(p)}\,(\gamma)\,/\,V^{*}_{m(p)}\,(\gamma)\,. \tag{45}$$

5. *Real and imaginary shadow boundaries*—Let us write equation (1) in the form

$$f_\mathrm{v} = \sum_{p=0}^{n}\ \sum_{m(p)} f_{m(p)}\ (\gamma)\quad \text{with }\ \gamma = \gamma_\mathrm{v}^{+}\ \text{ and }\ \gamma = \gamma_\mathrm{v}^{-}\,, \tag{46}$$

$$f_{m(p)}\ (\gamma) = \begin{cases} -\,f_D\,(\gamma-\pi) + f_D\,(\gamma+\pi) & \text{when}\quad \xi < 0 \qquad (47')\\ -f_D\,(\gamma-\pi) - f_D\,(\gamma+\pi) + g_{m(p)}\ (\gamma) & \text{when}\ \ 0 < \xi < 2\pi \qquad (47'')\\ +\,f_D\,(\gamma-\pi) - f_D\,(\gamma+\pi) & \text{when}\quad \xi > 2\pi\,, \qquad (47''') \end{cases}$$

$$f_D\,(\gamma) = \Phi_{m(p)}\ (\gamma)\ \exp\ (\,i\,k_\mathrm{v}\,r\,)\,, \tag{48}$$

$$g_{m(p)}\ (\gamma) \equiv 0\quad \text{when } p > p^{*}\,. \tag{49}$$

Quantity γ in these formulas varies in the interval

$$0 \le \gamma \le \varepsilon_\mathrm{v}\,. \tag{50}$$

By solving equation (5) relative to γ and substituting the result into equation (50) we get the interval of variable ξ, i.e.,

$$0 \le \xi - \pi + \mathrm{Re}\ \alpha_{m(p)} \le \varepsilon_\mathrm{v} \tag{51}$$

or

$$\pi - \mathrm{Re}\ \alpha_{m(p)} \le \xi\,, \tag{52}$$

$$\xi \le \varepsilon_\mathrm{v} + \pi - \mathrm{Re}\ \alpha_{m(p)}\,. \tag{53}$$

The previous section showed that we can consider the diffracted wave f_D as a correction, smoothing the discontinuity of a plane wave $g_{m(p)}$ at its shadow boundary $\xi = 0$ or $\xi = 2\pi$. On the strength of inequalities (52) - (53) and equation (49) such interpretation is not possible for every item of sum (46). However, we can extend this interpretation to every item by introducing the idea of *imaginary shadow boundaries* of real and imaginary plane waves. Following Sommerfeld [Frank and Mises, 1935] we can use a concept of *Riemann's multifold surface* and consider expression (47) as a function of a point on the Riemann's surface

$$r \geq 0, \; -\infty < \xi < \infty, \tag{54}$$

"forgetting" relation (49). Then we can interpret quantity $g_{m(p)}(\gamma)$ as a plane wave, existing in the interval $0 < \xi < 2\pi$ with a couple of shadow boundaries $\xi = 0$ and $\xi = 2\pi$. The quantities $f_D(\gamma - \pi)$ and $f_D(\gamma + \pi)$ can be interpreted as diffracted waves, smoothing discontinuities of the mentioned plane wave at its shadow boundaries $\xi = 2\pi$ and $\xi = 0$, respectively.

The interval (52) - (53), where such interpretation has a direct physical sense, is called *a physical Riemann's sheet.* The domain (54) without interval (52) - (53) is called *a mathematical sheet* of Riemann's surface. The plane waves $g_{m(p)}$ and shadow boundaries, which do not belong to the physical sheet, are called *imaginary waves and shadow boundaries.*

It follows from inequalities (52) - (53) and (47'') that the plane wave $g_{m(p)}$ exists at any point of the physical Riemann's sheet, if two following inequalities are satisfied simultaneously:

$$\pi - \operatorname{Re} \alpha_{m(p)} > 0, \tag{55}$$

$$2\pi > \varepsilon_v + \pi - \operatorname{Re} \alpha_{m(p)}. \tag{56}$$

In this case both shadow boundaries $\xi = 0$ and $\xi = 2\pi$ are imaginary (Figure 10a, Figure 26a).

If the two inequalities

$$\pi - \operatorname{Re} \alpha_{m(p)} < 2\pi, \tag{57}$$

$$2\pi < \varepsilon_v + \pi - \operatorname{Re} \alpha_{m(p)} \tag{58}$$

are satisfied simultaneously, the plane wave $g_{m(p)}$ has the shadow boundary $\xi = 2\pi$ on the physical sheet [$\alpha_k^+ + \pi$ in Figure 10(b), $\alpha_k^- + \pi$ in Figure 10(c)], and the shadow boundary $\xi_0 = 0$ is imaginary [Figure 26(b)].

If the inequalities

$$\pi - \text{Re}\ \alpha_{m(p)} < 0\,, \tag{59}$$

$$0 < \varepsilon_v + \pi - \text{Re}\ \alpha_{m(p)} \tag{60}$$

are satisfied simultaneously, the shadow boundary $\xi = 0$ belongs to the physical sheet [$\alpha_k^- - \pi$ in Figure 10(b), $\alpha_k^+ - \pi$ in Figure 10(c)] and the shadow boundary $\xi_0 = 2\pi$ is imaginary [Figure 26(c)].

On the strength of equations 1(11) and (6) inequalities (55), (57), and (59) cease to hold true with p increasing. In all such cases the corresponding plane waves and their shadow boundaries are imaginary. When $p > p^*$, all plane waves are imaginary [Figure 26(d)].

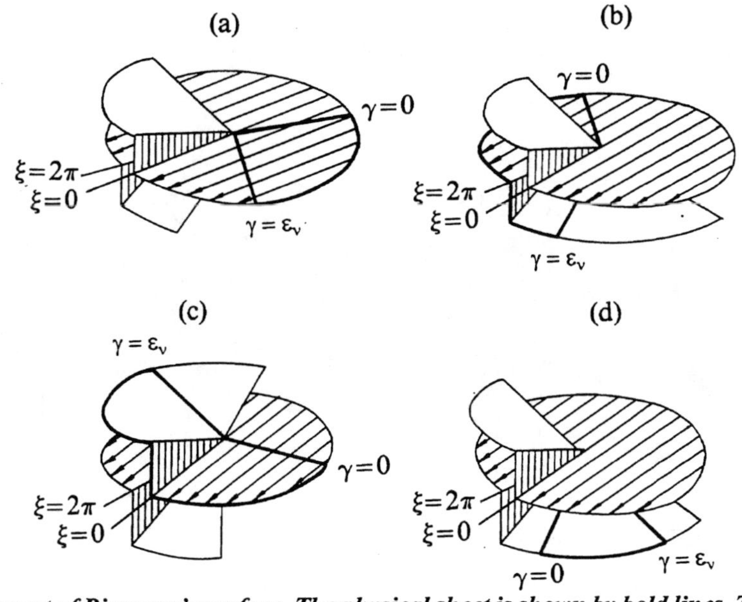

Figure 26. The element of Riemann's surface. The physical sheet is shown by bold lines. The domain of the plane wave is shaded.

6. *Virtual wave concept*—Until now we have been considering the case of the fixed direction of incidence, given by equation (7). For every value of the fixed direction of incidence we had to identify the $m(p)^{th}$ reflected/transmitted wave (3), which was considered as a function of the coordinate γ. Let us now consider the reflected/transmitted wave as a function of the mentioned coordinate γ and the direction of incidence α. By denoting such a function $F^*_{m(p)}(\gamma, \alpha)$ we have

$$F^*_{m(p)}(\gamma, \alpha) = H_{m(p)}[Q_{m(p)}(\alpha)] \exp\left\{ i k_v r \cos[\gamma - Q_{m(p)}(\alpha)]\right\}, \tag{61}$$

where α can be any real or complex number. In the particular case of $\alpha = \alpha_{m(0)}$ we have

$$F^*_{m(p)}(\gamma, \alpha_{m(0)}) = F_{m(p)}(\gamma), \tag{62}$$

where $F_{m(p)}(\gamma)$ is determined by equation (4).

Let us fix the coordinate $\gamma = \text{const}$ and choose the value $\alpha = \alpha_\gamma$ so that the following relation holds true:

$$\gamma = Q_{m(p)}(\alpha_\gamma). \tag{63}$$

The value α_γ can be found from equation IV.2(1)

$$\alpha_\gamma = P_{m(p)}(\gamma). \tag{64}$$

Then equation (61) can be written as

$$F^*_{m(p)}(\gamma, \alpha_\gamma) = H_{m(p)}(\gamma) \exp(i k_v r). \tag{65}$$

By using equation (65) we can write the edge-diffracted wave (48) in the form

$$f_D(\gamma) = F^*_{m(p)}(\gamma, \alpha_\gamma)\, W[w_{m(p)}(\gamma)], \tag{66}$$

where $w_{m(p)}(\gamma)$ is determined by equations (12) - (13) with

$$V_{m(p)}(\gamma) = (\alpha_\gamma - \alpha_{m(0)})/\alpha'_\gamma, \quad \alpha'_\gamma = P'_{m(p)}(\gamma). \tag{67}$$

This expression admits the following interpretation: let us call the quantity (64) *the virtual direction of incidence.* Let us call the reflected/transmitted wave (61) and propagating in the direction (64), *the virtual wave.* This wave is completely determined by equations (64) and (65). It follows from equation (66) that the edge-diffracted wave front

r = const corresponds to the envelope of the virtual wave fronts with γ = var . The edge-diffracted wave amplitude (11) is proportional to the virtual wave amplitude. The coefficient of proportionality W depends only on the deviation of the virtual direction of incidence $\alpha = \alpha_\gamma$ from a given direction $\alpha = \alpha_{m(o)}$.

Thus, the finding of the edge-diffracted wave (48) can be reduced to the finding of the virtual wave and the corresponding coefficient of proportionality. This interpretation of the obtained formulas can be called the *virtual wave concept.* This concept is useful for generalization of the discussed approach to the case of inhomogeneous media.

PART TWO

EDGE WAVES IN INHOMOGENEOUS MEDIA

Chapter VI

SOLUTION OF THE WAVE EQUATION IN THE BOUNDARY LAYER

1. Equation of the boundary layer

1. Definition—We now consider the reduced-wave equation

$$(\Delta + k^2) f = 0 , \; k = \omega / c , \tag{1}$$

where the wave velocity $c = c(M)$ depends on point M of an inhomogeneous medium. We look for high-frequency ($\omega \to \infty$) solutions of this equation in a narrow vicinity of the shadow boundary of an individual reflected/transmitted wave, where the geometrical theory of diffraction fails. In Section V.3.2 we identified such a domain as the boundary layer. Here we extend this concept to the case of 3-D inhomogeneous media. To do so, we have to consider a geometrical scheme of rays and wave fronts that follows from the kinematic law of edge diffraction (see Chapter I, Section 6.).

Let us take two families of rays, determined by two corresponding sets of parameters (α_0, β_0) and (α, β). Each fixed pair of values $\alpha_0 = \text{const}$, $\beta_0 = \text{const}$ gives an individual ray of the first family. Each pair of values $\alpha = \text{const}$, $\beta = \text{const}$ gives a ray of the second family. We call the families (α_0, β_0) and (α, β) *the congruencies of reflected/transmitted* and *diffracted rays*, respectively.

Any of the expressions $\alpha_0 = \text{const}$ or $\beta_0 = \text{const}$ gives a surface, formed by the rays of the congruence (α_0, β_0). Any of the expressions $\alpha = \text{const}$ or $\beta = \text{const}$ gives a surface, formed by the rays of the congruence (α, β). We will consider the specific case when the congruencies under consideration have a common surface. We suppose the latter can be given simultaneously as $\alpha_0 = \text{const}$ or $\alpha = \text{const}$. Let τ_0 and τ be the eikonals along the congruencies (α_0 , β_0) and (α , β) , respectively. Then the equation of the common surface can be written

$$\tau_0 = \tau . \tag{2}$$

According to the kinematic law of edge diffraction this relation defines *the shadow boundary* (Figure 27).

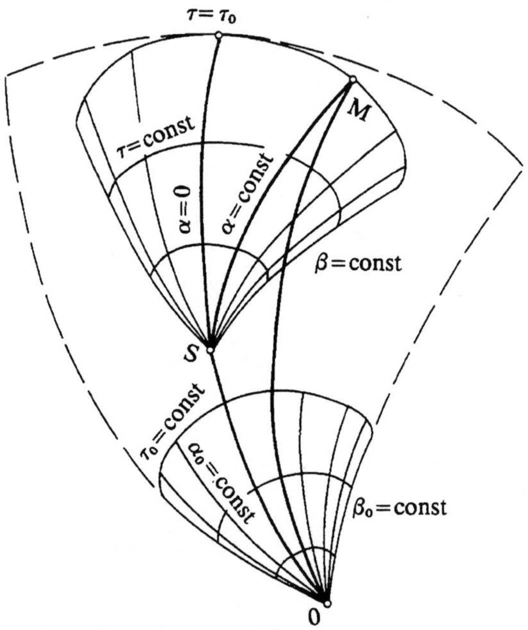

Figure 27. Ray coordinate surfaces β_0 = const ***and*** β = *const* **.**

The proximity of an arbitrary point M to the surface (2) can be estimated by the quantity

$$T = | \omega [\tau_0 (M) - \tau (M)] | . \tag{3}$$

We call a domain *the neighborhood of the shadow boundary* or *the boundary layer*, if its points satisfy the inequality

$$| \omega [\tau_0 (M) - \tau (M)] | < C \quad \text{with } \omega \to \infty , \tag{4}$$

where the constant C does not depend on ω . According to the estimate of Section V.3.2 we can take $C \approx 2 \pi$.

We are going to look for solutions of equation (1) in the domain (4).

2. *Two forms of solution*—Let us look for the solution of equation (1) in the form

$$f = AG \exp(i\omega\tau), \quad (\nabla\tau)^2 = 1/c^2, \tag{5}$$

where G is some given function. By inserting equation (5) into (1) we get a differential equation for the unknown function

$$G\nabla^2 A + B_1 \nabla A + B_2 A = 0, \tag{6}$$

$$B_1 = 2(i\omega G\nabla\tau + \nabla G), \tag{7}$$

$$B_2 = i\omega(G\nabla^2\tau + 2\nabla\tau\nabla G) + \nabla^2 G. \tag{8}$$

The way of integration of this equation depends on the choice of function G. We will consider two kinds of the given function.

Take

$$G = G_D, \tag{9}$$

where G_D complies with the transport equation

$$G_D \nabla^2\tau + 2\nabla\tau\nabla G_D = 0. \tag{10}$$

This is the typical choice of G in diffraction theory (Fock, 1965). Then $B_2 = \nabla^2 G_D$. By using the formal relation

$$\nabla^2(AG_D) = G_D\nabla^2 A + A\nabla^2 G_D + 2\nabla A\nabla G_D \tag{11}$$

we can write equation (6) in the form

$$\nabla^2(AG_D) + 2i\omega G_D\nabla\tau\nabla A = 0. \tag{12}$$

Now let us take

$$G = G_0, \tag{13}$$

where G_0 complies with the transport equation

$$G_0 \nabla^2 \tau_0 + 2 \nabla \tau_0 \nabla G_0 = 0 . \tag{14}$$

From the formulas of the scalar multiplication

$$\nabla\tau_0\nabla G_0 = c^{-1} \mid \nabla G_0 \mid \cos(\nabla\tau_0, \nabla G_0), \nabla\tau\nabla G_0 = c^{-1} \mid \nabla G_0 \mid \cos(\nabla\tau, \nabla G_0) \tag{15}$$

we have the relation

$$\nabla\tau\nabla G_0 = \gamma \nabla\tau_0 \nabla G_0 , \text{ and} \tag{16}$$

$$\gamma = \cos(\nabla\tau, \nabla G_0)/\cos(\nabla\tau_0, \nabla G_0) . \tag{17}$$

From equations (14) and (16) we have

$$\nabla\tau \nabla G_0 = -(\gamma G_0/2) \nabla^2 \tau_0 . \tag{18}$$

By substituting equations (13) and (18) into equation (6) we derive:

$$G_0 \nabla^2 A + B_1 \nabla A + B_2 A = 0 , \tag{19}$$

$$B_1 = 2(i \omega G_0 \nabla \tau + \nabla G_0), \tag{20}$$

$$B_2 = i \omega [(\nabla^2 \tau - \gamma \nabla^2 \tau_0) G_0] + \nabla^2 G_0 . \tag{21}$$

We are looking for high-frequency solutions with $\omega \to \infty$. Suppose that at the points of space under consideration the following inequalities hold true:

$$\mid \nabla\tau \mid \gg \mid \nabla G_0 \mid / \omega \mid G_0 \mid , \quad \mid \nabla^2\tau - \gamma\nabla^2\tau_0 \mid \gg \mid \nabla^2 G_0 \mid / \omega \mid G_0 \mid \quad \text{with } \omega \to \infty . \tag{22}$$

Then

$$B_1 \sim 2 i \omega G_0 \nabla\tau , B_2 \sim i \omega (\nabla^2\tau - \gamma\nabla^2\tau_0) G_0 \text{ with } \omega \to \infty . \tag{23}$$

By substituting these expressions into equation (19) we get

$$\nabla^2 A + 2 i \omega \nabla\tau \nabla A + i \omega (\nabla^2\tau - \gamma\nabla^2\tau_0) A = 0 . \tag{24}$$

We will solve equation (24) in Section 2. Here we will simplify equation (12) by taking into consideration condition (4). To do so, it is necessary to express the differential operators in a coordinate form.

3. Ray coordinates—Let us introduce an orthogonal coordinate system, connected with the congruence of diffracted rays. Let (τ, α, β) be the ray coordinate system, where each pair of values $\alpha = \text{const}$, $\beta = \text{const}$ singles out an individual ray. The coordinate surface $\beta = \text{const}$ will correspond to a cone of diffracted rays and the surface $\alpha = 0$ will coincide with the surface (2).

Now we can write the differential operators as

$$\nabla = \nabla_\tau + \nabla_\alpha + \nabla_\beta, \tag{25}$$

$$\nabla^2 = \nabla_\tau^2 + \nabla_\alpha^2 + \nabla_\beta^2, \tag{26}$$

$$\nabla_\gamma = g_{\gamma\gamma}^{-1/2}(\partial/\partial\gamma)\, \boldsymbol{i}_\gamma, \tag{27}$$

$$\nabla_\gamma^2 = J^{-1}\partial\,[(J/g_{\gamma\gamma})\,\partial/\partial\gamma]/\partial\gamma, \tag{28}$$

$$g_{\gamma\gamma} = \sum_{n=1}^{3} (\partial x_n/\partial\gamma)^2, \tag{29}$$

where $\boldsymbol{i}_\gamma$ are the unit vectors of coordinate axes and J is the Jacobian of the transformation from Cartesian coordinates (x_1, x_2, x_3) to ray (τ, α, β) coordinates.

Because the ray coincides with the coordinate line, there are well-known relations

$$g_{\tau\tau} = c^2, \quad \nabla\tau = \nabla_\tau \tau, \tag{30}$$

$$\nabla\tau\, \nabla\varphi = \nabla_\tau \tau \bullet (\nabla_\tau + \nabla_\alpha + \nabla_\beta)\,\varphi = \nabla_\tau \tau \bullet \nabla_\tau \varphi = c^{-2}\,\partial\varphi/\partial\tau, \tag{31}$$

where φ is an arbitrary function. Note that the first expression in equation (30) can be obtained by equating equation 1.2(9) with quantity $\nabla\tau$ described by equations (25) and (27)

In the chosen coordinate system the solution of transport equation (10) looks like

$$G_D = (g_{\tau\tau}/J)^{1/2} = (c^2/J)^{1/2}. \tag{32}$$

We can write condition (4) in the ray coordinate form by representing the eikonal τ_0 as a function of ray coordinates $\tau_0 = \tau_0(\tau, \alpha, \beta)$ and expanding it into the power series over α

$$\tau_0(\tau, \alpha, \beta) = \sum_{k=0}^{\infty} a_k(\tau, 0, \beta)\,\alpha^k, \text{ and} \tag{33}$$

$$a_k(\tau, 0, \beta) = (1/k!)(\partial^k \tau_0 / \partial \alpha^k)_{\alpha=0}. \tag{34}$$

The two first coefficients of the series satisfy relations

$$a_0(\tau, 0, \beta) = \tau_0(\tau, 0, \beta) = \tau, \text{ and} \tag{35}$$

$$a_1(\tau, 0, \beta) = 0. \tag{36}$$

Relation (35) follows from the coincidence of surfaces $\alpha = 0$ and equation (2) while relation (36) is the result of derivation over α with $\alpha = 0$ in the direction normal to $\nabla\tau_0$.

By taking into account equations (35) - (36) we rewrite equation (33) in the form

$$\tau_0(M) - \tau(M) = \sum_{k=2}^{\infty} a_k(\tau, 0, \beta)\,\alpha^k. \tag{37}$$

Suppose, the coefficient $a_2(\tau, 0, \beta)$ does not turn to zero for values of τ and β under consideration. Then it follows from equation (37) that condition (4) with $\omega \to \infty$ can be satisfied when $\alpha \to 0$ only. Therefore, we can neglect all items with $k > 2$ in series (37). Then

$$\tau_0(M) - \tau(M) = a_2(\tau, 0, \beta)\,\alpha^2. \tag{38}$$

By substituting equation (38) into equation (4) we get

$$|\,\omega\,\alpha^2 a_2(\tau, 0, \beta)\,| < C \quad \text{with } \omega \to \infty. \tag{39}$$

This inequality defines the boundary layer, where we are going to look for solutions of equations (12) and (24)

4. Approximate equation—Because condition (39) holds true with $\alpha \to 0$, we can simplify equation (12) by fixing slowly changing functions at $\alpha = 0$ in equations (28) and (29)

$$g_{\gamma\gamma} = g_{\gamma\gamma}(\tau, \alpha, \beta) = g_{\gamma\gamma}(\tau, 0, \beta), \tag{40}$$

$$J = J(\tau, \alpha, \beta) = J(\tau, 0, \beta), \tag{41}$$

$$G_D = G_D(\tau, \alpha, \beta) = G_D(\tau, 0, \beta). \tag{42}$$

Substituting equations (40) and (41) into equation (28), we get

$$\nabla_\alpha^2 = \frac{1}{g_{\alpha\alpha}(\tau, 0, \beta)} \frac{\partial^2}{\partial \alpha^2}, \tag{43}$$

$$\nabla_\gamma^2 = \frac{1}{J(\tau, 0, \beta)} \frac{\partial}{\partial \gamma} \left[\frac{J(\tau, 0, \beta)}{g_{\gamma\gamma}(\tau, 0, \beta)} \frac{\partial}{\partial \gamma} \right] \quad \text{with } \gamma = \tau, \beta. \tag{44}$$

By introducing a new variable

$$\phi = \alpha / \omega \tag{45}$$

and using equations (43) - (44), we rewrite equation (26) as

$$\nabla^2 = \nabla_\tau^2 + \omega \nabla_\phi^2 + \nabla_\beta^2, \tag{46}$$

$$\nabla_\phi^2 = \frac{1}{g_{\alpha\alpha}(\tau, 0, \beta)} \frac{\partial^2}{\partial \phi^2}$$

and equation (26) as

$$\left[\frac{1}{\omega} (\nabla_\tau^2 + \nabla_\beta^2) + \nabla_\phi^2 \right] (A G_D) + 2 i G_D \nabla \tau \nabla A = 0 . \tag{47}$$

Because the solution of equation (47) must be continuous, together with its first and second derivatives when $\omega \to \infty$, we can neglect the small terms containing cofactor ω^{-1}, i.e.,

$$\nabla_\phi^2 (A G_D) + 2 i G_D \nabla \tau \nabla A = 0 . \tag{48}$$

Returning to variable $\alpha = \phi / \sqrt{\omega}$, we can again write equation (48) in the form of equation (12) with

$$\nabla^2 = \nabla^2_\alpha \quad \text{with} \quad \alpha \to 0 \tag{49}$$

where ∇^2_α is determined by equation (43). Equations (42) and (49) yield

$$\nabla^2 (AG_D) = G_D \nabla^2_\alpha A \quad \text{with} \quad \alpha \to 0 . \tag{50}$$

By taking into consideration equations (31), (43), (49), and (50), we can rewrite equation (12) as

$$\mu \frac{\partial^2 A}{\partial \alpha^2} + 2 i \omega \frac{\partial A}{\partial \tau} = 0 , \tag{51}$$

$$\mu = \mu(\tau, 0, \beta) = (c^2 / g_{\alpha\alpha})_{\alpha = 0} . \tag{52}$$

Thus, the integration of the reduced-wave equation (1) within the boundary layer (4) can be reduced to the integration of equation (24) or equation (51). Solutions of these equations do not coincide because of the different choice of the cofactor G in their initial representation (5).

2. Linearly independent solutions

1. Kummer's equation—Here we show that equation 1(24) in the domain 1(39) can be reduced to an ordinary differential equation. To do this, we look for its solution in the form of function

$$A = A(z, \alpha, \beta) \quad \text{with} \quad z = i\omega(\tau_0 - \tau) = \alpha^2 p(\tau, \beta), \quad p = i\omega\, a_2(\tau, 0, \beta,) \tag{1}$$

where α_2 is determined by equation 1(34) and express the differential operations in a coordinate form.

By differentiating we get

$$\nabla^2 A = \sum_{\gamma = z,\alpha,\beta} \left[\sum_{\mu = z,\alpha,\beta} \left(A_{\gamma\mu} \nabla \gamma \nabla_\mu + A_\gamma \nabla \gamma \right) \right] ,$$

$$\nabla z = \frac{1}{\alpha} \left(2 z \nabla \alpha + \alpha^3 \sum_{\gamma = \tau,\beta} p_\gamma \nabla \gamma \right) , \tag{2}$$

$$\nabla^2 z = \frac{1}{\alpha^2}\left\{ 2z(\nabla\alpha)^2 + 2z\alpha\nabla^2\alpha + \alpha^2 \sum_{\gamma=\tau,\beta}\left[p_{\gamma\gamma}(\nabla\gamma)^2 + p_\gamma \nabla^2\gamma \right] \right\},$$

where the bottom indices denote partial derivatives.

To develop the scalar product

$$\nabla\tau\nabla A = \nabla\tau\,(A_z\nabla z + A_\alpha\nabla\alpha + A_\beta\nabla\beta) = A_z\nabla\tau\nabla z \tag{3}$$

we use the representation

$$2\nabla\tau\nabla z = (2\nabla\tau - \nabla\tau_0 + \nabla\tau_0)\nabla z = [\nabla(\tau-\tau_0) + \nabla(\tau+\tau_0)]\nabla z =$$
$$\nabla(\tau-\tau_0)\nabla z + \nabla(\tau+\tau_0)\nabla z. \tag{4}$$

It follows from equations (1) that

$$\nabla(\tau-\tau_0) = -\nabla z / i\omega. \tag{5}$$

Notice also that

$$\nabla(\tau+\tau_0)\nabla z = -i\omega\nabla(\tau+\tau_0)\nabla(\tau-\tau_0) = -i\omega(\nabla\tau+\nabla\tau_0)(\nabla\tau-\nabla\tau_0) =$$
$$= -i\omega\left[(\nabla\tau)^2 - (\nabla\tau_0)^2\right] = -i\omega(c^{-2}-c^{-2}) = 0. \tag{6}$$

By substituting equations (4), (5), and (6) into equation (3) we derive

$$\nabla\tau\nabla A = -\frac{A_z(\nabla z)^2}{2i\omega}. \tag{7}$$

By substituting equations (2) and (7) into equation I(24) we can write the equation under consideration in the form

$$b_1 A_{zz} + b_2 A_{\alpha\alpha} + b_3 A_{\beta\beta} + b_4 A_{z\alpha} + b_5 A_{z\beta} + b_6 A_z + b_7 A_\alpha + b_8 A_\beta + b_9 A = 0 \tag{8}$$

$$b_1 = 4z^2(\nabla\alpha)^2 + \alpha^6 \sum_{\gamma=\tau,\beta} p_\gamma^2(\nabla\gamma)^2,$$

$$b_2 = \alpha^2(\nabla\alpha)^2,$$

$$b_3 = \alpha^2 (\nabla \beta)^2,$$

$$b_4 = 2\alpha^4 p_\alpha (\nabla \alpha)^2,$$

$$b_5 = 2\alpha^4 p_\beta (\nabla \beta)^2,$$

$$b_6 = 2z(1-2z)(\nabla \alpha)^2 + 2\alpha z \nabla^2 \alpha + \alpha^2 \sum_{\gamma=\tau,\beta} \left[p_{\gamma\gamma} (\nabla \gamma)^2 + p_\gamma \nabla^2 \gamma + \alpha^4 p_\gamma^2 (\nabla \gamma)^2 \right],$$

$$b_7 = \alpha^2 \nabla^2 \alpha ,$$

$$b_8 = \alpha^2 \nabla^2 \beta ,$$

$$b_9 = i\omega \alpha^2 (\nabla^2 \tau - \mu \nabla^2 \tau_0) \approx i\omega (\nabla^2 \tau - \nabla^2 \tau_0) = -\alpha^2 \nabla^2 z \text{ with } \alpha \to 0 .$$

The coefficients of equation (8) are functions of the point in 3-D space (z, α, β). In the neighborhood of the coordinate line $\alpha = 0$, i.e., in the domain 1(39), these coefficients are regular slowly changing functions of α. Therefore, in the mentioned domain we can use the approximation

$$b_n(z, \alpha, \beta) = b_n(z, 0, \beta) \quad \text{with } n = 1, 2, \ldots 9. \tag{9}$$

Then equation (8) turns into the confluent hyper-geometrical equation — Kummer's equation

$$z A_{zz} + \left(\frac{1}{2} - z \right) A_z - \frac{1}{2} A = 0 . \tag{10}$$

2. *Pair of fundamental solutions*—The two linearly independent solutions (the fundamental solutions) of equation (10) are confluent hyper-geometrical functions (Abramowitz and Stegun, 1972)

$$A_1 = \Phi(1/2,\ 1/2;\ z) = \exp z, \tag{11}$$

$$A_2 = \sqrt{z}\ \Phi(1, 3/2; z) = \sqrt{\pi}\ [(\exp z)/2 - W(w)], \tag{12}$$

$$w = (2iz/\pi)^{1/2}, \tag{13}$$

where function $W(w)$ is determined by equation (D.1) of Appendix D.

We can see that in the domain 1(39) the solutions are functions of the only variable z. Because z depends on α^2 [see equation (1)], the value of the solution coincides at the symmetrical points (τ, α, β) and $(\tau, -\alpha, \beta)$. So, functions (11) - (12) can be regarded as the solutions of the initial equation (8) either for $\alpha < 0$ or for $\alpha > 0$. However, we want to get a solution, valid simultaneously in both domains. Such a solution must be continuous together with its derivatives at $\alpha = 0$. Let us check this condition.

Note first that both solutions (11) - (12) are continuous at $\alpha = 0$. By differentiating solution (11) as a composite function we learn that all its first and second partial derivatives are continuous at $\alpha = 0$. To differentiate solution (12), we use relations (D.(13) - D.(14) of Appendix D. Then we have

$$(\partial A_2/\partial\tau)_{\alpha=0} = (\partial^2 A_2/\partial\tau^2)_{\alpha=0} = (\partial^2 A_2/\partial\alpha^2)_{\alpha=0} = 0, \tag{14}$$

$$\partial A_2/\partial\alpha = 2i\omega a_2 \alpha A_2 + \delta \times (i\omega a_2)^{1/2}, \text{ and} \tag{15}$$

$$\delta = \alpha \times (\alpha^2)^{-1/2}, \tag{16}$$

where $a_2 = a_2(\tau, 0, \beta)$ is determined by equation 1(34). Derivatives (14) comply with the mentioned condition. Therefore, we must consider the derivative (15).

Because the value of δ in equation (16) depends on the direction of approaching the surface $\alpha = 0$

$$(\delta)_{\alpha=\pm 0} = [\alpha \times (\alpha^2)^{-1/2}]_{\alpha=\pm 0} = (\text{sign } \alpha)_{\alpha=\pm 0} = \pm 1, \tag{17}$$

the value of the derivative (15) at $\alpha = 0$ also depends on the mentioned direction

$$(\partial A_2/\partial\alpha)_{\alpha=\pm 0} = \pm (i\omega a_2)^{1/2}. \tag{18}$$

As a result, the derivative under consideration has a discontinuity at $\alpha = 0$

$$(\partial A_2/\partial\alpha)_{\alpha=+0} - (\partial A_2/\partial\alpha)_{\alpha=-0} = 2(i\omega a_2)^{1/2}. \tag{19}$$

Therefore, we have to replace solution (12) with a solution free of this flaw.

Let us take the expression

$$A^* = \delta \times A_2 \text{, and} \tag{20}$$

$$\delta = \text{sign } \alpha , \tag{21}$$

where A_2 is determined by equation (12). Then

$$(A^*)_{\alpha=0} = (\partial A^* / \partial \tau)_{\alpha=0} = (\partial^2 A^* / \partial \tau^2)_{\alpha=0} = (\partial^2 A^* / \partial \alpha^2)_{\alpha=0} = 0 , \tag{22}$$

$$(\partial A^* / \partial \alpha)_{\alpha=\pm 0} = (i \omega a_2)^{1/2} . \tag{23}$$

The derivative (23) is continuous at $\alpha = 0$

$$(\partial A^* / \partial \alpha)_{\alpha=+0} - (\partial A^* / \partial \alpha)_{\alpha=-0} = 0 . \tag{24}$$

We see that expression (20) satisfies the previously mentioned condition of continuity.

That any solution of equation (10) can be expressed through a linear combination of its fundamental solutions is well known. We can take solution (11) and (20) as the fundamental pair. Then we get the general solution of equation (10) in the form

$$A = C'_1 A_1 + \delta \times C'_2 A_2 , \tag{25}$$

where C'_1 and C'_2 are arbitrary constants. This solution complies with the previously mentioned conditions of continuity and smoothness at $\alpha = 0$.

3. Boundary layer—By substituting equations (25), (11), (12), and 1(13) into equation 1(5) we get

$$f = C'_1 f_0 + \delta \sqrt{\pi} \; C'_2 (f_0/2 - f_D) , \tag{26}$$

$$f_0 = G_0 \exp (i \omega \tau_0) , \tag{27}$$

$$f_D = G_0 W(w) \exp (i \omega \tau) , \tag{28}$$

$$w = [2 \omega (\tau - \tau_0)/\pi]^{1/2}, \; \delta = \text{sign } \alpha , \tag{29}$$

where G_0 complies with the transport equation 1(14).

Expression (26) gives the solution of wave equation in the boundary layer 1(4), depending on two arbitrary constants C'_1 and C'_2. To interpret this solution, we express these constants through new constants C_1 and C_2 as

$$C'_1 = C_1 + C_2/2, \quad C'_2 = -C_2/\sqrt{\pi}\,. \tag{30}$$

Then solution (26) can be written in the form

$$f = C_1 f_0 + C_2 f', \tag{31}$$

$$f' = s f_0 + \delta f_D, \quad s = (1 - \delta)/2\,. \tag{32}$$

By taking $C_2 = 0$ we get the ray method solution

$$f = C_1 f_0\,. \tag{33}$$

Note, this solution is valid simultaneously in both domains $\alpha < 0$ and $\alpha > 0$ and is continuous at $\alpha = 0$. Note also, that the solution does not depend on the choice of the ray coordinate system (τ, α, β).

By taking $C_1 = 0$, $C_2 = 1$ we get the second linearly independent solution

$$f = f', \tag{34}$$

which can be rewritten in the form

$$f = f_0 - f_D \quad \text{when } \alpha < 0, \tag{35}$$

$$f = f_D \quad \text{when } \alpha > 0\,. \tag{36}$$

Interpretation of these expressions leads to the generalization of ideas of Section V.3.2 on the case of 3-D inhomogeneous media. To do so, we define wave f_0 formally as

$$f_0 = f_0(\tau, \alpha, \beta) \quad \text{when } \alpha < 0, \tag{37}$$

$$f_0 = 0 \quad \text{when } \alpha > 0\,. \tag{38}$$

We can call domains $\alpha < 0$ and $\alpha > 0$ *the illuminated* and *the shadow domains* of the wave (37) - (38), respectively. We can call the surface $\alpha = 0$ *the shadow boundary* of the mentioned wave. Note, solution (33) is valid in both domains $\alpha < 0$ and $\alpha > 0$. Not to contradict this fact, we can call functions G_0 and τ_0 in domain $\alpha > 0$ *the continuations of the amplitude and the eikonal of the wave (37) - (38) into the shadow zone.* We can call the function f_D *the diffracted wave*, propagating along the congruence of diffracted rays (α, β). We can consider f_D as the edge-diffracted wave.

We can interpret solution (35) - (36) as a result of the interference of waves f_0 and f_D in the neighborhood of the shadow boundary. This type of interpretation can be reduced to considerations of Section V.3.2. Specifically, the considerations of Section V.3.2 allow us to take $C \approx 2\pi$ in equation 1(4).

Note that while solving Kummer's equation we considered the coordinate β as a parameter, therefore, the constants of integration (30) depend on the parameter β. Thus, equation (31) gives a solution which contains two arbitrary slowly changing functions $C_1(\beta)$ and $C_2(\beta)$ of the ray coordinate β.

3. Solution of equation of transverse diffusion

1. General solution—An equation in the form 1(51) is well-known in the asymptotic theory of diffraction (Fock, 1965; Malyuzhinetz, 1959). According to the current concepts about wave mechanisms, it can be interpreted as an equation of diffusion with the imaginary diffusion coefficient $-i\mu/2\omega$. Such an interpretation allows one to consider diffraction phenomena as a transverse diffusion of the wave energy flux from one ray tube to others across wave fronts. Therefore, an equation of form 1(51) is called *the equation of transverse diffusion* (Malyuzhinetz, 1959). Here we are going to get a general solution of this equation.

Let us seek the solution of equation 1(51) by the method of separation of variables

$$A = U(\tau)\, V(\alpha), \tag{1}$$

where U does not depend on α and V does not depend on τ. By substituting expression (1) into equation 1(51) we have

$$(2\omega V)^{-1}\partial^2 V/\partial\alpha^2 + i(\mu U)^{-1}\partial U/\partial\tau = 0. \tag{2}$$

Because the first term does not depend on τ and the second term does not depend on α, equation (2) can be split in two ordinary differential equations

$$(2\omega V)^{-1}\partial^2 V/\partial\alpha^2 = \zeta, \text{ and } i(\mu U)^{-1}\partial U/\partial\tau = -\zeta, \tag{3}$$

where ζ is an arbitrary number. The general solutions of these equations look like

$$V = C^{+} V^{+}(\zeta) + C^{-} V^{-}(\zeta), \quad U = \exp(-i\rho\zeta), \tag{4}$$

$$V^{\pm}(\zeta) = \exp\,[\pm\,\alpha(2\,\omega\,\zeta)^{1/2}], \tag{5}$$

$$\rho = -\int_{a}^{\tau} \mu\, d\tau, \tag{6}$$

where C^{+}, C^{-}, a are arbitrary constants. By substituting equations (4) into equation (1) we get

$$A = \exp\,(-i\rho\zeta)\,[C^{+} V^{+}(\zeta) + C^{-} V^{-}(\zeta)]. \tag{7}$$

Because any linear combination of expression (7) satisfies equation 1(51), the general solution can be represented by the integral

$$A = (2\pi)^{-1/2} \int_{-\infty}^{\infty} [C^{+}(\zeta)\, V^{+}(\zeta) + C^{-}(\zeta)\, V^{-}(\zeta)]\ \exp\,(-i\rho\zeta)\,d\zeta, \tag{8}$$

where $C^{+}(\zeta)$ and $C^{-}(\zeta)$ are arbitrary functions of the variable of integration.

We consider high-frequency solutions with $\omega \to \infty$. It is easy to see that under this condition integral (8) exists, if

$$\pm\,\alpha(2\,\omega\,\zeta)^{1/2} < 0 \quad \text{when } \zeta > 0. \tag{9}$$

This condition can be satisfied, if we take the arbitrary functions

$$C^{+}(\zeta) \equiv 0 \quad \text{when } \alpha > 0, \quad C^{-}(\zeta) \equiv 0 \quad \text{when } \alpha < 0. \tag{10}$$

Then integral (8) can be written

$$A = (2\pi)^{-1/2} \int_{-\infty}^{\infty} C^{+}(\zeta)\; V^{\pm}(\zeta)\; \exp\,(-i\rho\zeta)\,d\zeta, \tag{11}$$

where it is necessary to take plus for $\alpha < 0$ and minus for $\alpha > 0$.

This integral gives a solution depending on an arbitrary function $C^{\pm}(\zeta)$ of the variable of integration.

2. Fourier integrals—Next we show that integral (11) can be considered as the Fourier transform of function $C^{\pm}(\zeta)\ V^{\pm}(\zeta)$.

By using equations (6) and 1(52) we can introduce the pair of inverse functions

$$\tau = \tau(\rho), \quad \rho = \rho(\tau). \tag{12}$$

Note that on the strength of the theorem on the derivative of the inverse function and equation (6) the following relation holds true:

$$d\tau(\rho)/d\rho = [d\rho(\tau)/d\tau]^{-1} = -1/\mu(\tau). \tag{13}$$

Let us find the interval of variation $\rho(\tau)$ by analyzing the integral (6). To do so, we use the following representation of quantity 1(29)

$$g_{\alpha\alpha}^{1/2} = R(d\varepsilon/d\alpha), \tag{14}$$

where R is the radius of curvature of the intersection of the surface $\tau = \text{const}$ by the surface $\beta = \text{const}$. Here the differential $d\varepsilon$ corresponds to the angular size of an elementary arc length along the coordinate line $\tau = \text{const}$, $\beta = \text{const}$, if we look at this element from the center of curvature $R = 0$. By substituting equation (14) into (6) we have

$$\rho(\tau) = -\int_a^{\tau} \varphi(\tau)\ R^{-2}(\tau)\, d\tau, \quad \varphi = c^2 (d\varepsilon/d\alpha)^{-2}. \tag{15}$$

Let $\varphi(\tau)$ be limited. Then

$$\rho(a) = 0. \tag{16}$$

We take $\tau = 0$ at an edge point. Then in conformity with the law of edge diffraction (see Section 6 of Introduction) we have $R(0) = 0$. By using an approximate relation $\tau = R/c$ with $\tau \to 0$, we can write equation (15) as

$$\rho(\tau) = \varphi(0)\ c^{-2}(0) \int_{\alpha}^{\tau} \tau^{-2}\, d\tau = (d\varepsilon/d\alpha)^{-2}\ (\tau^{-1} - \alpha^{-1}). \tag{17}$$

From this relation we have

$$\rho(\tau) \to \pm\infty \quad \text{when } \tau \to \pm 0, \tag{18}$$

By taking $a \to -\infty$ we can write equations (16) and (18) in the form

$$\rho(\tau) \to \pm\infty \quad \text{when } \tau(\rho) \to \pm 0 \tag{19}$$

$$\rho(\tau) \to \pm 0 \quad \text{when } \tau(\rho) \to -\infty .$$

Because the quantity ρ is defined in the interval $-\infty < \rho < \infty$, we can introduce the following integral:

$$C^{\pm}(\zeta)\, V^{\pm}(\zeta) = (2\pi)^{-1/2} \int_{-\infty}^{\infty} A(\rho) \exp(i\rho\zeta)\, d\rho . \tag{20}$$

The pair of relations (11) and (20) can be regarded as a pair of the Fourier transforms, connecting the solution $A(\rho)$ of equation 1(51) with an arbitrary function $C^{\pm}(\zeta)$.

3. *Problem of conjugation along the shadow boundary*—Now proceeding to the edge-diffracted wave in the boundary layer, according to Section V.3.2, the wavefield in the boundary layer can be represented as the sum of the reflected/transmitted wave

$$f_0 = \Phi_0 \exp(i\omega\tau_0), \tag{21}$$

which has a discontinuity at the shadow boundary $\alpha = 0$, and the edge-diffracted wave

$$f_D = \Phi_D \exp(i\omega\tau), \tag{22}$$

which smoothes this discontinuity. If the wave defined in equation (21) is represented in the edge-diffracted wave's ray coordinates

$$f_0 = \begin{cases} f_0(\tau, \alpha, \beta) & \text{when } \alpha < 0 \\ 0 & \text{when } \alpha > 0, \end{cases} \tag{23}$$

then the condition of continuity of the total wavefield at the shadow boundary can be written

$$(f_0 + f_D)_{\alpha=-0} = (f_D)_{\alpha=+0} . \tag{24}$$

The description of the edge-diffracted wave, complying with condition (24), was given in Section V.3.2. Here we use condition (24) to obtain a more general description of the edge-diffracted wave, which can be useful for deriving the uniform formula (see Section VII.2.3). We also use the form of solution 1(5), 1(9) and (11), depending on an arbitrary function $C^{\pm}(\zeta)$. The arbitrary function will be found from condition (24).

We look for the amplitude of an edge-diffracted wave in the form 1(5), 1(9),

$$\Phi_D = A\, G_D\,, \tag{25}$$

were the cofactor A is determined by equation (11), and the cofactor G_D complies with transport equation 1(10).

The reflected/transmitted wave amplitude can be written as

$$\Phi_0 = A_0\, G_D\,,\quad A_0 = \Phi_0\, G_D^{-1}\,. \tag{26}$$

We can consider the value of quantity A_0 at the shadow boundary either as a function of the edge wave's ray coordinates

$$A_0(\tau) = A_0(\tau, \alpha, \beta) \quad \text{with } \alpha = 0\,, \tag{27}$$

or as a function of variable ρ

$$A_0[\tau(\rho)] = A_0[\tau(\rho), \alpha, \beta] \quad \text{with } \alpha = 0\,. \tag{28}$$

We suppose that this function allows the Fourier transform

$$A_0[\tau(\rho)] = (2\pi)^{-1/2} \int_{-\infty}^{\infty} \kappa(\zeta)\, \exp\,(-i\rho\zeta)\, d\zeta\,, \tag{29}$$

$$\kappa(\zeta) = (2\pi)^{-1/2} \int_{-\infty}^{\infty} A_0[\tau(\rho)]\, \exp\,(i\rho\zeta)\, dp\,. \tag{30}$$

By substituting equations (22), (25), (11) and (21), (26), (29) into condition (24) we derive

$$\kappa(\zeta) + C^{+}(\zeta) = C^{-}(\zeta)\,. \tag{31}$$

This condition is satisfied for any ζ, if

$$C^{+}(\zeta) = -\kappa(\zeta)/2\,,\quad C^{-}(\zeta) = \kappa(\zeta)/2\,. \tag{32}$$

By substituting equations (32) into (11) we get

$$A = \pm (2\pi)^{-1/2} \int_{-\infty}^{\infty} \kappa(\zeta)\, \eta(\zeta) \exp(-i\rho\zeta)\, d\zeta, \tag{33}$$

$$\eta(\zeta) = (1/2) \exp[-|\alpha|(2\omega\zeta)^{1/2}], \tag{34}$$

where it is necessary to take plus for $\alpha > 0$ and minus for $\alpha < 0$.

Equations (25) and (33) describe the amplitude of an edge-diffracted wave complying with condition (24).

4. Forms of the conjugation problem solution—Here we rewrite the edge-diffracted wave amplitude in the form more convenient for analysis. By taking into account the tabular integral

$$\psi(\rho) = (2\pi)^{-1/2} \int_{-\infty}^{\infty} \eta(\zeta) \exp(-i\rho\zeta)\, d\zeta =$$

$$= \begin{cases} (i\omega\alpha^2/4)^{1/2} \rho^{-3/2} \exp(-i\omega\alpha^2/2\rho) & \text{when } \rho > 0 \\ 0 & \text{when } \rho < 0, \end{cases} \tag{35}$$

where $\eta(\zeta)$ is determined by equation (34), we can write the Fourier integral (33) in the form of a convolution

$$\int_{-\infty}^{\infty} \kappa(\zeta)\eta(\zeta) \exp(-i\rho\zeta)\, d\zeta = \int_{0}^{\infty} \psi(\xi) A_0(\rho - \xi)\, d\xi. \tag{36}$$

By substituting equations (33) and (36) into (25) we get

$$\Phi_D = \pm (2\pi)^{-1/2} G_D \int_{0}^{\infty} A_0[\tau(\rho - \xi)]\, \psi(\xi)\, d\xi, \tag{37}$$

where it is necessary to take plus for $\alpha > 0$ and minus for $\alpha < 0$.

We obtain another useful form of equation (37) by introducing a new variable of integration $\lambda = \tau(\rho - \xi)$. According to equations (12) and (6) we have

$$\rho - \xi = \rho(\lambda) \text{ or } \xi = \rho - \rho(\lambda), \; d\xi/d\lambda = \mu(\lambda), \tag{38}$$

where $\mu(\tau)$ is determined by equation 1(52). The new limits of integration follow from equations (19)

$$\lambda = \tau(\rho - \xi) = 0 \text{ when } \xi \to \infty, \ \lambda = \tau(\rho - \xi) = \tau(\rho) = \tau \text{ when } \xi \to 0. \tag{39}$$

Equation (37) can be written

$$\Phi_D = \mp(2\pi)^{-1/2} G_D \int_0^\tau \psi\,[\rho - \rho(\lambda)]\, A_0(\lambda)\,\mu(\lambda)\, d\lambda, \tag{40}$$

where it is necessary to take minus for $\alpha > 0$ (the shadow zone) and plus for $\alpha < 0$ (the illuminated zone). Function $\mu(\tau)$ is determined by equation 1(52).

5. Approximation in a vicinity of the shadow boundary—By introducing a parameter

$$p = \omega\alpha^2 / 2\rho \tag{41}$$

we can rewrite equation (35) in the form

$$\psi(\xi) = (p\rho i/2)^{1/2}\, \xi^{-3/2} \exp(-ip\rho/\xi) \text{ with } \xi > 0. \tag{42}$$

By introducing a new variable $x = (\rho/\xi) - 1$ in integral (37) and taking into account equation (42) we have

$$\Phi_D = \pm(ip/4\pi)^{1/2} G_D \exp(-ip) \int_{-1}^{\infty} (x+1)^{1/2}$$
$$A_0\{\tau[\rho x/(x+1)]\} \exp(-ipx)\, dx, \tag{43}$$

where it is necessary to take plus for $\alpha > 0$ and minus for $\alpha < 0$.

Here we consider this integral when parameter p is small enough. Because of the cofactor $\sqrt{p}$ outside the integral, the contribution to the integral from any limited interval $x <$ const tends to zero when $p \to 0$. This allows us to simplify the integral by using the approximation

$$x + 1 \approx x \quad \text{when } x >> 1. \tag{44}$$

Then

$$A_0\{\tau[\rho x/(x+1)]\} \approx A_0[\tau(\rho)] = A_0(\tau, 0, \beta). \tag{45}$$

We consider the case of high frequencies $\omega \to \infty$. Parameter (41) is small with $\omega \to \infty$, if $\alpha \to 0$. Hence, we can use the approximation

$$A_0\ (\tau, 0, \beta) \approx A_0(\tau, \alpha, \beta) \quad \text{when } \alpha \to 0. \tag{46}$$

By substituting approximate expressions (44) - (46) into equation (43) and taking into account equations (26) we get

$$\Phi_D = \pm\ \Phi_0\ I \exp\ (-ip), \tag{47}$$

$$I = (ip/4\pi)^{1/2} \int_{-1}^{\infty} x^{-1/2} \exp\ (-ipx)\, dx =$$

$$= (i/4\pi)^{1/2} \left(\int_0^{\infty} + \int_{-p}^{0} \right) y^{-1/2} \exp\ (-iy)\, dy, \tag{48}$$

where it is necessary to take plus for $\alpha > 0$ and minus for $\alpha < 0$.

By expressing these integrals through the Fresnel integrals

$$(i/4\pi)^{1/2} \int_0^{\infty} y^{-1/2} \exp(-iy)\, dy = (i/2)^{1/2}\ [C(\infty) - iS(\infty)] = 1/2, \tag{49}$$

$$(i/4\pi)^{1/2} \int_{-p}^{0} y^{-1/2} \exp(-iy)\, dy = (i\pi)^{-1/2} \int_0^{\sqrt{p}} \exp(it^2)\, dt$$
$$= F(\sqrt{p}\,) - 1/2, \tag{50}$$

we get

$$I = F\ (\sqrt{p}\,), \tag{51}$$

where F is determined by equation (D.16). By fixing a branch of the square root by the condition $arg\ \sqrt{p} = \pi$, we get in accordance with equation (D.17) the expression

$$I = W(w) \exp\ (ip), \quad w = (2p/\pi)^{1/2}, \tag{52}$$

where W is determined by equation (D.1). Note that an attempt to fix a square root branch by condition $arg\ \sqrt{p} = 0$ leads to the wrong result—the edge-wave amplitude increases when $|\alpha| \to \infty$.

By substituting equation (52) into (47), we get the approximate formula

$$\Phi_D = \pm \Phi_0 \, W(w), \quad w = (\omega \, \alpha^2 / \pi \, \rho)^{1/2}, \tag{53}$$

where it is necessary to take plus for $\alpha > 0$ and minus for $\alpha < 0$. This formula is valid for small values of w only.

6. Approximation of the geometrical theory of diffraction—Now we consider a case of big values of parameter (41). To do so, we introduce the new variable in integral (40)

$$t = \omega \, \alpha^2 / 2 \, [\rho - \rho(\lambda)] = p / [1 - \rho(\lambda)/\rho], \tag{54}$$

where p is determined by equation (41). By taking into consideration equations (12) - (13) we have

$$\lambda = \tau(\chi), \; \chi = \rho(1 - p/t), \tag{55}$$

$$d\lambda / dt = [d\tau(\chi)/d\chi] \, d\chi / d\tau = - \, p \rho / [t^2 \mu(\chi)], \tag{56}$$

and equation (40) can be written in the form

$$\Phi_D = \pm (i/4\pi)^{1/2} \, G_D \int_0^\infty A_0[\tau(\chi)] \, t^{-1/2} \exp(-it) \, dt, \tag{57}$$

where it is necessary to take plus for $\alpha > 0$ and minus for $\alpha < 0$.

Suppose that the integrand is finite at $t = 0$ (we will see this, when a medium is homogeneous). Suppose that it is possible to neglect the contributions to the integral with $t \to \infty$, if parameter p is sufficiently large [note that the integral (43) for small values of p has been formed by contributions with $x \to \infty$]. Then we can replace the infinite interval of integration in equation (57) by the finite interval

$$\varepsilon < t < T, \tag{58}$$

where ε is small enough and T is sufficiently large.

Then quantity (55) can be approximated as

$$\chi = (\rho/t)(t - p) \approx - \, p\rho/t = - \, \omega \, \alpha^2 / 2t \quad \text{when } p \gg T. \tag{59}$$

Because in this case the integral does not depend on $\rho = \rho(\tau)$, equation (57) can be written

$$\Phi_D = \pm \, \Psi\,(\alpha,\beta)\; G_D, \tag{60}$$

$$\Psi(\alpha,\beta) = (i/4\pi)^{1/2} \int_0^{\infty} A_0[\tau(\tilde{\chi})]\, t^{-1/2} \exp(-it)\,dt, \tag{61}$$

$$\tilde{\chi} = -\,\omega\,\alpha^2/2t,$$

where $\Psi(\alpha,\beta)$ does not depend on τ.

This function complies with the transport equation I.2(11) and, therefore, can be used to obtain the edge wave in the framework of the geometric theory of diffraction. The cofactor Ψ is constant along an individual diffracted ray $\alpha = \text{const}$, β const. Hence, it can be found as well by using the description of the edge-diffracted wave in the small neighborhood of the edge ($\tau \to 0$), where the medium can be considered locally homogeneous. We do so in Section 4.4.

4. Case of homogeneous medium

1. Integral formula—Here we consider the integral 3(57) in the case of a constant wave velocity $c = \text{const}$.

Let us take $\tau = \ell / c$, where ℓ, is the distance from the edge along the diffracted ray, α is a dihedral angle between planes intersecting over the tangent to the edge (plane $\alpha = 0$ touches the shadow boundary), and β is a half of the vertex angle of the diffraction cone (Figure 28). Then the coefficient 1(29) with $\gamma = \alpha$ is determined by equation (E-7),

$$g_{\alpha\alpha} = (c\,\tau\,\sin\,\beta)^2. \tag{1}$$

By using this expression we can write equations 1(52), 3(6), 3(12), 3(55), and 3(41) as

$$\begin{gathered}\mu(\tau) = (\tau\,\sin\beta)^{-2},\ \rho(\tau) = (\tau\sin^2\beta)^{-1},\ \tau(\rho) = (\rho\,\sin^2\beta)^{-1},\\ \chi = (t-p)/(t\tau\sin^2\beta),\ \tau(\chi) = t\tau/(t-p),\ p = (\omega\,\tau\,\alpha^2\,\sin^2\beta)/2.\end{gathered} \tag{2}$$

By using equation (E.18) we can write equation 1(32) in the form

$$G_D = [r_D^{-1}\,\tau\,R_D(\tau)\,\sin^2\,\beta]^{-1/2},\ \text{and} \tag{3}$$

$$R_D(\tau) = c\,\tau + r_D, \tag{4}$$

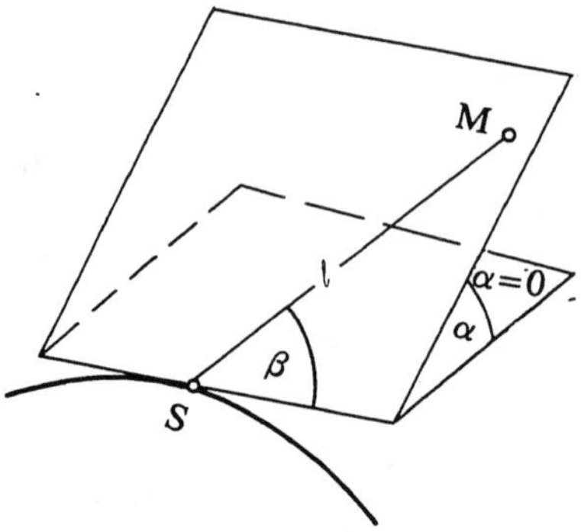

Figure 28. Ray coordinates in the homogeneous medium.

where r_D is the radius of curvature of the section of the edge-diffracted wave front by the plane $\alpha = 0$ at the edge.

Let the amplitude of the reflected/transmitted wave 3(21) be described by the ray method as

$$\Phi_0 = B\,G_0\,, \tag{5}$$

where G_0 complies with the transport equation 1(14). Cofactor B does not depend on the eikonal τ_0 of this wave. In an homogeneous medium the following relation holds true:

$$G_0 = (\,c\,/\,R_1\,R_2\,)^{1/2}\,, \tag{6}$$

where R_1 and R_2 are principal radii of the wave front.

Let us denote the value of amplitude (5) on the shadow boundary as

$$\Phi_0^* = \Phi_0\,(\,\tau\,,\alpha\,,\beta\,)\quad \text{with}\ \alpha = 0\,, \tag{7}$$

where $(\,\tau\,,\alpha\,,\beta\,)$ are the ray coordinates of the edge-diffracted wave. The principal radii of curvature on the shadow boundary can be written in the form

$$R_n\,(\,\tau\,) = c\,\tau + r_n \quad \text{with}\ n = 1\,,2\,, \tag{8}$$

where r_1 and r_2 are the corresponding principal radii of curvature of the wave front at the edge. By substituting expressions (6) - (8) into equation (5) we have

$$\Phi_0^* = \sqrt{c}\; B\, [R_1(\tau)\, R_2(\tau)]^{-1/2}. \tag{9}$$

By substituting equations (3) and (9) into 3(26) and 3(27) we have

$$A_0(\tau) = B \sin\beta \times [c\tau R_D(\tau)/r_D R_1(\tau)\, R_2(\tau)]^{1/2}. \tag{10}$$

As a result of transformation 3(55), this expression can be written

$$A_0[\tau(\chi)] = B \sin\beta \times \{c\tau(\chi) R_D[\tau(\chi)]/r_D R_1[\tau(\chi)] R_2[\tau(\chi)]\}^{1/2}, \tag{11}$$

where $\tau(\chi)$ is determined in equations (2). As a result of the same transformation, equations (4) and (8) can be written in the form

$$R_n[\tau(\chi)] = [c\tau t/(t-p)] + r_n = R_n(\tau)(t-z_n)/(t-p), \tag{12}$$

$$z_n = p r_n / R_n(\tau) \quad \text{with } n = D, 1, 2 \tag{13}$$

By substituting equations (12) into (11) and taking into account the expression for $\tau(\chi)$ from (2), we have

$$A_0[\tau(\chi)] = \Phi_0^* G_D^{-1}\, [t(t-z_D)/(t-z_1)(t-z_2)]^{1/2}. \tag{14}$$

By substituting equation (14) into 3(57) we get an integral formula for the amplitude of the edge-diffracted wave,

$$\Phi_D = \pm\, \Phi_0^*\, \mathfrak{F}\,(z_D, z_1, z_2), \tag{15}$$

$$\mathfrak{F}\,(z_D, z_1, z_2) = (1/2\sqrt{\pi}) \int_0^\infty [i(t-z_D)/(t-z_1)(t-z_2)]^{1/2} \exp(-it)\, dt, \tag{16}$$

$$z_n = (\omega\tau\alpha^2 \sin^2\beta)/2L_n,\; L_n = (c\tau + r_n)/r_n, \tag{17}$$

where it is necessary to take plus in the shadow zone ($\alpha > 0$) and minus in the illuminated zone ($\alpha < 0$).

2. *Special situations*—The function of three variables (16) has an obvious property

$$\mathfrak{F}\,(u, u, z) = \mathfrak{F}\,(u, z, u) = \mathfrak{F}\,(z, z, z) = \mathfrak{F}\,(z), \tag{18}$$

$$\mathcal{F}(z) = (i/4\pi)^{1/2} \int_0^\infty (t - z)^{-1/2} \exp(-it)\,dt. \tag{19}$$

By introducing a new variable of integration $y = t - z$, we can rewrite equation (19) in the form

$$\mathcal{F}(z) = I \exp(-iz), \quad I = (i/4\pi)^{1/2} \int_{-z}^\infty y^{-1/2} \exp(-iy)\,dy. \tag{20}$$

This integral is a type of equation 3(48). Therefore, we can use the transformations 3(48) - 3(52) with $p = z$. Then we get

$$\mathcal{F}(z) = W(w), \quad w = (2z/\pi)^{1/2}. \tag{21}$$

In special situations, when function (16) complies with relations (18), equation (15) can be written

$$\Phi_D = \pm\, \Phi_0^* \, W(w), \quad w = (2z/\pi)^{1/2}, \tag{22}$$

where it is necessary to use plus for $\alpha > 0$ and minus for $\alpha < 0$. Let us consider these situations.

1. Let the reflected/transmitted wave be plane, i.e., $r_D \to \infty$, $r_1 \to \infty$, $r_2 \to \infty$. Then

$$z = z_D = z_1 = z_2 \quad \text{with } L_D = L_1 = L_2 = 1, \tag{23}$$

and in equation (22) we have

$$w = |\alpha| \sin\beta \times (\omega\tau/\pi)^{1/2}. \tag{24}$$

2. Let the reflected/transmitted wave be spherical, i.e., $r_D = r_1 = r_2$. Then

$$z = z_D = z_1 = z_2. \tag{25}$$

In equation (22) we have

$$w = |\alpha| \sin\beta \times (\omega\tau/\pi\, L_D)^{1/2}. \tag{26}$$

3. Let one of the planes of the principal normal section of the reflected/transmitted wave front coincide with the shadow boundary $\alpha = 0$. Let it be $r_2 = r_D$, for example. Then $z_2 = z_D$ and we have

$$z = z_1 . \tag{27}$$

In equation (22) we have

$$w = |\alpha| \sin \beta \times (\omega \tau / \pi L_1)^{1/2} . \tag{28}$$

4. Let the wavefield be the same in any plane, perpendicular to the edge (2-D case). We can get this situation by taking $\beta = \pi/2$, $r_D \to \infty$, $r_2 \to \infty$. Then $z_D = z_2$, and we have

$$z = z_1 \quad \text{with } \beta = \pi/2 \tag{29}$$

In equation (22) we have

$$w = |\alpha| (\omega \tau / \pi L_1)^{1/2} . \tag{30}$$

3. Approximate formula—Any diffracted ray $\alpha = \text{const}$, $\beta = \text{const}$ can be related to the corresponding reflected/transmitted ray $\alpha = 0$, $\beta = \text{const}$, belonging to the same cone of diffracted rays $\beta = \text{const}$. Let Π_φ be the plane containing this pair of rays. Let Π_1 be the plane of the principal section of the reflected/transmitted wave front at the ray $\alpha = 0$, $\beta = \text{const}$. Let φ be the dihedral angle between Π_φ and Π_1. Let r_φ and r_1 be radii of curvature of sections of the reflected/transmitted wave front at the ray $\alpha = 0$, $\beta = \text{const}$ at the edge by planes Π_φ and Π_1, respectively. According to Euler's formula we have

$$r_\varphi^{-1} = r_1^{-1} \cos^2 \varphi + r_2^{-1} \sin^2 \varphi . \tag{31}$$

Let us write the following identity:

$$[(t-z_D)/(t-z_1)(t-z_2)]^{1/2} = (t-z_\varphi)^{-1/2} + v(t), \tag{32}$$

$$v(t) = \left\{ [(t-z_\varphi)(t-z_D)]^{1/2} - [(t-z_1)(t-z_2)]^{1/2} \right\} / [(t-z_\varphi)(t-z_1)(t-z_2)]^{1/2}, \tag{33}$$

where z_φ is any number, and take z_φ as

$$z_\varphi = (\omega \tau \alpha^2 \sin^2 \beta)/2 L_\varphi , \; L_\varphi = (c\tau + r_\varphi)/r_\varphi . \tag{34}$$

By substituting equation (32) into (16) we have

$$\mathcal{F}\,(z_D, z_1, z_2) = \mathcal{F}\,(z_\varphi) + \kappa, \tag{35}$$

$$\kappa = (i/4\pi)^{1/2} \int_0^\infty v(t)\, \exp\,(-it)\, dt, \tag{36}$$

where $\mathcal{F}$ is determined by equation (19) with $z = z_\varphi$. By representing $\mathcal{F}\,(z_\varphi)$ in the form of equation (21) we can rewrite equation (35) as

$$\mathcal{F}\,(z_D, z_1, z_2) = W(w) + \kappa, \tag{37}$$

$$w = |\alpha|\, \sin\,\beta \times (\omega\tau/\pi L_\varphi)^{1/2}. \tag{38}$$

Let us consider the behavior of each term of equation (37), when it approaches the shadow boundary $\alpha = 0$. Function (16) with $\alpha = 0$ turns into integral [3(49)]

$$\mathcal{F}\,(0, 0, 0) = 1/2. \tag{39}$$

According to equation D(11) of Appendix D the first term with $\alpha = 0$ is

$$W(0) = 1/2. \tag{40}$$

Equation (33) shows that with $\alpha \to 0$ the integrand in equation (36) tends to zero at every point of the interval of integration. Hence, we have

$$\kappa = 0 \quad \text{with } \alpha = 0. \tag{41}$$

Thus, this is the first term of equation (37) that smooths the discontinuity of the reflected/transmitted wave at its shadow boundary. The second term has nothing to do with correction of discontinuity and can be skipped in the boundary layer. However, it is not possible to neglect this term, if we want to continue function (37) outside the boundary layer (see Section VII.2.3). Thus, in the boundary layer function (37) can be approximated as

$$\mathcal{F}\,(z_D, z_1, z_2) \approx W(w), \tag{42}$$

where w is determined by equation (38).

One can consider equation (38) as the function in a 2-D space (τ, θ) with $\theta = \alpha\, \sin\, \beta$. The quantity θ allows a simple geometric interpretation, if we unroll the part of diffracted cone $\beta = \text{const}$, bounded by planes $\alpha = 0$ and $\alpha = \text{const}$ on the plane surface. As a result, we get a circular sector with the central angle $\theta = \alpha \sin \beta$. Hence, a pair of numbers (τ, θ) corresponds to polar coordinates on the plane surface or, what is the same thing, the polar coordinates on the surface of this cone. Thus, in the frame of approximation (42) the diffraction effect is described on each diffraction cone separately.

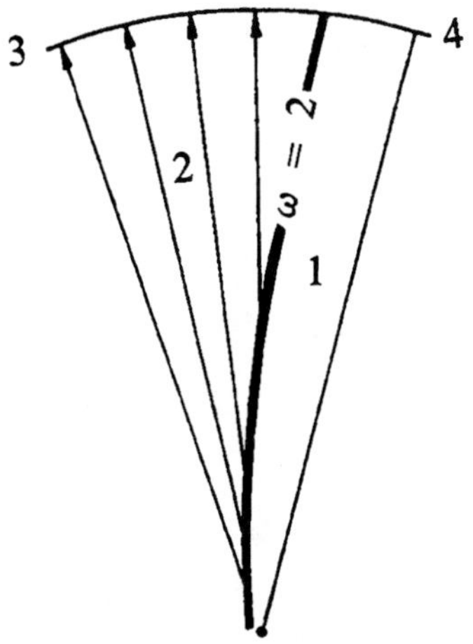

Figure 29. Radiation from the surface of the boundary layer. 1 – boundary layer; 2 – region of ray representations; 3 – front of edge-diffracted wave; 4 – shadow boundary.

4. Asymptotic formula for $z_n \to \infty$—As mentioned in the commentary to equation 3(60) the function $\Psi(\alpha, \beta)$ could also be found by using the description of the edge-diffracted wave in a small neighborhood of the edge, where the medium can be considered as locally homogeneous. This can be done by asymptotic analysis of equation (15) under the condition

$$p = (\omega \tau \alpha^2 \sin^2 \beta)/2 \to \infty . \tag{43}$$

The asymptotic value of integral (16) under this condition, i.e., with $|z_n| \to \infty$, is formed by contributions from the neighborhood of the point $t = 0$. Let us find this value by introducing a new variable of integration $x = -t/p$, where p is determined by equation (43). Then equation (16) can be written in the Fourier integral form

$$\mathcal{F}(z_D, z_1, z_2) = i(ip/4\pi)^{1/2} \int_{-\infty}^{0} f(x) \exp(ipx)\, dx, \tag{44}$$

$$f(x) = [(x + L_D^{-1})/(x + L_1^{-1})(x + L_2^{-1})]^{1/2} . \tag{45}$$

By using the well-known asymptotic representation of integrals of the Fourier type

$$\int_{-\infty}^{0} f(x)\ \exp\ (ipx)\,dx \sim (ip)^{-1} f(0) + O(p^{-2}) \quad \text{with } p \to \infty \tag{46}$$

we get an asymptotic representation of function (44)

$$\mathfrak{F}\ (z_D, z_1, z_2) \sim (i L_1\ L_2/4\,\pi\, p\, L_D)^{1/2} \quad \text{with } p \to \infty\ . \tag{47}$$

By substituting (47) into (15) and taking into consideration equations (3) and (9), we get the sought asymptotic formula

$$\Phi_D = \pm\ \Psi\ (\alpha\,, \beta)\, G_D\,, \tag{48}$$

$$\Psi(\alpha\,, \beta) = \Phi_0^*(0)\,(i/2\,\pi\,\omega\,\alpha^2)^{1/2}\,, \tag{49}$$

$$\Phi_0^*(0) = \Phi_0^* \quad \text{with } \tau = 0\,, \tag{50}$$

where it is necessary to take plus for $\alpha > 0$ and minus for $\alpha < 0$. The term $\Phi_0^*(0)$ corresponds to the reflected/transmitted wave amplitude at the edge.

Expression (48) complies with the transport equation given by I.1(11). The similar expression 3(60) has been obtained for the case of inhomogeneous media. Because function $\Psi(\alpha, \beta)$ does not depend on τ, formula (49) holds true for inhomogeneous media 3(60) as well.

5. *Wave mechanisms*—Here we interpret obtained formulas from the standpoint of the heuristic concept of Fock (Fock, 1965; Malyuzhinetz, 1959), which regards the phenomenon of diffraction as a transverse diffusion of energy in the directions tangential to the wavefronts. As a solution of the equation of transverse diffusion 1(51) expression (15) describes the diffusion of energy from the shadow boundary of the reflected/transmitted wave in the direction of the coordinate line α. Since equation 1(51) does not contain derivatives with respect to β, the process of diffusion occurs independently in each cone of diffracted rays, and there is no redistribution of energy between cones.

The antisymmetry of expression (15) with respect to coordinate α relative to the shadow boundary expresses the energy balance in the diffusion process: the inflow of energy into the shadow region ("plus" sign) is equal to the out-flow from the illuminated region ("minus" sign). The diffusion process leads to the equalization of amplitudes in the directions tangential to the front and to smoothing the boundary of the geometric shadow. Since the rate of equalization is finite, the process of energy transport (reflected/transmitted wave) and transverse diffusion are separated in time. In this case the process of expansion of the region of space encompassed by transverse diffusion in time has the character of a propagating wave, which we call the edge-diffracted wave and describe by expressions 3(22) and (15).

Outside the small vicinity of the shadow boundary, called the boundary layer, which is characterized approximately by the expression $w(\tau, \alpha, \beta) \lesssim 2$, the transverse diffusion diminishes out and is replaced by the energy transport mechanism. The transport mechanism within the scope of modernized ray concept is described by the asymptotic formula (48), which is valid outside the boundary layer but in a small angular vicinity of the shadow boundary. The wave mechanism described by this formula is related to the radiation from the surface of the boundary layer $w(\tau, \alpha, \beta) \approx 2$ and is conceived schematically in the following way. When the front of the diffracted wave leaves the boundary layer the energy, accumulated because of the transverse diffusion, on the surface of the boundary layer enters the ray tubes and is transported farther according to the law of the conservation of flux. In this case the diffracted wave is as though radiated by the surface of the boundary layer (Figure 29).

The diffraction coefficient (16) describing the investigated wave mechanisms is represented by us in the form of a sum (35). To describe the diffracted wave in the boundary layer it is sufficient to take into account only the first term. But this approximation is not sufficient for describing the effect of the radiation from the boundary layer, and both terms in expression (35) must be taken into account. The presence of the second term in (35) is because of noncoincidence of the planes of the principal normal sections of the fronts of the reflected/transmitted and diffracted waves on the shadow boundary.

Chapter VII

SCATTERING BY THE EDGE

Here we will derive a uniform formula of the edge-wave amplitude, valid throughout the entire domain of the existence of this wave. The idea of such a description is based on the merging formulas of the boundary layer and geometric theory of diffraction. According to the mentioned theory (see Section 1.7), the edge-wave amplitude can be obtained by its continuation along diffracted rays, if it is known in a small vicinity of the edge. The edge-wave amplitude near the edge can be found by solving some standard diffraction problem, which produces a similar congruence of diffracted rays in the vicinity of the edge (Keller, 1962). As a standard, we use the problem of diffraction of a plane wave on a 3-D system of wedge-shaped regions. We will continue the edge-wave amplitude, obtained from the solution of this problem, outside the neighborhood of the edge in accordance with the geometric theory of diffraction. The obtained formulas fail in the neighborhoods of the shadow boundaries of the reflected/transmitted waves, i.e., in the boundary layers. In the boundary layers we can use the formulas of Chapter VI. However, the formulas are invalid outside the boundary layers. To get the uniform description of the edge-wave amplitude, we generalize the boundary layer formulas in such a way that they correctly behave outside the boundary layers.

We give a physical interpretation of obtained formulas in the form of a concept of scattering by the edge. This concept can be expressed in the simplest form not in the usual Euclidean space but on a Riemann multifold surface (Frank and Mises, 1935). The other, less illustrative, way of interpretation is the generalization of the plan-waves theory to the complex directions of propagation. Here we prefer the latter, because it allows us to express all ideas in more or less ordinary terms.

We illustrate the concept of scattering by the edge by a detailed analysis of some numerical examples of the diffraction on an acoustic wedge, embedded in a different acoustic medium.

1. Deep shadow zone

1. Continuation from a vicinity of the edge—Let us consider a system of wedge-shaped regions, formed by N curvilinear interfaces with a common curvilinear edge. Inside each domain the wave velocity and medium density are continuous functions of a current position in a 3-D space. Let a concentrated source, placed in one of these regions, generate the stationary wave of a high frequency ω . The interaction of this wave with the interfaces generates in each domain the wavefields, which comply with reduced wave equations

$$(\Delta + k_\nu^2) f_\nu = 0 , \; k_\nu = \omega / c_\nu \; (\nu = 1 , 2 , \ldots N) , \tag{1}$$

where c_ν is the wave velocity. The problem is to find solutions of these equations with $\omega \to \infty$ under the boundary conditions at interfaces.

Suppose that the wavefield of the concentrated source can be described by the ray method. Then the components of the sought-after wavefields, corresponding to reflected/transmitted waves, also can be found by the ray method. However, such a description of the sought wavefields is not sufficient because of the shadow boundaries caused by the edge. To get a continuous high-frequency asymptotic description, it is necessary to take into account the edge-diffracted wave. Here we will find this wave in the framework of the geometric diffraction theory by continuation of the edge wave from a small vicinity of the edge along the diffracted rays.

Let a congruence of diffracted rays in the ν–th region be defined as a family of space curves depending on the pair of some parameters α and β so that every pair of fixed values $\alpha = \text{const}$ and $\beta = \text{const}$ describes an individual ray. Then we can introduce ray coordinates $(\tau_\nu , \alpha , \beta)$, where τ_ν is an edge-diffracted wave eikonal. The geometric theory of diffraction gives the following description of the edge wave

$$F_\nu^D = \Phi_\nu^D \exp (i \omega \tau_\nu) , \; (\nabla \tau_\nu)^2 = 1 / c_\nu^2 , \tag{2}$$

$$\Phi_\nu^D = \Psi_\nu (c_\nu^2 / J_\nu)^{1/2} , \tag{3}$$

where c_ν is the wave velocity and J_ν the Jacobian of the transformation from Cartesian coordinates to ray coordinates $(\tau_\nu , \alpha , \beta)$. Cofactor Ψ_ν does not depend on τ_ν , i.e., it is constant along an individual diffracted ray.

Thus, the problem can be reduced to finding the quantity $\Psi_\nu (\alpha , \beta)$. Because this quantity does not depend on τ_ν , it is sufficient to look for it in a small vicinity of the edge, where the problem essentially can be simplified due to the local approximations.

2. *Local approximations*—In a small vicinity of the edge we introduce the local cylindrical coordinates

$$r = r(S),\ \theta = \theta(S), z = z(S), \tag{4}$$

with the axis z oriented along the tangent to the edge at a given point S of the edge so that plane $z = 0$ contains point S (Figure 3). The tangent planes $\theta = \theta_\nu$ ($\nu = 1, 2, \dots N$) to the interfaces separate space in the neighborhood of point S into the wedge-shaped regions $\theta_\nu \le \theta_\nu \le \theta_{\nu+1}$. In the following we also use the following designations for the angular coordinates of the tangent planes: $\theta_\nu^+ = \theta_\nu$, $\theta_\nu^- = \theta_{\nu+1}$. In a small vicinity of the point S on the edge the set of interfaces can be approximated by a system of half-planes with a common rectilinear edge (example of such approximation for $N = 2$ is shown in Figure 3). The section of interfaces by plane $z = 0$ (Figure 30) can be approximated by the system of 2-D wedge-shaped regions shown in Figure 5.

Let F_k be the incident wave given in the region with $\nu = k$. In the small neighborhood of point S we can consider an incident wave locally plane (see equation I(18)), i.e.,

$$F_k = \Phi^* \bar{f}^*,\ \Phi^* = F_k(S), \tag{5}$$

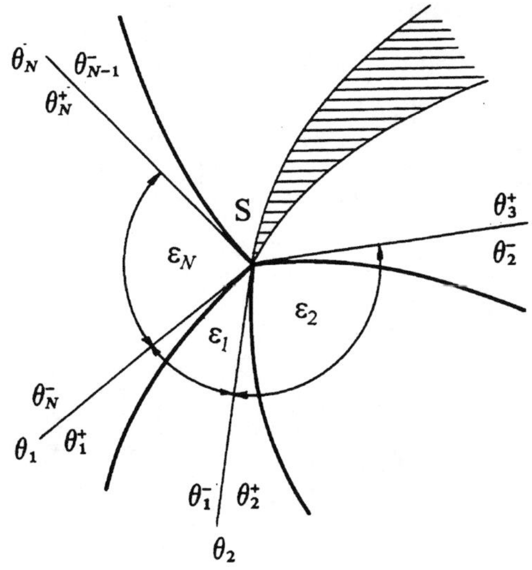

Figure 30. Section of the media by plane $z = 0$.

where $\bar{f}^*$ is the plane wave of the same type used in equation I.(41). In the coordinate system (4) this expression can be written as

$$F_k = \Phi^* f^* \exp(i k_k z \cos q_k), \tag{6}$$

$$f^* = \exp[i k_k^* r \cos(\theta - \theta_0)], \tag{7}$$

$$k_k^* = k_k \sin q_k, \; k_k = \omega / c_k(S), \tag{8}$$

where $c_k(S)$ is the wave velocity at S, q_k is the acute angle between the incident ray and the tangent to the edge at S, $\theta = \theta_0$ is the coordinate plane containing the incident wave vector at S.

By using the local plane approximation of interfaces and the local homogeneous approximation of the medium properties $c_v = c_v(S)$, we can reduce the problem of finding the sought wavefield in a small vicinity of S to the problem of diffraction of the plane wave (6) in the system of wedge-shaped regions with half-plane interfaces with the common rectilinear edge.

3. 3-D diffraction problem—Let $F_v(r, \theta, z)$ be the solution of the above mentioned 3-D diffraction problem. It was shown in Section I.5 that the solution of 3-D problem $F_v(r, \theta, z)$ can be reduced to the solution of 2-D problem $F_v(r, \theta)$ by using relations 1.(42) - 1.(44). Therefore, in the small neighborhood of an individual point S of the edge we can generalize the obtained 2-D solutions on the case of 3-D diffraction problem by means of multiplication by the exponent, according to equation 1.(43), and substitution of wave numbers, according to equation 1.(46).

Thus, the 3-D solution can be represented in the form

$$F_v(r, \theta, z) = \Phi^*[F_v(r, \theta)]_{c_v = c_v^*} \times \exp(i k_v z \cos q_v), \; k_v = \omega / c_v, \tag{9}$$

$$c_v^* = c_v / \sin q_v, \tag{10}$$

where the angles q_v and q_k are connected by relation 1.(29)

$$\cos q_v = (c_v / c_k) \cos q_k \tag{11}$$

Unknown functions $F_v(r, \theta)$ can be found by solving the 2-D diffraction problem (see Chapter II). It is easy to see that the 2-D solution $F_v(r, \theta)$ is the special case of a 3-D solution $F_v(r, \theta, z)$ when $q_k = \pi/2$.

4. Edge-diffracted wave—By using relations discussed in the previous section, we can express the amplitude and eikonal of the edge-diffracted wave in a small neighborhood of an individual point S on the edge

$$F_\nu^D\,(r,\theta,z) = \Phi_\nu^D(r,\theta,z)\ \exp\ [\,i\,\omega\,\tau_\nu(r,\theta,z)\,] \tag{12}$$

through the corresponding quantities in plane $z\ =\ \text{const}$ (Figure 3) as

$$\Phi_\nu^D(r,\theta,z) = \Phi^*\,[\,\Phi_\nu^D(r,\theta)\,]_{c_\nu=c_\nu^*}\,, \tag{13}$$

$$\tau_\nu(r,\theta,z) = [\,\tau_\nu(r,\theta)\,]_{c_\nu=c_\nu^*} + (z/c_\nu)\ \cos\ q_\nu\,, \tag{14}$$

where $\Phi_\nu^D(r,\theta)$ and $\tau_\nu(r,\theta)$ are the amplitude and eikonal, respectively, of the edge-diffracted wave V.3(9) in a 2-D space (r,θ).

These expressions allow a simple geometric interpretation. Expression $\tau_\nu(r,\theta,z) = t$, where t is time, is the equation of the wavefront of an edge-diffracted wave. Because

$$[\,\tau_\nu(r,\theta)\,]_{c_\nu=c_\nu^*} = (r/c_\nu)_{c_\nu=c_\nu^*} = (r\ \sin\ q_\nu)/c_\nu\,, \tag{15}$$

this expression can be rewritten in the form

$$(r\ \sin\ q_\nu + z\ \cos\ q_\nu)/c_\nu = t\,. \tag{16}$$

This is the equation of a cone. The normal to the surface of this cone forms an acute angle q_ν with axis z, i.e., coincides with the diffracted ray. The conical wave front (16) propagates along the diffracted rays with velocity c_ν. The front ascribed by equation (15) in plane $z = \text{const}$ propagates with velocity $c_\nu^* = c_\nu/\sin\ q_\nu$, i.e., the velocity of the wave process in plane $z = \text{const}$ depends on the angle q_ν. The substitution of c_ν by c_ν^* reflects this fact.

By substituting equation [V.3(42)] into equation (13) we have

$$\Phi_\nu^D(r,\theta,z) = \Phi^*\,(c_\nu^*/r)^{1/2}\,(A_\nu)_{c_\nu=c_\nu^*}\,, \tag{17}$$

where A_ν is determined by equation V.3(43).

To write this expression in the form of equation (3), we have to choose ray coordinates α and β, which specify the diffracted ray. The diffracted ray can be determined uniquely by its unit vector at an individual point S of the edge. Therefore we can take

$$\alpha = \theta(S)\,,\quad \beta = q_\nu(S)\,, \tag{18}$$

where θ is a cylindric coordinate (4) and q_v the acute angle between the ray unit vector and the tangent to the edge. Then a pair of expressions $\alpha = \text{const}$, $\beta = \text{const}$ determines the tangent to the ray as the line of intersection of the coordinate plane $\theta(S) = \text{const}$ with the diffraction cone $q_v(S) = \text{const}$.

Equation (18) of Appendix E describes the Jacobian of transformation from the Cartesian coordinates to the ray coordinates (τ_v, θ, q_v). In the specific case of diffraction of the plane wave $(r_D \to \infty)$, the mentioned formula turns into

$$J_v = c_v \, \ell \, \sin^2 q_v, \quad \ell = r/\sin q_v, \tag{19}$$

where ℓ is the distance from the edge along the diffracted ray. This expression corresponds to the approximation of the Jacobian of transformation from the Cartesian coordinates to the ray coordinates (τ_v, α, β) in a small vicinity of an individual point of the edge, where the previously used local approximations hold true.

By taking into consideration equations (19) and (10), we can rewrite the second cofactor in equation (17) in the form

$$(c_v^*/r)^{1/2} = (c_v^2/J_v)^{1/2}. \tag{20}$$

By substituting equation (20) into (17) we get

$$\Phi_v^D(r, \theta, z) = \Psi_v (c_v^2/J_v)^{1/2}, \tag{21}$$

$$\Psi_v = \Phi^* (A_v)_{c_v = c_v^*}, \tag{22}$$

where A_v is determined by equation V.3(43).

Equation (21) describes the amplitude of an edge-diffracted wave (2) - (3) in a small vicinity of the edge. Because cofactor Ψ_v does not depend on τ_v, formula (22) holds true for any distances from the edge. Thus, the edge wave in the system of wedge-shaped inhomogeneous regions with curvilinear interfaces is described for any distance from the edge by equations (2) - (3), where cofactor Ψ_v is determined by equation (22). Formula (22) fails in the neighborhoods of the shadow boundaries of the reflected/transmitted waves, where quantity A_v increases infinitely.

2. Merging formulas of boundary layer and deep shadow zone

1. Continuation along shadow boundaries—To get the description of the edge-diffracted wave, valid throughout the domain of its existence, we have to use an explicit description of the reflected/transmitted waves in the neighborhoods of their shadow boundaries. This can be done by the continuation of the reflected/transmitted waves from the neighborhood of the edge according to equation I.(13). Here we will derive the corresponding formulas.

In the small vicinity of an individual point of the edge the reflected/transmitted waves can be represented in a locally plane approximation (Section I.3). This type of description can be derived from equation 1(9) by using the approach of Section V.3.1. Then the sum of the reflected/transmitted waves in the neighborhood of the point of an edge can be written in the form

$$F_\nu^* = \Phi^* (F_\nu^0)_{c_\nu = c_\nu^*} \times \exp\,(i k_\nu z \cos q_\nu)\,, \tag{1}$$

where F_ν^0 is determined by equation V.3(2). Note that here instead of the coordinate θ angles $\gamma = \gamma_\nu^\pm$ (Figure 31), determined by equation II.2(3), are used.

By continuing equation (1) from the neighborhood of point S' on the edge to an arbitrary point M according to equation I.(13), we get the sum of reflected/transmitted waves

$$F_\nu^*(M) = \sum_{p=0}^{p^*} \sum_{m(p)} F_{m(p)}^0(\gamma) \quad \text{with } \gamma = \gamma_\nu^+ \text{ and } \gamma = \gamma_\nu^-, \tag{2}$$

where $m(p)$ is the index of the reflection/transmission graph. Here it is necessary to take $\gamma = \gamma_\nu^+$, if the $m(p)^{-th}$ wave is formed at the interface $\theta = \theta_\nu^+$, and $\gamma = \gamma_\nu^-$, if it is formed at the interface $\theta = \theta_\nu^-$.

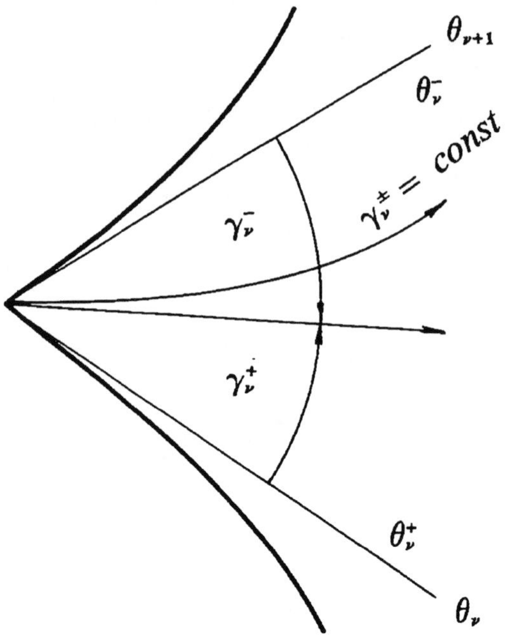

Figure 31. Angles $\gamma_\nu^\pm$ in equation VII.2(1).

Let $\gamma = \gamma_{m(p)}$ be an angular coordinate of the $m\,(p)^{th}$ shadow boundary. Every wave has two shadow boundaries

$$\gamma_{m(p)} = \alpha^*_{m(p)} - \pi \quad \text{and} \quad \gamma_{m(p)} = \alpha^*_{m(p)} + \pi\,, \tag{3}$$

$$\alpha^*_{m(p)} = [\,\mathcal{Q}_{m(p)}(\alpha_{m(0)})\,]_{c_\nu = c^*_\nu}\,, \tag{4}$$

where $\alpha_{m(0)}$ and $\mathcal{Q}_{m(p)}$ are determined by equations V.3(7) and IV.2(4), respectively. Only one of these shadow boundaries can belong to domain $\theta_\nu \le \theta \le \theta_{\nu+1}$ under consideration. The other is imaginary (see Section V.3.5). In the neighborhood of shadow boundaries (3) an individual reflected/transmitted wave has the following description:

$$F^0_{m(p)}(\gamma) = \begin{cases} F^0_{m(p)}(\xi^*) & \text{when } \xi^* < 2\pi\,, \quad (5') \\ 0 & \text{when } \xi^* < 0 \text{ or } \xi^* > 2\pi\,, \quad (5'') \end{cases}$$

$$\xi^* = \gamma + \pi - \alpha^*_{m(p)}\,. \tag{6}$$

In the illuminated zone [equation (5')] the reflected/transmitted wave is written as

$$F^0_{m(p)}(\gamma) = \Phi^0_{m(p)} \exp [i\omega \tau_{m(p)}(\gamma)], \quad (\nabla \tau_{m(p)})^2 = 1/c^2_\nu, \tag{7}$$

where $\Phi^0_{m(p)}$ is the amplitude and $\tau_{m(p)}(\gamma)$ the eikonal. The amplitude is given by the expressions

$$\Phi^0_{m(p)} = C_{m(p)}/L_{m(p)}, \quad C_{m(p)} = \Phi^* [H_{m(p)}(\alpha^*_{m(p)})]_{c_\nu = c^*_\nu}, \tag{8}$$

$$L_{m(p)} = [c^2_\nu(S')J_{m(p)}(M)/c^2_\nu(M) J_{m(p)}(S')]^{1/2}, \tag{9}$$

where $H_{m(p)}$ is determined by equation IV.1(18). The cofactor $L_{m(p)}$ accounts for the geometric spreading of the reflected/transmitted ray tubes [see equation I.(13)] in the process of their continuation from the point S' on the interface to an arbitrary point M. Symbol $J_{m(p)}$ denotes the Jacobian of transformation from the Cartesian coordinates to the ray coordinates of the reflected/transmitted wave.

2. *Boundary layer*—By analogy with equation V.3(10), we look for the edge-diffracted wave at an arbitrary point M in the form

$$F^D_\nu = \sum_{p=0}^{n} \sum_{m(p)} [F^D_{m(p)}(\gamma - \pi) - F^D_{m(p)}(\gamma + \pi)] \quad \text{with } \gamma = \gamma^+_\nu \text{ and } \gamma = \gamma^-_\nu, \tag{10}$$

$$F^D_{m(p)}(\gamma) = \Phi^D_{m(p)}(\gamma) \exp [i\omega \tau_\nu(\gamma)], \tag{11}$$

where each term must comply with the following condition at the shadow boundary equation (3) of the reflected/transmitted wave [equation (5)]

$$[F^0_{m(p)}(\gamma) + F^D_{m(p)}(\gamma - \pi)]_{\gamma = \alpha^*_{m(p)} + \pi - 0} = [F^D_{m(p)}(\gamma - \pi)]_{\gamma = \alpha^*_{m(p)} + \pi + 0},$$

$$[F^0_{m(p)}(\gamma) - F^D_{m(p)}(\gamma + \pi)]_{\gamma = \alpha^*_{m(p)} - \pi + 0} = -[F^D_{m(p)}(\gamma + \pi)]_{\gamma = \alpha^*_{m(p)} - \pi - 0}. \tag{12}$$

In the other words, the term $F^D_{m(p)}(\gamma - \pi)$ must smooth the discontinuity of the wavefield [equation (5)] at $\xi^* = 2\pi$ and the term $F^D_{m(p)}(\gamma + \pi)$ at $\xi^* = 0$.

The simplest description of the amplitude of an individual wave (11) in the boundary layer, forming the neighborhood of an individual reflected/transmitted wave shadow boundary, is given by equation VI.2(28). In the notation of this section the mentioned formula looks like

$$\Phi^{D}_{m(p)}(\gamma) = \pm\, \Phi^{0}_{m(p)}(\gamma)\, W(w), \tag{13}$$

$$w = \left\{ 2\omega\, [\, \tau_{v}(\gamma) - \tau_{m(p)}(\gamma)\,]/\pi \right\}^{1/2}, \tag{14}$$

where it is necessary to take minus in the illuminated zone (5') and plus in the shadow zone (5'').

The amplitude of wave (11) in the boundary layer also can be described by equation VI.3(40) by rewriting the formula in the notation of this section. However, we will use the formula VI.3(40) to get a more general description of the edge-diffracted wave.

3. *Uniform formula*—To get the description, valid throughout the domain of existence of the edge-diffracted wave, we will introduce an expression of the type of equation VI.3(40). To do so, we write all quantities from formula VI.3(40) in the notation of this section. The ray coordinates in the new notation look like

$$\tau = \tau_{v},\ \alpha = \gamma - \gamma_{m(p)},\ \beta = q_{v}. \tag{15}$$

Quantity VI.1(32) is written as

$$G_{D} = (\, c_{v}^{2}/J_{v}\,)^{1/2}, \tag{16}$$

where J_v is the Jacobian of transformation from the Cartesian coordinates to the ray coordinates (15). Function VI.3(27) looks like

$$A_{0}(\lambda) = A_{m(p)}(\lambda) = \Phi^{0}_{m(p)}(\lambda)/G_{D}(\lambda) \ \text{ with } \lambda = \tau_{v}, \tag{17}$$

$$\Phi^{0}_{m(p)}(\tau_{v}) = C_{m(p)}\,/L_{m(p)}(\tau_{v}), \tag{18}$$

where

$$L_{m(p)}(\tau_{v}) = L_{m(p)}(\tau_{v}, \gamma - \gamma_{m(p)}, q_{v}) \ \text{ with } \gamma = \gamma_{m(p)} \tag{19}$$

$$G_{D}(\tau_{v}) = G_{D}(\tau_{v}, \gamma - \gamma_{m(p)}, q_{v}) \ \text{ with } \gamma = \gamma_{m(p)}. \tag{20}$$

By substituting equations (15) - (17) into VI.3(40) we can describe the amplitude of wave (11) in the boundary layer. However, the description fails in the deep shadow zone. Next show how the description can be expanded into the deep shadow zone.

Let us look for the amplitude of the wave (11) in the form of an integral of type VI.3(40)

$$\Phi^D_{m(p)}(\gamma) = -s(2\pi)^{-1/2}\, G_D \int_0^{\tau_v} \psi\,[\rho(\tau_v) - \rho(\lambda)]\, A_{m(p)}(\lambda)\, \mu(\lambda)\, d\lambda, \tag{21}$$

$$\psi(\rho) = (i\omega\alpha^2/4)\,\rho^{-3/2} \exp(-i\omega\alpha^2/2\rho), \tag{22}$$

$$\rho(\tau_v) = -\int_{-\infty}^{\tau_v} \mu(\tau_v)\, d\tau_v, \tag{23}$$

$$\mu(\tau_v) = c_v^2(\tau_v, \gamma, q_v)/g_{\gamma\gamma}(\tau_v, \gamma, q_v), \tag{24}$$

$$A_{m(p)}(\tau_v) = \Phi^0_{m(p)}(\tau_v)\, G_D^{-1}(\tau_v), \tag{25}$$

$$G_D(\tau_v) = G_D(\tau_v, \gamma, q_v), \tag{26}$$

where $s = -1$ in the illuminated zone (5') and $s = +1$ in the shadow zone (5'').

Unlike in equation (18), we take quantity $\Phi^0_{m(p)}$ in the form

$$\Phi^0_{m(p)}(\tau_v) = \Phi^*\,[H_{m(p)}(\gamma)]_{c_v = c_v^*}\,/L_{m(p)}(\tau_v), \tag{27}$$

$$L_{m(p)}(\tau_v) = L_{m(p)}(\tau_v, \gamma, q_v). \tag{28}$$

We consider the expression:

$$F^*_{m(p)} = \Phi^0_{m(p)}(\tau_v)\exp(i\omega\tau_v), \tag{29}$$

where $\Phi^0_{m(p)}(\tau_v)$ is determined by equation (27), as a generalization of the virtual wave concept V.3(65) to the case of 3-D inhomogeneous media. The generalization consists in taking into account the factor of the geometric spreading $L_{m(p)}(\tau_v)$ in a 3-D ($c_v = c_v^*$) inhomogeneous medium. Because $L_{m(p)}(\tau_v) \to 1$ with $\tau_v \to 0$, expression (29) turns into equation V.3(65) in a small vicinity of the edge, when $c_v = c_v^*$. Here we use the virtual wave concept in the form of equation (29).

If we take the quantity α according to the corresponding expression from (15) and replace expressions (25) - (28) by expressions (17) - (20), we will get the above-mentioned description of the edge-diffracted wave amplitude VI.3(40) in the boundary layer. However, we now consider the quantity α to be unknown and the quantities (25) - (28) as the functions of an arbitrary point of space $(\tau_\nu, \gamma, q_\nu)$. The problem is to find such a function $\alpha = \alpha(\gamma)$, which guarantees the coincidence of expressions (10) and (21) with equation 1(21) in the deep shadow zone, and equation (21) with equation VI.3(40) in the boundary layer.

Let us look for an unknown function under condition of coincidence of equations (10) and (21) with equation 1(21) in the deep shadow zone, where the geometric theory of diffraction holds true. In this zone integral (21) can be approximated by asymptotic formulas [VI.3(60)] and [VI.4(49)], which in the notation of this section can be written

$$\Phi^D_{m(p)}(\gamma) \sim s\,\Psi_{m(p)}(\gamma)\,G_D(\gamma) \quad \text{with} \ |\,\omega\,\alpha^2/2\,\rho(\tau_\nu)\,| \to \infty, \tag{30}$$

$$\Psi_{m(p)}(\gamma) = (-2\,\pi\,i\,\omega\,\alpha^2)^{-1/2}\,[\Phi^0_{m(p)}(\gamma)]_{\tau_\nu=0}, \tag{31}$$

$$[\Phi^0_{m(p)}(\gamma)]_{\tau_\nu=0} = \Phi^*\,[H_{m(p)}(\gamma)]_{c_\nu=c_\nu^*}, \tag{32}$$

where equation (32) gives the amplitude value at the edge.

By equating equations (10) and (30) with equation [1(21)] we have the following relation in the deep shadow zone:

$$s\,\Psi_{m(p)}(\gamma) = \Phi^*\,(-2\,\pi\,i\,\omega)^{-1/2}\,[\Lambda_{m(p)}(\gamma)]_{c_\nu=c_\nu^*}, \tag{33}$$

where $\Lambda_{m(p)}$ is determined by equation V.3(45). Here it is necessary to take minus in domain (5') and plus in domain (5''). By substituting equations (31) and V.3(45) into equation (33) we have the relation:

$$s^{-1}\,(\alpha^2)^{1/2} = s^{-1}_{m(p)}(\gamma)\,[V^*_{m(p)}(\gamma)]_{c_\nu=c_\nu^*}, \tag{34}$$

where $V^*_{m(p)}$ and $s_{m(p)}$ are determined by equations V.3(13) and V.3(14)

From the definition of s and equations V3.(19) and V.3(34) we have

$$s = s_{m(p)}(\gamma). \tag{35}$$

Now to make equations (10) and (30) and equation 1(21) coincident, it is sufficient to take

$$\alpha = [\, V^{*}_{m(p)}\ (\gamma)\,]_{c_v = c_v^*} \; . \tag{36}$$

Equations (21) through (28), where s and α are determined by equations (35) and (36), guaranty the correct description of quantity (11) in the deep shadow zone. We will show that these expressions give the correct description of the mentioned quantity in the boundary layers, forming neighborhoods of the reflected/transmitted waves (5).

From equation V.2(34) we have an approximate relation

$$[\, V^{*}_{m(p)}\ (\gamma)\,]_{c_v = c_v^*} \approx \gamma - \alpha^{*}_{m(p)} \quad \text{when } \gamma \to \alpha^{*}_{m(p)} \, , \tag{37}$$

where $\alpha^{*}_{m(p)}$ is determined by equation (4). Then

$$[\, V^{*}_{m(p)}\ (\gamma \pm \pi)\,]_{c_v = c_v^*} \approx \gamma - \gamma_{m(p)} \quad \text{when } \gamma \to \gamma_{m(p)} \, , \tag{38}$$

where $\gamma_{m(p)}$ is the ray coordinate in the shadow boundary, determined by equation (3). One can see from equations (36) and (38) that under this approximation quantity α is described by the corresponding expression from equation (15), which holds true in the boundary layer. On the other hand, when $\gamma \to \gamma_{m(p)}$, functions (25) through (28) tend to their limiting values (17) through (20), i.e., to their approximations in the boundary layer. As a result, equation (21) turns into equation VI.3(40) describing the edge-diffracted wave amplitude in the boundary layer.

Thus, equations (21) through (28), where s and α are determined by equations (35) and (36), give the uniform description of quantity (11) throughout the whole domain of existence of the edge-diffracted wave.

4. *Case of homogeneous media*—If the wave velocity is constant c_v = const (see Section VI.4.1), the uniform formula (21) turns into

$$\Phi^{D}_{m(p)}(\gamma) = s_{m(p)}(\gamma)\ \Phi^{0}_{m(p)}\ \mathfrak{F}\ (z_D \, , \, z_1 \, , \, z_2) \, , \tag{39}$$

$$\Phi^{0}_{m(p)} = \Phi^{*}\ [\, H_{m(p)}(\gamma)\,]_{c_v = c_v^*} \times (L_1 L_2)^{-1/2} \, , \tag{40}$$

$$z_n = \left\{ \omega\, \tau_v\ [\, V^{*}_{m(p)}(\gamma)\,]^{2}_{c_v = c_v^*} \times \sin^2 q_v \right\} / 2\, L_n \, , \tag{41}$$

$$L_n = (c_v \tau_v + r_n)/r_n, \tag{42}$$

where r_1 and r_2 are the principal radii of curvature of the front of the $m\,(p)^{th}$ virtual reflected/transmitted wave at the edge ($\tau_v = 0$), r_D is the radius of curvature of the section of this wave front by the plane $\gamma =$ const at the edge. Function $\mathfrak{F}$ is determined by equation VI.4(16).

In specific cases, when function VI.4(16) satisfies relations VI.4(18), equation (39) can be written in its simplest form

$$\Phi^D_{m(p)}(\gamma) = s_{m(p)}(\gamma)\,\Phi^0_{m(p)}\,W(w), \tag{43}$$

$$w = S(\omega\tau_v/\pi L)^{1/2}\,[V^*_{m(p)}(\gamma)]_{c_v = c_v^*}, \tag{44}$$

where

$$\begin{array}{lll} S = \sin q_v,\ L = 1 & \text{in the case of relation VI.4(23)}, \\ S = \sin q_v,\ L = L_D & \text{in the case of relation VI.4(25)}, \\ S = \sin q_v,\ L = L_1 & \text{in the case of relation VI.4(27)}, \\ S = 1,\quad L = L_1 & \text{in the case of relation VI.4(29)}, \end{array} \tag{45}$$

Function $W(w)$ is determined by equation (D.1).

5. Case of 2-D inhomogeneous media—Let the characteristics of media and wavefields depend only on two space coordinates. We come to this case by dropping the dependence on the ray coordinate q_v.

Let us look for a uniform formula for the edge-diffracted wave amplitude in the form of equation (13)

$$\Phi^D_{m(p)}(\gamma) = s\,\Phi^0_{m(p)}(\gamma)\,W(w_{m(p)}), \tag{46}$$

$$\Phi^0_{m(p)}(\gamma) = \Phi^*\,H_{m(p)}(\gamma)/L_{m(p)},\ L_{m(p)} = L_{m(p)}(\tau_v, \gamma), \tag{47}$$

where $s = -1$ in the illuminated zone (5') and $s = +1$ in the shadow zone (5''). Here the quantity $w_{m(p)}$ is unknown. We can find this quantity from the condition of coincidence of equations (10) and (46) with equation 1(21) when $q_v = \pi/2$, in the deep shadow zone.

By analogy with the case of diffraction of the plane wave, we define the deep shadow zone by condition V.3(38), i.e., $w_{m(p)} \rightarrow \infty$. Then by replacing function $W(w_{m(p)})$ by its asymptotic formula (D.9) of Appendix D we can rewrite equation (46) in the form

$$\Phi^D_{m(p)}(\gamma) \sim s\,\Phi^0_{m(p)}(\gamma)(\pi\, w_{m(p)} \sqrt{2}\,)^{-1} \exp(i\pi/4). \tag{48}$$

By equating equations (10) and (48) with equation 1(21), when $q_v = \pi/2$, and taking into account relation (35) we get

$$w_{m(p)} = V^*_{m(p)}(\gamma)(\omega/\pi)^{1/2}\,[L_{m(p)}(\tau_v,\gamma)\; G_D(\tau_v,\gamma)]^{-1}, \tag{49}$$

$$G_D = (c_v^2 / J_v)^{1/2}, \; s = s_{m(p)}(\gamma), \tag{50}$$

where J_v is the Jacobian of transformation from the Cartesian coordinates (x_1, x_2) to the ray coordinates (τ_v, γ).

When the medium is homogeneous, equation (49) coincides with equation VI.4(30) under condition (37), i.e., in the boundary layer. In an inhomogeneous medium equation (49) can be reduced to equation VI.4(30) by expressing the Jacobians through radii of curvatures of wave fronts in the boundary layer (we drop the proof of this statement). Thus, equations (11), (46), (49), (50) give the uniform description of the edge-diffracted wave throughout the domain of its existence.

3. Reflections/transmissions

1. Plane waves—We begin the interpretation of obtained formulas with the generalization of the geometric theory of plane waves. It consists of the expansion of the theory on arbitrary, real and complex, values of the angles of incidence and reflection/transmission.

Let us begin with a 2-D case. Suppose, we are to find a wavefield, due to a given incident plane wave in a system of homogeneous wedge-shaped regions. The simplest attempt to find such a wavefield is to superpose all plane waves, arising as reflections/transmissions at interfaces. The corresponding computations include finding the directions of propagations according to Snell's law, the multiplication of amplitudes by the reflection/transmission coefficients and the summation of all waves existing at a point under consideration. A set of such waves, as in the case of parallel interfaces, can be put in the order by the reflection/transmission graph, showing all the possible directions of propagation or all the possible sequences of the reflections/transmissions.

If we restrict ourselves to the consideration of those waves, which really exist in the wedge-shaped regions, any succession of the reflections/transmissions is finite (unlike with the parallel interfaces, when every succession is unlimited). Indeed, after some finite number of reflections/transmissions, the Snell's law gives the direction, which does not intersect the interfaces. However, if one gives up the clarity of representation and uses Snell's law formally, any succession of reflections/transmissions can be made infinite.

2. *Generalization of plane waves theory*—When using Snell's law, we usually take the angle of incidence less or equal $\pi/2$. That is, this limitation is obvious from a physical viewpoint—the incident ray must impinge upon the interface, not to be radiated by the interface. That is, this limitation that cuts any reflection/transmission succession in the wedge-shaped regions—the angle of incidence turns bigger than $\pi/2$. However, if we lift the limitation on the angle of incidence α and admit that it can have any real and complex value $0 \leq |\alpha| < \infty$, $-\infty < \arg\alpha < \infty$, we get some angles of the "reflection/transmission" from Snell's law as well, provided we can determine the inverse trigonometric functions uniquely. Then, regarding the reflection/transmission coefficients as functions of the angle of incidence, given in the infinite complex domain, we can create an infinite set of plane waves in the form of infinite successions of reflections/transmissions. Such a set can also be put in the order by the reflection/transmission graph.

Let us proceed to the single-valued determination of the directions of propagation of plane waves. Instead of using angles of incidence and reflection/transmission, it is more convenient to use the angles between the positive direction of the ray and the direction from the edge of the corresponding interface illuminated by the ray to its infinite part. This angle has to be measured from the interface in the direction of that domain, where the ray under consideration is given (Figure 32 a, b). In such a reference system Snell's law can be written as

$$(\cos\,\alpha_m)/\,c_m = (\cos\,\alpha_n)/c_n, \tag{1}$$

where c_i are the wave velocities and α_i the previously mentioned angles. To find the directions of propagations, this expression must be solved relative to the corresponding angle

$$\alpha_m(\alpha_n) = \arccos\,[(c_m/c_n)\,\cos\,\alpha_n], \tag{2}$$

and the single-valued branch of the inverse trigonometric function must be fixed by the conditions:

$$\alpha_m(\alpha_n) = \alpha_n \text{ when } c_m = c_n;\ \alpha_m(\alpha_n \pm \pi) = \alpha_m(\alpha_n) \pm \pi;$$

$$\alpha_m(-\alpha_n) = -\alpha_m(\alpha_n). \tag{3}$$

The single-valued branch of the derivative of this function

$$\alpha'_m(\alpha_n) = d\alpha_m/d\alpha_n = (\sin \alpha_n)/[(c_n/c_m)^2 - \cos^2 \alpha_n]^{1/2} \tag{4}$$

must be fixed by the conditions:

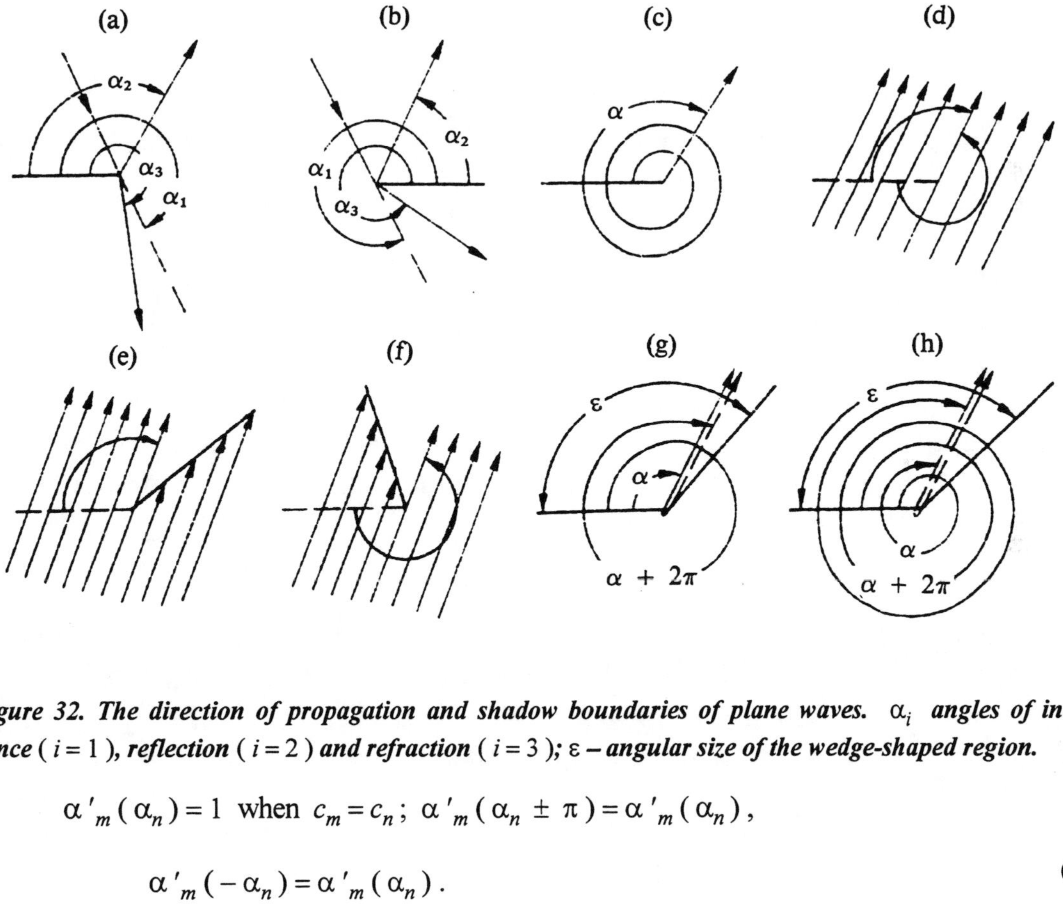

Figure 32. The direction of propagation and shadow boundaries of plane waves. α_i ***angles of incidence*** ($i = 1$), ***reflection*** ($i = 2$) ***and refraction*** ($i = 3$); ε ***– angular size of the wedge-shaped region.***

$$\alpha'_m(\alpha_n) = 1 \text{ when } c_m = c_n;\ \alpha'_m(\alpha_n \pm \pi) = \alpha'_m(\alpha_n),$$

$$\alpha'_m(-\alpha_n) = \alpha'_m(\alpha_n). \tag{5}$$

Now Snell's law determines uniquely any real (and complex) directions of rays relative to a correspondent semi-infinite interface. The corresponding angles can be, for example, more than 2 π (Figure 32 c). The arising plane waves are described by expressions similar to

$$f = A \exp(ikx \operatorname{ch} \delta - kz \operatorname{sh} \delta), \tag{6}$$

where x and z are the distances along the ray and perpendicular to the ray, respectively; k is the wave number; δ is the imaginary part of the angle between the ray and the direction of the interface, which has formed this ray. If $\delta = 0$, the plane wave is homogeneous. If not, the wave is inhomogeneous. The wave propagates with the velocity $c / \text{ch}\, \delta$, and its amplitude changes as $\exp(-kz\ \text{sh}\, \delta)$ in the direction perpendicular to the ray.

3. Domain of existence—When interfaces are semi-infinite, it is necessary to determine the domain of existence of the plane wave. In the usual Euclidean space this determination can be made by choosing the domain, filled with the rays of the corresponding wave, i.e., according to the rules of geometric acoustics. However, this is not sufficient when $-\infty < \text{Re}\, \alpha < \infty$.

Let (r, θ) be a polar coordinate system with its origin at the corner point $r = 0$. Let the angular coordinate vary in the infinite interval $-\infty < \theta < \infty$, which means that, in fact, we consider the infinitely folded Riemann space. Its "physical" sheet $(-\pi < \theta < \pi)$ corresponds to the usual Euclidean space. We suppose that a plane wave, propagating in the complex direction α, can be nonzero only in one of the two following domains:

$$\text{Re}\, \alpha \le \theta \le \text{Re}\, \alpha + 2\pi \quad \text{or} \quad \text{Re}\, \alpha - 2\pi \le \theta \le \text{Re}\, \alpha \tag{7}$$

The question of choosing between these inequalities is solved automatically in the process of formal transformations (2) - (3), if the domain of the given incident wave is inferred from the physical considerations.

4. Set $\mathfrak{M}$—Let $\mathfrak{M}$ denote the infinite branching set of reflected/transmitted plane waves (including a given incident wave), obtained by the above-mentioned formal operations. The reflection/transmission graph, describing the set $\mathfrak{M}$, is determined uniquely, if the domain of the given incident wave is chosen. The graph does not depend on the specific values of parameters characterizing the given incident wave, the angular dimensions of the wedge-shaped regions, medium properties, the boundary conditions, if these parameters do not tend to some limits, which can change the number of waves in the region or at an interface (for example, transition from elastic medium to acoustic, the elimination of a region by tending its angular dimension to zero, etc.). Thus, an attempt to find the wavefield in the system of wedge-shaped regions with the common corner point can be reduced to constructing the set $\mathfrak{M}$.

5. Shadow boundaries—Consideration of plane waves is not sufficient to get even a rough approximation of the wavefield in the wedge-shaped regions. The deficiency of such an approximation appears in the form of shadow boundaries. The field of any plane wave is nonzero only at the points through which the corresponding reflected/transmitted rays pass. This domain is separated from the domain where the corresponding wave does not exist by the shadow boundary, i.e., by the ray which propagates from the edge of the corresponding interface. The shadow zone can appear in the field of the incident wave as well.

Each plane wave has two shadow boundaries the directions of which differ by 2π. Note, from the geometric point of view the existence of two shadow boundaries can be explained by the freedom of choosing the reference system. The direction of propagation relative to some given direction can be measured clockwise or counterclockwise (Figure 32 d). Then by inserting an imaginary screen, the edge of which coincides with the origin of the polar coordinate system, in the wave-field and changing the orientation of the screen relative to the direction of propagation of the wave we can observe, in principle, each of two previously mentioned shadow boundaries separately (Figure 32 e, f).

Only one of the two mentioned shadow boundaries can belong to a wedge-shaped region, where the corresponding wave exists (Figure 32 g). The other shadow boundary is imaginary and can be traced by the formal mathematical continuation of the wave from the domain, where this wave exists (or observed experimentally), through the interfaces into the imaginary (Riemann's) space. It can happen that a wedge-shaped region is fully illuminated by some wave. Then both shadow boundaries are imaginary (Figure 32 h). It also can happen that the domain of existence of the wave, the direction of propagation which is determined by the previously mentioned formal operations, does not intersect at all with the corresponding wedge-shaped region, at the boundary of which the wave is formed. In this case both shadow boundaries are imaginary and any point of the region belongs to the shadow zone.

6. 3-D case—Let (x, y, z) be a system of Cartesian coordinates, plane $y = 0$ which coincides with the interface, and (r, θ, z) a system of cylindrical coordinates, plane $z = 0$ which coincides with the plane $x\,0\,y$. Then the plane wave can be written as

$$f_j = A_j \exp\left\{ i\,k_j\,[\,r \sin q_j \cos(\theta - \alpha_j^*) + z \cos q_j\,]\right\} \tag{8}$$

$$x = r \cos\theta, \quad y = r \sin\theta, \quad k_j = \omega / c_j,$$

where the direction of the wave vector is characterized by the value of the angular coordinate $\theta = \alpha_j^*$ and the angle q_j formed by the wave vector with axis z.

Snell's law can be written

$$(\cos q_m)/c_m = (\cos q_n)/c_n, \quad (\cos \alpha_m^*)/c_m^* = (\cos \alpha_n^*)/c_n^* \tag{9}$$

where $c_j^* = c_j / \sin q_j$ is the apparent wave velocity along that normal to axis z, which belongs to the plane $\theta = \alpha_j^*$ (Figure 33).

Representations (8) and (9) allow us to reduce the problem of finding the reflected/transmitted waves to a 2-D problem in plane $z = 0$. Suppose that axis z coincides with the edge and quantities q_0, α_o^*, c_0 are related to a given incident wave. Then for any multiple reflected/transmitted wave the first expression from equation (9) gives

$$q_j = \arccos [(c_j/c_0) \cos q_0]. \tag{10}$$

Hence, the problem of finding the set $\mathfrak{M}$ of plane waves in the 3-D case can be reduced to using the second relation of equation (9). The latter differs from equation (1) in the respect that it only deals with the apparent velocity c_j^* instead of the true velocity c_j. Therefore, by replacing in equations (1) through (5) quantities c_i by

$$c_i^* = c_i / \sin \left\{ \arccos [(c_i/c_0) \cos q_0] \right\} \tag{11}$$

we can find all angles α_i^* for all plane waves in set $\mathfrak{M}$, using the same technique as in the 2-D case. In the other words, replacing the true velocities with the apparent velocities, according to equation (11), we can find the traces of all wavefronts in the plane $z = 0$. But it is enough, because the trace of the wavefront in plane $z = 0$ and equation (10) determines the wave vector in the 3-D space.

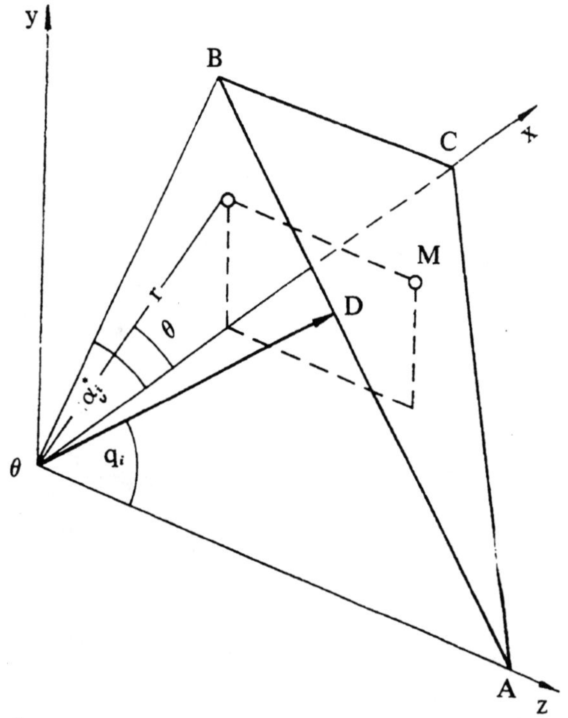

Figure 33. The plane front in a 3-D space. ABC – front; M – running point of the front; OD – normal to the front; BC – trace of the front on the plane $z = 0$.

7. General case—The generalization of the Snell's law to the arbitrary complex values of the angles of incidence and reflection/transmission allows us to expand the idea of infinitely branching sequence of reflections/transmissions to the case of inhomogeneous wedge-shaped regions with curvilinear interfaces. The set of such reflections/transmissions, in principle, can be found by the ray method, if the values of reflection/transmission angles are free of any limitations, and the branches of trigonometric functions in Snell's law [equation (2)] are fixed by conditions (3) and (5). Only the finite number of such waves would exist in the usual Euclidean space and could be observed experimentally. The other waves would be imaginary. However, it is necessary to take all of them into consideration to understand the mechanism of scattering by the edge.

The shadow boundaries can be found by methods of the plane wave theory. In a small vicinity of an isolated point M_0 on the edge it is possible to use the following local approximation. The media can be considered as locally homogeneous, the interfaces and the wave fronts plane, and the edge rectilinear. Hence, in the small vicinity of M_0 we can approximate the previously mentioned infinite set of reflections/transmissions by a corresponding set $\mathfrak{M}$ of plane waves. The continuation of directions of propagation of these waves from each point of the edge in accordance with the kinematic equations gives all real and imaginary shadow boundaries in the parametric form

$$q_i = q_i(M_0), \quad \theta = \alpha_i^*(M_0), \tag{12}$$

where $q_0(M_0)$ and $\alpha_0^*(M_0)$ are the parameters of the incident ray at M_0.

Note that the curvature of interfaces causes additional reflections/transmissions and new shadow boundaries. However, there is no reason to consider these phenomena (scattering by the curvilinear interface) here, because they have nothing to do with the edge.

4. Diffractions

1. Corrections for discontinuities—We begin a 2-D case. The existence of shadow boundaries shows that the set $\mathfrak{M}$ of plane waves is not sufficient to describe the wavefield in the wedge-shaped regions. Therefore, we look for corrections to the set $\mathfrak{M}$ that guarantee the continuity of the wavefield. To find these corrections, we use the following considerations. The corner point of a wedge-shaped region acts like a secondary source of oscillations generating the diffracted wave. The diffracted wave of angular frequency ω can be written

$$f_D = A_D \exp(ikr), \quad k = \omega/c, \quad i^2 = -1, \tag{1}$$

where c is the wave velocity and r is the distance from the corner point. The fronts of plane and diffracted waves touch at the shadow boundaries. Therefore, with each isolated shadow boundary we can connect an individual component of the diffracted wave (or an individual diffracted wave), which can provide the needed correction for discontinuity, i.e.,

$$A_D = \sum_n A_{Dn}, \tag{2}$$

where summation is carried out over indexes of real and imaginary shadow boundaries of that part of the set $\mathfrak{M}$ of plane waves which propagate with the velocity c (in the following we skip indexes of summation for brevity). Then each plane wave is associated with the pair of diffracted waves whose fronts touch the plane wave front at its shadow boundaries. This representation is very convenient, because the corrections for discontinuities at the set $\mathfrak{M}$ can be introduced at each shadow boundary independently. Formulas for such corrections follow from the analysis of wavefields in Section V.3.

2. Corrections to the incident wave—Let us consider diffracted waves, which are connected with shadow boundaries of the given incident wave. Depending on the mutual orientation of the direction of incidence and interfaces, the shadow boundary can be real or imaginary (Figure 34 a, b). If the incident wave illuminates both interfaces at once, both shadow boundaries are imaginary (Figure 34 c). But in any situation an individual diffracted wave is connected with each shadow boundary (real or imaginary).

Let (r, β) be polar coordinates with the origin at the corner point and $\beta = 0$ at the shadow boundary under consideration. Let the angle β vary in the interval $0 \le |\beta| \le 3\pi$. Therefore, the position of point (r, β) relative to the shadow boundary is given not in the ordinary Euclidean space but in the multifold Riemann space, the meaning of which is clear from Figure 34. Note, that the case $|\beta| > 2\pi$ can occur, when the corresponding shadow boundary is imaginary only.

The amplitude of the diffracted wave, connected with the shadow boundary $\beta = 0$ (real or imaginary), has the description:

$$A_D = \pm A\, W(w), \quad w = (2r/\lambda)^{1/2}\, |\beta|, \quad \lambda = 2\pi c/\omega, \tag{3}$$

where A is the amplitude and c is the velocity of the incident wave. Here it is necessary to take minus, if at the point (r, β) the incident wavefield is nonzero (the illuminated zone), and plus, if it is zero (the shadow zone). The cofactor $W(w)$ is determined by the expression:

$$W(w) = (1/2\sqrt{\pi})\, \Gamma(1/2, -i\pi w^2/2)\, \exp(-i\pi w^2/2), \tag{4}$$

where $\Gamma(1/2, z)$ is an incomplete gamma function. The amplitude of a diffracted wave, formed by the contributions from both shadow boundaries, is the sum of expressions (3) with the consideration of the mentioned sign rules. Note that the values of β in equation (3) differ by 2π at different shadow boundaries.

3. Corrections to the reflected/transmitted waves—Let us consider now the diffracted wave, connected with an isolated shadow boundary (real or imaginary) of a reflected/transmitted plane wave.

Let $(0 \le r < \infty,\ 0 \le \gamma \le \varepsilon)$ be polar coordinates with $\gamma = 0$ at the interface, where the wave under consideration is formed by the last reflection/transmission. Here ε is the angular size of the wedge-shaped region, where the wave under consideration is given. The angle γ is measured from the interface to the inner part of the region. Simultaneously with region (r, γ) we consider the region, where the incident wave is given. In this region we can identify the interface, the perturbation of which by the incident wave generates the wave under consideration as a result of successive reflec-

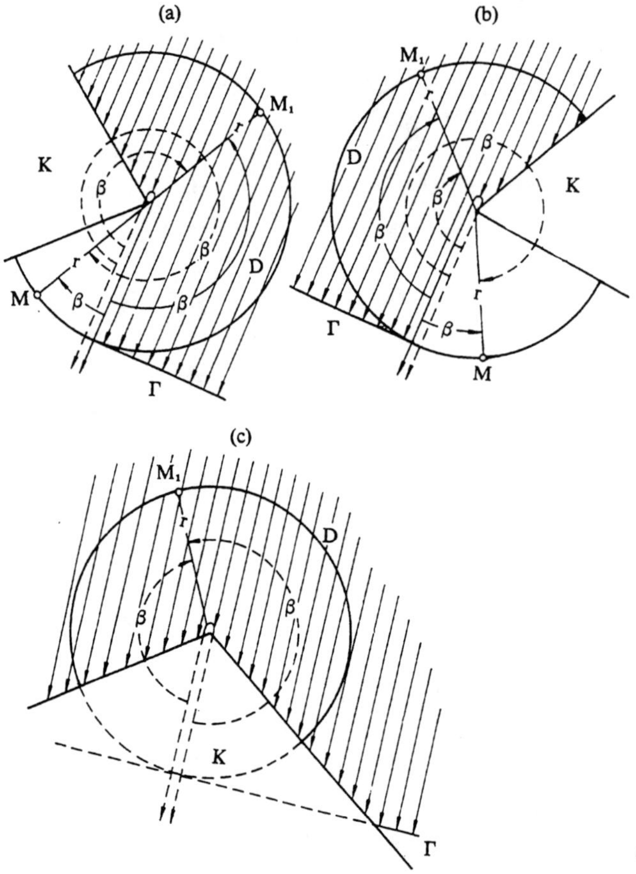

Figure 34. Shadow boundaries of the incident wave for different mutual orientation of the directions of propagation and interfaces. Γ – incident wave; D – diffracted wave; K – wedge; M and M_1 – current points of space. The domain of the incident wave is shaded.

tions/transmissions. We characterize the direction of propagation of the incident wave relative to the mentioned interface by the angle α, whose rule of measurement was given in Section 3.2 (Figure 32 a, b). This angle can take any complex values.

Let $\alpha = P$ be the direction of propagation of the incident wave relative to the mentioned interface. Let $\alpha = \psi$ be the direction of propagation of the incident wave with the shadow boundary of the reflected/transmitted wave under consideration passing through the point (r, γ). Then we connect the polar angle γ at the point of observation with some possible direction of propagation ψ of the incident wave (obviously, in general case $\psi \neq P$). The quantity $\psi(\gamma)$ can be always obtained by using Snell's law. The reflected/transmitted wave, propagating in the direction $\gamma(\psi)$, can be called the *virtual wave.* This wave exists in our imagination only and cannot be observed experimentally.

Let $A(\gamma)$ be the amplitude of the virtual wave. Then the amplitude of the diffracted wave, connected with the shadow boundary under consideration, can be written

$$A_D = \pm A(\gamma) W(w), \ w = E(2R)^{1/2}, \ R = r/\lambda, \ E = (\psi - P)/(d\psi/d\gamma), \tag{5}$$

where the minus sign has to be taken in the illuminated zone and the plus sign in the shadow zone. When computing the derivative, it is necessary to take into account conditions 3(5). The signs of real and imaginary parts of E have to be taken positive. The amplitude of a diffracted wave, formed by the contributions from both shadow boundaries of the wave under consideration, is the sum of expressions (5) with consideration of the mentioned rule of signs. Thus, finding the amplitude of the diffracted wave can be reduced to finding the virtual wave amplitude and the diffraction cofactor.

If media are inhomogeneous, the wave fronts and rays are curvilinear. The direction of any ray passing through the corner point can be determined by the direction of its unit vector at the corner point. Then directions of propagation of all waves under consideration can be determined by the corresponding quantities from the previous section: $\alpha = P$ for the incident wave, $\alpha = \psi$ for the virtual wave, and γ for the diffracted wave. The diffracted wave amplitude can be written again in the form (5), where

$$r = cI/c'L. \tag{6}$$

Here I is the spreading of the diffracted ray field (the cross section of the ray tube is $I d\gamma$), L is the geometrical spreading of the virtual wave ($L = 1$ at the corner point), and c' is the value of the wave velocity at the corner point. All quantities in equation (5) are functions of the position in space.

4. Characteristics of scattering—We can write equation (5) in the form which is invariant with respect to insignificant factors. The ratio $A^* = A_D/A(\gamma)$ can be called *the normalized amplitude of scattering* and written

$$A^* = \pm W(w). \tag{7}$$

This formula is more convenient, because it excludes from consideration the effect of factor $A(\gamma)$, reflecting the specific type of conditions at interfaces (the rigid contact of media, the viscous friction, etc.). This factor, which can be easily taken into account in the framework of the plane wave theory, has nothing to do with the understanding of scattering —the normalized amplitude of scattering does not depend on the type of boundary conditions and always has the form $W(w)$. The invariance of relation (7) with respect to all other factors appears as the fact that their total effect is taken into account only by the quantity w. This quantity can be called *the geometric characteristic of scattering,* because it depends on the quantities, reflecting the kinematics of wave process.

It is the function of two quantities, one R, which reflects the conditions of scattering along the distance, and the other E along the directions. This is clear if we consider function w in the spaces of polar coordinates (R, Re E) and (R, Im E). The polar curvilinear mesh of the space of observation (R, γ) can be transformed into these spaces in accordance with the expression for $E(\gamma)$ from equation (5). The real and imaginary parts of function w are determined by expressions

$$\mathrm{Re}\, w = \sqrt{2R}\ \ \mathrm{Re}\, E, \text{ and } \mathrm{Im}\, w = \sqrt{2R}\ \ \mathrm{Im}\, E, \tag{8}$$

and can be depicted by the level lines in planes (R, Re E) and (R, Im E), respectively. These lines, representing a family of spirals, are shown in Figure 35. Values of Re w or Im w are shown above the lines. There is also a mesh of polar coordinates, formed by circles R = const (values of $2\pi R$ are shown at the vertical ray) and by rays Re E = const or Im E = const (their values are shown at the rays).

5. *Radiation zone*—Let us consider a domain, where $|w| >> w_o$. Here w_0 is a "big" number ($w_0 \sim 2$), admitting the asymptotic representation of the function

$$W(w) \sim (1/aw)[1+O(w^{-1})],\ a = \pi\sqrt{2}\ \exp(-3\pi i/4).$$

Then

$$A^* = \pm\ 1/aw = \pm\ 1/aE\sqrt{2R},\ \ |w| >> w_o. \tag{9}$$

Equation (9) expresses the law of conservation of the energy flux into diffracted ray tubes. Here the scattering effect consists of the transport of the energy along ray tubes without the redistribution between the tubes. The quantity $R^{-1/2}$ has the role of the geometrical spreading and characterizes the decrease of the normalized amplitude of scattering along the distance. The quantity $1/E(\gamma)$ can be called *the scattering indicatrix* and characterizes the intensity of scattering along the directions. Domain $|w| >> w_0$, where this mechanism takes place, is called *the radiation zone.* In this zone the geometric characteristic of scattering w has the clear physical meaning—it is inversely proportional to the normalized amplitude of scattering with the coefficient of proportionality $\pm 1/a$.

The quantity E is proportional to the angle $\psi - P$ that has the role of "an aiming parameter"—to shoot a diffracted ray from the corner point $(0, \gamma)$ to the point of observation (R, γ), it is necessary to change the direction of the incident wave from given P to virtual ψ. The coefficient of proportionality $(d\psi/d\gamma)^{-1}$, depending on γ,

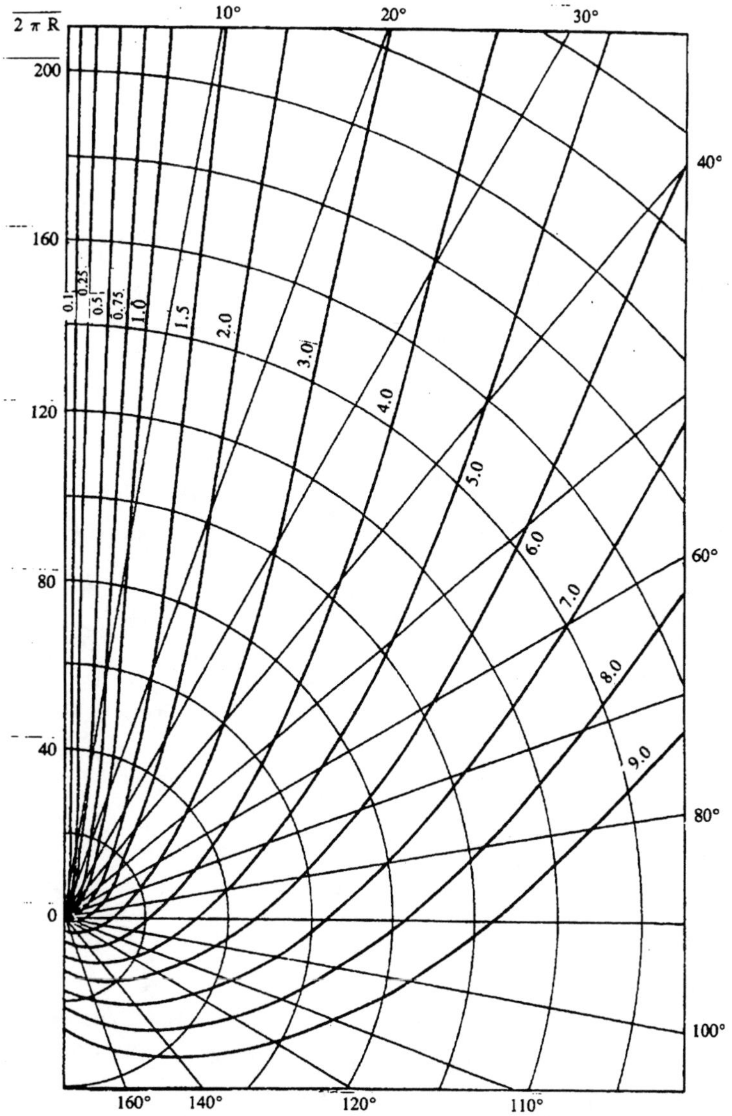

Figure 35. Lines w = const ***in spaces*** $(R, \operatorname{Re} E)$ ***and*** $(R, \operatorname{Im} E)$ ***in equation VII.4(8).***

characterizes the refracting properties of the set of interfaces participating in the formation of the virtual ray.

6. *Boundary layer*—Let us consider the domain $|w| <$ const near the shadow boundary $\gamma = \gamma_0$, where approximation (9) fails. If functions $A(\gamma)$ and $\psi(\gamma)$ are regular in the vicinity of point $\gamma = \gamma_0$, the following approximations hold true:

$$A(\gamma) \approx A(\gamma_0),\ E(\gamma) \approx \gamma - \gamma_0 \quad \text{with } \gamma \to \gamma_0 . \tag{10}$$

Then using equations D.(17) of Appendix D, we can write the sum of reflected/transmitted f and diffracted f_D waves in the form

$$f + f_D = fF(\mp v),\ F(v) = \int_{-\infty}^{v} \exp\,[\,i(x^2 - \pi/4)\,]\,dx/\sqrt{\pi}\ , \tag{11}$$

$$v = (\pi w^2/2)^{1/2},$$

where $F(v)$ is the Fresnel integral. This expression holds true in the domain of the mutual existence of both waves (then it is necessary to take plus in front of v) and in the shadow zone (then function $f(\gamma)$ must be continued analytically into this zone and minus must be taken in front of v).

One may regard equation (11) as a generalization of the Fresnel-Kirchoff's theory of diffraction to the 2-D case of reflecting/refracting interfaces in inhomogeneous media (the mentioned theory was formulated for ideal by reflecting boundaries between homogeneous media). The Fresnel integral $F(v)$ allows graphic representation by the Cornu spiral (Janke et al., 1960). There are tables of this integral as a function of parameter v (Abramowitz and Stegun, 1972; Janke et al., 1960).

Thus, when $\gamma \to \gamma_0$, the computation of the diffraction field [equation (11)] is reduced to the multiplication of the given wave f by the diffraction coefficient $F(v)$, properties of which are well-known. At the shadow boundary, i.e., with $v = 0$, this coefficient has the value $F(\pm 0) = 1/2$. When v increases, this coefficient changes rapidly and its modulus decreases. That is why the neighborhood of the shadow boundary is the domain of the rapid change of the diffracted wave. In the theory of diffraction, domains of such kind are called *boundary layers*. The mechanism of scattering there has a diffusion character.

7. Intermediate regions—Approximate expressions (9) and (10) fail in the *intermediate regions*, dividing the boundary layer from the radiation zone, and in domains of nonanalyticity of functions $A(\gamma)$ and $\psi(\gamma)$. Expressions (5) and (7) hold true everywhere (the boundary layer, intermediate regions, the radiation zone), except domains of nonanalyticity of functions $A(\gamma)$ and $\psi(\gamma)$.

Function $W(w)$ in the mentioned formulas is easily tabulated and has the clarity of representation. This function transforms conformally complex plane w into complex plane W. Figure 23 shows the transformation of the rectangular coordinate mesh of the first quadrant of plane w into plane W (this quadrant is the domain of w in formulas under consideration). Note, the line Im $w = 0$ of the mentioned figure can be transformed into the Cornu spiral by using representation $W \exp [-i\pi w^2/2]$ with Im $w = 0$. Figure 23 can be used for the direct calculation of $W(w)$ in the boundary layer and intermediate regions.

8. 3-D case (plane waves)—Here we take the case of diffraction of the plane wave on a 3-D system of wedge-shaped homogeneous regions with rectilinear interfaces. The position of an isolated shadow boundary is determined by the expression $\theta = \alpha_i^*$, where α_i^* is determined by equation 3(9). The front of the diffracted wave, smoothing the discontinuity at this shadow boundary, is the cone with the vertex semiangle $\pi/2 - q_i$, where q_i is determined by equation 3(10). Each point of the edge radiates the cone of diffracted rays with the same semivertex angle 3(10). The diffracted wave amplitude is again described by equation (3) with

$$w = (2r^*/\lambda)^{1/2} \,|\beta \sin q_0|, \tag{12'}$$

and by equation (5) with

$$w = (E \sin q_i)(2R^*)^{1/2}, \quad R^* = r^*/\lambda, \tag{12''}$$

where the distances r^* and R^* are taken along the diffracted ray. When computing E, all true velocities c_i must be replaced by the apparent ones 3(11). Angles β, γ, ψ and P are taken in plane $z = 0$.

9. 3-D case (homogeneous media)—Let the incident wave front, the interfaces, and the edge be curvilinear. Consider an arbitrary point M on the diffracted ray which is emitted from some point M_0 on the edge. The diffracted wave amplitude has the following description:

$$A_D(M, M_0) = \pm A(\gamma)\,\mathfrak{F}(z_D, z_1, z_2), \quad z_m = \pi w^2/2L_m, \tag{13}$$

$$\mathfrak{F}(z_D, z_1, z_2) = (1/2\sqrt{\pi}) \int_0^\infty [\,i(t-z_D)/(t-z_1)(t-z_2)]^{1/2} \exp(-it)\,dt, \tag{14}$$

$$L_m = (r_m + r^*)/r_m, \tag{15}$$

where $A(\gamma)$ is the amplitude of the virtual wave at M. The quantity w is determined by equations (12). Parameters γ, r^*, R^*, q_i, E were determined in previous formulas. However, now they are the functions of the point on the edge $\gamma = \gamma(M_0)$, $q_i = q_i(M_0)$, $E = E(M_0)$. When computing $E(M_0)$, the true velocities must be replaced by the apparent ones 3(11). Quantities $r_1 = r_1(M_0)$ and $r_2 = r_2(M_0)$ are the principal radii of curvature of the virtual wave front at M_0. Quantity $r_D = r_D(M_0)$ is the radius of curvature of the section of the diffracted wave front by plane γ = const at M_0.

The sum of reflected/transmitted f and diffracted f_D waves in a vicinity of the shadow boundary $\gamma = \gamma_0$ (the boundary layer) can be written in the form of equation (11) with

$$v = |(\gamma - \gamma_0)\sin q_i|(\pi r^*/\lambda L_0)^{1/2}, \; L_0 = (r_0 + r^*)/r_0, \tag{16}$$

where $r_0 = r_0(M_0)$ is the radius of curvature of the section of the virtual wave front at M_0 by the plane perpendicular to the shadow boundary.

Far away from the shadow boundary (the radiation zone) expression (13) has the form similar to equation (9)

$$A_D/A(\gamma) = \pm 1/(aE\sin q_i)(2R^* L_D)^{1/2}, \tag{17}$$

and describes the nomalized amplitude of scattering in terms of the geometric theory of diffraction.

In fact, the complicated integral description (14) is necessary in the intermediate regions only. If the planes of the principal sections of fronts of the reflected/transmitted f and diffracted f_D waves coincide ($r_1 = r_0$, $r_2 = r_D$ or $r_1 = r_D$, $r_2 = r_0$), expression (14) has the form

$$\mathfrak{F}(z_D, z_1, z_2) = W(w/\sqrt{L_0}), \tag{18}$$

where w is determined by equations (12).

The curvature of interfaces leads to the reflections/refractions of diffracted waves and forms the secondary shadow boundaries of diffracted waves (Figure 36). The phenomena of reflection/refraction of diffracted waves, in principle, can be described by the standard methods in the radiation zone. The scattering from the secondary shadow boundaries in the case under consideration is a difficult and, so far, unsolved problem.

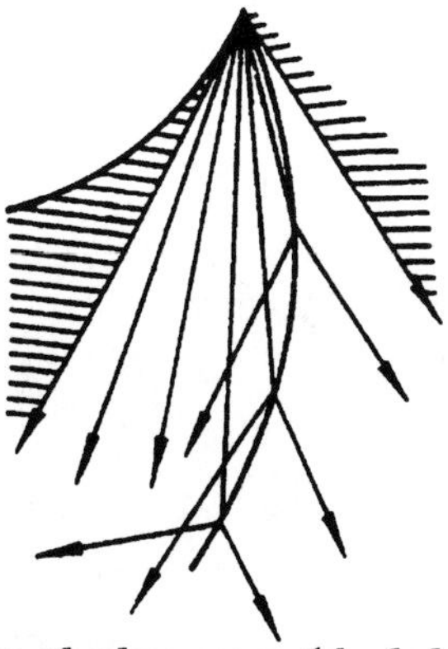

Figure 36. Formation of the secondary shadow zones (shaded regions) and reflection/transmission of edge-diffracted waves at the curvilinear interfaces.

5. Scattering on a wedge

We now study the main dynamic characteristics of diffracted waves and their dependence on the principal factors determining the scattering phenomenon for the simplest example of diffraction of a plane sound wave on a wedge-shaped interface. Let there be two wedge-shaped regions of two-dimensional space ($r \geq 0 \; -\pi \leq \theta \leq \pi$) filled with fluid media of different densities ρ_1 and ρ_2 and different wave velocities c_1 and c_2 (see Figure 37). In one of the media a plane incident pressure wave of unit amplitude propagates in the direction $\theta = \theta_0$. As a result of the interaction of this wave with the interfaces of the media $\theta = \pm \beta$, additional pressure oscillations occur in each of the media. At the interfaces of the media the fields of pressures and components of the particle velocity normal to the interface are continuous.

In the geometrical acoustic approximation the simplest wave picture occurs in the case when the plane waves with one reflection from the interfaces and one refraction through the interfaces occur. Examination of precisely this situation, but with the consideration of scattering phenomena, follows. We consider the medium where the reflected waves exist only. The wave fronts occurring in this medium are shown in Figure 37. The regularities of the change in the amplitude of the diffracted wave along its front r = const are examined everywhere hereafter.

Reflected waves with fronts $A_1 B_1$ and $A_2 B_2$ (see Figure 37) are components of the set $\mathfrak{M}$ of plane waves (see Section 3.4) for a pair of acoustic media with a wedge-shape interface. The amplitude of the diffracted wave $D_1 D D_2$ represents the superposition of contributions associated with each individual shadow boundary of the complete system of plane waves. However, it is expedient to begin a study of the dynamic characteristics of the diffracted wave with an examination of the contribution associated with an individual shadow boundary and then proceed to the consideration of the contributions from the other shadow boundaries (real and imaginary).

1. Scattering from an individual shadow boundary—We now examine a contribution of the reflected wave $A_1 B_1$ to the amplitude of the diffracted wave from shadow boundary $O B_1$, which is determined by equation [4(5)]. First we consider that the wave propagation velocities in both media are the same ($c_1 = c_2$) and only the densities differ ($\rho_1 \neq \rho_2$). In this case the reflection coefficient does not depend on the angle of incidence $A(\gamma) = (\rho_2 - \rho_1)/(\rho_2 + \rho_1)$, and the scattering indicatrix has the form $1/E = 1/(\theta - \theta_1)$, where θ_1 is an angular coordinate of the shadow boundary OB_1. In Figure 38 the lines with index 1 show in an arbitrary scale the distribution of the amplitude of the diffracted wave along the front when $\beta = 135°$, $\theta_0 = 180°$, $R = r/\lambda = 250/2\pi n$, $n = 1, 5$, and 20 for two different ρ_1/ρ_2 ratios. We note that the variations of parameters β and θ_0 lead only to a shift of the curves along the horizontal axis and the variations of parameter ρ_1/ρ_2 only change the vertical scale of the graph of the modulus of the amplitude. The variation of parameter R leads to a nonuniform compression or extension of the curves in the direction of the horizontal axis—with an increase in R the curves are compressed; the smaller the difference $|\theta - \theta_1|$ the greater the compression. The last property follows directly from the character of the curves $w(R, E)$ = const given in Figure 35, since in the investigated case $|E| = |\theta - \theta_1|$. By virtue of the noted properties of the graphs under condition $c_1 = c_2$, it is most convenient to study the general character of the change in amplitude along the front of the diffracted wave.

A characteristic feature of the indicated curves, which is inherent only to the case $c_1 = c_2$, is the property of the symmetry of the graphs of the modulus and argument relative to the angular coordinate of the shadow boundary. The change in modulus is symmetric relative to the point $\theta = \theta_1 = \pi/2$. The graph of the argument, shifted by $\pi/2$ along the vertical axis, is antisymmetric relative to this same point. The indicated properties show that the diffracted wave plays the role of a smoothing correction applied to the reflected wave. The discontinuity of its field and the signs of the discontinuity are such that the sum of the diffracted and reflected waves is a continuous function of θ in the neighborhood of the shadow boundary. In this case the properties of symmetry of the graphs, i.e., their dependence only on the difference $(\theta - \theta_1)$, express the fact that the discontinuity of the field of the reflected wave along the shadow boundary can be regarded as the sole cause of the scattering phenomenon.

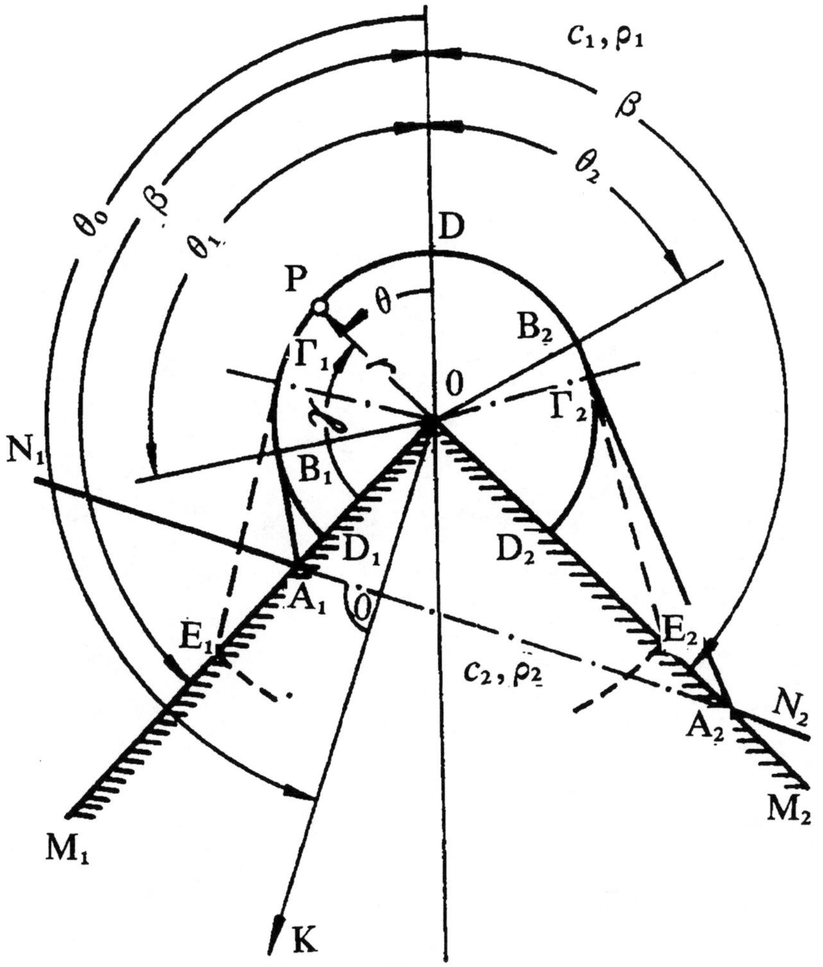

Figure 37. Wave fronts at the wedge. ***N_1A_1, A_2N_2 – incident wave; OK – direction of incidence; A_1B_1, A_2B_2 – reflected waves; D_1DD_2 – diffracted wave; $E_1\Gamma_1$, $E_2\Gamma_2$ – head diffracted waves for $c_2 > c_1$; M_1O, M_2O – interfaces.***

Another characteristic feature of the investigated curves is the rate of their change with distance from the shadow boundary. Two regions are clearly distinguished on both sides of the shadow boundary $\theta = \pi/2$. In one region, immediately adjacent to the shadow boundary $\theta = \theta_1$, the amplitude reaches a maximum value and rapidly changes with the increase of $|\theta - \theta_1|$. This is the *boundary layer*, where the Fresnel approximation 4(11) is valid. Far from the shadow boundary the amplitude of the diffracted wave is relatively small and changes slowly with the increase of $|\theta - \theta_1|$. This is the *radiation zone*, where the equation of the geometric ray theory 4(9) is valid. The interval of inflection of the curves separating the indicated zones corresponds to the *intermediate region*, where equations 4(9) and 4(11) are not suitable. A decrease of wavelength for a fixed r emphasizes the indicated characteristics of the graphs and the localization of the

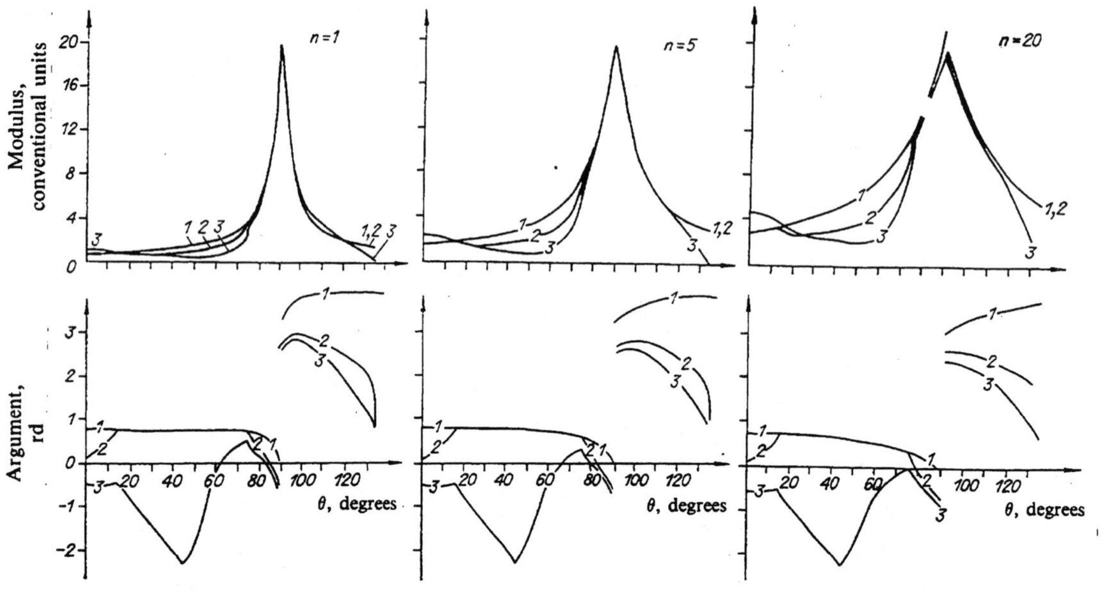

(a)

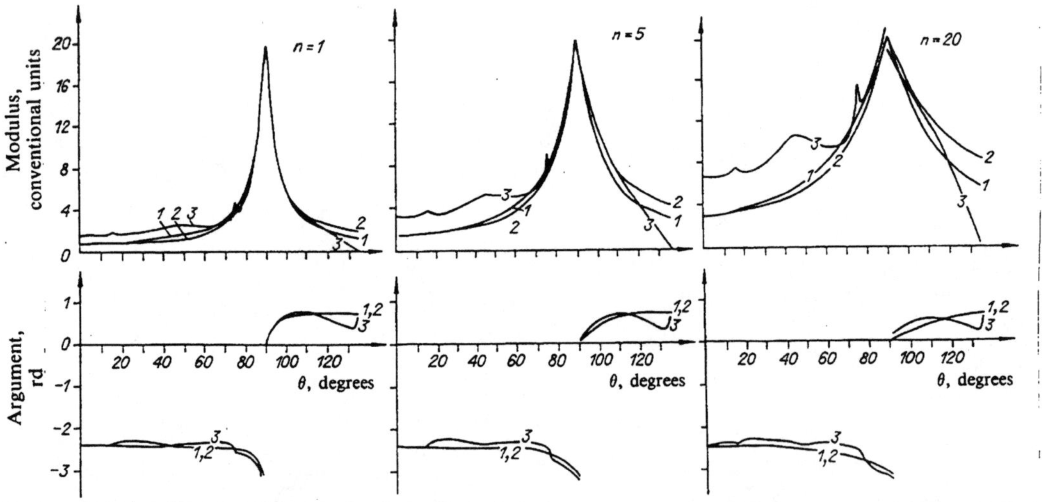

Figure 38. Distribution of the modulus and argument of the complex amplitude of the edge-diffracted wave along the front $\beta = 135°$, $\theta_0 = 180°$, $R = 250/2\pi n$. ***1– discontinuous component (contribution from shadow boundary*** OB_1***) when*** $c_1 = c_2$***; 2 – same, when*** $c_1 \neq c_2$***; 3 – same, with consideration of the background. (a)*** $c_1/c_2 = 1/2$, $p_1/p_2 = 1/2$; ***(b)*** $c_1/c_2 = 2/1$, $\rho_1/\rho_2 = 2/1$.

regions (at the limit when $\lambda = 0$ the boundary layer disappears and a sharp shadow boundary – a discontinuity – appears).

2. *Effect of reflection coefficient*—The particular example used gives a general idea about the character of change in the amplitude of the diffracted wave along the front. However, in a more general case the noted regularities are complicated by the effect of factors which for $c_1 = c_2$ are not manifested. One factor is the dependence of the reflection coefficient $A(\gamma)$ on angle γ. When $c_1 \neq c_2$ the reflection coefficient is determined by the expression

$$A(\gamma) = (a_2 - a_1)/(a_2 + a_1), \quad (1)$$

$$a_1 = \rho_1 c_1 / \sin\gamma, \quad a_2 = \rho_2 c_2 \, [1 - (c_2/c_1)^2 \cos^2\gamma]^{-1/2},$$

where $\gamma = 135° - \theta$. In Figure 38 the curves with index 2 depict the amplitude of the diffracted wave when $c_1/c_2 = 1/2, 2/1$ (the graph of the modulus is normalized so that the calculated value for $\theta = \theta_1$ coincides with the corresponding values for the case $c_1 = c_2$). The noncoincidence of these curves with those obtained earlier for $c_1 = c_2$ is because of the dependence of the reflection coefficient on angle γ. The effect of this factor is felt systematically in the radiation zone. In the boundary layer it gradually levels out and as $\theta \to \theta_1$ the Fresnel approximation 4(11) is again sufficient there. When $c_1/c_2 = 1/2$ the presence of anomalous deviations in the intermediate region is because of an abrupt change of function (1) in the neighborhood of the branch point $\gamma = \arccos(c_1/c_2)$ corresponding to the point of contact Γ_1 of the fronts of the diffracted $D_1 D D_2$ and head $E_1 \Gamma_1$ waves (see Figure 37). This point is singular for analytic function (1), and in its neighborhood the examined approximation 4(5) is insufficient (such situations occur in equations of the ray method in the neighborhood of critical rays).

Another factor complicating the character of the curves being considered is the ability of the reflecting/transmitting interfaces to deflect the rays occurring when $c_1 \neq c_2$. This factor is manifested in that $E \neq \theta - \theta_1$ when $c_1 \neq c_2$. However, in the example used of a single reflection of the wave of the same type this factor does not act, i.e., $E = \theta - \theta_1$.

3. *Discontinuous component and background*—The complete field of the diffracted wave which, for example, should be observed in an experimental study of the diffraction represents a superposition of the contributions from all shadow boundaries (real and imaginary) of the set $\mathfrak{M}$ of plane waves. The number of such boundaries is infinite. However, in the mathematical modeling of diffraction we can take into account contributions only from a finite number of shadow boundaries corresponding to the finite

sequence of reflections/transmissions of plane waves. The rate of convergence of the sum of the indicated contributions to the complete field can be studied numerically so far. Examples of such study will be shown in Subsection 9. Here in calculations of the complete field of the diffracted wave we confine ourselves to four successive reflections/transmissions in each branch of the reflection/transmission graph. For a given incident wave this corresponds to consideration of the contributions from 62 shadow boundaries, of which only two are real.

The result of calculating the amplitude of the diffracted wave with the indicated number of successive reflections/transmissions is given in Figure 38 (curves with index 3) for the same values of parameters for which the graphs marked by index 2 were calculated. The situation in the given example is characterized by the fact that only one shadow boundary OB_1 falls in the investigated interval of variation of the polar coordinate $0 \leq \theta \leq 135°$. The presence of a boundary layer associated with this shadow boundary also determined a general character of the graphs of the modulus and argument of the amplitude of the diffracted wave. For the contributions associated with the other shadow boundaries the investigated interval of variation of θ corresponds to the radiation zone. Therefore, it is convenient to regard the total contribution from all shadow boundaries except OB_1 as a *background* which accompanies the scattering effect related to boundary OB_1 – the *discontinuous component* (graphs 2). At this stage a detailed quantitative study of the characteristics of the background is hardly advisable, since its properties are determined by the effect of numerous components associated with the satisfaction of the boundary conditions during successive reflections/transmissions (we will point out some characteristics of the background later). Now, we obtain better physical conclusions by investigating the character of the deviations of the total amplitude (graphs 3) from its discontinuous component (graphs 2) caused by the presence of the background.

In the example used the presence of the background is felt least of all in the boundary layer. Here it is manifested in a relatively small shift of the graphs vertically and in the occurrence of a discontinuity of the graph of the modulus at the shadow boundary. These deviations are easily explained. In the boundary layer the background component is considerably smaller in modulus compared to the discontinuous component, which compensates the discontinuity of the reflected wave on the shadow boundary (curves 2). Consideration of the "small" correction leads to small deviations. Since the background is continuous with respect to θ on the shadow boundary, its consideration disturbs the symmetry of the distribution of the amplitude relative to the shadow boundary: the value of the discontinuity of the graphs of the modulus when $\theta = 90°$ corresponds to the modulus of the background at this point.

On passing from the boundary layer to the intermediate regions the effect of the background becomes more substantial. In the radiation zone the presence of the background completely changes the character of the total curves, they are not similar to the discontinuous components 2. Compensation of the discontinuity of the reflected wave along an individual shadow boundary is no longer the decisive factor here (this factor was the principal one on graphs 2) but the entire collection of conditions characterizing oscillation of the system of the wedge-shaped media as a whole. For example, the difference of graphs 2 and 3 when $\theta = 135°$ is related to the fact that consideration of the background component permits coordinating the conditions on reflecting boundary OM_1. Therefore, in the radiation zone it no longer makes sense to separate the field of the diffracted wave into a discontinuous component and background – here both components are equally substantial and their separation does not give any advantages in a physical analysis.

4. Effect of distance from the corner point—The investigated example enables us to obtain an idea about the character of the distribution of the amplitude of the diffracted wave along the front. However, the noted characteristics of the distribution can be manifested differently for different values of the parameters determining the process as a whole. The distance in wavelengths from the corner point $R = r/\lambda$ is the most substantial factor affecting localization of zones with different scattering mechanisms (boundary layer, radiation zone). The effect of this factor in Figure 38 is traced upon the variation of n. However, it is most simple to trace it when $c_1 = c_2$. Figure 39 shows the graph of the modulus and argument of the amplitude of the diffracted wave for various values of R (the values of the modulus are normalized so that their values coincide when $\theta = 90° + 0$). The values of the other parameters are the same as for graph 2 in Figure 38 for $\rho_1/\rho_2 = 1/2$ with the exception of the ratio c_1/c_2, which for simplifying the shape of the curves is assumed equal to unity. We see from these graphs that a decrease in parameter R leads to the extension of the boundary layer, which agrees with its definition $|w| < w_0$ in Section 4.6. For small values of R the intermediate regions expand, and localization of the boundary layer and radiation zone become less distinct. These tendencies are displayed especially strongly near the interface of the media ($90° < \theta \leq 135°$), where the low-frequency background has the same order with respect to the modulus as the discontinuous component (here the background contains a "nonray" component generated by the reflection of the discontinuous component from the interface). The background component for small R plays a substantial role not only in the radiation zone but also in the entire range of variation of θ, including the boundary layer. Conversely, for large R the boundary layer and radiation zone are localized most vividly and the effect of the background in the boundary layer is small.

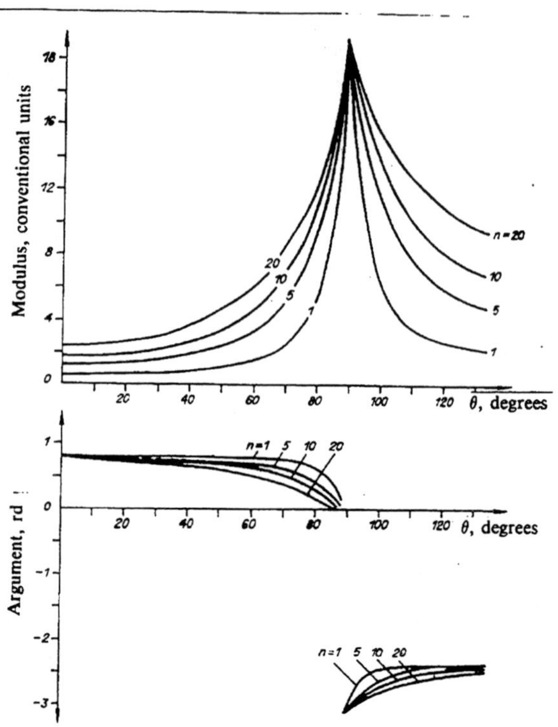

Figure 39. Distribution of the modulus and argument of the amplitude of edge-diffracted wave along the front when $\beta = 135°$, $\theta_0 = 180°$, $\rho_1/\rho_2 = 1/2$, $c_1 = c_2$, *for various* $R = 250/2\pi n$. *The values of* n *are given at the curves.*

A comparison of the results of calculations by the equation of the Fresnel approximation (curves 1) with a more accurate approximation of the scattering theory under consideration (curves 2) is given in Figure 40. The comparison shows that the effectiveness of the Fresnel approximation when describing the scattering in the boundary layers increases with the distance of the observation point from the corner point.

5. *Properties of media*—We will examine what effect the properties of the media have on the character of the distribution of the amplitude of the diffracted wave. The results of the calculations for the case $R = 250/2\pi$, $\beta = 135°$, $\theta_0 = 180°$ with various values of rations c_1/c_2 and ρ_1/ρ_2 are given in Figure 41. We see from this figure that the zones with different scattering mechanisms, as a rule, are distinguished rather clearly—the general character of the curves remains the same as in the graphs of Figure 38. However, in individual cases ($c_1/c_2 = 2/1$, $\rho_1/\rho_2 = 1/2$) substantial deviations from the described character of the curves can occur. This case is characterized by a small value of the coefficient of reflection of wave $A_1 B_1$. Therefore, the contribution of the discontinu-

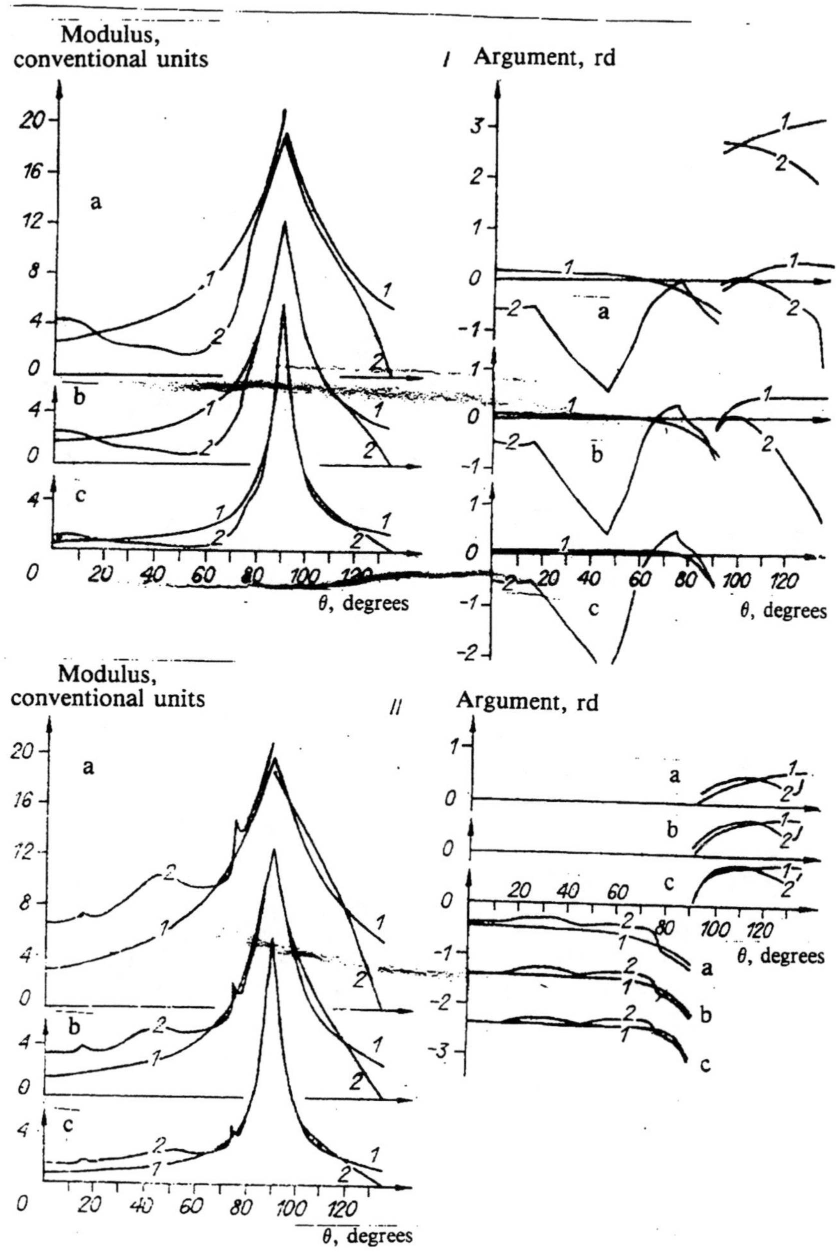

Figure 40. Comparison of the examined scattering theory (curves 2) with the Fresnel approximation (curves 1), (1) $\beta = 135°$, $\theta_0 = 180°$, $R = 250/2\pi n$. ***(I)*** $c_1/c_2 = 1/2$, ***II*** $\rho_1/\rho_2 = 1/2$; *II)* $c_1/c_2 = 2/1$, $\rho_1/\rho_2 = 2/1$; ***(a)*** $n = 20$; ***(b)*** $n = 5$; ***(c)*** $n = 1$.

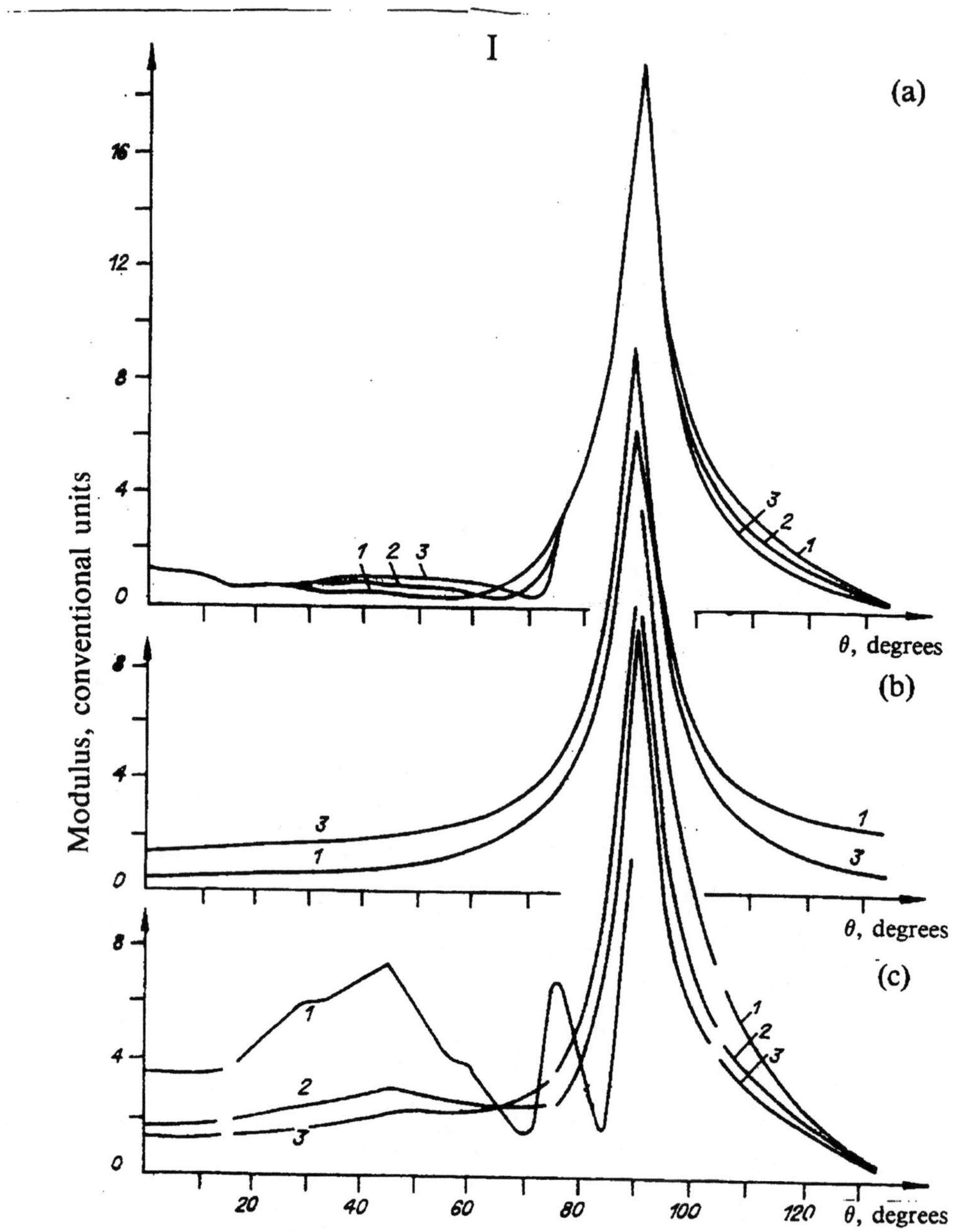

Figure 41. Distribution of the modulus (I) and argument (II) of the amplitude of the edge-diffracted wave along the front for $\beta = 135°, \theta_0 = 180°, R = 250/2\pi$ *for various parameters of the contracting media. (a)* $c_1/c_2 = 1/2$; *(b)* $c_1/c_2 = 1/1$; *(c)* $c_1/c_2 = 2/1$; *(1)* $\rho_1/\rho_2 = 1/2$; *(2)* $\rho_1/\rho_2 = 1/1$; *(3)* $\rho_1/\rho_2 = 2/1$.

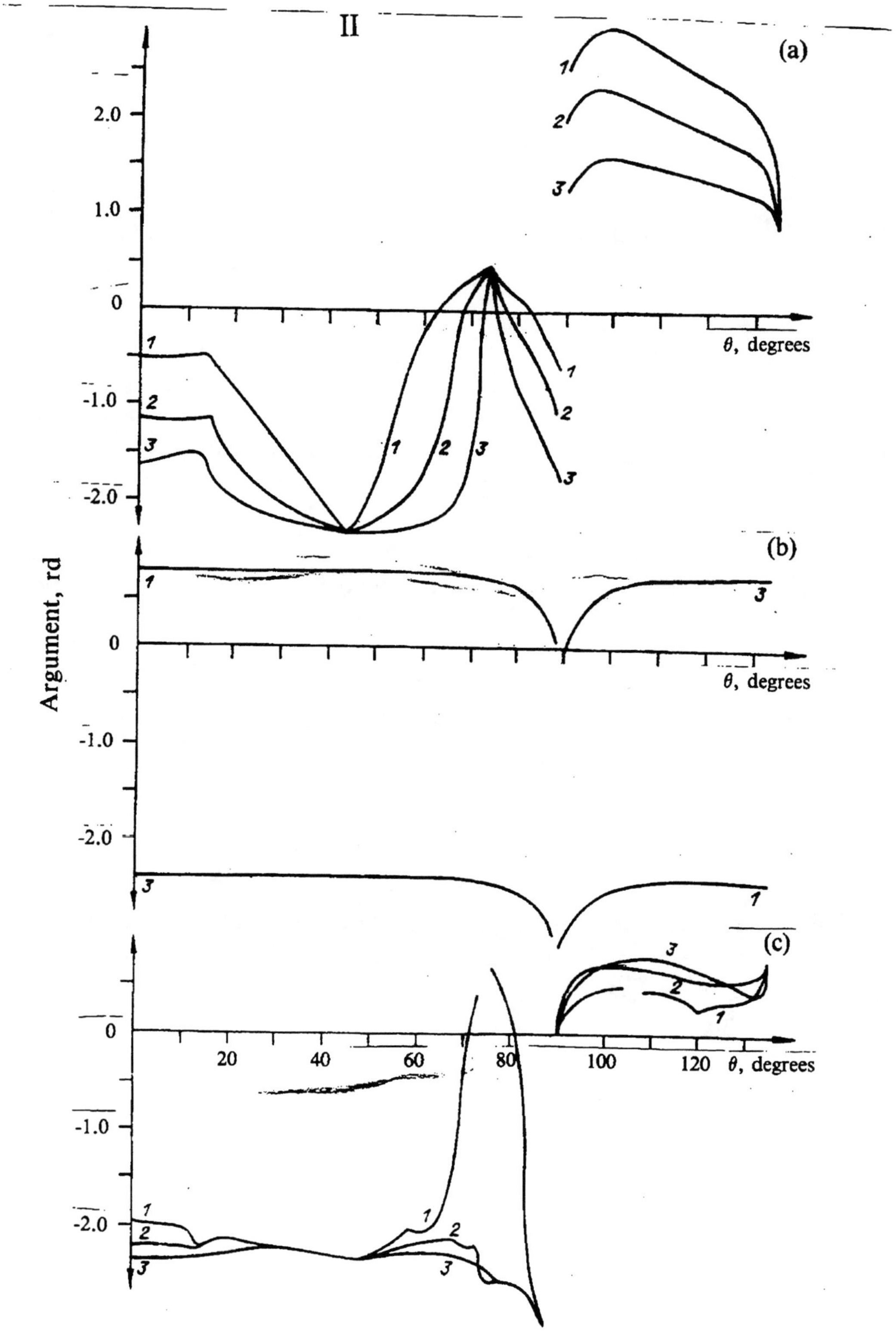
II
(a)
(b)
(c)
2.0
1.0
0
-1.0
-2.0
θ, degrees
Argument, rd
20
40
60
80
100
120
1
2
3

ous component is commensurate with the background, and the Fresnel approximation in the boundary layer is clearly insufficient. We see from the graphs presented that the properties of the contacting media have a substantial effect on the value of the amplitude of the diffracted wave in the radiation zone and intermediate regions, and also on its distribution along the front.

6. *Angle of wedge*—Figures 42 and 43 show the distribution of the amplitude of the diffracted wave along the front for various angles of the wedge β , respectively, for cases $c_1/c_2 = 1/2$ and $c_1/c_2 = 2/1$ when $\rho_1 = \rho_2$, $R = 250/2\pi$, $\theta_0 = 180°$. The general form of these distributions is similar to that described and is characterized by a well-defined localization of the zones with different wave mechanisms. The modulus of the amplitude is always maximum at the shadow boundary (point B_1 in Figure 37). When $\beta = 165°$, 150°, 135°, 120°, and 105° the position of this shadow boundary is characterized, respectively, by the following values of the angular coordinate $\theta = 150°$, 120°, 90°, 60°, and 30°. In the boundary layer (except curves 4 and 5 in Figure 42 and curve 1 in Figure 43) the amplitude of the diffracted wave is described with sufficient accuracy by the equations of the Fresnel approximation 4(11). The values and character of the distribution of the amplitude along the front in the radiation zone substantially depend on the value of β .

The local anomalies of the graphs of the modulus and argument are because of the points of nonanaliticity of functions $A(\gamma)$ and $E(\gamma)$, in the neighborhoods of which equation 4(5) is insufficient. One of such singular points when $c_1/c_2 = 1/2$ is a point of contact of the fronts of the diffracted and head waves (point Γ_1 in Figure 37). When $\beta = 165°$, 150°, 135°, 120°, 105°, the position of this point is characterized, respectively, by the following values of the angular coordinate $\theta = 105°$, 90°, 75°, 60°, 45° and easily can be distinguished in Figure 42 by the anomalies of the modulus and argument of the diffracted wave. When $\beta = 105°$ point Γ_1 is in the boundary layer. This causes the sharp deviation from the Fresnel character of scattering in the boundary layer (the right additional peak of curve 5 in Figure 42). When $\beta = 120°$ (curve 4 in Figure 42) points B_1 and Γ_1 coincide. Therefore, in this case expressions 4(5) and 4(11) are not sufficient though equation 4(5) is sufficient in the radiation zone.

7. *Angle of incidence*—Figure 44 shows the distribution of the amplitude of the diffracted wave along the front for various directions of propagation of the incident wave $\theta_0 = 180°$, 165°, 150° in cases $\beta = 135°$, $\rho_1 = \rho_2$, $R = 250/2\pi$, $c_1/c_2 = 1/2$, and $c_1/c_2 = 2/1$. Owing to the non-symmetry of the graphs the interval of variation of the angular coordinate is assumed $-\beta \le \theta \le \beta$. The graphs of the modulus are given in an arbitrary scale – all their values are divided by the value of the reflection coefficient at

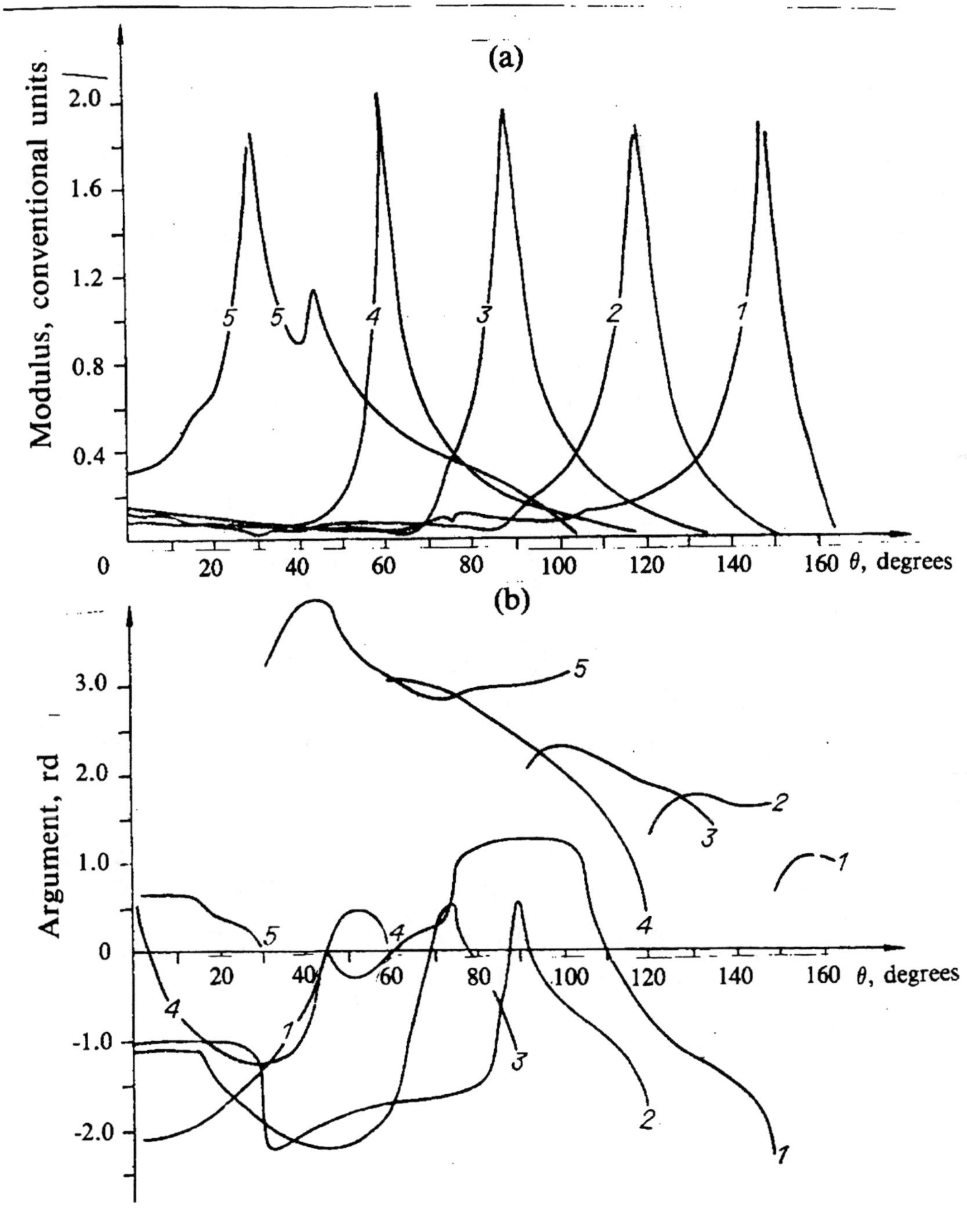

Figure 42. Distribution of the modulus (a) and argument (b) of the amplitude of the edge-diffracted wave along the front for $\theta_0 = 180°, \rho_1 = \rho_2, c_1/c_2 = 1/2, R = 250/2\pi$ *for various wedge angles. (1)* $\beta = 165°$; *(2)* $\beta = 150°$; *(3)* $\beta = 135°$; *(4)* $\beta = 120°$; *(5)* $\beta = 105°$.

point B_1. The general form of the distribution of the amplitude along the front, characterized by alternation of the boundary layers, intermediate regions, and radiation zones, is similar to that examined in the preceding examples. The right and left maxima of the graphs of the modulus correspond to the shadow boundaries of the pair of reflected waves (points B_1 and B_2 in Figure 37). The anomalies when $c_1/c_2 = 1/2$ and $\theta = \pm 75°$ are because of the singular point of function (1) corresponding to the points Γ_1 and Γ_2 in Figure 37. The anomalies when $c_1/c_2 = 1/2$ and $\theta = \pm 15°$ and when $c_1/c_2 = 2/1$ and $\theta = \pm 75°, \pm 15°$, are also because of points of nonanalyticity. We see from the graphs presented that variation of parameter θ_0 has relatively little effect on the character of distribution of the amplitude along the front in the radiation zone.

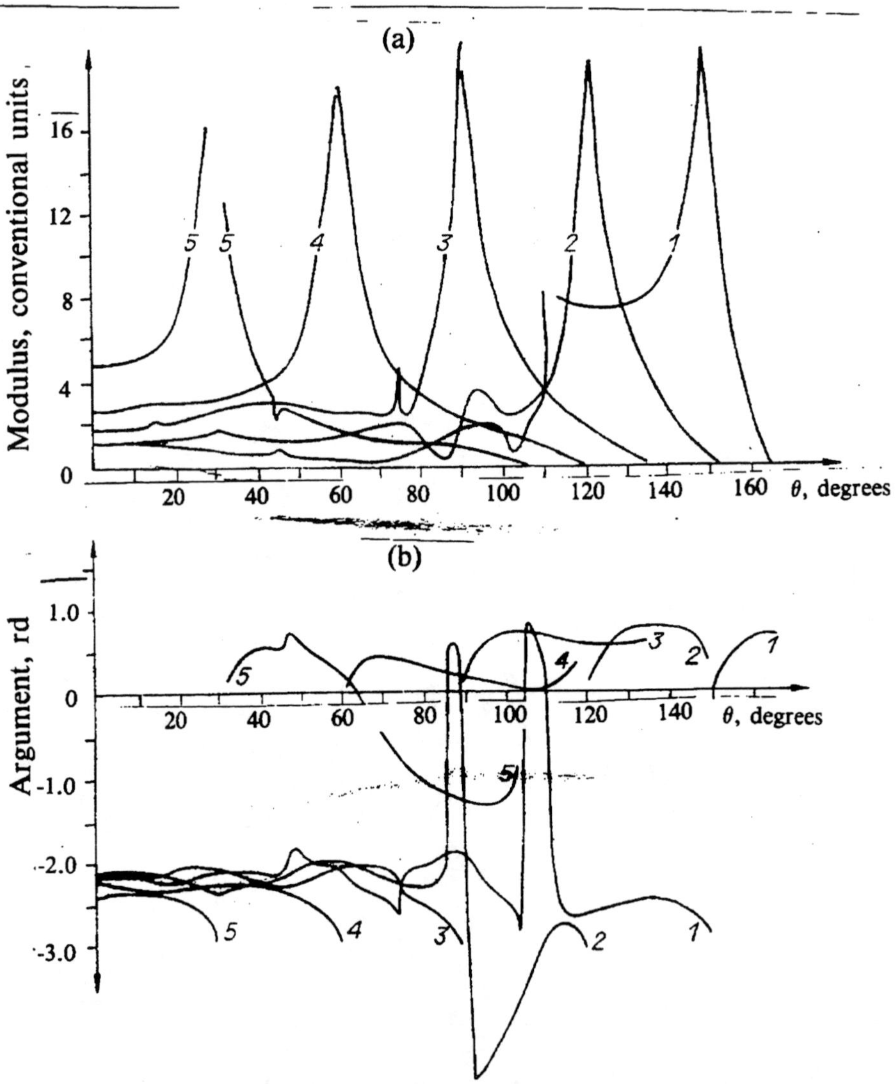

Figure 43. Distribution of the modulus (a) and argument (b) of the amplitude of the edge-diffracted wave along the front for $\theta_0 = 180°$, $\rho_1 = \rho_2$, $c_1/c_2 = 2/1$, $R = 250/2\pi$ *for various wedge angles. (1)* $\beta = 165°$; *(2)* $\beta = 150°$; *(3)* $\beta = 135°$; *(4)* $\beta = 120°$; *(5)* $\beta = 105°$.

8. Scattering of a cylindrical wave—Figure 45 shows the distribution of the modulus (a) and argument (b) of the amplitude of the diffracted wave along the front in the case of incidence on a wedge-shaped interface by a cylindrical wave whose origin is located at the axis of symmetry of the interface $M_1\ O\ M_2$ (see Figure 37). The graphs were calculated for the following values of the parameters $c_1 = c_2$, $\rho_1/\rho_2 = 1/2$, $R = 250/2\pi$, $\beta = 135°$for various ratios r/r_0, where r_0 is the distance from the source to the corner point of the boundary $M_1\ O\ M_2$. The graphs, when $r/r_0 = 0$, correspond to the curves with index 1 in Figure 41b. To eliminate the effect of the geometrical divergence of the incident wave the values of the modulus of the diffracted wave are multiplied by $\sqrt{r_0}$.

We see from Figure 45 that the effect of the curvature of the incident wave front is most substantial in the neighborhood of the shadow boundary of the reflected wave ($\theta = 90°$). With increase of the ratio r/r_0 this effect is manifested in the extension of the boundary layer and increase of the relative contribution of the background, the value of which is characterized by the magnitude of the jump of the graph of the modulus when $\theta = 90°$. In the radiation zone the curvature of the incident wave front when $r/r_0 \leq 20$ has practically no effect on the characteristics of the scattered radiation.

9. Effect of successive approximations—Here we consider some examples of a numerical study of the convergence of successive approximations carried out by Malyshkin (1990). They deal with the case of nonstationary oscillations caused by a plane incident wave propagating in the domain $|\theta| \gtrless \beta$ in the direction $\theta_0 = 180°$. The shape of the incident pulse in all examples is $f(t) = t \exp(-100\,t) \sin(209\,t)$ with $t > 0$, where t is time in seconds. When changing to the nonstationary case, the Hilbert transformation for narrow-band signals was used. The points of observation are taken along the line $r/\lambda = \text{const}$, where $\lambda = 2\pi c_v/209$ is the apparent wavelength in the domain of observation and c_v the wave velocity in the same domain.

An example of the seismogram of the nonstationary wavefield, refracted in domain $|\theta| > \beta = 175°$ in the case of $c_1/c_2 = 2$, $\rho_1/\rho_2 = 2$ with $c_2 = 1$ km/s, and $r/\lambda = 33.1$, is given in Figure 46. The wavefield is represented by a superposition of two wave sequences, symmetrical relative to the axis of the domain of observation, and the diffracted wave. Each of these wave sequences consists of the refracted wave and six reflected waves. The direction of the sixfold reflected ray almost coincides with the interface where it is formed. Therefore, the sixfold reflected wave is absent in the seismogram—all points of observation are in its shadow zone. The strong diffracted wave is visible at the end of the wave train.

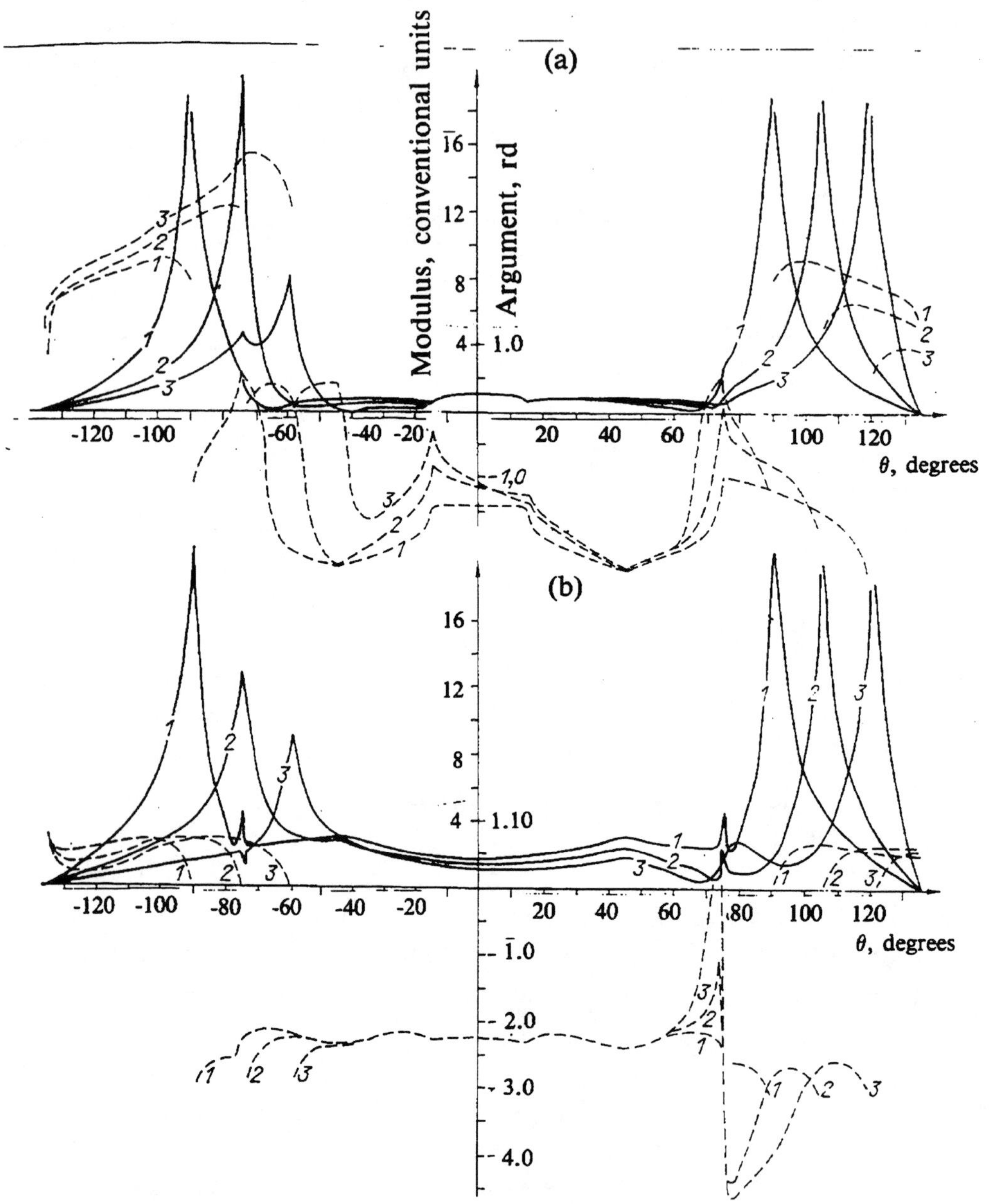

Figure 44. Distribution of the modulus (solid lines) and argument (dashed lines) of the amplitude of the edge-diffracted wave along the front for $\beta = 135°$ $\rho_1 = \rho_2$, $R = 250/2\pi$, $c_1/c_2 = 1/2$ ***(a) and*** $c_1/c_2 = 2/1$ ***(b) as a function of the direction of the incident wave. (1)*** $\theta_0 = 180°$; ***(2)*** $\theta_0 = 165°$; ***(3)*** $\theta_0 = 150°$.

Because the number of reflections/transmissions in the wedge-shaped regions is always finite, the problem of convergence of successive approximations arises only when calculating the diffracted wave. Figure 47 shows how the diffracted wave changes with the number of interactions increasing in different situations. Each individual curve corresponds to the trace of the diffracted wave at a fixed point of space. Each column of traces is calculated at the fixed point of observation for a different number of interactions (the number of interactions is shown against the corresponding trace).

Figures 47a, b correspond to the mentioned case (Figure 46) for points $\theta = 180°$ (a) and $\theta = 177°$ (b). Figure 47c corresponds to the case of the diffracted wave in the domain $|\theta| > \beta = 157°$ with $c_1/c_2 = 1/3$, $\rho_1/\rho_2 = 1/3$, $\theta = 180°$, $r/\lambda = 11.1$. Figures 2d - 2g correspond to the case of the diffracted wave in the domain $|\theta| < \beta = 157°$ with $c_1/c_2 = 1/3$, $\rho_1/\rho_2 = 1/3$, $r/\lambda = 33.1$, $\theta = 87°$ (d), $\theta = 57°$ (e), $\theta = 27°$ (f), $\theta = 0°$ (g). In Figure 47c the amplitudes are diminished five times at the first and second traces, and two times at the third trace. All examples show that the successive approximations converge, because after some interactions the results of calculation practically do not change. However, the character of the change of the diffracted wave with the number of interactions increasing is different in different examples.

Figures 47a and b demonstrate the character of the convergence in the case of many imaginary shadow boundaries with real directions of propagation. The effect of these shadow boundaries steadily increases in the process of multiple reflections (corresponding waves are visible in Figure 46). The contributions from some imaginary shadow boundaries (interactions numbers 5 and 6) are especially large because the profile of observation belongs to the correspondent boundary layers. The relatively large intensity of the diffracted wave is due to this fact.

Figure 47c corresponds to a specific case when the incident rays do not refract into the domain of observation – Snell's law gives the complex direction of reflection. So, this figure demonstrates the character of convergence in a case of many imaginary shadow boundaries with the complex directions of propagation. The process of convergence has an oscillating character and is approximately stabilized after nine interactions.

Figures 47d - 47g show how the character of convergence changes in the deep shadow when the point of observation moves in the direction from the boundary layer to the shadow (from situation "d" to situation "g"). One can see that the deeper the shadow is, the fewer interactions are necessary.

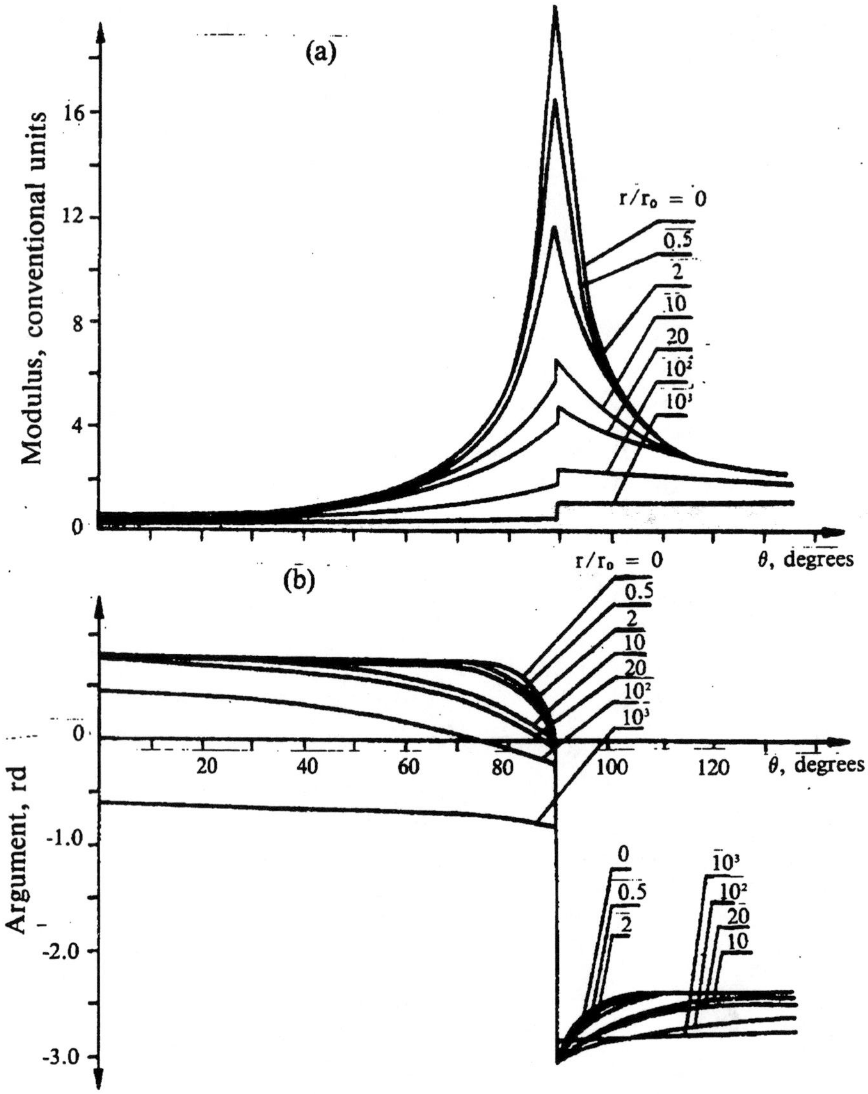

Figure 45. Effect of the ratio r/r_0 on the modulus (a) and argument (b) of the amplitude of the edge-diffracted wave. $c_1 = c_2$; $\rho_1/\rho_2 = 1/2$; $R = 250/2\pi$, $\beta = 135°$.

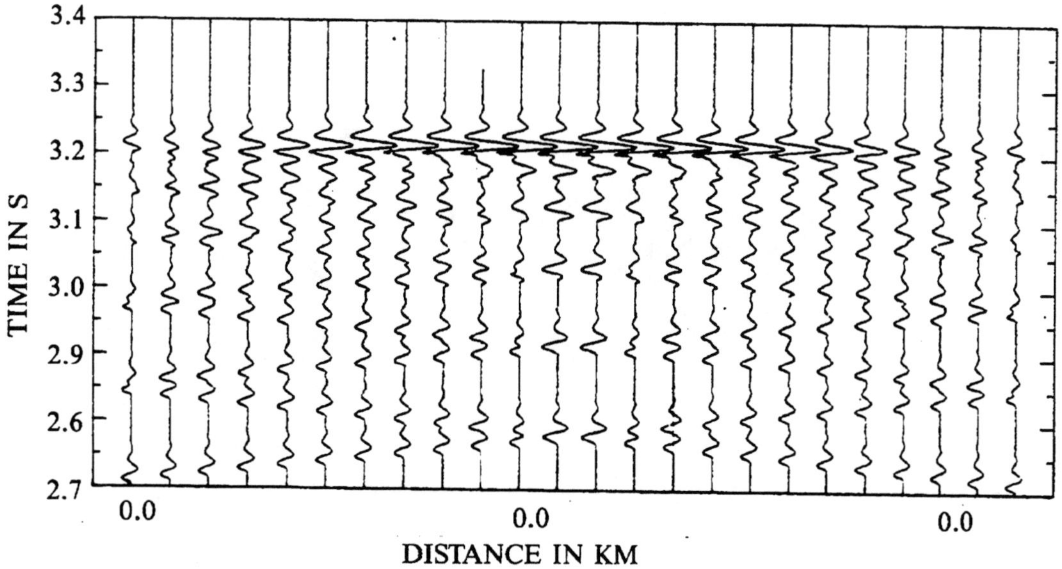

Figure 46. Theoretical seismogram of the total wavefield, refracted through the wedge-shaped interface into domain $|\theta| > 175°$; ***(Malyshkin, 1990).*** $\beta = 175°$; $\theta_0 = \theta\ 180°$; $c_1 / c_2 = 2$; $\rho_1 / \rho_2 = 2$; $r\lambda = 33.1$. λ ***-apparent wavelength***

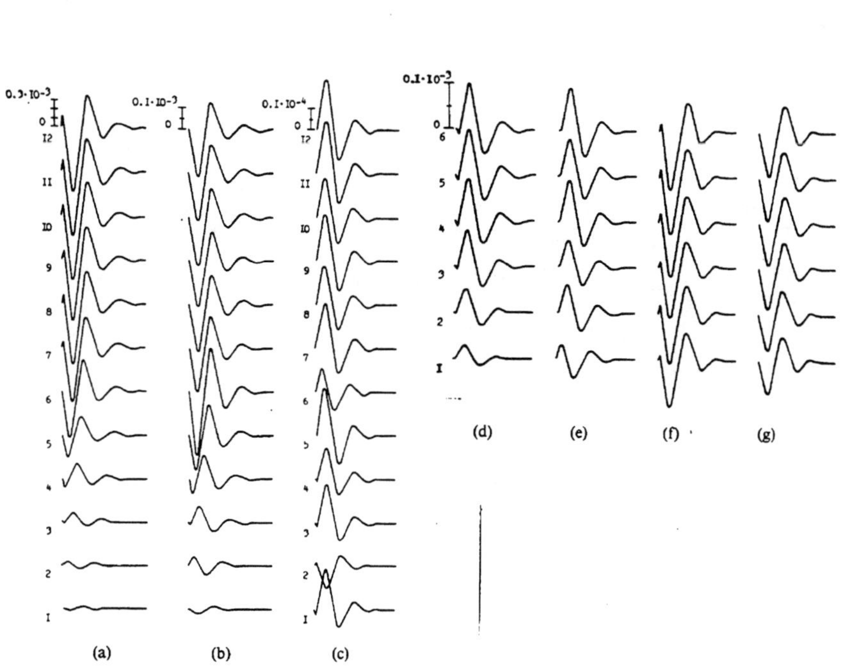

Figure 47. Theoretcial seismograms of the edge-diffracted wave demonstrating the convergence of the successive approximations for different situations (Malyshkin, 1990). The number of interactions is shown at the traces. Further explanation in text.

The character of convergence can be shown in the graphic form. Let $f(p)$ correspond to the value of the wave V.3.(9) obtained by p interactions for the fixed apparent frequency $\tilde{\omega} = 2\pi c_v/\lambda$. If the successive approximations converge, there is the number of interactions n providing the necessary accuracy of computations. Then quantity $f(n)$ corresponds to the desired value and the convergence can be characterized by the quantities

$$\delta_1(p) = |f(p)/f(n)|, \quad \delta_2(p) = arg\,[f(p)/f(n)]$$

Figure 48 shows the graphs of functions (2) for two situations. The solid lines correspond to seismograms in Figure 47a with $n = 12$, the dash lines to Figure 47d with $n = 6$.

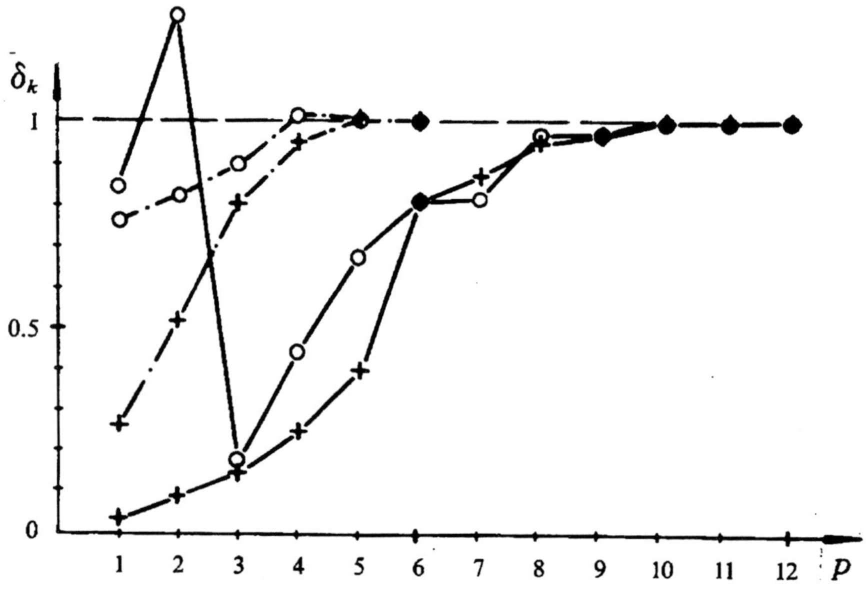

Figure 48. Graphs of convergence of the modulus (crosses) and argument (circles) of the edge-diffracted wave related to Figure 47a with $n = 12$ (solid lines) and Figure 47d with $n = 12$ (dash lines) (Malyshkin, 1990).

Chapter VIII

EDGE WAVES IN THE BOUNDARY LAYERS

The most intensive diffraction effects smoothing the discontinuities at shadow boundaries are localized in the boundary layers. Outside the boundary layers the scattering effect has a character of a less intensive diffraction background. The very possibility of dividing the edge-diffracted wave into the boundary layer approximation and the background prompts a simple approximate way to describe wavefields in inhomogeneous block media with diffracting edges. It is based on representation of the wavefield as the superposition of two parts. The first part is described by the ray method and has discontinuities at the shadow boundaries, which are caused by the edges of interfaces. The second part, which is the superposition of edge-diffracted waves taken in the boundary layer approximation, smoothes the discontinuities at the shadow boundaries of the reflected/transmitted waves. The existence of the diffraction background is neglected. The total wavefield complies with given conditions at interfaces in the ray-method approximation. Such an approach results in a modification of the ray method by considering the diffraction phenomena only in the boundary layers.

In Chapter VIII we consider the special problem of finding edge-diffracted waves in the boundary-layer approximation. It is essential that there is no necessity to deal with the equations of motion to state this problem. Therefore, the final result is equally fair for scalar and vector waves of any physical origin (optics, acoustics, elastodynamics, electrodynamics, etc.). First we consider the statement of this problem for a scalar case.

1. Smoothing a discontinuity

1. Definitions—Let the expression

$$f = \sum_{m} f_m \tag{1}$$

represent the superposition of reflected/transmitted waves at some point M in space in the approximation of the ray method. Here every single wave f_m exists within a pertinent domain of continuity, which can be called the *primary illuminated zone* of this wave. If the interfaces have edges there may be a domain in which wave f_m does not exist (defined as $f_m = 0$). Such a domain can be called the *primary shadow zone* of the wave being considered. The singly connected surface dividing these zones can be called the *primary shadow boundary*. Let mn be the symbol of an individual primary shadow boundary of wave f_m . Let Ω^+_{mn} be the symbol of the primary shadow zone, caused by the mn^{th} shadow boundary, and Ω^-_{mn} the symbol of the corresponding primary illuminated zone.

We will try to smooth the discontinuities of waves f_m at their shadow boundaries by the corresponding edge-diffracted waves. Let e_{mn} be the unit vector of the tangent to a diffracted ray emanating from that edge, which caused the mn^{th} shadow boundary. Then the differential equation

$$d\,(\,e_{mn}/\,c_m\,)\;/\,ds\;=\;\nabla\,(\,1\,/\,c_m\,) \tag{2}$$

determines the congruence of diffracted rays, emanated by that edge. Here c_m is the wave propagation velocity, and ds is the differential of the arc length of the ray. On this congruence we can introduce the wave

$$f_{mn}\;=\;\Phi_{mn}\;\exp\;(\,i\,\omega\,\tau_{mn}\,)\,,\quad \nabla\,\tau_{mn}\;=\;e_{mn}/\,c_m\,, \tag{3}$$

connected with the mn^{th} shadow boundary. The latter can be given implicitly by equation

$$\tau_{mn}\;=\;\tau_m\,. \tag{4}$$

Equation (3) determines the *edge-diffracted wave.*

By adding the corresponding edge-diffracted waves f_{mn} to each individual wave f_m we can introduce the superposition

$$f = \sum_m\,(f_m\,+\,\sum_n\,f_{mn})\,. \tag{5}$$

This wavefield must be continuous at every primary shadow boundary. We will state the problem of finding edge waves, equation (3), under this condition.

2. *Condition at a shadow boundary*—Let τ_{mn} , η , ζ be the ray coordinates of wave f_{mn}. Here η and ζ give the congruence of diffracted rays, i.e., every pair of fixed values η = const and ζ = const determines an individual ray. Let coordinate surface $\eta\,=\,0$ coincide with the mn^{th} shadow boundary, equation (4), and the primary shadow zone of wave f_m coincide with domain $\eta\,>\,0$. Let ζ be the angle between the edge and the diffracted ray. Then expression $\zeta\,=$ const gives a cone of diffracted rays.

Each item of sum (1) is considered a function of these coordinates

$$f_m = \Phi_m(\tau_{mn}, \eta, \zeta) \exp [i\omega \tau_m(\tau_{mn}, \eta, \zeta)]. \tag{6}$$

Then in the neighborhood of its shadow boundary this wave can be represented as the following discontinuous function:

$$\begin{aligned} f_m &= f_m(\tau_{mn}, \eta, \zeta) \quad &\text{when } \eta < 0, \\ f_m &= 0 \quad &\text{when } \eta > 0. \end{aligned} \tag{7}$$

Now the condition of the continuity of a wavefield [equation (5)] at the mn^{th} shadow boundary can be written as

$$[f_m(\tau_{mn}, \eta, \zeta) + f_{mn}(\tau_{mn}, \eta, \zeta)]_{\eta=-0} = [f_{mn}(\tau_{mn}, \eta, \zeta)]_{\eta=+0}. \tag{8}$$

3. Piecewise-analytic function given by its jump—To state the problem of finding the edge-diffracted wave under condition (8), we will recall one well-known mathematical problem (Muskhelishwily, 1968).

Let Γ be a smooth nonintersecting infinite curve in the complex plane of variable α. We choose the direction of curve Γ, as is shown by the arrow in Figure 49, and define the left (+) and the right (-) sides of this curve. Let $\varphi(\alpha)$ be some function given at Γ and let the function at Γ be Hölder continuous,

$$|\varphi(\alpha + \Delta\alpha) - \varphi(\alpha)| \le C|\Delta\alpha|^{\mu} \text{ with } \Delta\alpha \to 0, \ 0 < \mu < 1 \tag{9}$$

and decreasing at infinity

$$|\varphi(\alpha)| \to 0 \text{ when } \alpha \to \infty \ (\alpha \in \Gamma), \tag{10}$$

where C is an arbitrary positive constant. Let $F(\alpha)$ be an unknown piecewise-analytic function discontinuous at Γ. We denote $F^+(\alpha)$ and $F^-(\alpha)$ the boundary values of this function at the left and right sides of Γ, respectively.

The problem is to find function $F(\alpha)$ under the following conditions:

$$F^+(\alpha) - F^-(\alpha) = \varphi(\alpha) \text{ with } \alpha \in \Gamma, \text{ and} \tag{11}$$

$$|F(\alpha)| \to 0 \text{ when } \alpha \to \infty. \tag{12}$$

The only solution is

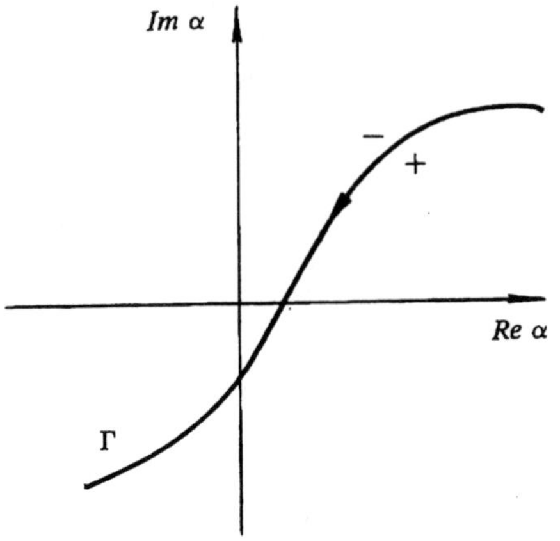

Figure 49. Contour of integration in equation VIII.1(13).

$$F(\eta) = (2\pi i)^{-1} \int_{\Gamma} (\alpha - \eta)^{-1} \varphi(\alpha)\, d\alpha \tag{13}$$

where η is a complex variable.

4. Formulation of the problem—We formulate the problem of finding a smoothing correction f_{mn} to discontinuous function (7) under condition (8) with $\omega \to \infty$. The preceding problem influences the statement of this problem. Here we consider the formal statement of the problem without substantiating the taken assumptions. The necessary substantiation is given in Section 2.7.

Suppose, that for values of τ_{mn} and ζ being considered, the function (7) allows a continuation into the complex plane of variable η along some contour Γ, satisfying conditions of Section 3 (Figure 49). Suppose, that at this contour this function is Hölder continuous [equation (9)] and disappears at infinity

$$|f_m(\tau_{mn}, \eta, \zeta)| \to 0 \text{ when } \eta \to \infty \ (\eta \in \Gamma). \tag{14}$$

We will look for function $f_{mn}(\tau_{mn}, \eta, \zeta)$ among piecewise-analytic functions of variable η under the following boundary condition:

$$f^{+}_{mn}(\tau_{mn}, \eta, \zeta) - f^{-}_{mn}(\tau_{mn}, \eta, \zeta) = f_m(\tau_{mn}, \eta, \zeta) \text{ with } \eta \in \Gamma, \tag{15}$$

where $f^{+}_{mn}(\tau_{mn}, \eta, \zeta)$ and $f^{-}_{mn}(\tau_{mn}, \eta, \zeta)$ correspond to the values of this function at the left-hand and right-hand sides of contour Γ, respectively. Condition (8) is a specific case of condition (15), when $\mathrm{Im}\,\eta = 0$ and intervals of the real axis $\mathrm{Re}\,\eta < 0$ and $\mathrm{Re}\,\eta > 0$ are at the right-hand and left-hand sides of the contour Γ, respectively. So, unlike with the initial condition (8), we introduce the boundary condition (15) at some contour Γ in the complex plane of η.

We put the following additional restrictions on the sought function in the complex plane of η:

$$|f_{mn}(\tau_{mn}, \eta, \zeta)| \to 0 \quad \text{when } \eta \to \infty . \tag{16}$$

It follows from Subsection 3 that conditions (15) and (16) are sufficient to solve the problem under consideration uniquely. The solution is given by expression (13)

$$f_{mn}(\tau_{mn}, \eta, \zeta) = (2\pi i)^{-1} \int_{\Gamma} (\alpha - \eta)^{-1} f_m(\tau_{mn}, \alpha, \zeta)\, d\alpha . \tag{17}$$

This is an integral of Cauchy's type, the properties of which are well-known (Muskhelishwily, 1968). It tends to zero when $\eta \to \infty$. It has a discontinuity when $\eta = 0$. However, the superposition of equations (7) and (17) is a continuous and analytic function of η in the neighborhood of surface $\eta = 0$. Note, if function (7) is a solution of some linear differential equation (for example, wave equation) in domain $\eta < 0$, then the mentioned superposition complies with the same equation for $\eta < 0$ as well as for $\eta > 0$.

Equation (17) determines a piecewise-analytic function of the complex variable η. We will consider this function for real values of η only. Therefore, in the following, the variable η is real. Function (17) of a real variable η complies with condition (8), i.e., it smooths the discontinuity of the reflected/transmitted wave at its shadow boundary. Because the reflected/transmitted wave corresponds to a high-frequency asymptotic solution of equations of motion, expression (17) has meaning when $\omega \to \infty$. The asymptotic value of integral (17) with $\omega \to \infty$ will be considered next.

2. The boundary layer approximation

1. High-frequency asymptotics—We correct discontinuities in the high-frequency wavefield 1(1). Hence, we have to take into account only a high-frequency approximation of integral 1(17) with $\omega \to \infty$. To do so, we rewrite this integral in a more convenient form. By substituting variable α with $\alpha + \eta$, and taking into account equation 1(6), we derive

$$f_{mn} = (2\pi i)^{-1} \int_L \Phi_m(\tau_{mn}, \alpha+\eta, \zeta) \exp [i\omega\tau_m(\tau_{mn}, \alpha+\eta, \zeta)] \alpha^{-1} d\alpha . \tag{1}$$

Discussion of the specific form of contour L will follow.

A characteristic feature of this integral is the exponent depending on a "large parameter" ω. When $\omega \to \infty$, the integrand is a rapidly oscillating function of the variable of integration. As a result of such oscillation, different parts of the contour of integration can contribute quite differently to the asymptotic value of the integral. The basic idea of asymptotic analysis of integrals from rapidly oscillating analytic functions is the deformation of the contour of integration to some special form, which allows simplification of the integrand due to the local approximations (Felsen and Marcuvitz, 1973). A similar approach has been used for integral V.1(1). Here we use the same approach to get a high-frequency approximation of integral (1).

Let contour L pass through the *saddle point* $\alpha = \alpha^*$ of the integrand which is the minimax point of the exponent cofactor in the complex plane of α. At the saddle point the following equation holds true:

$$d\tau_m(\tau_{mn}, \alpha+\eta, \zeta)/d\alpha = 0 \quad \text{when } \alpha = \alpha^* . \tag{2}$$

Let contour L in the neighborhood of the saddle point coincide with the *steepest descent path* satisfying the following conditions:

$$\begin{aligned} &\text{Im } [i\omega\tau_{m\tau}(\tau_{mn}, \alpha+\eta, \zeta)] = \text{Im } [i\omega\tau_m(\tau_{mn}, \alpha^*+\eta, \zeta)], \text{ and} \\ &\text{Re } [i\omega\tau_m(\tau_{mn}, \alpha+\eta, \zeta)] < 0 . \end{aligned} \tag{3}$$

Then the leading term of the high-frequency approximation of integral (1) with $\omega \to \infty$ can be obtained by integrating along the contour (3) in a narrow vicinity of the saddle point and using the local approximation of the integrand. This is done in the following sections.

2. *Saddle point*—Let us show that equation (2) is satisfied when $\alpha^* = -\eta$. To do so, we first write the mentioned equation for the real axis $\text{Im } \alpha = 0$. By denoting

$$\alpha = x + iy, \ \text{Re } \tau_m = u, \ \text{Im } \tau_m = v, \tag{4}$$

we can write the derivative of the function of the complex variable in the form

$$d\tau_m / d\alpha = \partial u/\partial x + i\partial v/\partial y . \tag{5}$$

Suppose

$$\operatorname{Im} \tau_m(\tau_{mn}, \alpha + \eta, \zeta) \equiv 0 \quad \text{when } \operatorname{Im} \alpha = 0 . \tag{6}$$

Then from equation (5) we get the following form of equation (2):

$$\partial \tau_m(\tau_{mn}, x+\eta, \zeta)/\partial x = 0 , \tag{7}$$

where τ_m is a real quantity.

Let us write equation (7) as a directional derivative

$$\partial \tau_m(\tau_{mn}, x+\eta, \zeta)/\partial x = |\nabla \tau_m(\tau_{mn}, x+\eta, \zeta)| \cos[\nabla \tau_m(\tau_{mn}, x+\eta, \zeta), \nabla x] = 0. \tag{8}$$

Suppose

$$\nabla \tau_m(\tau_{mn}, x + \eta, \zeta) \neq 0 . \tag{9}$$

Then equation (8) turns into the following

$$\cos[\nabla \tau_m(\tau_{mn}, x + \eta, \zeta), \nabla x] = 0 . \tag{10}$$

In equation (8) we differentiate along the direction of vector $\nabla x = \nabla \eta$, which is tangential to the edge-diffracted wave front. On the other hand, vectors $\nabla \tau_m$ and ∇x are mutually perpendicular only at the shadow boundary 1(4), i.e., when $x + \eta = 0$. We see that equation (10) is satisfied when $x = -\eta$. Hence, equation (2) has the saddle point

$$\alpha^* = -\eta . \tag{11}$$

It is clear that in the neighborhood of this point assumptions (6) and (9) hold true.

3. Steepest descent path—Here we will find the steepest descent path in the neighborhood of the saddle point (11).

Let us expand the eikonal from equation 1(6) into power series in the vicinity of the saddle point

$$\tau_m(\tau_{mn}, \alpha + \eta, \zeta) = \sum_{k=0}^{\infty} [\tau_m^{(k)}(0)/k!](\alpha + \eta)^k , \tag{12}$$

$$\tau_m^{(k)}(0) = [\,\partial^k \tau_m(\tau_{mn}, \alpha + \eta, \zeta)/\partial \alpha^k\,]_{\alpha = -\eta} \tag{13}$$

In a small neighborhood of the saddle point we can neglect all terms with $k \geq 3$ and take into account relations

$$\tau_m^0(0) = \tau_m(\tau_{mn}, 0, \zeta) = \tau_{mn}, \quad \tau_m^{(1)}(0) = 0, \tag{14}$$

following from equations 1.(4) and (2). Then equation (12) can be written

$$\tau_m(\tau_{mn}, \alpha + \eta, \zeta) = \tau_{mn} + [\,\tau_m^{(2)}(0)/2\,]\,(\alpha + \eta)^2. \tag{15}$$

By substituting equation (15) into (3) with $\alpha = x + iy$ we get equations of the steepest descent path in the form

$$(x + \eta)^2 = y^2, \quad \tau_m^{(2)}(0)(x + \eta)y > 0. \tag{16}$$

There are two rectilinear contours

$$x + \eta = y, \quad x + \eta = -y, \tag{17}$$

complying with the first equation from equations (16). The steepest descent path complies with the second equation from equations (16). Suppose

$$\mathrm{Im}\ \tau_m^{(2)}(0) = 0. \tag{18}$$

Then the second equation from equation (16) can be written

$$s(x + \eta)y > 0, \quad s = \mathrm{sign}\ \tau_m^{(2)}(0). \tag{19}$$

Thus, we can choose from equation (17) the proper equation for condition (19).

4. Local approximation—We consider integral (1) only in the vicinity of shadow boundary 1(4), i.e., in the vicinity of the coordinate surface $\eta = 0$. Then function $\tau_m(\tau_{mn}, \eta, \zeta)$ can be approximated by its power expansion over variable η in the vicinity of the surface $\eta = 0$. In this domain the third and the higher powers of the series can be dropped. The mathematical formalism for this type of approximation is similar to those considered in equations (12) - (15). The sought approximation can be directly obtained from equation (15) when $\alpha = 0$, i.e.,

$$\tau_m(\tau_{mn}, \eta, \zeta) = \tau_{mn} + \tau_m''(0)\,\eta^2/2, \tag{20}$$

where

$$\tau_m''(0) = [\,\partial^2 \tau_m(\tau_{mn}, \eta, \zeta)/\partial \eta^2\,]_{\eta=0}\,. \tag{21}$$

By using the following representation of the second derivative of a function of the complex variable

$$d^2 \tau_m / d\alpha^2 = \partial^2 u/\partial x^2 + i\partial^2 v/\partial y^2\,, \tag{22}$$

where all notations are given in equations (4) and in assumption (18), we get

$$\tau_m^{(2)}(0) = \tau_m''(0)\,. \tag{23}$$

By solving equation (20) relative to $\tau_m''(0)$ and taking into consideration equation (23) we obtain

$$\tau_m^{(2)}(0) = 2\,(\tau_m - \tau_{mn})/\eta^2\,, \tag{24}$$

where τ_m and τ_{mn} are the functions of the position in a 3-D space. Expression (24) is valid in a narrow vicinity of the shadow boundary.

Now we can determine quantity s in equation (19) as

$$s = \text{sign}\,(\tau_m - \tau_{mn})\,. \tag{25}$$

Taking into consideration equations (17), (19), and (25), we can write equations of the steepest descent path in the form

$$x + \eta = -\,y \quad \text{when } \tau_{mn} > \tau_m \text{ and}$$

$$x + \eta = +\,y \quad \text{when } \tau_{mn} < \tau_m\,. \tag{26}$$

5. *Edge-diffracted wave*—Let contour L in equation (1) coincide with the steepest descent path (26) in the neighborhood of the saddle point (11). Such a contour is shown in Figure 50a for $\tau_{mn} > \tau_m$ and in Figure 50b for $\tau_{mn} < \tau_m$. When $\omega \to \infty$, the asymptotic value of integral (1) is formed by the contribution from the small neighborhood of the saddle point. Hence, we can replace the integrand by its local approximation in the neighborhood of the saddle point.

We take the approximations standard for integrals of rapidly oscillating functions. We approximate the eikonal in the exponent cofactor by its power expansion (12) with $k < 3$, i.e., by equation (15). We approximate a slowly changing cofactor Φ_m by its value at the saddle point

$$\Phi_m(\tau_{mn}, \alpha + \eta, \zeta) \approx \Phi_m(\tau_{mn}, 0, \zeta). \tag{27}$$

By substituting equations (15) and (27) into (1) we get the sought asymptotic expression

$$f_{mn} = \Phi_m(\tau_{mn}, 0, \zeta)\ \exp(i\omega\tau_{mn}) \times I, \tag{28}$$

$$I = (2\pi i)^{-1} \int_L \alpha^{-1} \exp[i\omega\tau_m^{(2)}(0)(\alpha + \eta)^2/2]\, d\alpha, \tag{29}$$

where contour L is shown in Figure 50.

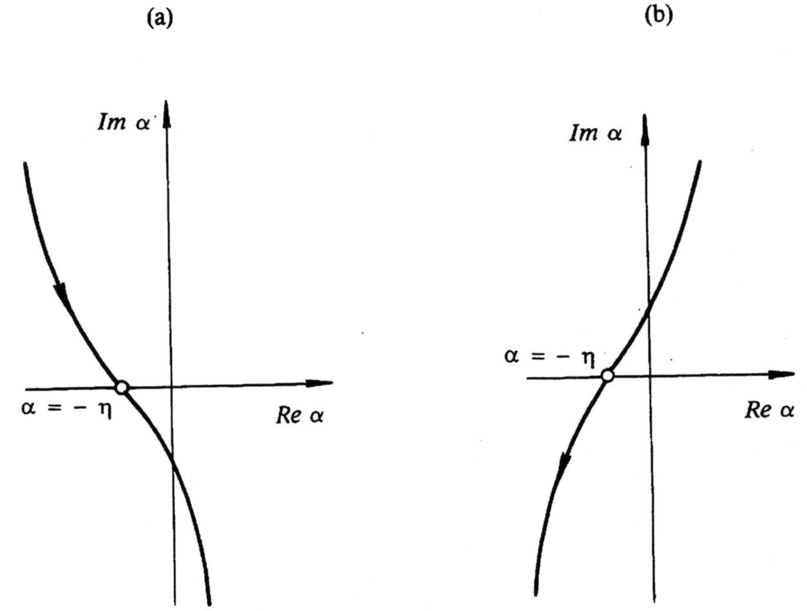

Figure 50. Contours of integration for $\tau_{mn} > \tau_m$ (a) and $\tau_{mn} < \tau_m$ (b) in equation VIII.2(29).

Let us rewrite this integral in a more convenient form. By introducing a new variable of integration

$$\tau = \alpha \times [-\omega\tau_m^{(2)}(0)/2]^{1/2}, \tag{30}$$

we can rewrite equation (29) in the form

$$I = (2\pi i)^{-1} \int_T \tau^{-1} \exp[-i(\tau - \beta)^2]\, d\tau, \tag{31}$$

$$\beta = -\eta[-\omega\, \tau_m^{(2)}(0)/2]^{1/2} \tag{32}$$

where contour T is similar to contour L.

We have considered a similar integral V.2(4). Therefore, by taking $h = -1$, $\beta_{-1} = \beta$ we have $I = -I_{-1}$, where I_{-1} is determined by equation V.2(4). Note that the minus sign here is because of the opposite directions of integration in equations (31) and V.2(4). From equation V.2(10) we have

$$\lim_{\beta \to \pm 0} I = -(1/2)\operatorname{sign}\beta = (1/2)\operatorname{sign}\eta. \tag{33}$$

From equations V.2(18), V.2(19), and V.2(23) we have

$$I = \operatorname{sign}\eta \times W(w), \quad w = \beta(2/\pi)^{1/2}, \tag{34}$$

where function $W(w)$ is determined by equation D.(1) of Appendix D.

By substituting equation (24) into (32) we can write the quantity w from equation (34) as

$$w = -[2\omega(\tau_{mn} - \tau_m)/\pi]^{1/2}. \tag{35}$$

Because function $W(w)$ depends on w^2 (see equation D.(1) of Appendix D), we can change the sign of this expression

$$w = [2\omega(\tau_{mn} - \tau_m)/\pi]^{1/2}. \tag{36}$$

By substituting equations (34) and (36) into (28) we can represent the edge wave in the form

$$f_{mn} = s_{mn}\Phi_m W(w_{mn}) \exp(i\omega\tau_{mn}), \quad w_{mn} = [2\omega(\tau_{mn} - \tau_m)/\pi]^{1/2} \tag{37}$$

$$s_{mn} = +1 \text{ within } \Omega^+_{mn}, \quad s_{mn} = -1 \text{ within } \Omega^-_{mn} \tag{38}$$

where Ω^{+}_{mn} and Ω^{-}_{mn} are symbols of the primary shadow and illuminated zones, respectively. Here quantity τ_m in domain Ω^{+}_{mn} corresponds to the continuation (for example, analytic continuation) of function $\tau_m(\tau_{mn}, \eta, \zeta)$ into the domain $\eta > 0$.

According to equation (28), cofactor Φ_m in equation (37) should be fixed at the shadow boundary, i.e., $\Phi_m = \Phi_m(\tau_{mn}, 0, \zeta)$. We show below that this cofactor also can be regarded as a function of position in space, i.e., $\Phi_m = \Phi_m(\tau_{mn}, \eta, \zeta)$. Then quantity Φ_m in domain Ω^{+}_{mn} corresponds to the continuation (for example, analytic continuation) of function $\Phi_m(\tau_{mn}, \eta, \zeta)$ in domain $\eta > 0$.

6. *Estimation of inaccuracy*—In deriving equation 1(17) we did not take into account conditions at the interfaces. Therefore, equation (37) can be used only in those regions, where the edge-diffracted wave amplitude is much larger then the inaccuracy, caused by neglecting conditions at interfaces. Such regions can be found by comparing asymptotic estimates of the field (37) and the mentioned inaccuracy.

It follows from the analysis of equation V.3(22) that the amplitude of wave (37) changes rapidly from the value of the relative order $O(1)$ to the value of the relative order $O(\omega^{-1/2})$, when quantity $|w_{mn}|$ changes from 0 to 2. When $|w_{mn}| > 2$, the amplitude has the order $O(\omega^{-1/2})$. The region of rapid change ($|w_{mn}| \lesssim 2$) corresponds to the *boundary layer*. The region of slow change ($|w_{mn}| > 2$) corresponds to the *deep shadow zone.*

If the boundary shadow is near the interface (grazing), the inaccuracy, caused by neglecting the conditions at interfaces, is of the order $O(1)$. An example of this type of inaccuracy is the mismatch between curves 2 and 3 in Figure 38b with $n = 20$. It is clear that equation (37) is invalid in such situations.

According to equations VII.1(12), VII.1(21) - VII.1(22) and V.3(42), the inaccuracy, caused by neglecting the conditions at interfaces, has the relative order $O(\omega^{-1/2})$, if the interfaces are in the deep shadow zone. It is essential that in the neighborhood of the shadow boundary the correction for conditions at interfaces is a continuous function of coordinate η. This very fact shows that the region of application of equation (37) is the boundary layer, where the edge-diffracted wave amplitude has the relative order

$O(1) \div O(\omega^{-1/2})$. In this region the inaccuracy of equation (37) is characterized by the value of the relative order $O(\omega^{-1/2})$.

Let us discuss now, if it is possible to replace value $\Phi_m(\tau_{mn}, 0, \zeta)$ by value $\Phi_m(\tau_{mn}, \eta, \zeta)$ in equation (37). Let f_{mn} and f_{mn}^* correspond to quantity (37) with $\Phi_m = \Phi_m(\tau_{mn}, 0, \zeta)$ and $\Phi_m = \Phi_m(\tau_{mn}, \eta, \zeta)$, respectively. Then $\delta f_{mn} = f_{mn} - f_{mn}^*$ corresponds to the inaccuracy, caused by replacing $\Phi_m(\tau_{mn}, 0, \zeta)$ with $\Phi_m(\tau_{mn}, \eta, \zeta)$. Unlike with f_{mn} and f_{mn}^*, quantity δf_{mn} represents a wave of the type 1(3) with the amplitude continuous at $\eta = 0$. On the strength of its continuity, the amplitude of this wave complies with the transport equation in the neighborhood of surface $\eta = 0$, i.e., it has the relative order $O(\omega^{-1/2})$. This estimate shows that the replacement of $\Phi_m(\tau_{mn}, 0, \zeta)$ by $\Phi_m(\tau_{mn}, \eta, \zeta)$ does not change the previously mentioned inaccuracy of the boundary-layer approximation.

7. Substantiation of taken assumptions—Now we can substantiate assumptions taken to formulate the problem of Section 1.4. Let us begin with the possibility of the continuation of function $f_m(\tau_{mn}, \eta, \zeta)$ in the complex plane of η along contour Γ under condition 1(14).

If the medium is homogeneous and wave f_m is plane, the mentioned assumption holds true for the contour Γ, placed in the *allowable domains* (see Section II.1.3. In this case quantity f_m at Γ corresponds to an inhomogeneous attenuating plane wave. Hence, this assumption holds true in the small neighborhood of an individual point of the edge, where the locally plane approximation of the reflected/transmitted waves is possible (see Sections VII.1.2 - VII.1.3.

To substantiate the assumption being considered in a general case of inhomogeneous media outside the neighborhood of the edge, we have to remember that the problem is stated under condition $\omega \to \infty$. Therefore, it is sufficient to show that this assumption holds true asymptotically when $\omega \to \infty$. Equations (20) and (27) show that in this case wave f_m can be approximated as follows:

$$f_m \approx \Phi_m(\tau_{mn}, 0, \zeta) \exp\left[\tau_{mn} + \tau_m''(0)\eta^2/2\right], \tag{39}$$

where $\tau_m''(0)$ is determined by equation (21). This expression allows a continuation in the complex plane of η along the steepest descent path and complies with condition 1(14), if values of $\Phi_m(\tau_{mn}, 0, \zeta)$ and $\tau_m''(0)$ are limited. Hence, the assumption under consideration does not put any additional restrictions on the function $f_m(\tau_{mn}, \eta, \zeta)$ above those, which exist in the ray method.

The second assumption concerns the class of solutions. We have been looking for the solution among the piecewise-analytic functions decreasing at infinity. To substantiate this assumption, it is enough to show that the solution obtained makes sense for the real values of η. The answer is clear: expression (37) in the boundary layer coincides with the earlier obtained solutions of the reduced wave equation. All this is enough to substantiate the statement of the problem.

8. Vector waves—Let the items of sum 1(1) be the vector waves

$$f_m = \Phi_m \exp(i\omega\tau_m), \quad \Phi_m = \boldsymbol{P}_m \varphi_m, \tag{40}$$

where $\boldsymbol{P}_m$ is a unit vector of polarization, and φ_m is a scalar. In an isotropic medium the vector $\boldsymbol{P}_m$ coincides with the tangent to the ray (a longitudinal wave) or is perpendicular to it (a transverse wave). Let $\boldsymbol{j}_1$, $\boldsymbol{j}_2$, $\boldsymbol{j}_3$ be the unit vectors of a certain fixed coordinate system (for example, the Cartesian one). By decomposing the vector amplitude of wave (40) on the above basis we have

$$f_m = \sum_{q=1}^{3} \boldsymbol{j}_q f_m^{(q)}, \tag{41}$$

$$f_m^{(q)} = \varphi_m^{(q)} \exp(i\omega\tau_m), \tag{42}$$

where $f_m^{(q)}$ are scalars.

Let us represent the sought edge-diffracted wave, equation 1(3), on the same basis

$$f_{mn} = \sum_{q=1}^{3} \boldsymbol{j}_q f_{mn}^{(q)}, \; f_{mn}^{(q)} = \varphi_{mn}^{(q)} \exp(i\omega\tau_{mn}), \tag{43}$$

where $f_{mn}^{(q)}$ are scalars. To find every individual scalar function $f_{mn}^{(q)}(\tau_{mn}, \eta, \zeta)$, we can use the same approach, which was used for finding function 1(3) and which allows us to determine three scalar functions:

$$f_{mn}^{(q)} = s_{mn} \varphi_{mn}^{(q)} W(w_{mn}) \exp(i\omega\tau_{mn}), \text{ with } q = 1, 2, 3. \tag{44}$$

By inserting equations (44) into (43) we get again equation (37), where Φ_m is the vector amplitude of wave (40).

This result has to be interpreted. Let $\boldsymbol{P}_{mn}$ be a unit vector of polarization of the edge-diffracted wave f_{mn}. In accordance with the zeroth order approximation of the ray method this vector must coincide with the tangent to the diffracted ray (a longitudinal wave) or be perpendicular to it (a transverse wave). But in vector equation (37) the obtained vector $\boldsymbol{P}_{mn}$ coincides with vector $\boldsymbol{P}_{mn}(\tau_{mn}, 0, \zeta)$ which is out of the line of the theory. In other words, the above approach gives an inaccuracy $\delta \boldsymbol{P} = \boldsymbol{P}_{mn}(\tau_{mn}, \eta, \zeta) - \boldsymbol{P}_m(\tau_{mn}, 0, \zeta)$. In fact, the real accuracy of the description of polarization is independent of the choice of any of the versions: $\boldsymbol{P}_m(\tau_{mn}, 0, \zeta)$, $\boldsymbol{P}_m(\tau_{mn}, \eta, \zeta)$, or $\boldsymbol{P}_{mn}(\tau_{mn}, \eta, \zeta)$, because in the boundary layer the corresponding $\delta \boldsymbol{P}$ represents the vector of polarization of the continuous asymptotic solution of equations of motion of the relative order $O(\omega^{-1/2})$. Because of this vector Φ_m may be regarded as well as a function of the current point $\Phi_m(\tau_{mn}, \eta, \zeta)$ and then continued into the shadow zone.

9. Reciprocity principle—We note one important property of equation (37). To calculate the quantities τ_m and τ_{mn} in terms which the quantity w_{mn} is expressed, it is necessary to construct two trajectories of wave propagation from the source to the observation point. One of them corresponds to the ray path within the scope of the usual Fermat principle. The other is also constructed according to the laws of the ray theory, but passes through the point of the diffracting edge (generalized Fermat principle). The propagation times over these trajectories correspond to the quantities τ_m and τ_{mn}. These quantities, consequently, and the quantity w_{mn} do not change if the source and observation point change places. The fields of the ray method waves f_m in this case do not change either (Cerveny et al., 1977). Therefore, expression (37) satisfies the reciprocity principle – it does not change its value if the source and observation point change places.

3. Criteria of applicability of geometrical seismics

1. Estimate of the deviation from geometrical seismics—The concept under consideration only supplements the ray theory. The need to use this concept arises in those cases when the observation point is in the regions of space where the change of various wave mechanisms occurs. In this connection the question arises, how to estimate the degree of admissibility of using the ray theory in each specific case?

Let wave f_m propagating in a known direction be observed at a certain point in space. If there are no shadow boundaries in the field of this wave, the observation results can be explained within the scope of the ray theory concepts. If there are shadow boundaries in the field of this wave, the influence of the edge effects related to them can be manifested at the observation point in the form of more or less considerable deviations from the laws of geometrical seismics. If the indicated deviations are not appreciable, the observation results can be explained with a practically acceptable accuracy by using the ray theory. Otherwise it is necessary to enlist diffraction concepts. How does one estimate quantitatively the magnitude of deviations from the laws of geometrical seismics?

The answer to this question is contained in the very mathematical form of notation of the wavefields 1(5) and 2(37). Suppose that in the field of wave f_m there is a single shadow boundary with which the diffracted wave f_{mn} is associated. If wave f_m exists at the observation point, then, according to equations 1(5), 2(37) and equation D(17) of Appendix D,

$$f=f_m+f_{mn}=f_m\left\{1-W(w_{mn})\exp\left[i\omega(\tau_{mn}-\tau_m)\right]\right\}$$
$$=f_m F\left[+w_{mn}(\pi/2)^{1/2}\right]. \tag{1}$$

This equation shows that the degree of deviation from the geometrical seismics $f = f_m$ is estimated quantitatively by the Fresnel integral F.

From practical considerations we can always allow some deviation from the geometrical seismics laws for which the influence of the edge effects is small and the observation result with a knowingly acceptable accuracy is explained on the basis of the ray theory. Let, for example, such limitation on the edge effects have the form

$$\left|(f-f_m)/f_m\right| = \left|f_{mn}/f_m\right| = \left|W(w_{mn})\right| < v, \tag{2}$$

where v is a given "small" number. This limitation is equivalent to the following inequality:

$$\left|w_{mn}\right| > N \quad \text{with} \quad \left|W(N)\right| = v \tag{3}$$

Thus the observed field f with a knowingly acceptable accuracy is described by geometrical seismics laws if condition (3) is fulfilled for the given v. A geometrical interpretation of this expression permits introducing convenient concepts for estimating the conditions of applicability of the ray theory.

2. *Neighborhood of the ray*—For subsequent constructions it is convenient to use the concept of an individual point of diffraction – a point in space at which the diffracted ray originates. A set of diffraction points forms a diffracting edge in space. Let us examine at first a simple case of an homogeneous medium when there are no interfaces between the source of a spherical wave and the observation point.

Since the quantity w_{mn} is a function of the point in space, inequality (3) isolates in space a certain region with boundary $w_{mn} = N$. To investigate the geometry of this boundary, we express the quantity w_{mn} by the second equation from 2(37) in terms of traveltime curves of the diffracted wave $\tau_{mn} = (r_0 + r)/c$ and geometrical seismic wave $\tau_m = R/c$ and write the equation $w_{mn} = N$ in the form

$$r_0 + r - R = (N/2)^2 \lambda, \ \lambda = 2\pi c/\omega, \tag{4}$$

where R and r_0 are, respectively, the distances of the observation point and diffraction point from the source, r is the distance from the diffraction point to the observation point, c is the propagation velocity, and λ is the wavelength.

We fix the position of the source and diffraction point and write equation (4) in the form

$$\rho_{10} - \rho_{20} = 1 - A_0, \ \rho_{10} = R/r_0, \ \rho_{20} = r/r_0, \ A_0 = (N/2)^2(\lambda/r_0), \tag{5}$$

where the index 0 means that the observation point O belongs to the surface being considered. Let P be the plane containing the source M, diffraction point D, and observation point O. The lines of intersection of the surface [equation (5)] with plane P form a family of confocal hyperbolas with focal radii ρ_{10} and ρ_{20}, depending on parameter A_0. The foci are located at points M and D, the distance between which is taken as the unit of measurement of the lengths. The dimensions of the real and imaginary axes of the hyperbolas are equal, respectively, to $(1 - A_0)$ and $[A_0(2 - A_0)]^{1/2}$. Only those branches of the hyperbolas for which $\rho_{10} \geq \rho_{20}$ have physical meaning. The family of these branches, depending on parameter A_0 is shown in Figure 51a. On rotating plane P relative to the straight line connecting the source with the diffraction point, the investigated branch of each hyperbola describes the surface of a hyperboloid.

Condition (3) is satisfied if the observation point belongs to the hyperboloid $A_0 \geq (N/2)^2(\lambda/r_0)$. We call the region of space bounded by the branch of the hyperboloid $A_0 = (N/2)^2(\lambda/r_0)$ and containing this point the *neighborhood of the diffraction point.* Obviously, condition (2) is fulfilled and the observed field is described by the geometrical seismic laws if the *observation point does not belong to the neighborhood of the diffraction point.* The union of neighborhoods of diffraction points belonging to one diffracting edge form a *boundary layer* related to an individual shadow boundary of the wave f_m. Therefore, we can also say that the observed field is described by the geometrical seismic laws if the observation point does not belong to the boundary layer.

Now we fix the position of the diffraction point and observation point, and we represent equation (4) in the form

$$\rho_{1M} - \rho_{2M} = 1 - A_M, \ \rho_{1M} = R/r, \ \rho_{2M} = r_0/r, \ A_M = (N/2)^2(\lambda/r), \tag{6}$$

where index M shows that the source belongs to the surface being investigated. The geometry of this surface is similar to that already investigated (for the quantity ρ_{i0} and A_0 the index 0 must be replaced by the index M). Now we must call the region of space bounded by the hyperboloid $A_M = (N/2)^2(\lambda/r)$ the neighborhood of the diffraction point. The condition of applicability of the geometrical seismic laws reduces to the requirement that the source does not belong to the neighborhood of the diffraction point. This criterion obviously follows from the preceding by virtue of the reciprocity principle, since the source and observation point can change places.

We will now consider the position of the source and the observation point to be fixed. Equation (4) is written in the form

$$\rho_{1D} + \rho_{2D} = 1 + A_D, \ \rho_{1D} = r/R, \ \rho_{2D} = r_0/R, \ A_D = (N/2)^2(\lambda/R), \tag{7}$$

where the index D indicates that the diffraction point belongs to the investigated surface. The lines of intersection of plane P with the surface form a family of confocal ellipses with focal radii ρ_{1D} and ρ_{2D}, depending on parameter A_D (Figure 51b). The foci are located at points M and O and the distance between them is taken for the unit of length. The dimensions of the semimajor and semiminor axes are equal, respectively, to $(1 + A_D)$ and $[A_D(2 + A_D)]^{1/2}$. On rotating plane P, relative to the straight line connecting the source with the observation point, the ellipses describe the surface of an ellipsoid of revolution. Condition (3) is fulfilled if the diffraction point belongs to the ellipsoid $A_D \geq (N/2)^2 (\lambda/R)$. We will call the region of space bounded by the ellipsoid $A_D = (N/2)^2 (\lambda/R)$ and containing the observation point the *neighborhood of the ray.* Obviously, the observed field is described by geometrical seismic laws if the *diffraction point does not belong to the neighborhood of the ray.*

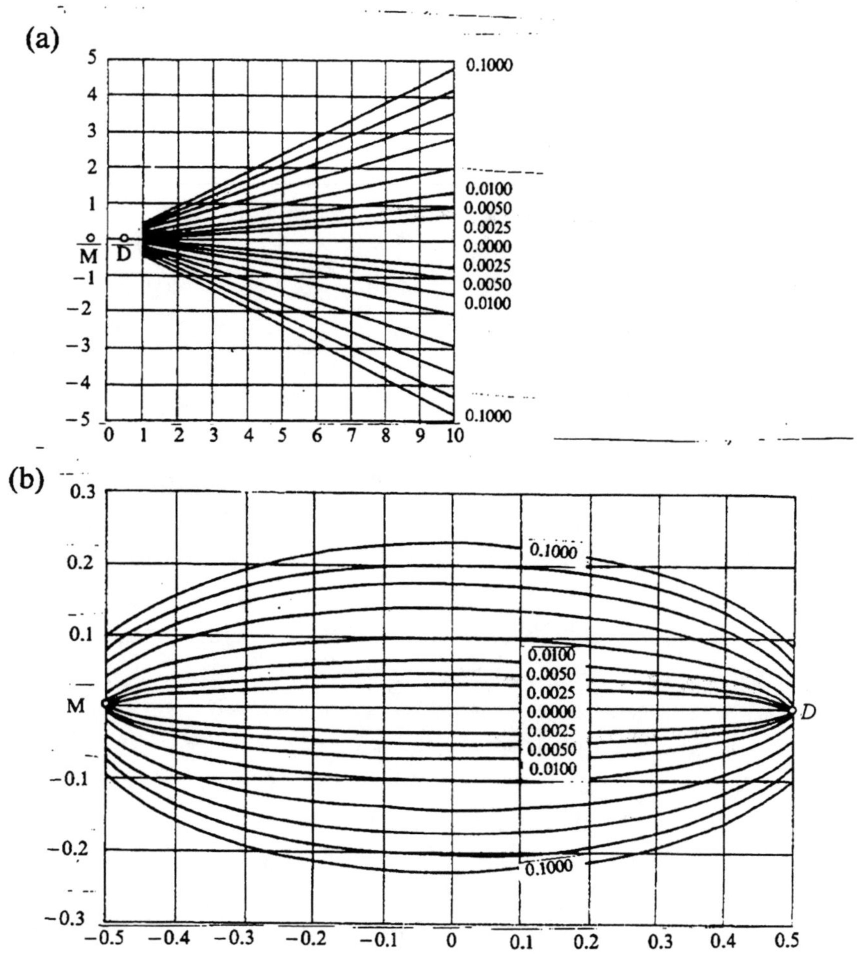

Figure 51. Neighborhood of the diffraction point (a) and neighborhood of the ray (b) in plane P of the normal section of the wavefronts for different values of the parameters A_i (the notations of the lines correspond to these values).

Thus, in the investigated simple case we have established two independent equivalent criteria permitting an estimate of the limits of applicability of the concepts of geometrical seismics. The problem of which of the indicated criteria should be used in interpretation is not related with the physics of the investigated phenomenon – the choice of any of them leads to the same estimate.

3. General case—We can now proceed to the general case of an inhomogeneous medium when the geometrical seismic wave f_m on the propagation path from the source to the observation point is reflected and refracted at interfaces. As previously, we will consider that there is a single diffraction point with which is associated only one diffracted wave f_{mn}. To calculate the quantities τ_m and τ_{mn} we must construct a pair of propagating trajectories of the waves "source – observation point" and "source – diffraction point – observation point." The propagation times along these trajectories correspond to the quantities τ_m and τ_{mn}. Each of the trajectories is a piecewise broken ray with points of the broken line at the interfaces of the medium (there is also a point of the broken line at the diffraction point).

The geometric interpretation of equation (3) again leads to the concepts about the neighborhood of the diffraction point and the neighborhood of the ray and to the corresponding criteria of estimating the applicability of the concepts of geometric seismics analogous to those previously given. The propagating trajectories of waves f_m and f_{mn} contain three characteristic points: the source, observation point, and diffraction point. If we fix any pair of these points, then under condition (3) the position of the unfixed characteristic point can no longer be chosen arbitrarily. The indicated condition defines a certain surface to which this point should belong. Since on the passage of this point across the interface of the medium any of the quantities τ_m and τ_{mn} change continuously (Fermat's principle), the indicated surface is also continuous at the interfaces of media. This surface separates the space into a pair of regions, and in only one is the condition (2) fulfilled. Depending on the type of unfixed characteristic point – the observation point, source, or the diffraction point – the region, where condition (2) is not fulfilled, can be defined anew as the neighborhood of the diffraction point or neighborhood of the ray. The criterion of validity of the concepts of geometrical seismics is again the condition that the unfixed characteristic point does not belong to the corresponding region of space – the neighborhood of the diffraction point, the neighborhood of the ray.

4. *Neighborhood of the reflection point*—When interpreting seismic prospecting data the most common case is when the diffraction points belong to the investigated reflecting/transmitting boundary (diffracting edges modeling the faults, pinch-outs, and oblique contacts of seismic interfaces). In these cases, for estimating the limits of applicability of the geometrical seismics laws it is sufficient to use instead of the neighborhood of the ray its cross section of the interface of the media – the *neighborhood of the reflection (or refraction) point.* The equations of the neighborhood of the reflection point are, in addition to expression (3), equations of the interface of media as surfaces in three-dimensional space

$$\mathfrak{F}(x, y, z) = 0. \tag{8}$$

The line of intersection of surfaces (3) and (8) corresponds to the boundary of the neighborhood of the reflection point.

If in equation (3) the quantity N is assigned in the form

$$N = \sqrt{2k} \quad \text{where } k = 1, 2, 3, \ldots, \tag{9}$$

then the difference of travel paths over trajectories "source – diffraction point – observation point" and "source – observation point" comprise a whole number of half-waves $k\lambda/2$. Actually, substituting equation (9) into (3) when $w_{mn} = N$ and using for w_{mn} an equation from 2(37), we obtain $c(\tau_{mn} - \tau_m) = k\lambda/2$. Thus, on assigning N in the form of equation (9) to surface equation (3) divides the reflecting/transmitting interface equation (8) into Fresnel half-wave zones which is used widely when analyzing wave mechanisms. Therefore, it is expedient to express the size of the neighborhood of the reflection point in the Fresnel zones. Using equations (2) and (3), we can estimate on the basis of v the error due to discarding any number of zones. From Figure 25 we see that the error stabilizes and becomes an order of magnitude less than the amplitude of the geometrical seismic wave when $k > 2$. Therefore, in equation (9) we should set $k = 2$. Then for parameters A_i in equations (5) - (7) we obtain the approximate expressions

$$A_0 = \lambda/r_0,\ A_M = \lambda/r,\ A_D = \lambda/R. \tag{10}$$

Figure 52 shows an example of the neighborhood of a ray for a three-layer seismic model of one of the regions of Western Siberia. The predominant frequency of oscillations is assumed equal to 10 Hz. Parameter A_D assigned according to the formula from equation (10). The discontinuities of the neighborhoods of the reflection/transmission points are because the error of computation.

4. Examples

Now we give some examples of using expressions (1.5) and (2.37) for the mathematical modeling of the edge diffraction phenomena in the simplest cases.

Example 1. Spectrum of the edge-diffracted wave—The knowledge of the spectral properties of seismic waves permits us to sometimes single out some waves by using the frequency filtering. In this connection a question arises: what are the properties of the frequency spectrum of the edge-diffracted wave? This example gives an answer in that simple case when the edge-diffracted wave is formed because of a single shadow boundary.

According to equation 2(37), the complex spectrum $f_{mn}(\omega)$ of the edge-diffracted wave is connected with the complex spectrum $f_m(\omega)$ of the geometrical seismic wave by the relation

$$f_{mn}(\omega) = W(w)\, f_m(\omega),\ w = \sqrt{\omega\tau},\ \tau = 2(\tau_{mn} - \tau_m)/\pi, \tag{1}$$

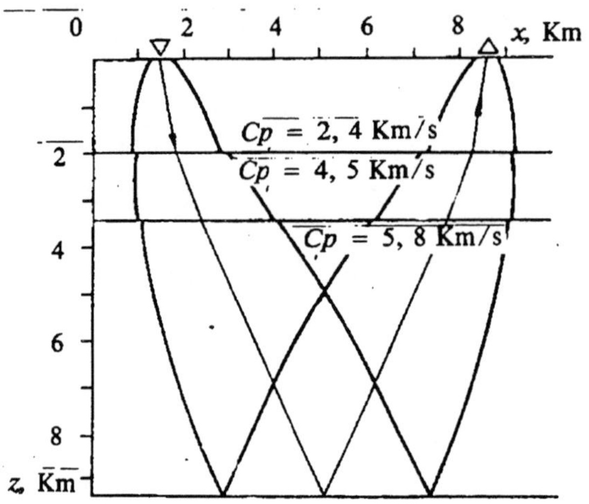

Figure 52. Example of constructing the neighborhood of the ray in the plane of the principal normal cross section of wavefronts for a three-layer seismic mode.

where cofactor $W(w)$ characterizes the transformation of the spectrum due to diffraction. We consider an example of spectrum (1) when the shape of the geometrical seismic wave pulse is

$$F_m(t) = t \exp(-\beta t) \sin \overline{\omega} t, \tag{2}$$

where $\overline{\omega}$ is the "apparent" frequency of oscillations and parameter β characterizes the shape of the envelope of the pulse.

Figure 53 shows examples of the modules of the complex frequency spectrum for different distances from the shadow boundary (variation of τ) and shapes of the geometric seismic wave pulse (variation of $\overline{\omega}$ and β). The position of the observation point relative to the shadow boundary is characterized by the quantity $s = \tau \pi 10^3$, values of which (0, 1, 4, 16, 64) are given at the curves. At the shadow boundary $s = 0$. The value $s = 4\pi 10^3/\overline{\omega}$, i.e., $w \approx 2$, corresponds to the outer boundary of the boundary layer. Therefore, the spectra in the boundary layer are displayed by the graphs with $s \le 64$ for $\overline{\omega}/2\pi = 25$ Hz, $s \le 16$ for $\overline{\omega}/2\pi = 100$ Hz, and $s \le 4$ for $\omega/2\pi = 500$ Hz. The rest of the graphs are related to the deep shadow zone where expression (1) fails.

In the first pair of columns the spectra of the narrow band pulses are given, in the second pair – spectra of the typical width of the seismic pulses, in the third – spectra of broad band pulses. Each group of the spectra for different τ and fixed $\overline{\omega}$ and β is given twice on the different scale. The right-hand groups of graphs are given on the natural scale, permitting for each ω to evaluate the relative change of the spectral density when parameter τ varies. The vertical scales of the left-hand groups of graphs for each τ are

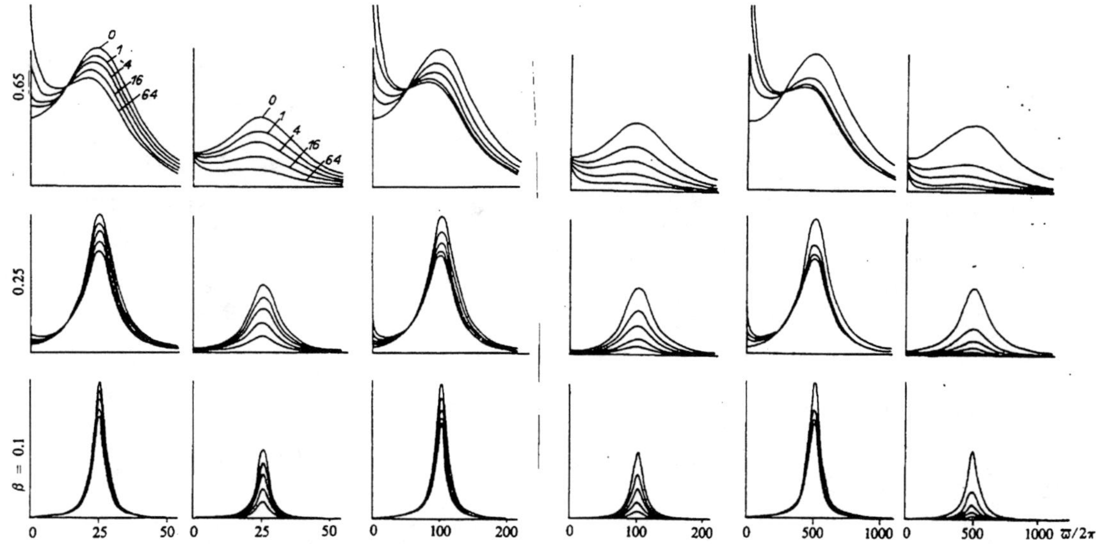

Figure 53. Modules of the complex frequency spectrum of the edge-diffracted wave. (From Klem-Musatov et al., 1975a).

chosen so that the transformation of the shape of the spectrum is underlined when parameter τ varies.

The graphs being considered show that the shape of the amplitude spectrum changes insignificantly on moving away from the shadow boundary (increasing of parameter τ), while the spectral density rapidly decreases. It follows from this example that the spectral criteria hardly can be effective in the experimental investigation of edge waves.

Example 2. Shape of the edge-diffracted wave pulse—Example 2, (Klem-Musatov et al., 1975a) illustrates the transformation of the wave pulse shape because of diffraction. The computational procedure consists in the Fourier transform of the spectra from the preceding example. The three left-hand columns of Figure 54 show the functions $F_{mn}(t)$ and $F_m(t)$ for different values of parameter $\bar{\omega}$, β, and τ. For each graph of $F_{mn}(t)$ the graph of function (2) is shown as a scale (in figures the latter seems to be shifted a bit to the left-hand side). Because only the transformation of the wave pulse shape is under consideration, the vertical scale of each function $F_{mn}(t)$ is chosen to give the clarity of representation.

These graphs show that the shape of the edge-diffracted wave pulse is slightly changing in its propagation. The magnitude of the first phase is slightly stretching and decreasing. The ratio between the amplitudes of the first and following phases is changing. The following phases are shifting toward the tail. The tendencies to the change of the shape with the variation of parameters τ , $\overline{\omega}$, and β are of the same kind as for the above discussed amplitude spectra. Outside the boundary layer the shape of the wave pulse is stabilized, and only the intensity of the wave changes. This example shows that the characteristics of the shape of the wave pulse hardly can be used to single out an edge-diffracted wave from experimental data.

Example 3. Approximate formula—The computation of the nonstationary edge-diffracted wave includes the Fourier transform. For some typical seismic pulses the Fourier transform can be replaced by the narrow band Hilbert transform. However, it is also possible to use the approximate formula (Klem-Musatov et al., 1975a)

$$F_{mn}(t) = |W(\overline{w})| F_m[t - \arg W(\overline{w})/\overline{\omega}], \quad \overline{w} = (\overline{\omega}\tau)^{1/2}, \tag{3}$$

where τ and $\overline{\omega}$ are determined in equations (1) and (2). In three right-hand columns of Figure 54 the comparison of the shapes of the wave pulses, computed according to equation (3) and by using the Fourier transform, is given. The mismatch of the curves characterizes the inaccuracy of the approximate formula (3).

Example 4. Diffraction on the half-plane—Now we consider the simplest situation making possible the experimental observation of a single edge-diffracted wave and the investigation of the dimensional change of the wave's intensity. It is the case of the reflection of the ultrasound wave from the "semi-infinite" plate in liquid. The reflecting half-plane is parallel to the surface of the liquid. The profiles of observation (on the surface of the liquid) form different angles α with the projection of the edge on the surface of observation. The comparison of the experimental and theoretical data, computed in accordance with equation 2(37), is shown in Figure 55. One can see that the boundary-layer approximation formula describes the edge-diffracted wave with sufficient accuracy.

Example 5. Diffraction on a small-throw fault—Small-throw faults play an important role in oil and gas prospecting. The existence of the seismic anomalies associated with such objects was noted and experimentally confirmed by Kovalevsky (1971) who successfully explained the relevant wave mechanisms at the empirical level. Here we consider an

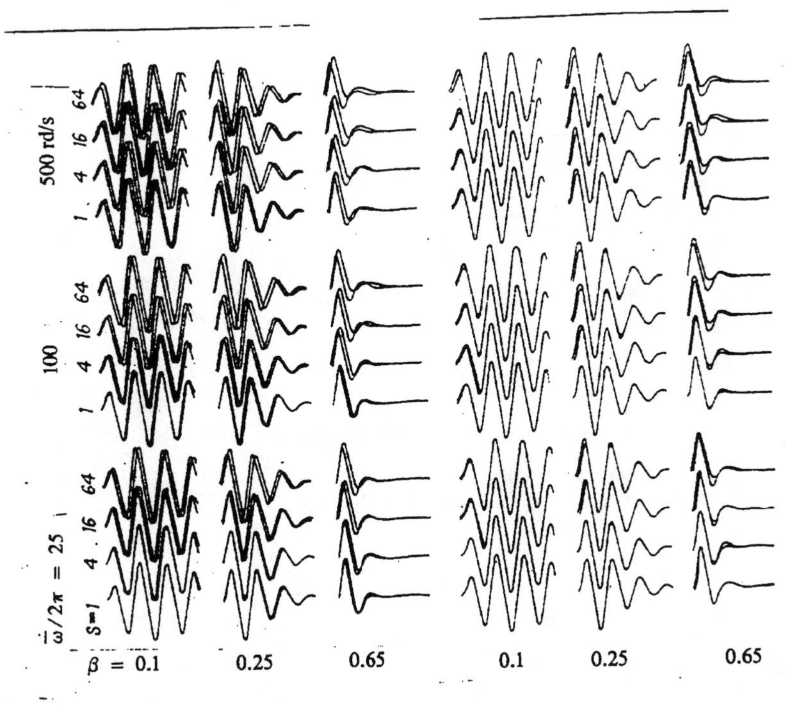

Figure 54. Shape of the edge-diffracted wave.

example of the mathematical modeling of such anomalies, taken from Klem-Musatov et al., (1976).

As the simplest model of a small-throw fault we can take a pair of half planes parallel to the observation surface (Figure 56). The seismic trace is put in correspondence to the common depth point (see Figure 56). The seismograms of longitudinal reflected waves with consideration of diffractions along the profile oriented across the strike of the fault are shown in Figure 57. In all seismograms the bottom traces correspond to the left-hand side of the model shown in Figure 56. Each individual seismogram is computed for the fixed value of parameter $\Delta h / \lambda$, where λ is the predominant wavelength.

More details concerning this type of seismic modeling are given in Klem-Musatov et al., (1976b). The characteristic feature of these seismograms is a more or less pronounced region of an anomalous decrease of the intensity of oscillations. The position of this region is controlled by the simple rule of "seismic deflection." Klem-Musatov et al., (1976b) show that the degree of relative attenuation of the intensity of oscillations at the mid-point of the mentioned region can be expressed by the formula

$$E \approx 2 \mid W(w^*) \mid^2 (1 + \cos \eta), \tag{4}$$

$$w^* = (\delta \cos \gamma)/[\sqrt{\lambda r} \sin \alpha], \quad \eta = (\Delta h \cos \gamma)/\lambda,$$

where γ is the angle of incidence at the fault, α is the angle between the observation profile and the project of the strike of the fault on the observation surface, and r is the distance from the source to the fault along the ray.

Figure 58a shows experimental seismograms of a 2-D physical modeling of the longitudinal waves reflected from the interface with the small-throw fault ($\Delta h = \lambda/4$). Here each seismogram corresponds to the fixed position of the source. The right-hand seismogram corresponds to the source, placed right above the fault. Figure 58b shows the corresponding theoretical seismograms, computed in accordance with equations 1(5) and 2(37). The good agreement between the experimental and theoretical seismograms justifies the above model of a small-throw fault.

Example 6. Diffraction in wedge-shaped regions—Seismic prospecting of geological structures of the pinching-out bed type and various adjoining boundaries is of great importance in the search for useful minerals. The simplest models of such geological structures are V-shaped homogeneous media with different elastic properties, having a common edge.

The simplest case corresponds to the reflection from a wedge-shaped boundary. The formation of the reflected wavefield with the consideration of diffractions can be explained graphically by the diagrams in Figure 59. The top middle seismogram is computed in accordance with ray method 1(1) and contains a shadow zone. Each of two seismograms in the far right column is computed in accordance with equation 2(37) and their sum is shown in the second row of the middle column. The bottom middle seismogram corresponds to expression 1(5).

Figure 60 shows the kinematic scheme of reflections and diffractions for the model of a pinch-out. Inside the pinched layer there are multiple reflections. As a result, there are many reflected waves with sharp shadow boundaries at the profile of observation. Only three of them are shown in Figure 60. They are shown with dashed lines (Γ_1, Γ_2 relating to interfaces 1 and 2, and Γ_3 to interface 3 with PP-transmission through interface 2). Figure 61 shows the correspondent theoretical seismograms. Note that all edge-diffracted waves from the common edge have the same eikonal and form a resultant diffracted wave.

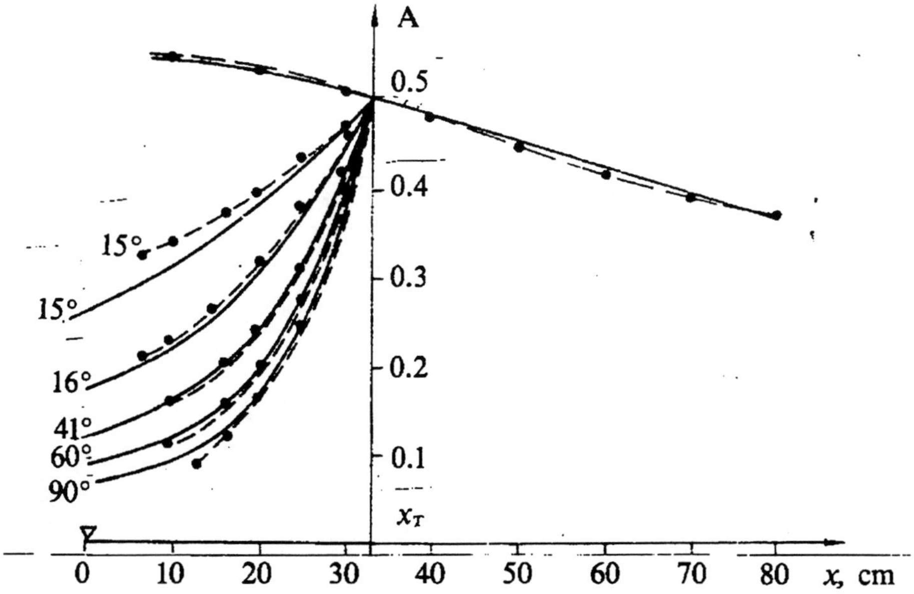

Figure 55. Experimental (dashed lines) and theoretical (solid lines) amplitude graphs of the edge-diffracted wave from a rectilinear edge. The top graphs correspond to the reflection from the infinite plane. (From Klem Musatov et al., 1975).

The following figures show examples of theoretical seismograms in the simplest models of wedge-shaped structures, (from Klem-Musatov et al., 1975b). The geological models and the system of observations are shown in Figure 62 with $H = 500$ m and $\alpha = 10°$. The value of the propagation velocities of the longitudinal waves (km/s) in the contacting media follows.

No. of Model	c_1	c_2	c_3	No. of Model	c_1	c_2	c_3
1-4	2.5	3.5		9	2.5	2.0	3.5
5	2.5	3.5	4.0	10	2.5	3.5	3.0
6	2.5	3.5	2.0	11	3.5	2.5	2.0
7	2.5	3.5	3.0	12	2.5	3.5	2.0
8	2.5	3.5	4.0	13	3.5	2.0	2.5

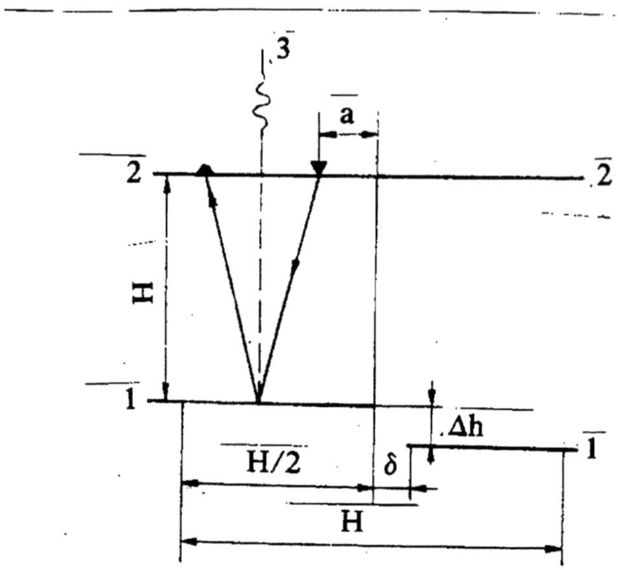

Figure 56. Model of the small-throw fault and the system of observation.

(1) – reflecting interface; (2) – surface of observation; (3) – seismic trace reduced to the reflection point. $H = 10\,\lambda$; $d = 2.5\,\lambda$; $\delta = 0.25\,\lambda$; λ ***– apparent wavelength. (From Klem-Musatov et al., 1976).***

The Poisson's ratio is 0.25 in all media; their densities are the same. The observation profile is oriented across the strike of the structure. The source of oscillations excites a P–wave with a uniform radiation characteristic. The shape of the radiated pulse is described by equation (2) for $\beta = 0.2$, $\overline{\omega} = 50$ Hz. Figure 63 presents theoretical seismograms and amplitude graphs of the first three phases of the vertical component of the longitudinal wave displacement vector for three different positions of the source, which are marked by black triangle. The x coordinate of the point of observation is written to the right of the vertical passing through the diffracting edge. The value of this quantity on the graphs is expressed in fractions of the "apparent" wave length $\lambda = 2\pi c_1/\overline{\omega} = 50$ m. Each trace of the seismogram is placed right above the point of observation. The detailed analysis of these seismograms is given in Klem-Musatov et al., 1975b.

Figure 64 shows experimental and theoretical amplitude graphs for some models. The ultrasound physical modeling was carried out in the contacting media "organic glass ($c_1 \approx 2.2$ km/s – paraffin($c_2 \approx 1.7$ km/s)."

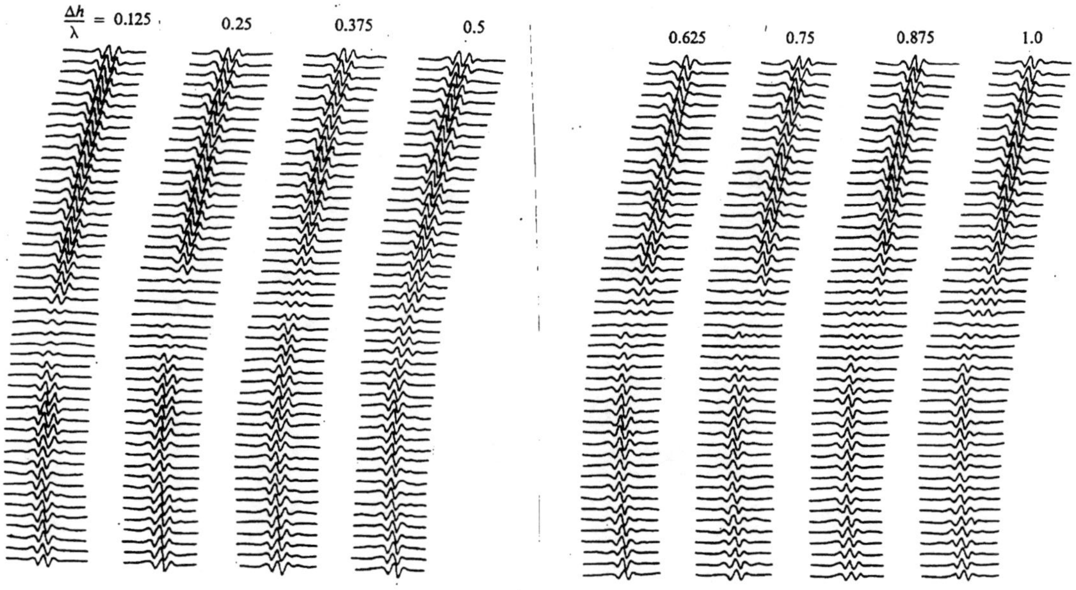

Figure 57. Theoretical seismograms of reflections from an interface disrupted by a small-throw fault.

Example 7. Diffraction on an interface with two edges—The edge-diffracted waves, described by equation 2(37), are included in a Norsk Hydro A/S, Research Centre 2-D seismic modeling package. Figures 65 and 66 demonstrate the contribution of the longitudinal and transverse edge-diffracted waves in the wave picture that can be observed in vertical seismic profiling. The source is placed at the earth's surface with the array of receivers (with vertical and horizontal components) in the vertical well.

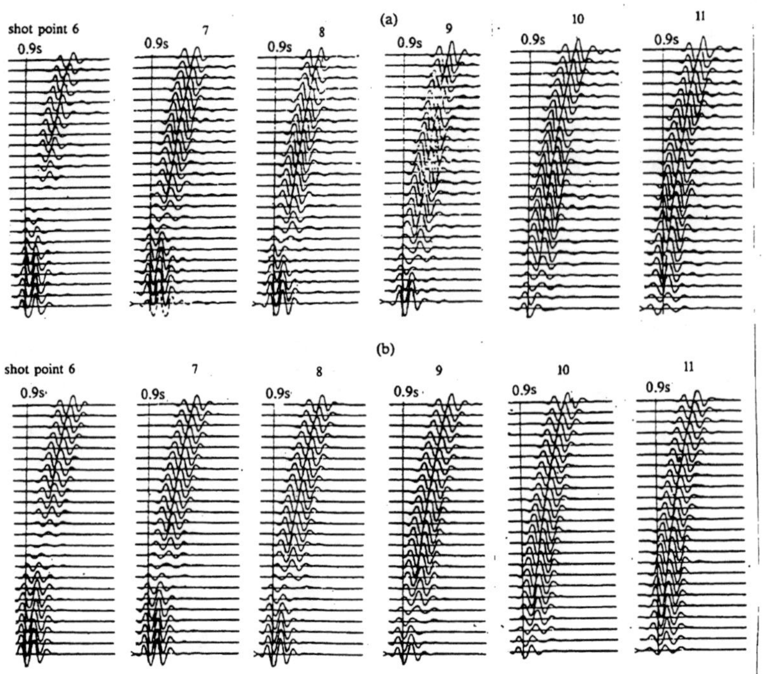

Figure 58. Experimental (a) and theoretical (b) seismograms for the model of a small-throw fault $\Delta h = \lambda / 4$. *(Landa and Maksimov, 1980).*

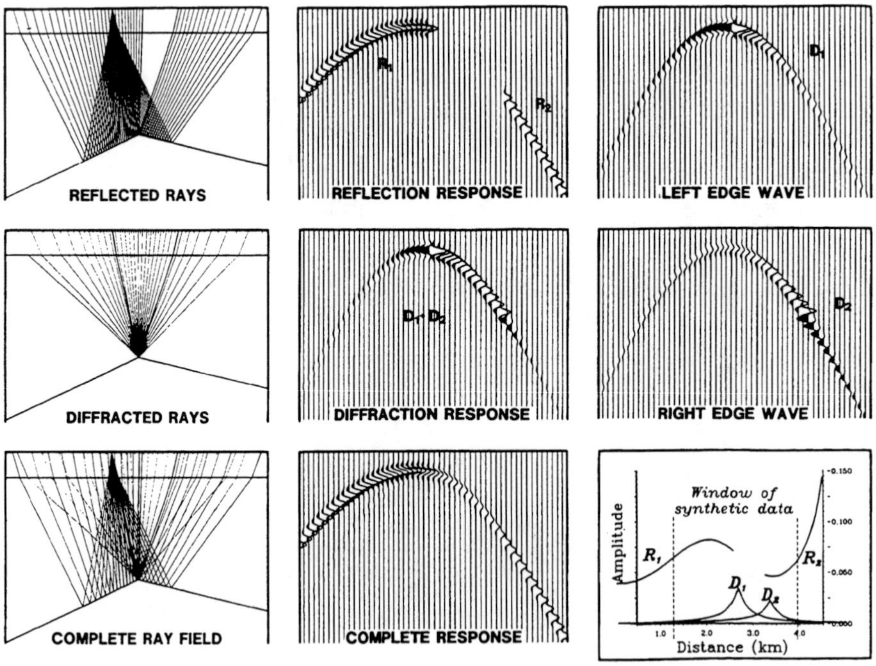

Figure 59. Formation of the reflected wavefield with the consideration of diffractions. (J. Pajchel et al., 1988).

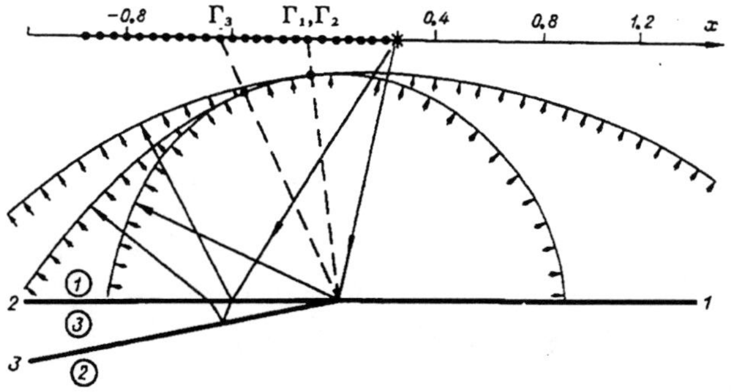

Figure 60. Model of a "pinch-out" and wavefronts in a cross-section with the projection of the observation system. The profile of observation is perpendicular to the edge. The angle of the pinch-out is 5° (Klem-Musatov and Aizenberg, 1985).

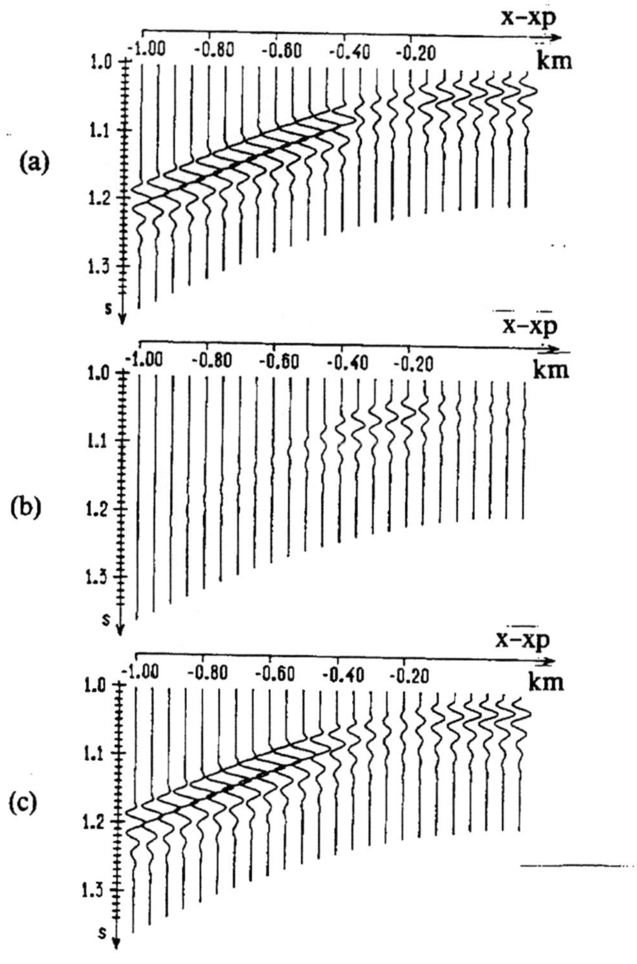

Figure 61. Theoretical seismograms for model of "pinch-out": (a) reflected waves, (b) edge waves, (c) total field. (Klem-Musatov and Aizenberg, 1985).

Example 8. Diffraction on a piecewise-broken interface—Example 8 is also from Research Centre of Norsk Hydro A/S reports. The geological model is shown in Figure 67. The target consists of a series of rotated fault blocks which have been modeled in terms of two sequences of broken reflectors. The edge-diffracted waves from the edges of these blocks have been computed in accordance with equation 2(37). The seismogram of normal incidence profiling (NIP) shown in Figure 68 (top) is dominated by the diffraction events. Most of the reflections are difficult to identify. However, after applying a straight forward FK-migration procedure from the seismic processing package the fault blocks of the model are revealed clearly (Figure 68, bottom).

Example 9. Diffraction in refracted waves—Example 9, taken from Lunyova and Kharlamov (1990), gives a comparison of the mathematical and 2-D ultrasound physical modeling of the refraction of a longitudinal wave at the interface containing diffracting edges. The form of the interface and the system of observation are shown in Figure 69a. The media properties are characterized by the following quantities:

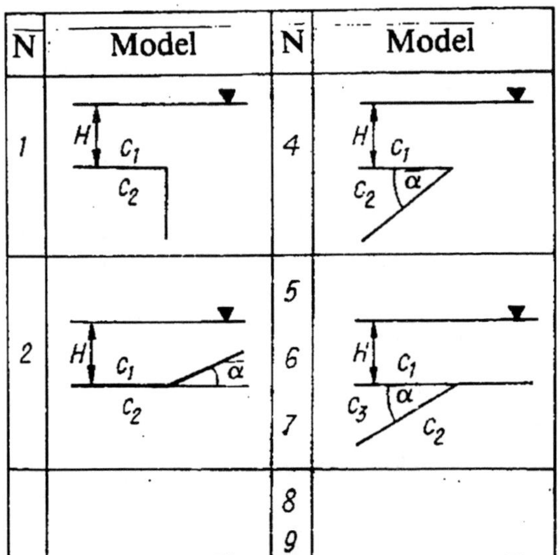

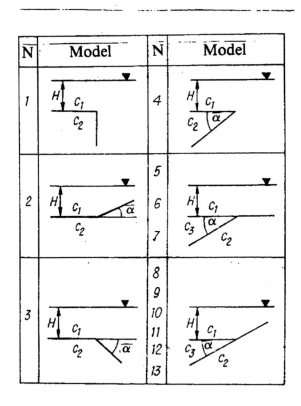

Figure 62. Models of media and the system of observation.

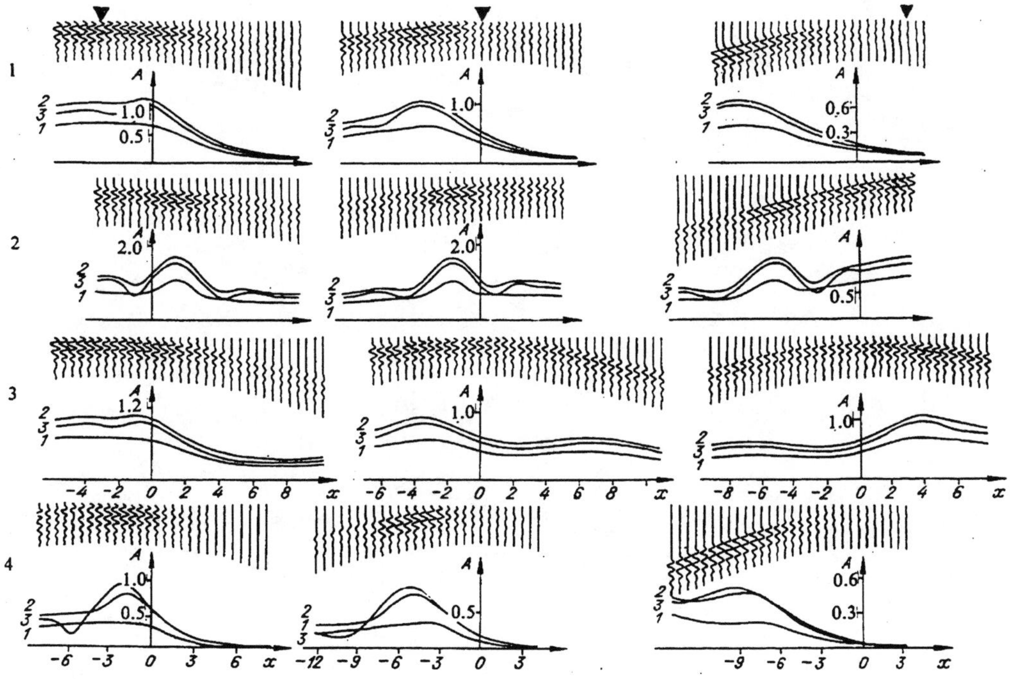

Figure 63. Theoretical seismograms and amplitude graphs of the first three phases of oscillations in different models. Numbers of the models are shown at the left.

$$v_{p1} = 5.35 \text{ km/s}, \quad v_{s1} = 3.1 \text{ km/s}, \quad \rho_1 = 0.132 \text{ g/cm}^3, \quad \lambda_1 = 5.35 \text{ cm},$$

$$v_{p2} = 2.3 \text{ km/s}, \quad v_{s2} = 1.3 \text{ km/s}, \quad \rho_2 = 0.123 \text{ g/cm}^3, \quad \lambda_2 = 2.3 \text{ cm},$$

where v_{pn} and v_{sn} are velocities of longitudinal and transverse waves respectively, ρ_n is the media density, λ_n is the "apparent" wave length, $n = 1$ in the incident wave domain, and $n = 2$ is the domain of observation. The distance from the source to the interface 18 - 20 λ_1 is chosen in such a way that at the profile of observation the wave fronts, refracted through the plane parts of the interface, are almost plane. The angle of incidence at the plane parts of the interface is 20°. The distance from the interface to the profile of observation is 3 λ_2. The curvilinear part of the interface ("dome") is a segment of a circle (its height is λ_2 and its base is 6 λ_2).

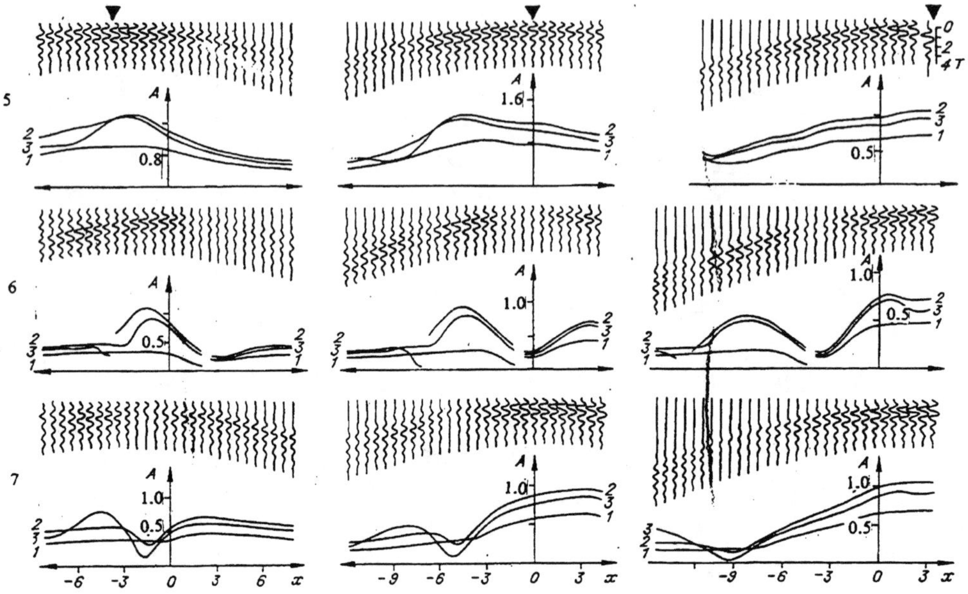

Figure 63. Theoretical seismograms and amplitude graphs of the first three phases of oscillations in different models. Numbers of the models are shown at the left.

PP– and *PS*–waves are formed due to refraction. There are four shadow boundaries in each of the wavefields because of the edges of the interface. The discontinuities at these shadow boundaries are smoothed by the corresponding edge-diffracted waves (see Figure 69a). The mathematical modeling was carried out by the *edge-diffracted wave superposition method* (Aizenberg and Klem-Musatov, 1980; Klem-Musatov et al., 1982; Klem-Musatov and Aizenberg, 1989), in which the curvilinear interface was approximated by a piecewise-plane surface with sufficiently small elements. In the case under consideration this approach leads directly to the result that could be obtained from equations 1(5) and 2(37), therefore, providing data required to check the accuracy of the boundary-layer approximation.

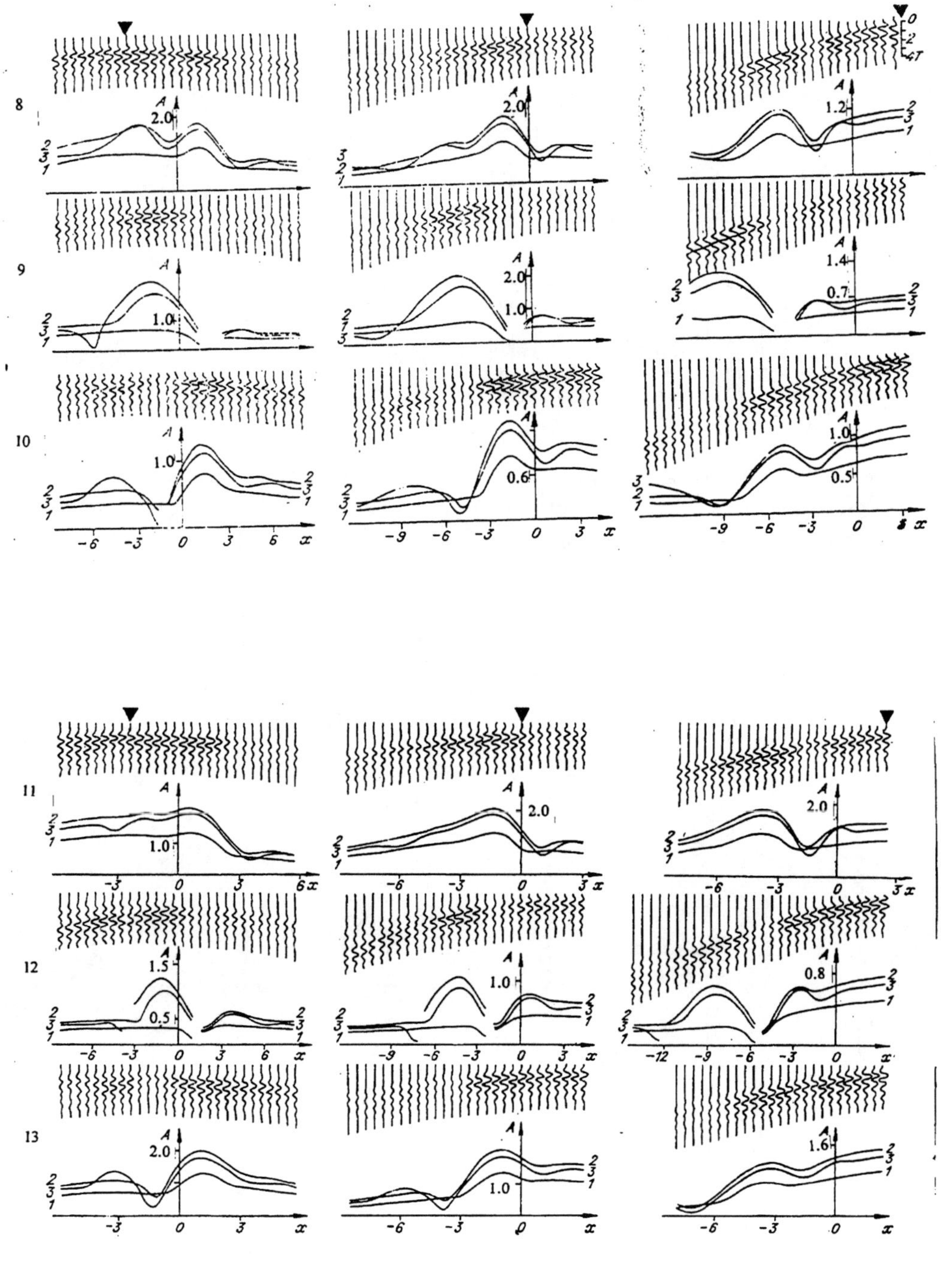

Figure 63. Theoretical seismograms and amplitude graphs of the first three phases of oscillations in different models. Numbers of the models are shown at the left.

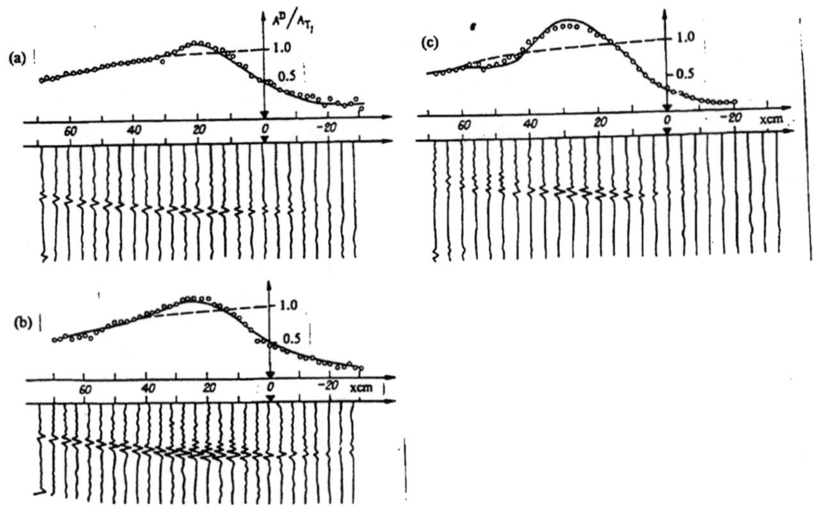

Figure 64. Experimental seismograms, experimental (circles) and theoretical (solid lines) amplitude graphs in the models of type 1 (a) and 4 for α = 20° (b) α = 5° (c). The dashed lines correspond to a theoretical amplitude of the wave, reflected from the horizontal part of the interface (Klem-Musatov et al., 1975).

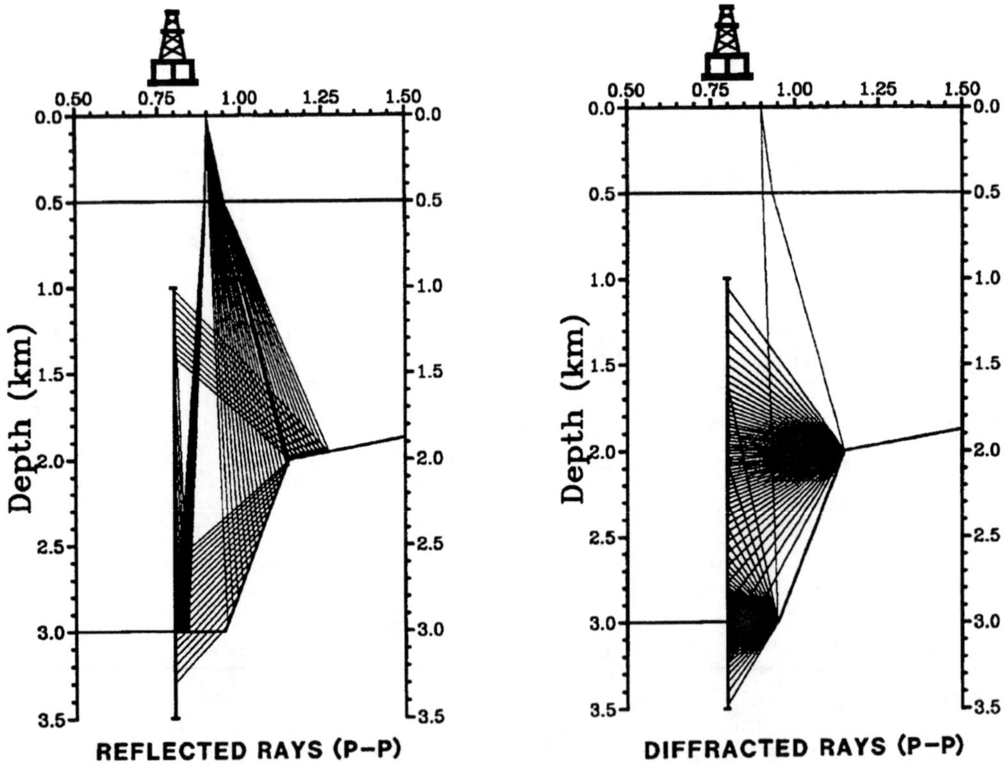

Figure 65. Ray diagrams for reflections and diffractions in a rig source (zero-offset) VSP (Pajchel et al., 1989).

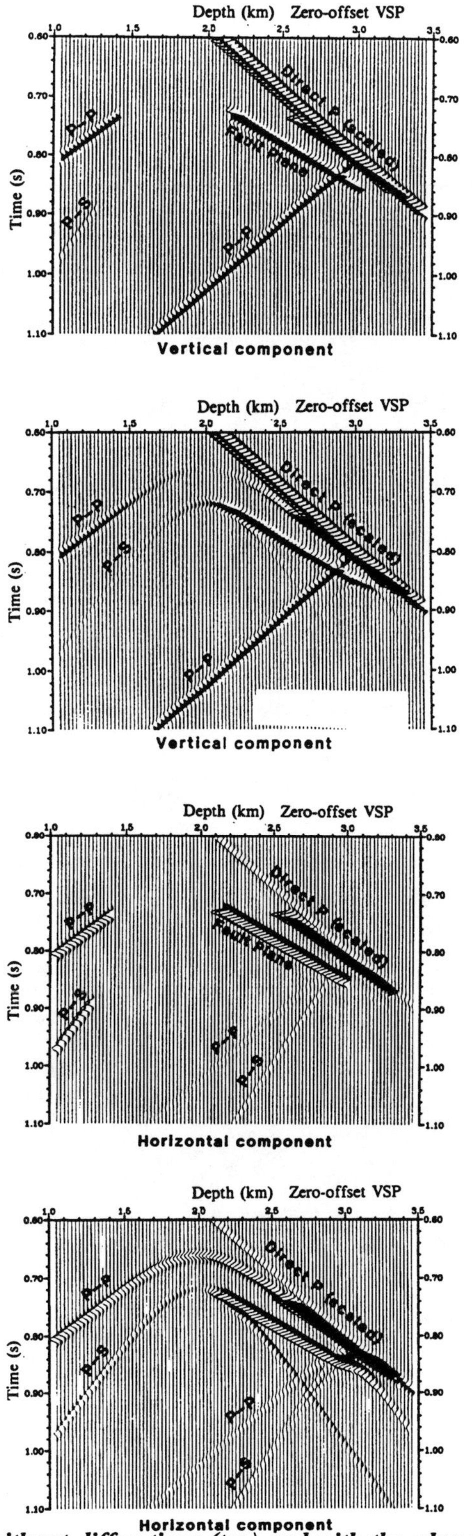

Figure 66. Zero-offset VSPs without diffractions (top) and with the edge-diffracted waves superimposed (bottom) (J. Pajchel et al., 1989).

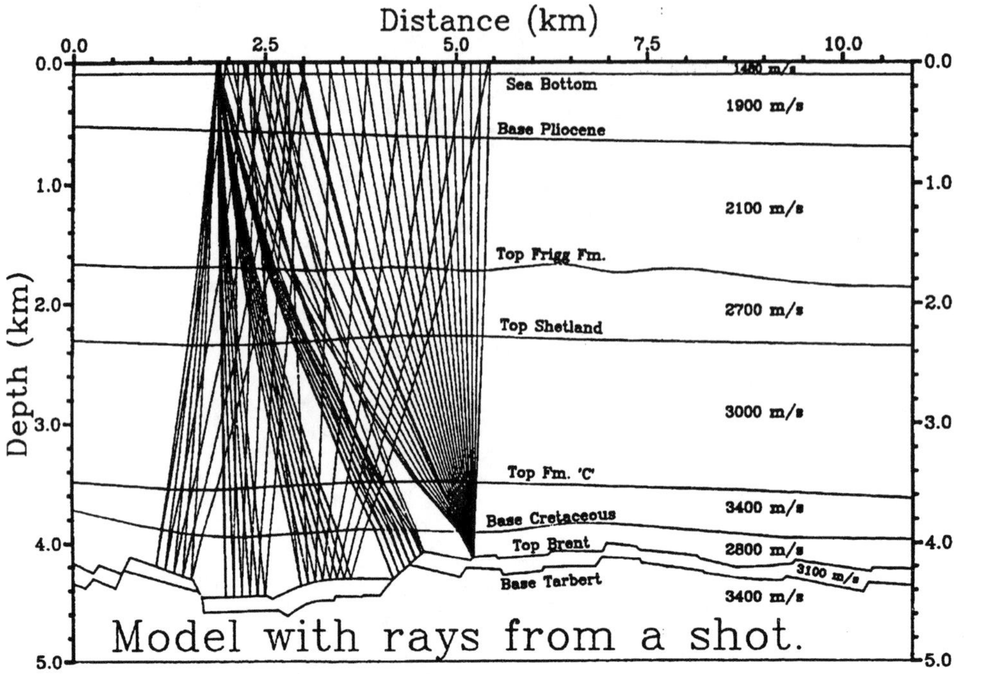

Figure 67. Geological model. (J. Pajchel et al., 1988).

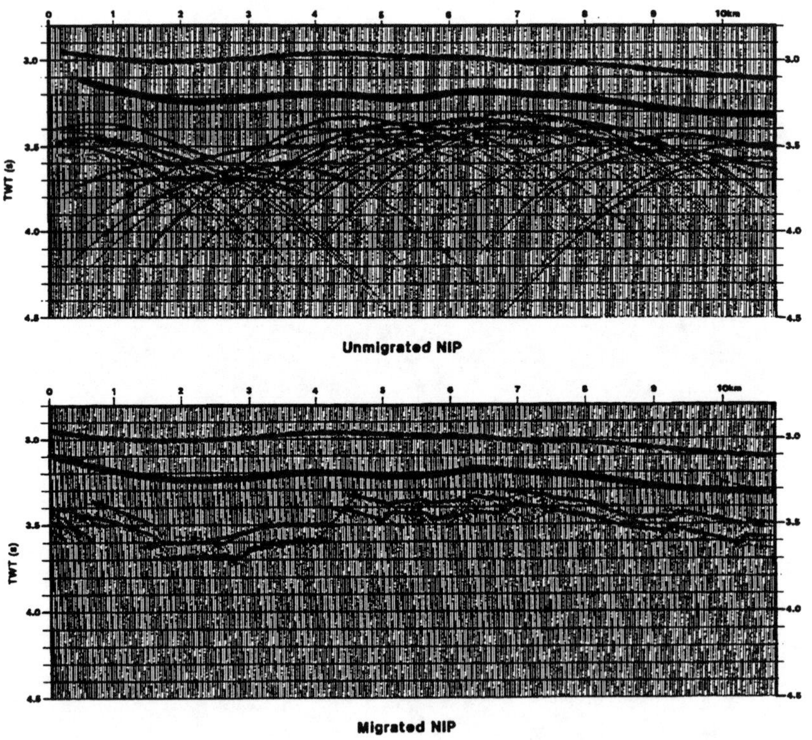

Figure 68. Theoretical seismograms and seismic migration of the normal incidence profiling (Pajchel et al., 1988).

Figure 69b shows the theoretical and experimental seismograms of the vertical z and horizontal x components of the displacement vector. To compare the theoretical and experimental data quantitatively, the coefficients of correlation along the corresponding traces for $z-$ and $x-$components were computed separately. The coefficient of correlation is 0.9 for the $z-$component, and 0.7 - 0.8 for the $x-$component. The decrease of the correlation for the horizontal component is because of the decrease of the signal/noise ratio compared to the vertical component. The amplitude graphs of $PP-$ and $PS-$waves along the profile of observation are shown in Figure 69c. The graphs show the second phase of oscillations (the positive maximum) in fractions of the maximum amplitude of the correspondent wave at the correspondent profile.

Example 10. Effect of the inhomogeneity of the medium—All preceding examples dealt with the cases of diffraction in the piecewise-homogeneous media when the rays were straight. A question, therefore, arises whether the inhomogeneity of the medium, i.e., the curvature of the rays, can influence the diffraction effects being considered? The following example, from Klem-Musatov and Tatarnikov (1976), partly answers this question.

Figure 70 shows the theoretical seismograms and amplitude graphs of the wavefield arising at a half-plane (model of type 1 in Figure 62) placed in the inhomogeneous medium. All notations coincide with those in Figure 63. The shape of the incident pulse is given at the right. The propagation velocity depends on the depth z as follows: $c = 2.5\,(1 + \beta z)$ km/s, where $z = 0$ at the profile of observation, and $z = 0.5$ km at the reflecting half-plane. The values of β are given in the figure at the left. This example shows that the inhomogeneity of the medium does not influence the character of the local diffraction effects.

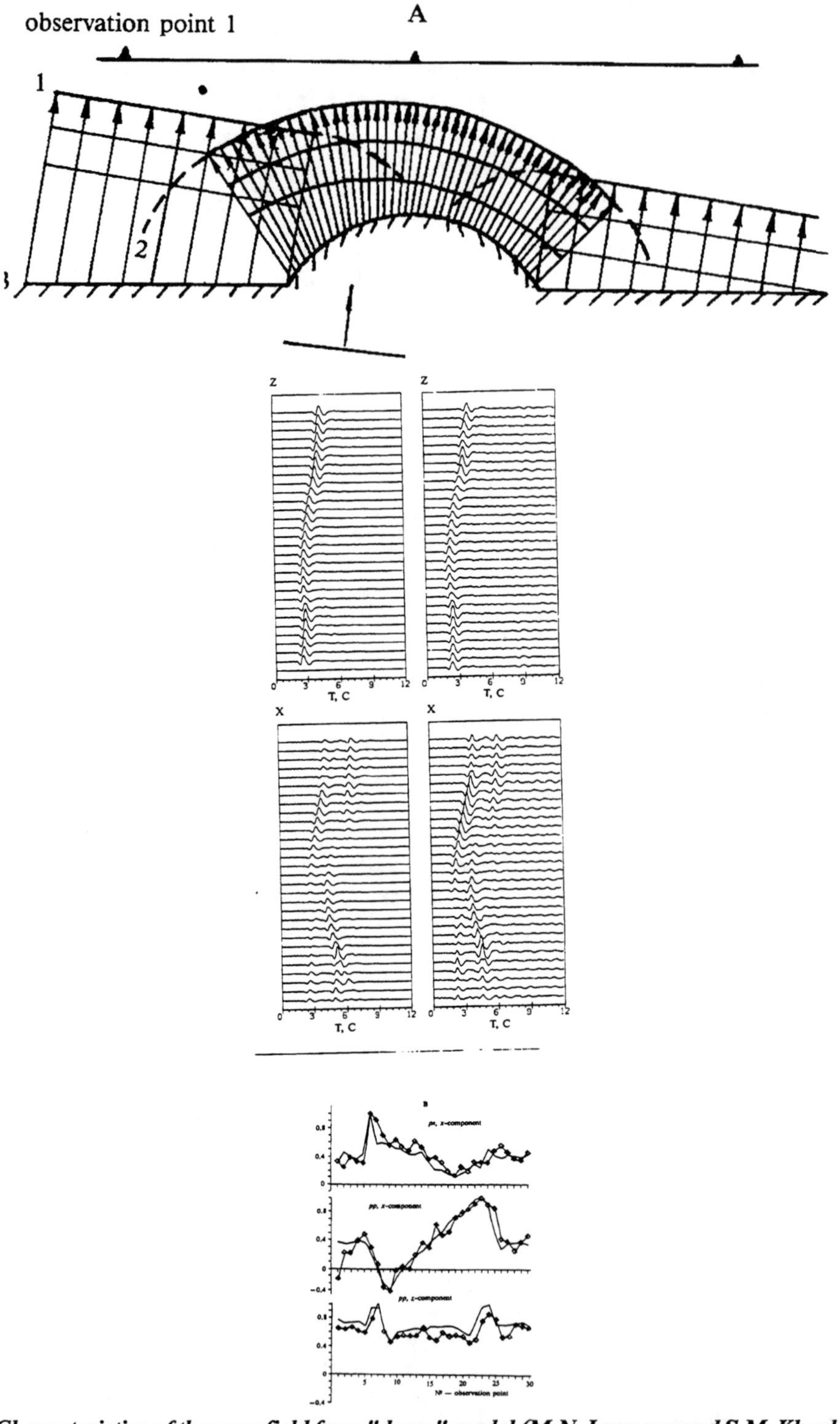

Figure 69. Characteristics of the wavefield for a "dome" model (M.N. Lunyova and S.M. Kharlamov, 1990). (A) scheme of propagation through the interface with the "dome"; (1) front of regular wave; (2) front of diffracted wave; (3) interface. (B) theoretical (left) and experimental (right) seismograms. (C) amplitude graphs.

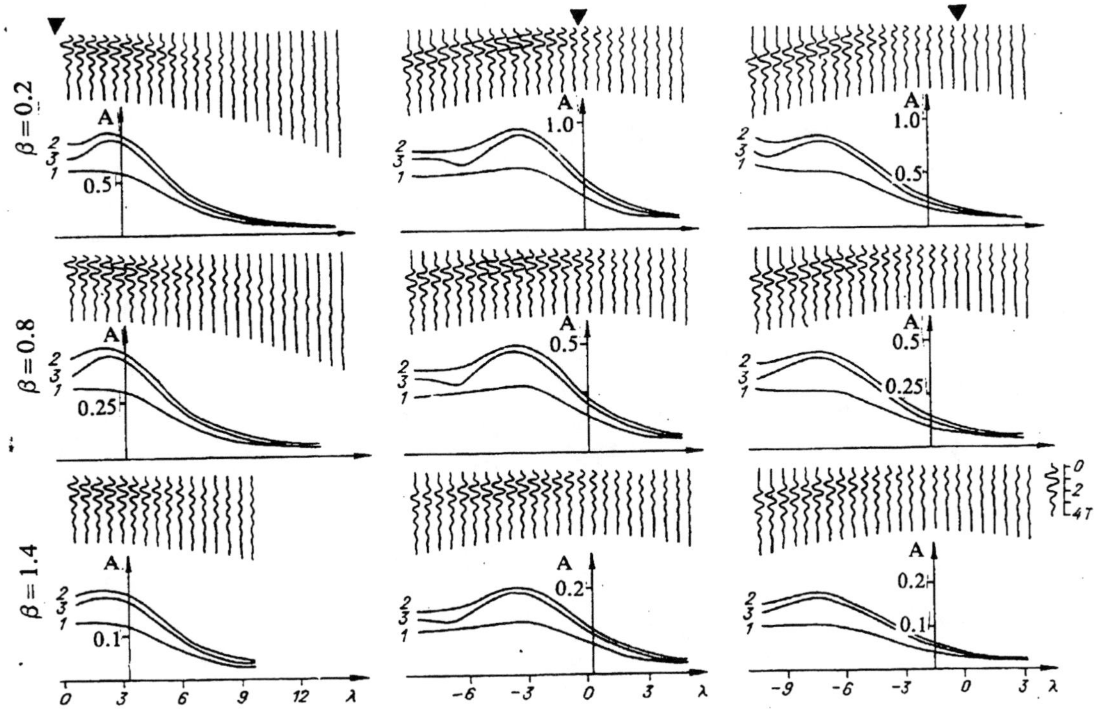

Figure 70. Edge diffraction in inhomogeneous medium. (Klem-Musatov and Tatarnikov, 1976).

Chapter IX

TIP WAVES

In 3-D block media the interfaces are represented by the surfaces of the curvilinear polyhedrons. Such surfaces include the vertices, where several diffracting edges can converge, and therefore, in 3-D block media the diffracting edges are not smooth. The latter limits the range of applicability of the approach described in Chapter VIII. The gist of the limitations becomes clear from the following example.

Figure 71a shows the geometry of the shadow boundary of the reflected/transmitted wave in the case of a broken edge. The edge consists of two semi-infinite parts RA and RB. Point R is not a regular point of the edge, because the tangent to the edge cannot be determined as a single value at R. The shadow boundary consists of two parts RAT and RBT.

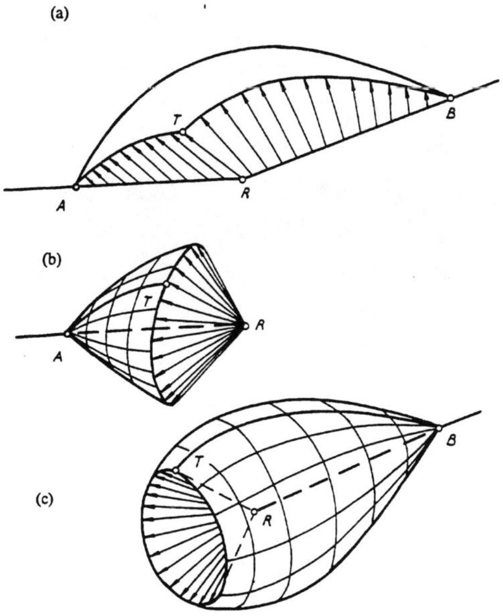

Figure 71. The form of a shadow boundary (a) and the edge-diffracted wavefronts (b) and (c) in a case of the broken edge.

Figures 71b and 71c show the fronts of the edge-diffracted waves arising at semi-edges RA and RB. The diffracted rays, caused by each individual semi-edge, form a *congruence.* However, the unification of two sets of diffracted rays, spreading from two semi-edges, is not a congruence. Each of two mentioned congruences exists only on one side of the cone of diffracted rays spreading from point R. Such a cone acts like a shadow boundary of the corresponding edge-diffracted wave, caused by the semi-edge. There are no edge-diffracted waves in the region where diffracted rays do not exist.

Thus, in the case of a broken edge we face the deficiency of the above considered approach, caused by the discontinuities of the edge wavefields. The problem is how to correct for these discontinuities. Here we show that the corresponding problem can be formulated and solved by the approach used in Chapter VIII. We begin with a scalar case and then generalize obtained formulas for the case of vector waves.

1. Original representations

1. Definitions—The point of break (or the end) of a smooth edge is called the *tip*. Every smooth part of an edge has two tips. The common tip of several edges forms a *vertex.*

The sizes of the edge-diffracted wave domains are limited because of the tips. A single edge-diffracted wave f_{mn} exists within the connected domain coinciding with the corresponding congruence of diffracted rays. This wavefield f_{mn} is continuous everywhere within its domain, with the exception of the primary shadow boundary, $\tau_{mn} = \tau_m$. This type of domain is called the *secondary illuminated zone* of wave f_{mn}. A domain of absence of the wave ($f_{mn} \equiv 0$) is called the *secondary shadow zone.* A simply connected surface dividing the above zones is called the *secondary shadow boundary* and looks like the surface of a curvilinear cone whose apex angle complies with the law of edge diffraction. In Figures 71b and 71c the secondary shadow boundaries correspond to the cones of edge-diffracted rays spreading from point R. An individual edge-wave f_{mn} can have two secondary shadow boundaries which we mark by the triple index mnp.

When the diffracting edges are not smooth, representation VIII.1(5) is not sufficient because of the discontinuities at the secondary shadow boundaries. To correct for these discontinuities, we look for the total wavefield in the form

$$f = \sum_m [\, f_m + \sum_n (f_{mn} + \sum_p f_{mnp})\,] , \tag{1}$$

where term f_{mnp} must smooth the discontinuity of wave f_{mn} at the mnp^{th} secondary shadow boundary. We now state a mathematical problem of finding f_{mnp}.

2. *Tip-diffracted wave*—We look for f_{mnp} in the form of a wave spreading from the vertex. To do so, we must introduce a corresponding congruence of diffracted rays. Because it is impossible to determine uniquely the tangent plane to the interface at the vertex, then Snell's law puts no limitations on the directions of rays arising at the vertex. This fact is known as the *law of vertex diffraction* (Keller, 1962), which reads "The incident ray generates rays leaving the vertex in all directions."

Let e_{mnp} be a unit vector of the tangent to the ray. Let this ray comply with the law of vertex diffraction at that tip, which gives the mnp^{th} secondary shadow boundary. Then the differential equation

$$d(e_{mnp}/c_m)/ds = \nabla(1/c_m) \tag{2}$$

determines the congruence of the *tip-diffracted rays.*

Let wave

$$f_{mnp} = \Phi_{mnp} \exp(i\omega\tau_{mnp}), \quad \nabla\tau_{mnp} = e_{mnp}/c_m \tag{3}$$

be connected with the mnp^{th} secondary shadow boundary. The latter can be given implicitly by the equation

$$\tau_{mnp} = \tau_{mn}. \tag{4}$$

The wave, equation (3), is called the *tip-diffracted wave.*

We will look for the terms f_{mnp} of sum (1) in the form of tip-diffracted waves (3), assuming that the eikonals τ_{mnp} are the given functions of the position in a 3-D space. Then the problem is to find the amplitudes Φ_{mnp} of the tip waves.

3. *Domains of continuity*—From now on we will consider an individual tip-diffracted wave. Figure 72 shows the pair of wavefronts $\tau_{mn} = t$ and $\tau_{mnp} = t$ where t is time. This figure helps introduce an idea of the domains of continuity of these waves.

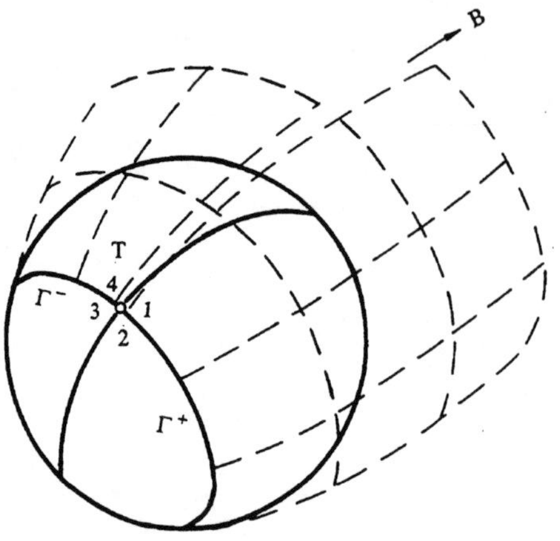

Figure 72. Separation of the space into domains of continuity (1, 2, 3, 4). The fronts of the edge (dashed lines) and tip (solid lines) diffracted waves touch at the secondary shadow boundary $\Gamma^-\Gamma^+$. ***TB – the primary shadow boundary.***

The secondary shadow boundary [equation (4)] divides the space into two parts: the secondary illuminated zone and the secondary shadow zone. Suppose that the primary shadow boundary $\tau_{mn} = \tau_m$ can be continued analytically into the secondary shadow zone. The continued surface also divides space into two parts. As a result, the continued primary shadow boundary $\tau_{mn} = \tau_m$ and the secondary shadow boundary (4) divide the domain of the wave f_{mn} into four parts as shown in Figure 72.

We number the parts 1, 2, 3, and 4, going around the line $\tau_{mnp} = \tau_{mn} = \tau_m$ clockwise or counterclockwise, so that the shortest way from the fourth part to the first part would coincide with the shortest way from the primary illuminated zone of the wave f_m to the primary shadow zone through the mn^{th} primary shadow boundary. The line $\tau_{mnp} = \tau_{mn} = \tau_m$ is called the *central ray*. The first and third domains have common points only at the *central ray*. The second and fourth domains have common points only at the same ray.

On crossing the central ray along the secondary shadow boundary, the edge-diffracted wave f_{mn} has a discontinuity because of the change of its sign VIII.2(38). So, the central ray divides the secondary shadow boundary into intervals of continuity of the edge-diffracted wave. We denote the boundary between the first and second domains by Γ^+, and between the third and fourth domains by Γ^-. The combination of the surfaces Γ^+ and Γ^- forms the secondary shadow boundary. At each of surfaces $\Gamma^\pm$ the edge-diffracted wave is continuous.

The tip wave, represented in equation (3), can be written in the form

$$f_{mnp} = f^{+} + f^{-}, \; f^{\pm} = \Phi^{\pm} \exp\,(i\,\omega\,\tau_{mnp}) \tag{5}$$

Let the sum $f_{mn} + f^{+}$ be continuous at the boundary Γ^{+} and the sum $f_{mn} + f^{-}$ be continuous at the boundary Γ^{-}. Under these conditions, we can find f^{+} and f^{-} in the same way used for finding f_{mn}.

4. Ray coordinates—Let τ_{mnp}, $\psi^{\pm}$, σ be the ray coordinates of the wave $f^{\pm}$. Here $\psi^{\pm}$ and σ give a congruence of the tip-diffracted rays, i.e., every pair of fixed values $\psi^{\pm} = \text{const}$ and $\sigma = \text{const}$ singles out an individual ray. Let the coordinate σ correspond to the distance from the central ray. For example, σ can be an arc length on the surface $\tau_{mnp} = \text{const}$. Let the coordinate $\psi^{\pm}$ correspond to the distance from the surface $\Gamma^{\pm}$. Let $\psi^{\pm}$ vary in the interval $-\pi \leq \psi^{\pm} \leq \pi$. The computation of ray coordinates can always be done by the corresponding scaling. We choose $\psi^{\pm}$ in such a way that the surface $\psi^{\pm} = 0$ would coincide with the surface $\Gamma^{\pm}$, and the surfaces $\psi^{\pm} = \pi$ and $\psi^{\pm} = -\pi$ would coincide with $\Gamma^{\mp}$ (Figure 73).

To express the value of $\psi^{\pm}$ through the value less than $\pi/2$ we introduce a special notation for the domains of continuity. Let Ω^{-}_{mnp} denote the combination of the first and third domains, and Ω^{+}_{mnp} denote the combination of the second and fourth domains (see Figures 72 and 73).

The following unit function

$$s_{mnp} = \begin{cases} +1 \text{ when } M \in \Omega^{+}_{mnp} \\ -1 \text{ when } M \in \Omega^{+}_{mnp}, \end{cases} \tag{6}$$

where M is a running point of space, is connected with function VIII.2(38) in the secondary illuminated zone by the relation

$$s_{mnp} = -\,s_{mn} \quad \text{when } \psi^{\pm} < 0, \tag{7'}$$

and in the secondary shadow zone by the relation

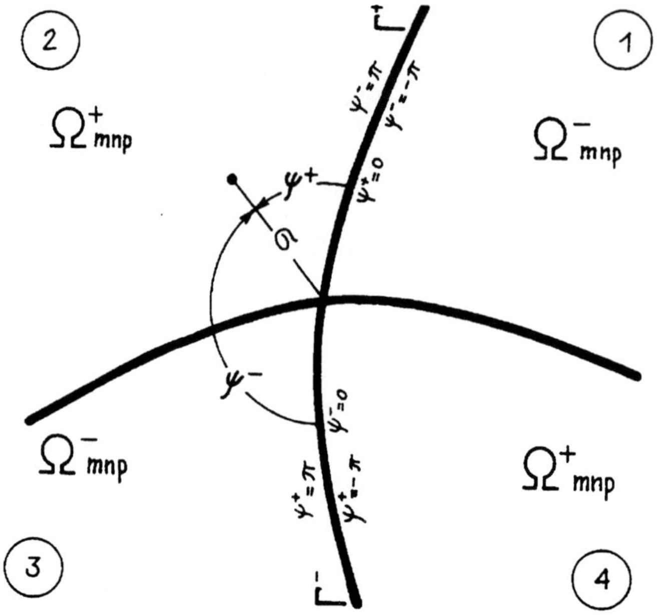

Figure 73. The domains of continuity and the ray coordinates of a tip diffracted wave at the surface τ_{mnp} = const .

$$s_{mnp} = s_{mn} \quad \text{when } \psi^{\pm} > 0 . \tag{7''}$$

To check that the following relations hold true is easy:

$$\psi^{\pm} = \pm\, s_{mnp}\, |\psi^{\pm}| \quad \text{when } |\psi^{\pm}| \le \pi/2 ,$$

$$\psi^{\pm} = \pm\, s_{mnp}\, (|\psi^{\mp}| - \pi) \quad \text{when } |\psi^{\pm}| > \pi/2 . \tag{8}$$

By using equation (8) and taking into consideration the relation

$$|\psi^{\pm}| + |\psi^{\mp}| = \pi , \tag{9}$$

we can express $\psi^{\pm}$ through its value less than $\pi/2$,

$$\psi^{+} = s_{mnp}\,|\psi^{+}| ,\ \psi^{-} = -\,s_{mnp}\,(|\psi^{+}| - \pi) ,\ \text{when } |\psi^{+}| < \pi/2 ,\ |\psi^{-}| > \pi/2 ,$$

$$\psi^{+} = s_{mnp}\,(|\psi^{-}| - \pi) ,\ \psi^{-} = -\,s_{mnp}|\psi^{-}| ,\ \text{when } |\psi^{+}| > \pi/2 ,\ |\psi^{-}| < \pi/2 , \tag{10}$$

5. *Representation of the edge-diffracted wave*—Let us consider the edge-diffracted wave f_{mn} as a function of the ray coordinates of the tip-diffracted wave.

The intersection of the primary shadow zone Ω^{+}_{mn} or the primary illuminated zone Ω^{-}_{mn} of wave f_m with the secondary illuminated zone can be determined, respectively, by the following inequalities:

$$-\pi/2 < \psi^{+} < 0 \quad \text{or} \quad -\pi/2 < \psi^{-} < 0 \tag{11}$$

Then function [VIII.2(38)] can be determined as

$$s_{mn} = \pm 1 \quad \text{when} \; -\pi/2 < \psi^{\pm} < 0 \,. \tag{12}$$

We consider the edge-diffracted wave in domain Ω^{+}_{mn} as a function of coordinate ψ^{+}, and in domain Ω^{-}_{mn} as a function of ψ^{-}. Then, taking into consideration equation (12), equation VIII.2(37) in the secondary illuminated zone can be written as

$$f_{mn}(\tau_{mnp}, \psi^{\pm}, \sigma) = \pm \Phi_m W(w_{mn}) \exp(i\omega\tau_{mn}) \quad \text{when} \; -\pi/2 < \psi^{\pm} < 0 \,. \tag{13}$$

By continuing this expression through the primary shadow boundary $\psi^{\pm} = -\pi/2$ we have

$$f_{mn}(\tau_{mnp}, \psi^{\pm}, \sigma) = \mp \Phi_m W(w_{mn}) \exp(i\omega\tau_{mn}) \quad \text{when} \; -\pi < \psi^{\pm} < -\pi/2 \,. \tag{14}$$

In the domain $\psi^{\pm} > 0$ the edge-diffracted wave does not exist.

Thus, the edge-diffracted wave can be represented either as a function of coordinates $(\tau_{mnp}, \psi^{+}, \sigma)$, i.e.,

$$\left.\begin{aligned} f_{mn} &= f_{mn}(\tau_{mnp}, \psi^{+}, \sigma) && \text{when} \; -\pi \le \psi^{+} < 0 \\ f_{mn} &= 0 && \text{when} \; 0 < \psi^{+} \le \pi \end{aligned}\right\} \tag{15'}$$

with the discontinuity at Γ^{+}, or as a function of coordinates $(\tau_{mnp}, \psi^{-}, \sigma)$, i.e.,

$$\left.\begin{aligned} f_{mn} &= f_{mn}(\tau_{mnp}, \psi^{-}, \sigma) && \text{when} \; -\pi \le \psi^{-} < 0 \\ f_{mn} &= 0 && \text{when} \; 0 < \psi^{-} \le \pi \end{aligned}\right\} \tag{15''}$$

with the discontinuity at Γ^{-}.

6. *Conditions at the secondary shadow boundary*—Let us consider the members of the sum, equation (5), as the functions of the corresponding ray coordinates

$$f^+ = f^+(\tau_{mnp}, \psi^+, \sigma) = f^+(\psi^+), \tag{16}$$

$$f^- = f^-(\tau_{mnp}, \psi^-, \sigma) = f^-(\psi^-),$$

dropping the dependence on τ_{mnp} and σ for brevity.

According to equation (5), the sum $f_{mn} + f^+$ is continuous at surface Γ^+. To write this condition, we represent the edge-diffracted wave by equation (15'). Then the corresponding condition can be written as

$$[f^+(\psi^+) + f_{mn}(\psi^+)]_{\psi^+=-0} = [f^+(\psi^+)]_{\psi^+=+0}, \tag{17'}$$

where the dependence of f_{mn} on τ_{mnp} and σ is dropped for brevity.

According to equation (5), the sum $f_{mn} + f^-$ is continuous at surface Γ^-. By representing f_{mn} in equation (15") we can write the corresponding condition as

$$[f^-(\psi^-) + f_{mn}(\psi^-)]_{\psi^-=-0} = [f^-(\psi^-)]_{\psi^-=+0}, \tag{17''}$$

We can write both conditions (17') and (17") in the form

$$[f^\pm(\psi^\pm) + f_{mn}(\psi^\pm)]_{\psi^\pm=-0} = [f^\pm(\psi^\pm)]_{\psi^\pm=+0}, \tag{18}$$

2. Smoothing the discontinuity

1. *Periodic functions*—It follows from the physical considerations that the functions being discussed must comply with the following condition of periodicity:

$$f_{mn}(\psi^\pm + 2\pi k) = f_{mn}(\psi^\pm), \tag{1}$$

$$f^\pm(\psi^\pm + 2\pi k) = f^\pm(\psi^\pm), \tag{2}$$

where k is an integer. Suppose that function $f^\pm$ allows a representation in the form of an infinite series

$$f^{\pm}(\psi^{\pm}) = \sum_{k=-\infty}^{\infty} F^{\pm}(\psi^{\pm} + 2\pi k), \tag{3}$$

where $F^{\pm}$ is some new unknown function. Then $f^{\pm}(\psi^{\pm})$ is the periodic function, because the replacement of $\psi^{\pm}$ by $\psi^{\pm} + 2\pi k$ leads only to a new designation of the index of summation.

By inserting equation (3) into condition 1(18) we derive

$$\left[\sum_{k=-\infty}^{\infty} F^{\pm}(\psi^{\pm}+2\pi k)+f_{mn}(\psi^{\pm})\right]_{\psi^{\pm}=-0} = \left[\sum_{k=-\infty}^{\infty} F^{\pm}(\psi^{\pm} + 2\pi k)\right]_{\psi^{\pm}=+0}. \tag{4}$$

Suppose that function $F^{\pm}$ complies with the following conditions of continuity at the secondary shadow boundary

$$\left[F^{\pm}(\psi^{\pm}) + f_{mn}(\psi^{\pm})\right]_{\psi^{\pm}=-0} = \left[F^{\pm}(\psi^{\pm})\right]_{\psi^{\pm}=+0}, \tag{5}$$

$$\left[F^{\pm}(\psi^{\pm} + 2\pi k)\right]_{\psi^{\pm}=-0} = \left[F^{\pm}(\psi^{\pm} + 2\pi k)\right]_{\psi^{\pm}=+0} \tag{6}$$

for any k except for $k = 0$. Then function $F^{\pm}$ complies with condition (4) as well.

2. *Non-periodic functions*—Let

$$\eta^{\pm} = \psi^{\pm} + 2\pi k \tag{7}$$

be a new variable, where k is an integer. When $-\pi \le \psi^{\pm} \le \pi$, this variable can have any value from the interval $(-\infty, \infty)$ and turn to zero for $\psi^{\pm} = 0$, $k = 0$ only.

It follows from equations (1) - (3) that we can consider functions

$$f_{mn}(\psi^{\pm}) = f_{mn}(\psi^{\pm} + 2\pi k) = f_{mn}(\eta^{\pm}), \tag{8}$$

$$f^{\pm}(\psi^{\pm}) = f^{\pm}(\psi^{\pm} + 2\pi k) = f^{\pm}(\eta^{\pm}), \text{ and} \tag{9}$$

$$F^{\pm}(\psi^{\pm} + 2\pi k) = F^{\pm}(\eta^{\pm}) \tag{10}$$

as the functions of a new variable $\eta^{\pm}$ in the infinite interval $(-\infty, \infty)$. Note that functions $f_{mn}(\eta^{\pm})$ and $f^{\pm}(\eta^{\pm})$ are periodic functions with the period 2π.

Function $F^{\pm}(\eta^{\pm})$ is non-periodic. Indeed, in accordance with condition (5), this function has a given jump at $\eta^{\pm} = 0$. On the other hand, in accordance with condition (6) this function is continuous at $\eta^{\pm} = 2\pi k$ for any k except for $k = 0$. To satisfy both conditions, this function has to be non-periodic.

Let us consider f_{mn} and $F^{\pm}$ as the functions (8) - (9) of variable $\eta^{\pm}$. Let $F^{\pm}$ comply with the following condition:

$$\left[F^{\pm}(\eta^{\pm}) + f_{mn}(\eta^{\pm}) \right]_{\eta^{\pm} = -0} = \left[F^{\pm}(\eta^{\pm}) \right]_{\eta^{\pm} = +0} . \tag{11}$$

Condition (11) coincides with condition (5), because $\eta^{\pm} = \psi^{\pm}$ with $k = 0$. If $F^{\pm}(\eta^{\pm})$ is continuous for $k \neq 0$, condition (6) is satisfied automatically.

Thus, expression (11) represents the condition of continuity of the wavefield at the secondary shadow boundary, if function $F^{\pm}(\eta^{\pm})$ is continuous for $|\eta^{\pm}| > 0$.

3. Smoothing function—The problem of finding the tip wave $f^{\pm}$ can be reduced to finding function $F^{\pm}(\eta^{\pm})$ under condition (11). A similar problem was considered in Section VIII.1.4, so we can use the same approach to formulate the problem of finding function $F^{\pm}$.

Suppose that for values τ_{mnp} and σ being considered function (8) allows a continuation into a complex plane over variable $\eta^{\pm}$ along some contour Γ, satisfying conditions of Section VIII.1.3 (Figure 49). Suppose that at this contour this function is Hölder continuous, equation VIII.1(9), and disappears at infinity

$$|f_{mn}(\eta^{\pm})| \to 0 \quad \text{when } \eta^{\pm} \to \infty \ (\eta^{\pm} \in \Gamma). \tag{12}$$

We will look for function $F^{\pm}(\eta^{\pm})$ among piecewise-analytic functions of the variable $\eta^{\pm}$ under the following boundary condition:

$$F_L^{\pm}(\eta^{\pm}) - F_R^{\pm}(\eta^{\pm}) = f_{mn}(\eta^{\pm}) \quad \text{with } \eta^{\pm} \in \Gamma, \tag{13}$$

where $F_L^{\pm}(\eta^{\pm})$ and $F_R^{\pm}(\eta^{\pm})$ correspond to the values of this function at the left-hand and right-hand sides of the contour Γ, respectively. Condition (11) is a specific case of condition (13), when Im $\eta^{\pm} = 0$ and intervals of the real axis Re $\eta^{\pm} < 0$ and Re $\eta^{\pm} > 0$ are at the right-hand and left-hand sides of the contour Γ, respectively. We impose the following additional restriction on the sought function in the complex plane of $\eta^{\pm}$:

$$| F^{\pm}(\eta^{\pm}) | \to 0 \quad \text{when } \eta^{\pm} \to \infty . \tag{14}$$

It follows from Section VIII.1.3 that conditions (13) and (14) are sufficient to solve the problem of finding function $F^{\pm}(\eta^{\pm})$ uniquely. The solution is given by expression VIII.1(13)

$$F^{\pm}(\eta^{\pm}) = (2\pi i)^{-1} \int_{\Gamma} (\alpha - \eta^{\pm})^{-1} f_{mn}(\alpha) \, d\alpha . \tag{15}$$

This integral possesses the same properties as integral VIII.1(17). It has a discontinuity when $\eta^{\pm} = 0$. However, the superposition of expressions 1(15) and equation (15) is a continuous and analytic function of $\eta^{\pm}$ in the neighborhood of coordinate surface $\eta^{\pm} = 0$. Therefore, function (15) complies with condition (4).

4. Summation of the infinite series—By substituting equation (7) into (15) we have

$$F^{\pm}(\psi^{\pm} + 2\pi k) = (2\pi i)^{-1} \int_{\Gamma} [\alpha - (\psi^{\pm} + 2\pi k)]^{-1} f_{mn}(\alpha) \, d\alpha . \tag{16}$$

By substituting this integral into equation (3) and changing the order of summation and integration we get

$$\begin{aligned} f^{\pm}(\psi^{\pm}) &= \sum_{k=-\infty}^{\infty} (2\pi i)^{-1} \int_{\Gamma} [\alpha - (\psi^{\pm} + 2\pi k)]^{-1} f_{mn}(\alpha) \, d\alpha = \\ &= (2\pi i)^{-1} \int_{\Gamma} f_{mn}(\alpha) \sum_{k=-\infty}^{\infty} [(\alpha - \psi^{\pm}) - 2\pi k]^{-1} \, d\alpha . \end{aligned} \tag{17}$$

The sum of the infinite series can be obtained by using the well-known decomposition of cotangent into partial fractions

$$(1/2) \cot (Z/2) = \sum_{k=-\infty}^{\infty} (Z - 2\pi k)^{-1} . \tag{18}$$

By using formula (18) we can rewrite equation (17) in the form

$$f^{\pm} = (4\pi i)^{-1} \int_{\Gamma} f_{mn}(\tau_{mnp}, \alpha, \sigma) \cot [(\alpha - \psi^{\pm})/2]\, d\alpha . \tag{19}$$

Integral (19) has the following properties: it tends to zero when $|\psi^{\pm}| \to \infty$, and it has a discontinuity at $\psi^{\pm} = 0$. However, the superposition of equation 1(15) and (19) is a continuous and analytic function of $\psi^{\pm}$ in the neighborhood of the surface $\psi^{\pm} = 0$. If function [1(15)] is a solution of some linear differential equation (for example, the wave equation) within domain $-\pi < \psi^{\pm} < 0$, the superposition of equations 1(15) and (19) complies with the same equation within the whole domain $-\pi < \psi^{\pm} < \pi$.

Equation (19) determines a piecewise analytic function of the complex variable $\psi^{\pm}$. We will consider this function for real values of $\psi^{\pm}$ only. Therefore, in this discussion the variable $\psi^{\pm}$ is real. Function (19) of real variable $\psi^{\pm}$ complies with condition 1(18), i.e., it smoothes the discontinuity of the edge-diffracted wave at the secondary shadow boundary. Because the edge-diffracted wave is described in a high-frequency approximation with $\omega \to \infty$, expression (19) has meaning when $\omega \to \infty$. The asymptotic value of integral (19) with $\omega \to \infty$ is considered later. To obtain the asymptotic formula, an explicit expression of function $\tau_{mn}(\tau_{mnp}, \psi^{\pm}, \sigma)$ must be used in the following sections.

5. *Local approximation*—To consider equation (19) in a small neighborhood of the central ray $\sigma = 0$ we can use a local approximation of the edge-diffracted wave eikonal.

Let us decompose function $\tau_{mn}(\tau_{mnp}, \psi^{\pm}, \sigma)$ into a power series over coordinate σ in the neighborhood of ray $\sigma = 0$, neglecting the third and higher powers,

$$\begin{aligned} \tau_{mn}(\tau_{mnp}, \psi^{\pm}, \sigma) &= \tau_{mn}(\tau_{mnp}, \psi^{\pm}, 0) + \sigma(\partial \tau_{mn}/\partial \sigma)_{\sigma=0} + \\ &+ (\sigma^2/2)(\partial^2 \tau_{mn}/\partial \sigma^2)_{\sigma=0} . \end{aligned} \tag{20}$$

Because $\tau_{mnp} = \tau_{mn} = \tau_m$ when $\sigma = 0$, we have

$$\tau_{mn}(\tau_{mnp}, \psi^{\pm}, 0) = \tau_{mnp} . \tag{21}$$

We can use the representation

$$(\partial \tau_{mn}/\partial \sigma)_{\sigma=0} = [\ |\nabla \tau_{mn}| \cos(\nabla \tau_{mn}, e_\sigma)\ ]_{\sigma=0}\ , \tag{22}$$

where e_σ is a unit vector of the coordinate σ line, i.e., the line of intersection of the coordinate surfaces τ_{mnp} = const and $\psi^{\pm}$ = const. Then

$$[\ \cos(\nabla \tau_{mn}, e_\sigma)\ ]_{\sigma=0} = 0\ . \tag{23}$$

Hence, we have

$$(\partial \tau_{mn}/\partial \sigma)_{\sigma=0} = 0\ . \tag{24}$$

By substituting equations (21) and (24) into (20) we derive

$$\tau_{mn}(\tau_{mnp}, \psi^{\pm}, \sigma) = \tau_{mnp} + a(\psi^{\pm})\sigma^2/2\ , \tag{25}$$

where

$$a(\psi^{\pm}) = (\partial^2 \tau_{mn}/\partial \sigma^2)_{\sigma=0}\ . \tag{26}$$

We rewrite this expression in the form independent of σ. Let point P belong to the primary shadow boundary

$$\psi^{\pm} = \pi/2 \quad \text{or} \quad \psi^{\pm} = -\pi/2\ . \tag{27}$$

Let point P and a running point M of the space belong to the same line of intersection of coordinate surfaces τ_{mnp} = const and σ = const, as shown in Figure 74. At point P expression (25) can be written as

$$\tau_{mn}(\tau_{mnp}, \psi_L, \sigma) = \tau_{mnp} + a(\psi_L)\sigma^2/2\ , \tag{28}$$

where ψ_L is the coordinate of the primary shadow boundary (27).

Now we can eliminate quantity $\sigma^2/2$ from equations (25) and (28) and write the result in the form

$$\tau_{mn} = \tau_{mnp} - (\tau_{mnp} - \tau^L_{mn})A\ , \tag{29}$$

where

$$A = a(\psi^{\pm})/a(\psi_L)\ , \ \text{and} \tag{30}$$

$$\tau_{mn}^{L} = \tau_{mn}(\tau_{mnp}, \psi_L, \sigma). \tag{31}$$

6. *Localization principle*—We can write quantity (30) in a more simple form. By solving equation (29) relative to A we have

$$A = (\tau_{mnp} - \tau_{mn})/(\tau_{mnp} - \tau_{mn}^{L}), \tag{32}$$

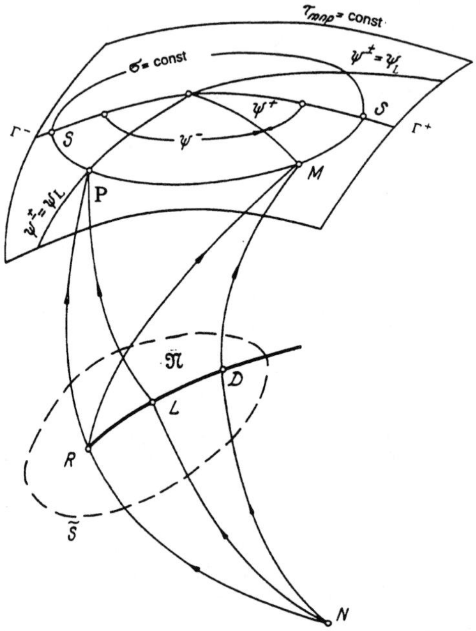

Figure 74. Rays corresponding to the traveltimes in equations IX.2(28) and IX.2(34).

where all eikonals depend on σ. On the other hand, in accordance with definitions (26) and (30), the same quantity can be written as

$$A = \left\{[\partial^2 \tau_{mn}(\tau_{mnp}, \psi^{\pm}, \sigma)/\partial\sigma^2] \,/\, [\partial^2 \tau_{mn}(\tau_{mnp}, \psi_L, \sigma)/\partial\sigma^2]\right\}_{\sigma=0}. \tag{33}$$

By comparing representations (32) and (33) we have

$$A = \lim_{\sigma \to 0} [(\tau_{mnp} - \tau_{mn})/(\tau_{mnp} - \tau_{mn}^{L})]. \tag{34}$$

To interpret this expression let R be the tip and let D and L be the edge diffraction points corresponding to the eikonals τ_{mn} and τ_{mn}^{L} respectively (Figure 74). Let $\mathfrak{N}$ be a domain bounded by some closed surface $\boldsymbol{S}$ and including all three points R, D, and L. We can always choose surface $\boldsymbol{S}$ so that the traveltimes along all the corresponding rays in Figure 74 from the source N to surface $\boldsymbol{S}$ are equal, and the traveltimes along corresponding rays from surface $\boldsymbol{S}$ to points M and P are equal too. Then all differences of the eikonals in equation (34) turn to zero outside the domain $\mathcal{N}$, and quantity (34) depends only on the differences of the corresponding traveltimes within domain $\mathcal{N}$.

When $\sigma \to 0$, points D and L tend to the tip R. Therefore, we can choose domain $\mathcal{N}$ with $\sigma \to 0$ as a small neighborhood of the tip R. Within such a small domain we can neglect the medium inhomogeneity and the curvatures of the interface and wavefronts. All this leads to the following localization principle: the quantity (34) can be found from the simplest diffraction problem of a spherical or plane wave striking the tip of the rectilinear edge in a homogeneous medium. Such a problem is considered in Appendix F where the following expression for quantity (34) is given:

$$A = \sin^2 \psi^{\pm} . \tag{35}$$

By substituting equation (35) into (29) we get

$$\tau_{mn} = \tau_{mnp} - (\tau_{mnp} - \tau_{mn}^{L}) \sin^2 \psi^{\pm} . \tag{36}$$

7. Variables ζ_{mnp} and ρ_{mnp}—Now we introduce new coordinates convenient for the description of tip waves.

By solving equations (36) relative to $\psi^{\pm}$ we derive

$$\psi^{\pm} = \arcsin\, [(\tau_{mnp} - \tau_{mn})/(\tau_{mnp} - \tau_{mn}^{L})]^{1/2} . \tag{37}$$

Let us consider quantity τ_{mn} in this expression as a function of $\psi^{\pm}$, i.e.,

$$\tau_{mn} = \tau_{mn}(\tau_{mnp}, \psi^{\pm}, \sigma) \ \text{ with } \tau_{mnp} = \text{const}, \ \sigma = \text{const} . \tag{38}$$

On varying $\psi^{\pm}$ in the interval $0 \le |\psi^{\pm}| \le \pi$ quantity (38) varies from $\tau_{mn} = \tau_{mnp}$, when $\psi^{\pm} = 0$ or $|\psi^{\pm}| = \pi$, to $\tau_{mn} = \tau_{mn}^{L}$, when $|\psi^{\pm}| = \pi/2$. At the same time, quantity (37) varies, respectively, from $\psi^{\pm} = 0$ to $\psi^{\pm} = \pi/2$ in the interval $0 \le \psi^{\pm} \le \pi/2$. Hence, expression (37) determines quantities $|\psi^{\pm}| \le \pi/2$ in equations 1(8) and 1(10).

We introduce a special symbol for quantity (37)

$$\zeta_{mnp} = \arcsin\,[\,(\tau_{mnp} - \tau_{mn})/(\tau_{mnp} - \tau^{L}_{mn})\,]^{1/2}. \tag{39}$$

Then equations [1(10)] can be rewritten as

$$\begin{aligned} \psi^{+} &= s_{mnp}\,\zeta_{mnp}, & \psi^{-} &= -\,s_{mnp}(\zeta_{mnp} - \pi) & &\text{when } |\psi^{+}| < \pi/2, \\ \psi^{+} &= s_{mnp}(\zeta_{mnp} - \pi), & \psi^{-} &= -\,s_{mnp}\,\zeta_{mnp} & &\text{when } |\psi^{-}| < \pi/2. \end{aligned} \tag{40}$$

Let us introduce the quantity

$$\rho_{mnp} = [\,2\,\omega\,(\tau_{mnp} - \tau^{L}_{mn})/\pi\,]^{1/2}, \tag{41}$$

where quantity τ^{L}_{mn} is a function of two coordinates

$$\tau^{L}_{mn} = \tau_{mn}(\tau_{mnp},\,\psi_{L},\,\sigma) = \tau_{mn}(\tau_{mnp},\,\sigma). \tag{42}$$

Therefore, quantity (41) also depends on two coordinates

$$\rho_{mnp} = \rho_{mnp}(\tau_{mnp},\,\sigma). \tag{43}$$

We can consider the quantities $(\tau_{mnp},\,\zeta_{mnp},\,\rho_{mnp})$ as coordinates of a running point of space in an individual domain of continuity (see Section 1.3).

By substituting equations (40) into (36) and expressing $(\tau_{mnp} - \tau^{L}_{mn})$ through ρ_{mnp} according to equation (41) we get

$$\tau_{mn} = \tau_{mnp} - (\pi\,\rho^{2}_{mnp}\,\sin^{2}\zeta_{mnp})/2\,\omega. \tag{44}$$

We will use the new variables in the final formulas.

8. Integral formula in a vicinity of the central ray—We have obtained integral (19) under condition 1(18). The latter assumes representation of the edge-diffracted wave by expression 1(13). By substituting equation (36) into 1(13) we get the following approximate representation of the edge-diffracted wave in a small vicinity of the central ray:

$$f_{mn}(\tau_{mnp},\psi^{\pm},\sigma) = \pm\,\Phi_{mn}(\tau_{mnp},\psi^{\pm},\sigma)\exp\left\{i\,\omega\,[\,\tau_{mnp} - (\tau_{mnp} - \tau^{L}_{mn})\sin^{2}\psi^{\pm}\,]\right\}, \tag{45}$$

$$\Phi_{mn}(\tau_{mnp},\psi^{\pm},\sigma) = \Phi_{m}\,W(w_{mn}), \tag{46}$$

where τ_{mn}^{L} is determined by equation (31). By substituting equation (45) into (19) we get

$$f^{\pm} = \Phi^{\pm} \exp\,(\,i\,\omega\,\tau_{mnp}\,)\,, \tag{47}$$

$$\Phi^{\pm} = (\,4\,\pi\,i\,)^{-1} \int_{\Gamma} S\,(\,\alpha\,)\,\exp\,[\,i\,\omega\,\varphi\,(\,\alpha\,)\,]\,d\,\alpha\,, \tag{48}$$

$$S(\,\alpha\,) = \pm\,\Phi_{mn}(\,\tau_{mnp}\,, \alpha\,, \sigma\,)\,\cot\,[\,(\,\alpha\,-\,\psi^{\pm}\,)/2\,]\,, \tag{49}$$

$$\varphi\,(\,\alpha\,) = -\,(\,\tau_{mnp} - \tau_{mn}^{L}\,)\,\sin^2\,\alpha\,. \tag{50}$$

These expressions describe integral (19) in a small vicinity of the central ray. Because the edge-diffracted wave is described in the high-frequency approximation with $\omega\,\rightarrow\,\infty$, these expressions are meaningful when $\omega\,\rightarrow\,\infty$.

3. High-frequency approximation

1. Contour of integration—When $\omega\,\rightarrow\,\infty$, the asymptotic value of integral 2(48) is formed by contributions within a small neighborhood of the saddle point $\alpha\,=\,\alpha^*$, which can be found from the equation

$$d\,\varphi\,(\,\alpha\,)/d\,\alpha\,=\,0 \quad \text{with } \alpha\,=\,\alpha^*. \tag{1}$$

By substituting equation 2(50) into equation (1) we can rewrite the latter in the form

$$\sin\,\alpha^*\,\cos\,\alpha^*\,=\,0\,. \tag{2}$$

Equation (2) has the following solutions:

$$\alpha^*\,=\,k\,\pi\,,\ \alpha^*\,=\,k\,\pi\,+\,\pi/2\,, \tag{3}$$

where *k* is an integer. We will choose the value of *k* below.

Let the contour of integration in equation 2(48) coincide with the *steepest decent path*, which is determined by the equations

$$\text{Re}\,[\,i\,\omega\,\varphi\,(\,\alpha\,)\,]\,<\,0\,,\ \text{and} \tag{4}$$

$$\text{Im}\,[\,i\,\omega\,\varphi\,(\,\alpha\,)\,]\,=\,\text{Im}\,[\,i\,\omega\,\varphi\,(\,\alpha^*\,)\,]\,. \tag{5}$$

By denoting

$$\alpha = x + iy\,,\ \alpha^* = x^* + iy^* \text{ with } y^* = 0\,,\ t = -(\tau_{mnp} - \tau_{mn}^L) \tag{6}$$

and using equation 2(50) we derive

$$\mathrm{Re}\,[\,i\varphi(\alpha)\,] = -\,(t/2)\,\sin 2x\ \mathrm{sh}\ 2y\,, \tag{7}$$

$$\mathrm{Im}\,[\,i\varphi(\alpha)\,] = t\,(\sin^2 x\ \mathrm{ch}^2\, y - \cos^2 x\ \mathrm{sh}^2\, y)\,, \text{ and} \tag{8}$$

$$\mathrm{Im}\,[\,i\varphi(\alpha^*)\,] = t\,\sin^2 x^*\,. \tag{9}$$

Using equation (7), we can rewrite inequality (4) as

$$t\,\sin 2\,x\ \mathrm{sh}\ 2y > 0\,. \tag{10}$$

Let $t > 0\,,\ y > 0$. Then inequality (10) is satisfied, if

$$\pi k < x < \pi k + \pi/2\,,\ \ k = 0\,, \pm 1\,, \pm 2\,,\ \dots\,. \tag{11}$$

Let $t > 0\,,\ y < 0$. Then inequality (10) is satisfied, if

$$\pi k - \pi/2 < x < \pi k\,,\ \ k = 0\,, \pm 1\,, \pm 2\,,\ \dots\,. \tag{12}$$

For $t < 0\,,\ y > 0$ inequality (10) is satisfied under conditions (12). For $t < 0\,,\ y < 0$ inequality (10) is satisfied under condition (11). The regions of the complex plane of α, where inequality (10) is satisfied, are shown in Figure 75 with hatching.

Using equations (8) and (9), we can write equation (5) as

$$\sin^2 x\ \mathrm{ch}^2\, y - \cos^2 x\ \mathrm{sh}^2\, y = \sin^2 x^*\,. \tag{13}$$

Let us introduce the quantity

$$\chi = x - x^*\,. \tag{14}$$

We consider this expression in a small vicinity of the saddle point, where $|\chi| \ll 1\,,\ |y| \ll 1$. Therefore, we can use the following approximations:

$$\begin{aligned} &\sin x = \sin\,(x^* + \chi) \approx \sin x^* + \chi\,\cos x^*\,,\\ &\cos x = \cos\,(x^* + \chi) \approx \cos x^* - \chi\,\sin x^*\,,\\ &\mathrm{sh}\ y \approx y\,,\ \ \mathrm{ch}\ y \approx 1\,. \end{aligned} \tag{15}$$

By substituting equations (15) into (13) and taking into account equation (2), i.e., $\sin x^* \cos x^* = 0$, we have

$$(\chi^2 - y^2) \cos^2 x^* - \chi^2 y^2 \sin^2 x^* = 0 \ .$$

By neglecting the term containing small quantity $\chi^2 y^2$, we get

$$\chi^2 = y^2 \ . \tag{16}$$

There are two lines $\chi = y$ and $\chi = -y$ complying with equation (16). For any given saddle point, determined by equations (3), it is necessary to choose the ones that belong to the allowable regions shown in Figure 75 with hatching.

Thus, there are many versions of choosing the contour of integration due to the existence of many saddle points (3). We choose the simplest version shown in Figure 76.

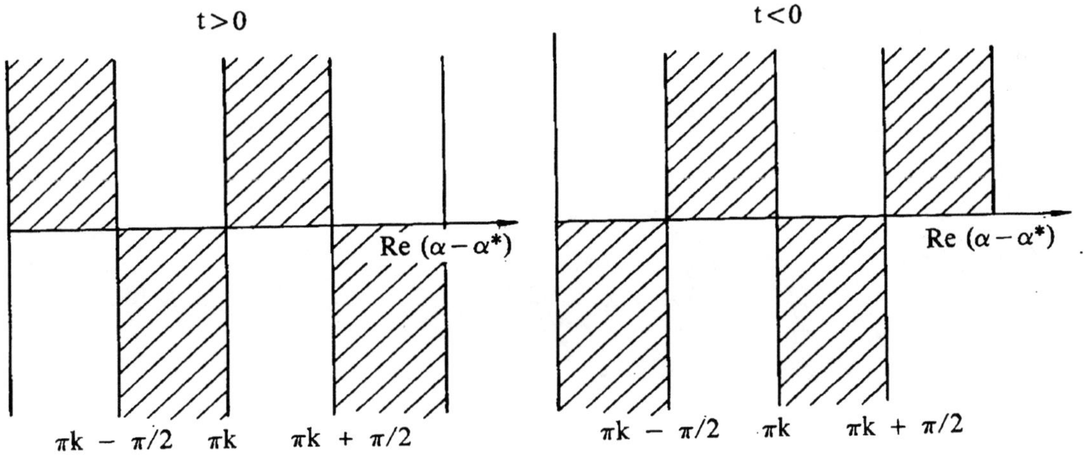

Figure 75. The allowable regions (shown with hatching) related to equation IX.3(10).

2. *Asymptotic formula*—The phase shift between the edge-diffracted and initial wave-fronts in expression for w_{mn} in equation VIII.2(37) is practically constant along the coordinate line $\tau_{mnp} = \text{const}$, $\sigma = \text{const}$ when $\zeta^{\pm}$ varies in the vicinity of the secondary shadow boundary $\zeta^{\pm} = 0$. Therefore, the edge-diffracted wave amplitude, equation 2(46), is a slowly changing function of $\zeta^{\pm}$ in the vicinity of point $\zeta^{\pm} = 0$. Hence, we can assume that quantity $\Phi_{mn}(\tau_{mnp}, \alpha, \sigma)$ in equation 2(49) is a slowly changing function of α in the vicinity of its regular point $\alpha = 0$. When integrating along the steepest descent path with $\omega \to \infty$, the slowly changing function Φ_{mn} can be approximated by its value at the saddle point $\alpha = 0$, i.e.,

$$\Phi_{mn}(\tau_{mnp}, \alpha, \sigma) \approx \Phi_{mn}(\tau_{mnp}, 0, \sigma). \tag{17}$$

Let us introduce a temporary notation

$$\Phi^0_{mn} = \Phi_{mn}(\tau_{mnp}, 0, \sigma). \tag{18}$$

Quantity (18) corresponds to the value of the edge-diffracted wave amplitude at the secondary shadow boundary. On the strength of the symmetry of the edge-diffracted wave amplitude relative to the primary shadow boundary, the following relation holds true:

$$\Phi^0_{mn} = [\Phi_{mn}(\tau_{mnp}, \psi^+, \sigma)]_{\psi^+=0} = [\Phi_{mn}(\tau_{mnp}, \psi^-, \sigma)]_{\psi^-=0}. \tag{19}$$

Using approximation (17) and relation (19), we can write function 2(49) as

$$S(\alpha) = \pm\, \Phi^0_{mn} \cot[(\alpha - \psi^{\pm})/2]. \tag{20}$$

We do not approximate the exponent 2(50) in the vicinity of the saddle point (an approach, based on such approximation, is given in Appendix D.3) and therefore we can obtain an asymptotic formula valid for any values of coordinate $\psi^{\pm}$.

By substituting equation (20) into equation 2(47) - 2(48) we derive

$$f^{\pm} = \pm\, \Phi^0_{mn}\, \Psi^{\pm} \exp(i\omega\tau_{mnp}), \tag{21}$$

$$\Psi^{\pm} = (4\pi i)^{-1} \int_{\Gamma} \cot[(\alpha - \psi^{\pm})/2] \exp[-i\omega(\tau_{mnp} - \tau^L_{mn}) \sin^2\alpha]\, d\alpha. \tag{22}$$

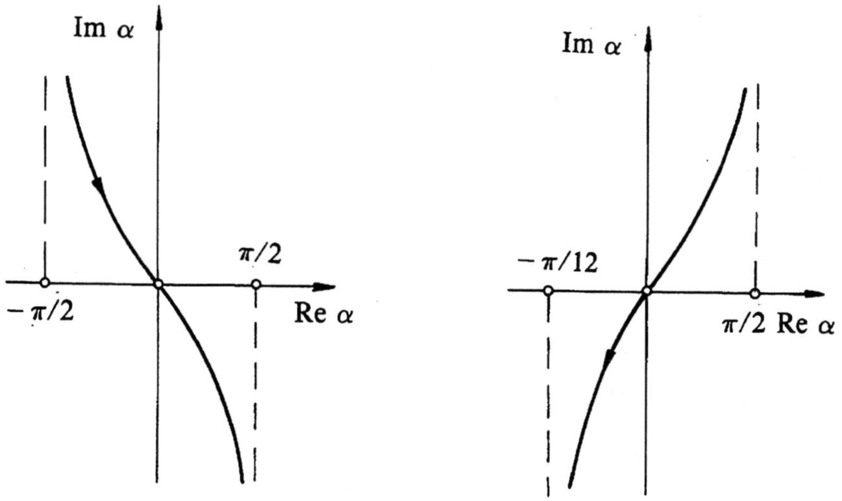

Figure 76. Contours of integration for $\tau_{mnp} > \tau^L_{mn}$ (left) and $\tau_{mnp} < \tau^L_{mn}$ (right) within the allowable regions shown in Figure 75.

By substituting these expressions into equation 1(5) we obtain the sought description of the tip wave

$$f_{mnp} = \Phi^0_{mn} \, (\Psi^+ - \Psi^-) \, \exp \, (i \, \omega \, \tau_{mnp}) \, . \tag{23}$$

3. *Function* $\Psi(\rho, \zeta)$—Let us consider cofactor $(\Psi^+ - \Psi^-)$ in equation (23). From equation 2(41) we have

$$\tau_{mnp} - \tau^L_{mn} = \pi \, \rho^2_{mnp} / 2 \, \omega \, . \tag{24}$$

By substituting equation (24) into equation (22) we can write the previously mentioned cofactor in the form

$$\Psi^+ - \Psi^- = (4 \pi i)^{-1} \int_\Gamma P(\alpha) \, \exp \, [-(i \pi \rho^2_{mnp}/2) \, \sin^2 \alpha \,] \, d\alpha \, , \tag{25}$$

where

$$P(\alpha) = \cot \, [(\alpha - \psi^+)/2] - \cot \, [(\alpha - \psi^-)/2] \, . \tag{26}$$

Let us transform function (26) to a more convenient form. By substituting equations 2(40) into (26) and using the well-known trigonometric formula of summation of cotangents we get

$$
\begin{aligned}
P(\alpha) &= 2\, s_{mnp} \cos \zeta_{mnp} \times (s_{mnp} \sin \alpha - \sin \zeta_{mnp})^{-1} \quad \text{when } |\psi^{+}| < \pi/2, \\
P(\alpha) &= 2\, s_{mnp} \cos \zeta_{mnp} \times (-s_{mnp} \sin \alpha - \sin \zeta_{mnp})^{-1} \quad \text{when } |\psi^{-}| < \pi/2.
\end{aligned} \tag{27}
$$

By using the obvious relation (see Figure 73)

$$\pm s_{mnp} = \text{sign } \psi^{\pm} \quad \text{with } |\psi^{\pm}| < \pi/2, \tag{28}$$

we can rewrite both equations (27) as

$$P(\alpha) = 2\, s_{mnp} \cos \zeta_{mnp} \times (\text{sign } \psi^{\pm} \times \sin \alpha - \sin \zeta_{mnp})^{-1} \tag{29}$$

We always can use $\text{sign } \psi^{\pm} \times \sin \alpha = \sin \alpha$ here when obviously $\psi^{\pm} > 0$. If $\psi^{\pm} < 0$, we get this relationship as a result of substituting the variable of integration α with $-\alpha$ in equation (25).

Substituting equation (29) into (25) and taking $\text{sign } \psi^{\pm} \times \sin \alpha = \sin \alpha$, we obtain

$$\Psi^{+} - \Psi^{-} = s_{mnp}\, \Psi(\rho_{mnp}, \zeta_{mnp}), \tag{30}$$

where the following function is introduced:

$$\Psi(\rho, \zeta) = (2\pi i)^{-1} \cos \zeta \times \int_{\Gamma} (\sin \alpha - \sin \zeta)^{-1} \exp[-(i\pi\rho^2/2) \sin^2 \alpha]\, d\alpha \tag{31}$$

Properties of this function are given in Appendix D2. Let us use the following representation:

$$\rho_{mnp} = \begin{cases} |\rho_{mnp}| & \text{when } \tau_{mnp} > \tau_{mn}^{L}, \\ i\,|\rho_{mnp}| & \text{when } \tau_{mnp} < \tau_{mn}^{L} \end{cases} \tag{32}$$

Then from equation D(58) of Appendix D we have

$$\Psi(i|\rho|, \zeta) = \text{Re } \Psi(|\rho|, \zeta) - i\, \text{Im } \Psi(|\rho|, \zeta). \tag{33}$$

If $0 \le \rho < \infty$, $0 \le \zeta \le \pi/2$, from equations (24), (30), (31), (39), (46), and (47) of Appendix D we have

$$\Psi(\rho,\zeta) \approx \Psi(0,\zeta) - (i\rho^2/8)\sin 2\zeta \times \ln(\pi\rho^2/8) \quad \text{when } \rho \to 0, \tag{34}$$

$$\Psi(\rho,\zeta) \sim \sum_{n=-\infty}^{\infty} [s_n^+ W(w_n^+) - s_n^- W(w_n^-)] \quad \text{when } \rho \to \infty, \tag{35}$$

$$w_n^\pm = |\psi^\pm - 2\pi n|\rho, \; s_n^\pm = \operatorname{sign}(\psi^\pm - 2\pi n), \; \psi^+ = \zeta, \; \psi^- = \pi - \zeta,$$

$$\Psi(0,\zeta) = 1/2 - \zeta/\pi, \; \Psi(\rho,0) = 1/2, \; \Psi(\rho,\pi/2) = 0 \tag{36}$$

Figure 77 shows the graphs of modulus and argument of the function $\Psi(\rho,\zeta)$.

4. Simplified formula—Let us introduce point S, determined by the expressions

$$\tau_{mnp} = \text{const}, \; \psi^\pm = 0, \; \sigma = \text{const}. \tag{37}$$

It is clear that there are two points, symmetric relative to the primary shadow boundary, that comply with these expressions (Figure 74).

From equations (19) and [2(46)] we have

$$\Phi_{mn}^0 = [\Phi_{mn}(\tau_{mnp},\psi^\pm,\sigma)]_{\psi^\pm=0} = \Phi_m(\tau_{mnp},0,\sigma)\, W[w_{mn}(\tau_{mnp},0,\sigma)] =$$

$$= \Phi_m(S)\, W[w_{mn}(S)]. \tag{38}$$

Using the second expression from VIII.2(37) and the definition of the secondary shadow boundary 1(4) in the form $\tau_{mn}(\tau_{mnp},0,\sigma) = \tau_{mn}(S) = \tau_{mnp}$, we have

$$w_{mn}(S) = \left\{2\omega\,[\tau_{mnp} - \tau_m(S)]/\pi\right\}^{1/2}. \tag{39}$$

By substituting equations (38), (39), (30), 2(41) and 2(39) into equation (23) and representing equation 2(31) in the form $\tau_{mn}^L = \tau_m(P)$, where point P is determined by expression 2(27) we obtain the tip-diffracted wave in the form

$$f_{mnp}(M,S,P) = s_{mnp}\,\Phi_m(S)\, W(\rho_{mnp}^S)\,\Psi(\rho_{mnp}^P,\zeta_{mnp}^P)\exp(i\omega\tau_{mnp}), \tag{40}$$

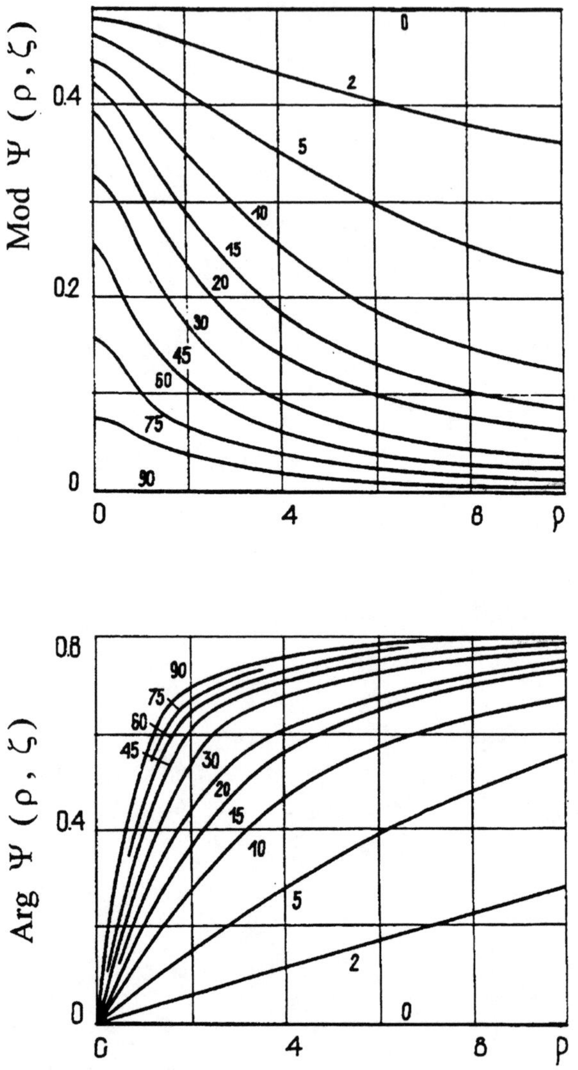

Figure 77. Modulus and argument of function $\Psi(\rho, \zeta)$. *Numbers at the curves give the values of* ζ, *expressed in degrees.*

$$\rho^S_{mnp} = \left\{ 2\omega \left[\tau_{mnp} - \tau_m(S) \right] / \pi \right\}^{1/2}, \tag{41}$$

$$\rho^P_{mnp} = \left\{ 2\omega \left[\tau_{mnp} - \tau_m(P) \right] / \pi \right\}^{1/2}, \tag{42}$$

$$\zeta^P_{mnp} = \arcsin \left\{ (\tau_{mnp} - \tau_{mn}) / \left[\tau_{mnp} - \tau_m(P) \right] \right\}^{1/2}, \tag{43}$$

where τ_{mnp} and τ_{mn} are the functions of a running point M of space (Figure 74).

These expressions can be simplified. Let us rewrite equation (40) in the form

$$f_{mnp}(M,S,P) = f_{mnp}(M) + \delta f, \tag{44}$$

where

$$f_{mnp}(M) = s_{mnp}\,\Phi_m\,H(\rho_{mnp},\zeta_{mnp})\,\exp\,(i\,\omega\,\tau_{mnp}), \tag{45}$$

$$H(\rho,\zeta) = W(\rho)\,\Psi(\rho,\zeta), \tag{46}$$

$$\rho_{mnp} = [\,2\,\omega\,(\tau_{mnp} - \tau_m)\,/\pi\,]^{1/2}, \tag{47}$$

$$\zeta_{mnp} = \arcsin\,[\,(\tau_{mnp} - \tau_{mn})/(\tau_{mnp} - \tau_m)\,]^{1/2}, \tag{48}$$

Here quantities Φ_m, τ_m, τ_{mn}, and τ_{mnp} are functions of a running point M of space. The quantity δf is the difference of expressions (40) and (45).

If

$$\tau_m(S) = \tau_m(P) = \tau_m(M), \tag{49}$$

expressions (40) and (45) coincide, i.e., $\delta f = 0$. This is the case of a homogeneous medium when the wave f_m is plane or spherical. However, it is easy to show that in a general case of inhomogeneous media we can neglect the term δf as well in equation (44) when $\omega \to \infty$.

Let us write the mentioned term in the form

$$\delta f = f_{mnp}(M,S,P) - f_{mnp}(M) = s_{mnp}\,Q\,\exp\,(i\,\omega\,\tau_{mnp}), \tag{50}$$

where quantity Q has the sense of the amplitude of the propagating wave. By substituting equations (40) and (45) into (50) and expressing function $\Psi(\rho,\zeta)$ according to equations D(20) and D(21) of Appendix D we can write quantity Q in the form

$$Q = (2\,\pi\,i)^{-1}\int_\Gamma F(\alpha)\,\exp\,(-i\,\omega\,\tau_{mnp}\,\sin^2\alpha)\,d\alpha, \tag{51}$$

$$F(\alpha) = \Phi_m(S)\,W(\rho^S_{mnp})\,h\,[\alpha,\zeta^P_{mnp},\tau_m(P)] - \\ - \Phi_m\,W(\rho_{mnp})\,h\,(\alpha,\zeta_{mnp},\tau_m), \tag{52}$$

$$h(\alpha, \zeta, \tau) = \cos\zeta \times (\sin\alpha - \sin\zeta)^{-1} \exp(i\omega\tau \sin^2\alpha). \tag{53}$$

The quantity (51) is a continuous function of a running point M of space. Indeed, it turns to zero at the primary shadow boundary in accordance with the third expression from equations (36) and at the secondary shadow boundary because of the coincidence of equations (40) and (45) when $M \to S$. Function (52) is continuous and finite at the contour of integration Γ, i.e., $|F(\alpha)| < C$, where C is some constant independent of ω. All this allows us to estimate an asymptotic value of the integral (51) with $\omega \to \infty$ by the saddle-point method in the neighborhood of the saddle point $\alpha = 0$. The standard calculations yield the following estimate: $Q \sim O(\omega^{-1/2})$, which is valid in the neighborhood of the central ray. Using this estimate and taking into account equation (50), we can represent equation (44) as

$$f_{mnp}(M, S, P) = f_{mnp}(M) + O(\omega^{-1/2}). \tag{54}$$

One can see that the inaccuracy of the description of the tip-diffracted wave by expression (54) corresponds to the inaccuracy of the boundary-layer approximation, which was considered in Section VIII.2(6). Thus, the tip-diffracted wave can be described by equations (45) - (48).

5. Substantiation of the statement of the problem—We, still, have to substantiate assumptions taken to formulate the problem of Section 2.3. It can be done in the same way used for the corresponding problem of finding the edge-diffracted wave (see Section VIII.2.7). In fact, it is enough to show that function 2(8) allows its continuation into the complex plane of $\eta^{\pm}$ under condition 2(12) along the contour Γ when $\omega \to \infty$. Equations 2(36) and (17) show that in the neighborhood of the central ray with $\omega \to \infty$ the mentioned function can be approximated as

$$f_{mn} \approx \Phi_{mn}(\tau_{mnp}, 0, \sigma) \exp\left\{ i\omega [\tau_{mnp} - (\tau_{mnp} - \tau^L_{mn}) \sin^2 \eta^{\pm}] \right\}. \tag{55}$$

This expression allows the continuation in the complex plane of $\eta^{\pm}$ along the steepest descent path and complies with condition 2(12), if the value of $\Phi_{mn}(\tau_{mnp}, 0, \sigma)$ is finite. Hence, the assumption under consideration does not put any additional limitations compared with those which were taken to find the edge-diffracted wave.

6. Vertex—It follows from the first expression in equation (36) that any point on the central ray $\rho_{mnp} = 0$ is the essential special point of the tip wave because its value depends on the direction along which this point is approached. Here we show that the total wavefield at the points on the central ray is determined uniquely. To do this, we consider the wavefield, caused by the diffraction on the vertex.

An interface in a small neighborhood of the vertex forms a curvilinear polyhedron (Figure 78). A single wave f_m is formed by the reflection/transmission at the face of the polyhedron. We label the face by the index m of the corresponding wave f_m.

If we now denote Ω_m and Ω_{mn} the domains of waves f_m and f_{mn}, respectively, and introduce the following unit functions

$$\delta_m = \begin{cases} 1 \text{ when } M \in \Omega_m , \\ 0 \text{ when } M \notin \Omega_m , \end{cases} \qquad \delta_{mn} = \begin{cases} 1 \text{ when } M \in \Omega_{mn} , \\ 0 \text{ when } M \notin \Omega_{mn} , \end{cases} \tag{56}$$

where M is a running point of space, then the wavefield, caused by the polyhedral interface, can be written as

$$f = \sum_m \left[\delta_m f_m + \sum_n \left(\delta_{mn} f_{mn} + \sum_p f_{mnp} \right) \right] . \tag{57}$$

Let us consider a contribution from an individual face of the polyhedron, omitting the symbol of summation over index m in this equation. We note that each wave f_{mn} is caused by one of two edges ($n = 1$ or $n = 2$) of the mth face, and each wave f_{mn} produces only one tip wave f_{mnp}. Because of this, equation (57) takes the form

$$f = \delta_m f_m + \sum_{n=1}^{2} \left(\delta_{mn} f_{mn} + f_{mnp} \right) . \tag{58}$$

Note, there are obvious relationships

$$s_{mnp} = - s_{mn} \text{ when } M \in \Omega_{mn} , \; s_{mnp} = s_{mn} \text{ when } M \notin \Omega_{mn} , \tag{59}$$

which can be rewritten in the form

$$s_{mnp} = - s_{mn} \text{ when } \delta_{mn} = 1 , \; s_{mnp} = s_{mn} \text{ when } \delta_{mn} = 0 . \tag{60}$$

Let us consider the case of $\sigma = 0$. From equation VIII.2(37), (36) and (45) with $\sigma = 0$ we have

$$f_{mn} = s_{mn} f_m / 2 , \tag{61}$$

$$f_{mnp} = s_{mnp} f_m \Psi (0 , \zeta_{mnp}) / 2 = s_{mnp} f_m (1/4 - \zeta_{mnp} / 2 \pi) ,$$

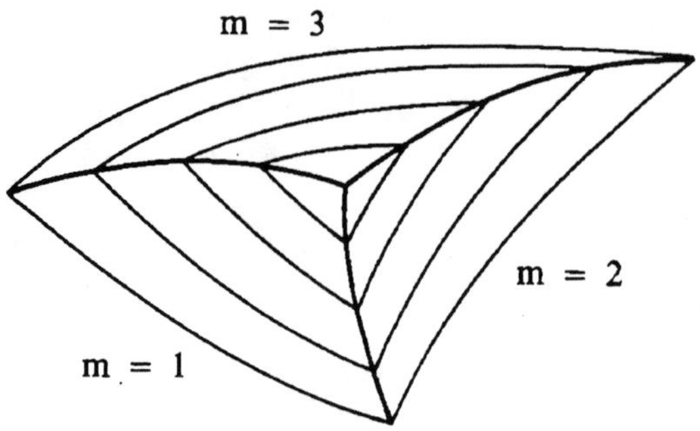

Figure 78. Vertex.

where f_m is taken at $\sigma = 0$.

By substituting equations (61) into (58) we obtain

$$f/f_m = \delta_m + \sum_{n=1}^{2} [\delta_{mn} s_{mn}/2 + s_{mnp}(1/4 - \zeta_{mnp}/2\pi)] =$$
$$= \delta_m + \sum_{n=1}^{2} (x - s_{mnp}\zeta_{mnp}/2\pi) \quad \text{when } \sigma = 0, \tag{62}$$

where

$$x = \delta_{mn} s_{mn}/2 + s_{mnp}/4 . \tag{63}$$

By substituting equations (60) into (63) we have

$$x = s_{mn}/4 . \tag{64}$$

By substituting equation (64) into (62) we obtain

$$f/f_m = \delta_m + \sum_{n=1}^{2} (s_{mn}/4 - s_{mnp}\zeta_{mnp}/2\pi) . \tag{65}$$

Let us rewrite equation (65) in the form

$$2\pi f/f_m = 2\pi\delta_m + \sum_{n=1}^{2} \xi_n , \tag{66}$$

$$\xi_n = s_{mn}\,\pi/2 - s_{mnp}\,\zeta_{mnp}\,. \tag{67}$$

The quantity ξ_n determines some direction of approaching the central ray. It can be illustrated graphically. Figure 79a shows the domains of continuity of the tip-diffracted wave with the corresponding values of s_{mn} and s_{mnp}. The indices of these domains are given in the circles. The primary and secondary shadow boundaries are shown by the straight lines (see also Figure 73). Using these figures, one can find the identities

$$\xi_n = \begin{cases} +\lambda_n & \text{when } \beta_n < \pi\,, \\ -\lambda_n & \text{when } \beta_n > \pi\,, \end{cases} \tag{68}$$

where λ_n and β_n are the angles between the primary shadow boundaries (the continuous lines in Figure 79b) and the direction of approaching (the dash line in Figure 79b) the central ray.

Let ε_m be the dihedral angle between the primary shadow boundaries at the central ray (Figure 80). This angle must be taken within the primary illuminated zone Ω_m. Using Figure 80, one can find the following identity:

$$\varepsilon_m = 2\,\pi\,\delta_m + \sum_{n=1}^{2} \xi_n\,, \tag{69}$$

where ξ_n is determined by equations (68). Now from equations (66) and (69) we obtain the value of the wavefield (58) at the central ray

$$f = f_m\,\varepsilon_m/2\,\pi \quad \text{when } \sigma = 0\,. \tag{70}$$

Thus, the wavefield at the central ray is uniquely determined by equation (70).

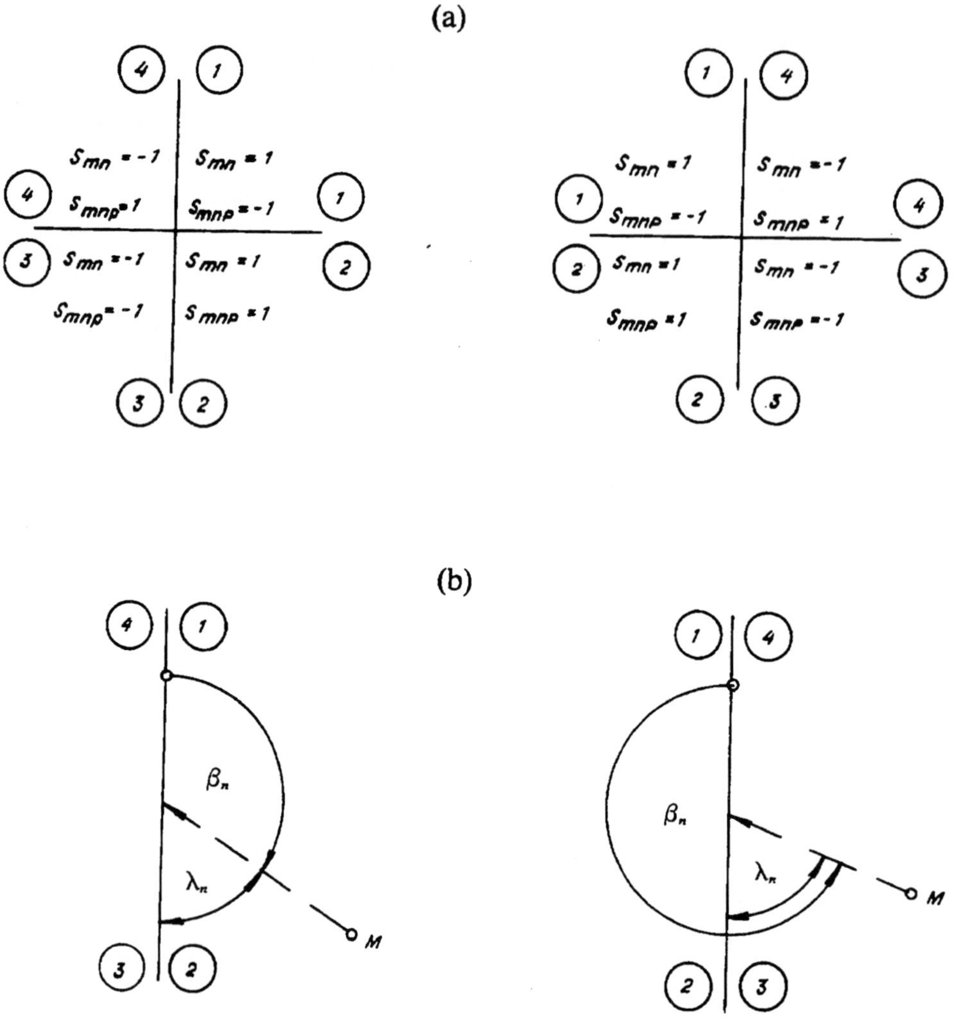

Figure 79. Interpretation of equation IX.3(66).

7. *Vector waves*—Now let us consider the case when the amplitude of the reflected/transmitted wave VIII.2(40) is a vector. Then the vector edge-diffracted wave can be written in the form VIII.2(43). Let us represent the tip-diffracted wave 1(3) in the same form

$$f_{mnp} = \sum_{q=1}^{3} j_q \, f^{(q)}_{mnp}, \; f^{(q)}_{mnp} = \varphi^{(q)}_{mnp} \exp \left(i \omega \tau_{mnp} \right), \tag{71}$$

where $f^{(q)}_{mnp}$ are scalars. To find each scalar function $\varphi^{(q)}_{mnp} (\tau_{mnp} , \psi^{\pm} , \sigma)$, we can use the same approach that was used in the scalar case, i.e., equations 1(5) - 3(48) and which allows us to find three scalar functions

$$f_{mnp}^{(q)} = s_{mnp}\ \varphi_m^{(q)}\ H(\rho_{mnp}, \zeta_{mnp})\ \exp\ (i\,\omega\,\tau_{mnp}) \quad \text{with } q = 1, 2, 3. \tag{72}$$

Substituting equation (72) into (71), we get equation (45) again, where Φ_m is the vector from equation VIII.2(40).

This result can be interpreted in the same way as for the edge-diffracted waves (see Section VIII.2.8). Let $\boldsymbol{P}_{mnp}$ be the unit vector of polarization of the tip-diffracted wave f_{mnp}. In accordance with the general theory, this vector with $\omega \to \infty$ must coincide with the unit vector of the tangent $\boldsymbol{e}_{mnp}$ to the tip-diffracted ray (for a longitudinal wave) or be perpendicular to $\boldsymbol{e}_{mnp}$ (for a transverse wave). However, the obtained vector coincides with the vector of polarization $\boldsymbol{P}_m$ of the reflected/transmitted wave. In fact, the real accuracy of description of the vector tip-diffracted wave is independent of this discrepancy because the latter is of no importance in the boundary layer approximation. The vector Φ_m can be considered as a function of a running point of space and continued analytically into the shadow zones.

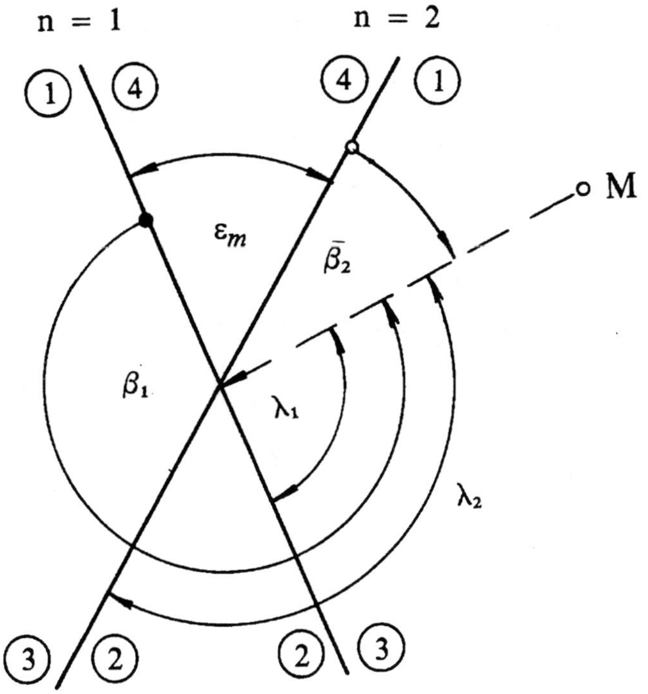

Figure 80. Interpretation of equation IX.3(66).

4. Ray method with consideration of diffractions

1. Streamlined formulas—The possibility to describe diffraction effects in the neighborhoods of the primary and secondary shadow boundaries with the simplest formulas leads to the modification of the ray method, which can be used in the media of block structure.

We can consider the total wavefield in such media as a superposition of three parts. The first part corresponds to the superposition of the reflected/transmitted waves, which can be described by a ray method, equations (6) - (12) of the Introduction. Here an individual m^{th} wave f_m can have discontinuities at its primary shadow boundaries, which we denote with the double index mn. The second part of the total wavefield corresponds to a superposition of the edge-diffracted waves, VIII.2(37), where each individual wave f_{mn} smoothes the discontinuity of the corresponding reflected/transmitted wave f_m at its mn^{th} primary shadow boundary. An individual edge-diffracted wave f_{mn} can have a discontinuity at its secondary shadow boundaries, which we label with the triple index mnp. The third part of the total wavefield corresponds to the superposition of the tip-diffracted waves 3(45), where each tip wave f_{mnp} smoothes the discontinuity of the corresponding edge wave f_{mn} at its mnp^{th} secondary shadow boundary.

Then the total wavefield can be written as

$$f = \sum_m [f_m + \sum_n (f_{mn} + \sum_p f_{mnp})], \tag{1}$$

$$f_m = \Phi_m \exp(i\omega\tau_m), \tag{2}$$

$$f_{mn} = s_{mn} \Phi_m W(w_{mn}) \exp(i\omega\tau_{mn}), \tag{3}$$

$$f_{mnp} = s_{mnp} \Phi_m H(\rho_{mnp}, \zeta_{mnp}) \exp(i\omega\tau_{mnp}), \tag{4}$$

$$w_{mn} = [2\omega(\tau_{mn} - \tau_m)/\pi]^{1/2}, \tag{5}$$

$$\rho_{mnp} = [2\omega(\tau_{mnp} - \tau_m)/\pi]^{1/2}, \tag{6}$$

$$\zeta_{mnp} = \text{arc sin } [\tau_{mnp} - \tau_{mn})/(\tau_{mnp} - \tau_m)]^{1/2}, \tag{7}$$

$$s_{mn} = +1 \quad \text{within } \Omega^+_{mn}, \quad s_{mn} = -1 \quad \text{within } \Omega^-_{mn}, \tag{8}$$

$$s_{mnp} = +1 \quad \text{within } \Omega^{+}_{mnp}, \quad s_{mnp} = -1 \quad \text{within } \Omega^{-}_{mnp}, \tag{9}$$

where summation is carried out over the indices of the reflected/transmitted waves and the primary and secondary shadow boundaries. Here Ω^{-}_{mn} and Ω^{+}_{mn} denote the corresponding primary illuminated and shadow zones of the mth reflected/transmitted wave relative to the mn^{th} primary shadow boundary. The symbols $\Omega^{\pm}_{mnp}$ denote the domains of continuity, determined in Section 1.3 (see Figures 72 and 73). The diffraction coefficients W and H are determined by equations D(1) of Appendix D, 3(46), and D.(20) - D.(29) of Appendix D. The eikonals τ_{mn} and τ_{mnp} must be computed in accordance with the kinematic law of the edge (Section 6 of the Introduction) and vertex (Section 1.2) diffraction. When computing the edge and tip-diffracted waves, we have to consider quantities Φ_m, τ_m, and τ_{mn} as the functions of a running point of space and continue them into the primary and secondary shadow zones (for example, analytically).

Expressions (3) and (4) describe the corresponding diffraction corrections with an inaccuracy of the relative order $O(\omega^{-1/2})$ with $\omega \to \infty$. Such an inaccuracy is acceptable only within those regions of space (the boundary layers), which can be determined implicitly by the equations

$$|w_{mn}| \lesssim 2, \quad |\rho_{mnp}| \lesssim 2 . \tag{10}$$

In these regions the intensity of diffractions is of the same order as that of reflections/transmissions when $\omega \to \infty$. Outside these regions the intensity of diffractions has the relative order $O(\omega^{-1/2})$, i.e., it is comparable with the above mentioned inaccuracy (deep shadow zones). Therefore, in the deep shadow zones the diffraction corrections (3) and (4) can be considered as a *diffraction background* (or a noise), which can be neglected comparing with the reflections/transmissions.

We will interpret the limitations in equation (10) in the simplest case of the reflection of a single wave from the interface in the form of a sector with two edges converging to the common point (Figure 81). Let O, P, and M denote the source, reflection point, and observation point, respectively. Let Q' and Q'' be the diffraction points, where the edge-diffracted rays are formed. Let R be the point of the tip diffraction.

Let $\tau(O,P,M)$ and $\tau(O,S,M)$ be the traveltimes along the trajectories OPM and OSM, where S is an arbitrary point of the interface. Now consider a region of the interface, given implicitly by the inequality

$$|\tau(O,S,M) - \tau(O,P,M)| \lesssim 2\pi/\omega . \tag{11}$$

According to Section VIII.3.4, this region can be called the *neighborhood of the reflection point* (NRP). The region is shaded in Figure 81. Point S belongs to NRP, if it belongs to the shaded region. By considering the positions of the diffraction points relative to NRP we can examine if a corresponding inequality from equation (10) holds true in any specific situation (see Section VIII.3.4).

If the diffracting edges do not belong to NRP (Figure 81a), none of the conditions of equation (10) holds true. The wavefield is described by the ray method (the transportation of the energy along trajectory OPM). The contributions along edge $OQ'M$, $OQ''M$ and tip ORM diffracted rays correspond to the diffraction background (noise). If the smooth part of the diffracting edge belongs to NRP (Figure 81b), only the first condition from equation (10) is satisfied for the corresponding edge wave. The contribution along the corresponding edge diffracted ray $OQ''M$ is of the same order as the contribution along the reflected ray OPM. The contributions along diffracted rays $OQ'M$ and ORM correspond to the diffraction background. If the reflection point and all diffraction points belong to NRP (Figure 81c), all conditions in equation (10) are satisfied. The contributions along all rays OPM, $OQ'M$, $OQ''M$ and ORM are of the same order. In this case the diffraction background is absent.

If all mentioned points, except for the reflection point, belong to NRP (Figure 81d), the observation point belongs to the primary shadow zone. All conditions (10) are satisfied. The wavefield is formed only by the contributions along edge $OQ'M$, $OQ''M$ and tip ORM diffracted rays. There is no diffraction background. If, besides, one of the diffraction points Q' does not belong to NRP (Figure 81e), the observation point belongs to the intersection of the corresponding primary and secondary shadow zones. The wavefield is formed by the contributions along the edge $OQ''M$ and tip ORM diffracted rays. There is no diffraction background. If only the tip diffraction point belongs to NRP (Figure 81f), the observation point belongs to the intersection of the secondary shadow zones. The wavefield is formed by the contributions along the tip ray ORM. The diffraction background is absent. At last, we can consider a case, when none of the points P, Q', Q'', R belongs to NRP, i.e., the interface has no NRP. However, there is the tip ray ORM. Then the wavefield must be formed by the contribution along this ray only. However, such a contribution corresponds to the diffraction background of the relative order $O(\omega^{-1})$.

We next consider some of the simplest examples illustrating the character of the approximation given by expression (1).

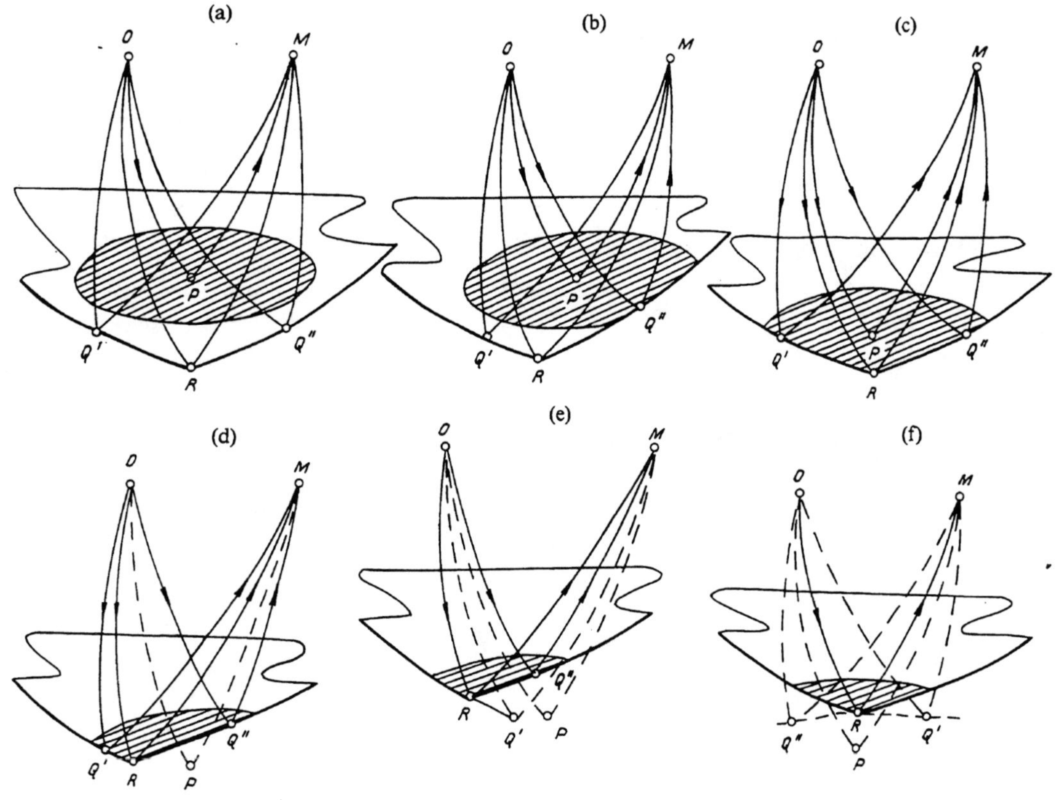

Figure 81. Estimate of applicability of the boundary layer approximation formulas IX.4(3) and IX.4(4) by using a concept of the neighborhood of the reflection point (shaded region). O ***– source;*** P ***– reflection point;*** M ***– point of observation;*** RQ' ***and*** RQ'' ***– edges;*** R ***– tip.***
(a): contributions along trajectories $OQ'M$, $OQ''M$, ***and*** ORM ***correspond to the diffraction background.***
(b): contribution along trajectory $OQ''M$ ***corresponds to the boundary layer approximation; contributions along trajectories*** $OQ'M$ ***and*** ORM ***correspond to the diffraction background.***
(c) and (d): contributions along trajectories $OQ'M$, $OQ''M$, ***and*** ORM ***correspond to the boundary-layer approximation.***
(e): contributions along trajectories $OQ''M$ ***and*** ORM ***correspond to the boundary-layer approximation;***
(f): contribution along trajectory ORM ***corresponds to the boundary-layer approximation.***

2. *Diffraction on the sector*—This example from Klem-Musatov and Aizenberg (1985) represents the simplest situation, in which it is necessary to consider the tip-diffraction effects. Let the interface be sector-shaped (Figure 82). The medium properties are characterized by the following quantities:

$$v_{p1} = 2.0 \text{ km}/s, \quad v_{s1} = 1.25 \text{ km}/s, \quad \rho_1 = 2.0 \text{ g}/\text{cm}^3,$$

$$v_{p2} = 2.5 \text{ km}/s, \quad v_{s2} = 1.5 \text{ km}/s, \quad \rho_2 = 2.4 \text{ g}/\text{cm}^3,$$

where v_{pn} and v_{sn} are the velocities of longitudinal and transverse waves, respectively, ρ_n is the medium density, $n = 1$ in the top medium, $n = 2$ in the bottom medium. The source of oscillations (which is marked by an asterisk in Figure 82) excites a P–wave with a uniform radiation characteristic. The shape of the radiated pulse is described by equation VIII.4(2) with $\beta = 50$ Hz, $\overline{\omega} = \pi / 0.03$ rd/s. To change to the nonstationary case, the Hilbert transformation for narrow-band signals was used. We will consider only the vertical component of the displacement vector of PP waves.

In this case the superposition (1) of P–waves can be written as

$$f = f_1 + \sum_{n=1}^{2} (f_{1n} + f_{1n1}), \tag{12}$$

where f_1 is the only reflected wave, f_{11} and f_{12} are the edge-diffracted waves, f_{111} and f_{121} are the tip waves. In Figure 82 the primary shadow boundaries are marked by the indices 11 and 12 and the secondary shadow boundaries by the indices 111 and 121. The domain of existence of the reflected wave is marked by the index 1 and the domains of the secondary illuminated zones are located on the left of the dashed lines.

Figures 83a and 84a show seismograms of the reflected wave f_1 for two profiles marked by I and II in Figure 82. We can see that the shortcoming of the ray method appears as the discontinuities of this wave at the primary shadow boundaries. Figures 83b and 84b show the total seismograms of edge-diffracted waves scattered from both edges. We can see that the shortcoming of edge-diffracted waves in this model appears as the discontinuities at the secondary shadow boundaries. Figures 83c and 84c show the total seismograms of tip waves. It is possible to see in Figure 84c the change of sign of their amplitudes at the secondary shadow boundaries 111 ($y = 0.95$ km) and 121 ($y = 1.66$ km). Figures 83d and 84d show the seismograms of the total wave fields formed by superposition (12). The total wavefield is regular everywhere.

3. *Diffraction on the pyramid*—Let the interface be pyramid-shaped (Figure 85). Let all parameters of the media and the source be the same as in the preceding example. Then

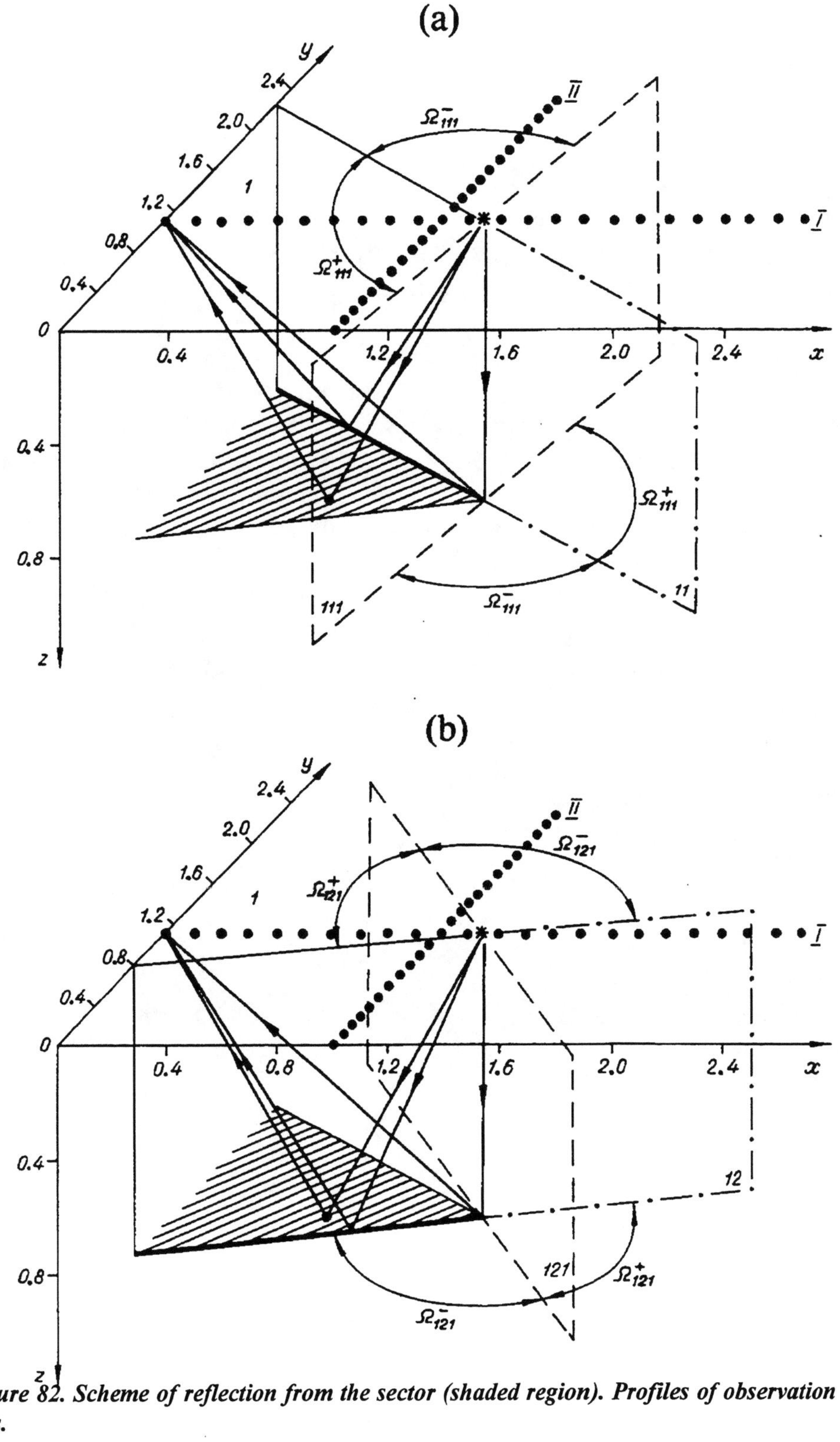

Figure 82. Scheme of reflection from the sector (shaded region). Profiles of observation are shown with dots.

the arising field of *P*–waves can be obtained by a direct superposition of the wavefields scattered by the individual faces of the pyramid

$$f = \sum_{m=1}^{3} [f_m + \sum_{n=1}^{2} (f_{mn} + f_{mn1})], \tag{13}$$

where m is the index of the face. Figure 86 shows the seismogram of the vertical component of a displacement vector of *P*–waves (Klem-Musalov and Aizenberg, 1985). Note, that all six tip waves have the same eikonal and form a common diffracted wave scattering from the vertex of the interface.

4. *Scattering by systems of small-throw faults*—The example used here is from Klem-Musalov and Aizenberg (1985). It is known that in seismic prospecting and deep seismic sounding, the observed waves often have a complex group (multiphase) character in spite of a rather simple source signal shape. The simplest example of the formation of multiphase groups is obtained from the examination of reflections from an interface disrupted by two systems of faults with a small throw.

Let the interface be disturbed by two intersecting systems of faults, where each system contains four parallel faults of an infinite extension (Figure 87). Unlike the previous examples, the elements of the interface differ in their number of edges and the edges differ in their number of tips. Let us mark the elements with four edges by $m = 1, 2, \ldots, 9$, those with three edges by $m = 10, 11, \ldots, 21$, and those with two edges by $m = 22, \ldots, 25$. Then the total field of *P*–waves can be written in the form

$$f = f^1 + f^2 + f^3, \tag{14}$$

$$f^1 = \sum_{m=1}^{9} [f_m + \sum_{n=1}^{4} (f_{mn} + \sum_{p=1}^{2} f_{mnp})],$$

$$f^2 = \sum_{m=10}^{21} [f_m + \sum_{n=1}^{2} (f_{mn} + f_{mn1}) + f_{m3} + f_{m31} + f_{m32}],$$

$$f^3 = \sum_{m=22}^{25} [f_m + \sum_{n=1}^{2} (f_{mn} + f_{mn1})].$$

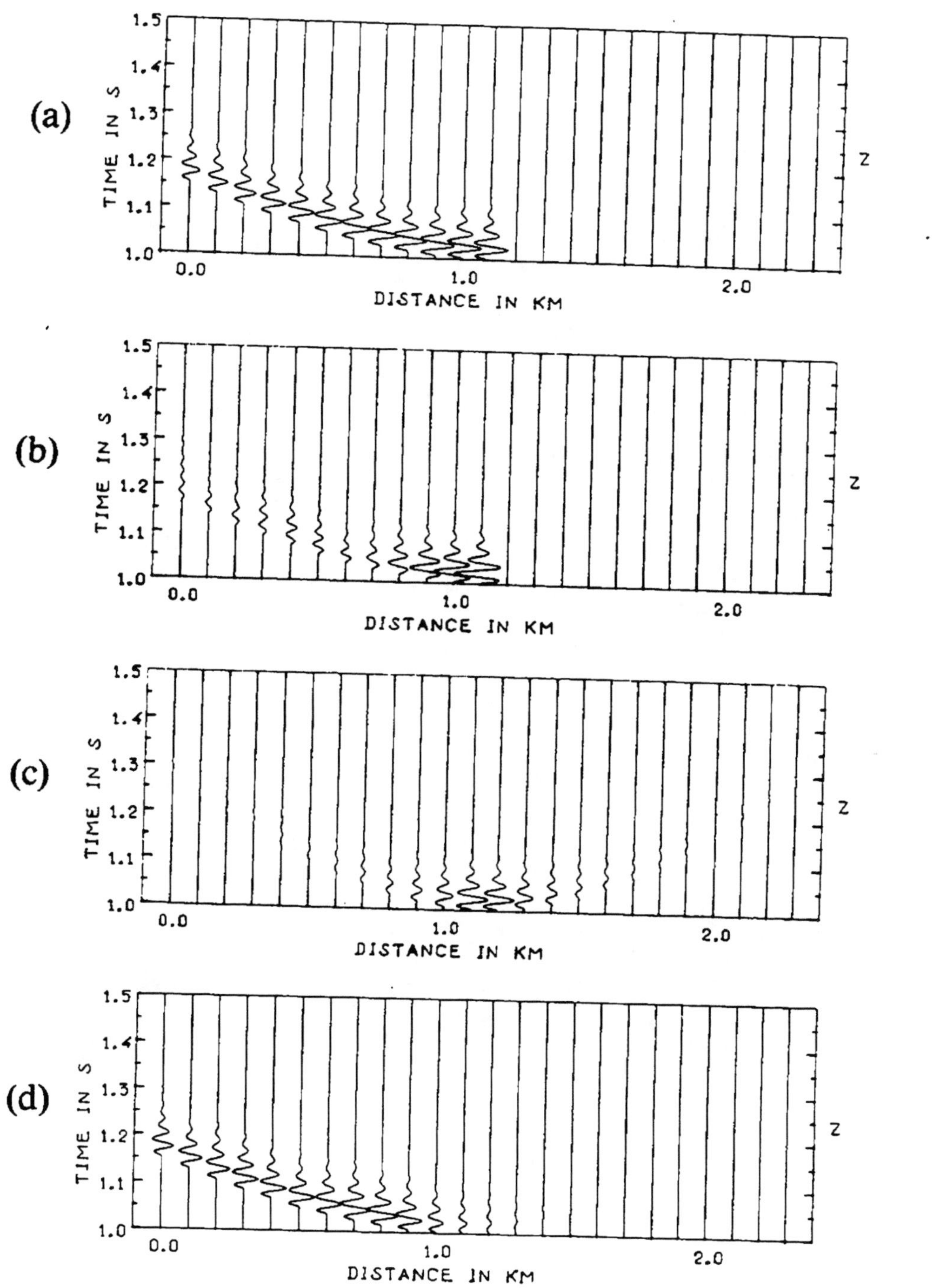

Figure 83. Theoretical seismograms for the sector model (profile I): (a) reflected wave, (b) edge-diffracted waves (1.5 times enlarged), (c) tip-diffracted waves (7.5 times enlarged), (d) total wave field.

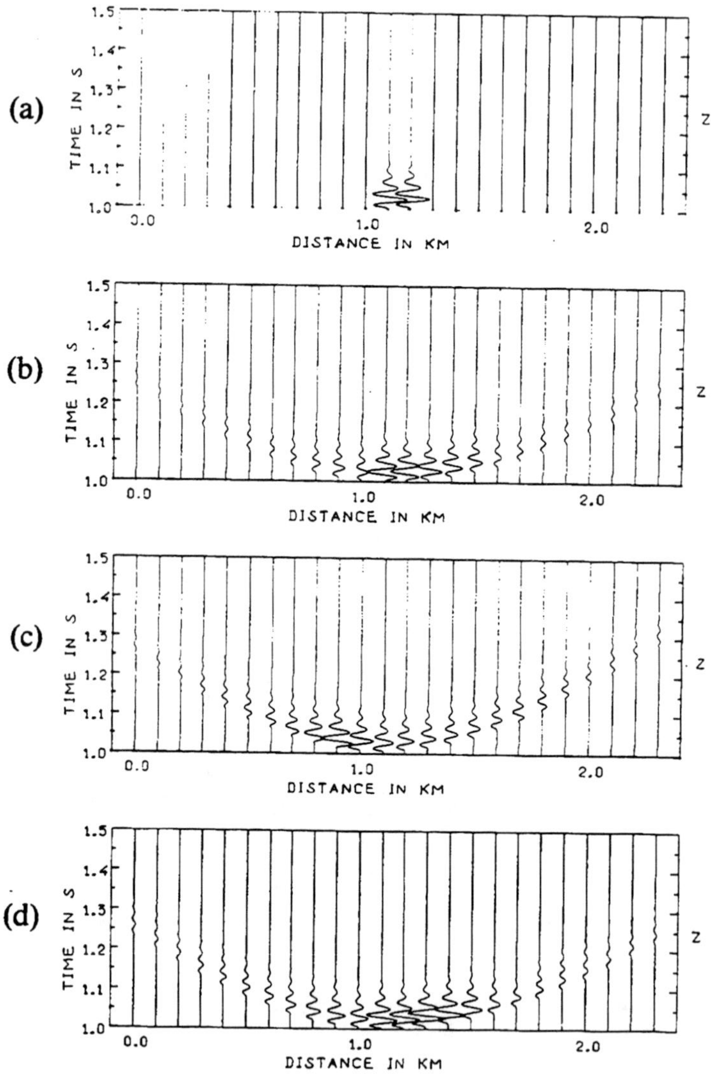

Figure 84. Theoretical seismograms for the sector model (profile II): (a) reflected wave (twice diminished), (b) edge-diffracted waves (1.66 times diminished), (c) tip-diffracted waves (4 times enlarged), (d) total wave field.

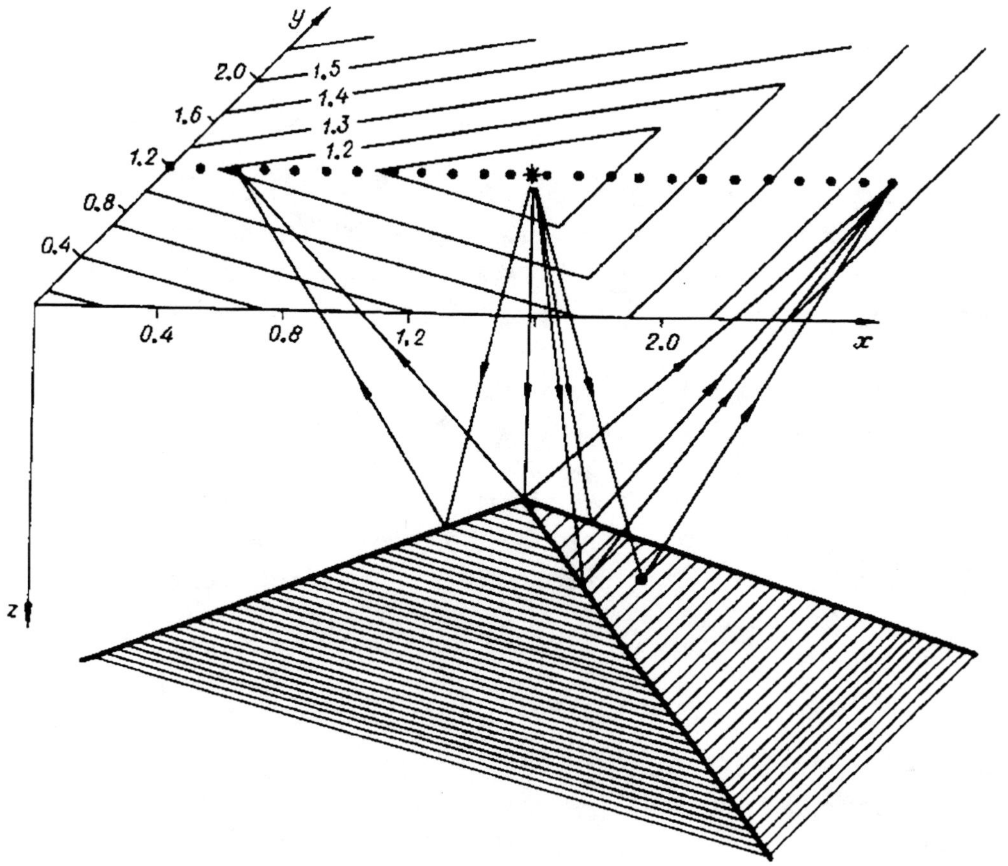

Figure 85. Pyramid model. Reflecting interface is given by depth lines on the plane of observation.

Let the minimum distance of the interface from the plane of observation be proportional to λ_p where λ_p is the P wavelength. The depth of each block of the interface is given by the formula

$$z = h + k\ \lambda_p/4\,, \tag{15}$$

where k is given in Figure 87. Let all parameters of the media and the source be the same as in Subsection 2. We will consider a system of normal incidence profiling (NIP), when the sources are matched with observation points (they are marked by crosses in Figure 87).

Figures 88 and 89 show the vertical component of the displacement vector of *PP* waves scattered by the disturbed interface for $h = 5\lambda_p$ and $h = 50\lambda_p$, respectively. Each horizontal row of traces corresponds to NIP seismogram along the profile $y = \text{const}$. Each vertical column of traces correspond to NIP seismogram along the profile $x = \text{const}$.

These examples show that for a relatively small depth ($h = 5\lambda_p$) the line-ups mainly represent the block structure of the interface with characteristic horizontal dimensions of the blocks of $2 - 3\lambda_p$ (and, obviously, larger). Under these conditions, the character of the wave patterns is determined by that part of the field which is controlled by the laws of geometrical seismics (ray transport of energy). The diffraction components (mechanism of transverse diffusion) have a secondary character, smoothing the characteristics of the field and complicating it by interference effects. With increasing depth of the interface, the role of diffraction components increases since the absolute dimensions of the zones of influence of diffusion mechanisms, NRP, increase. For a relatively great depth ($h = 50\lambda_p$), the diffusion mechanism plays the dominant role in the formation of fields from disturbed interfaces. Interference of diffraction components generates multiphase trains, the character of which depends on the degree of disturbance of the interface.

5. *Diffracted converted waves of PS–type*—When reflecting from an interface separating elastic media, an incident *P*–wave also generates converted waves of the *PS*–type. Because the reflection coefficient of *PS*–waves is zero at the normal incidence in the zero approximation of the ray theory the converted waves must be absent at NIP seismograms. This example shows that converted waves of the *PS*–type can be observed on NIP seismograms when the interface is disturbed by systems of small-throw faults.

The model of interface is similar to that in the preceding example (Figure 87) where the scales of coordinate axes must be multiplied by 5/3. The media properties are characterized by the following quantities:

$$v_{p1} = 2\ \text{km}/s, \quad v_{s1} = 1\ \text{km}/s, \quad \rho_1 = 2\ \text{g}/\text{cm}^3,$$

$$v_{p2} = 4\ \text{km}/s, \quad v_{s2} = 2\ \text{km}/s, \quad \rho_2 = 2\ \text{g}/\text{cm}^3,$$

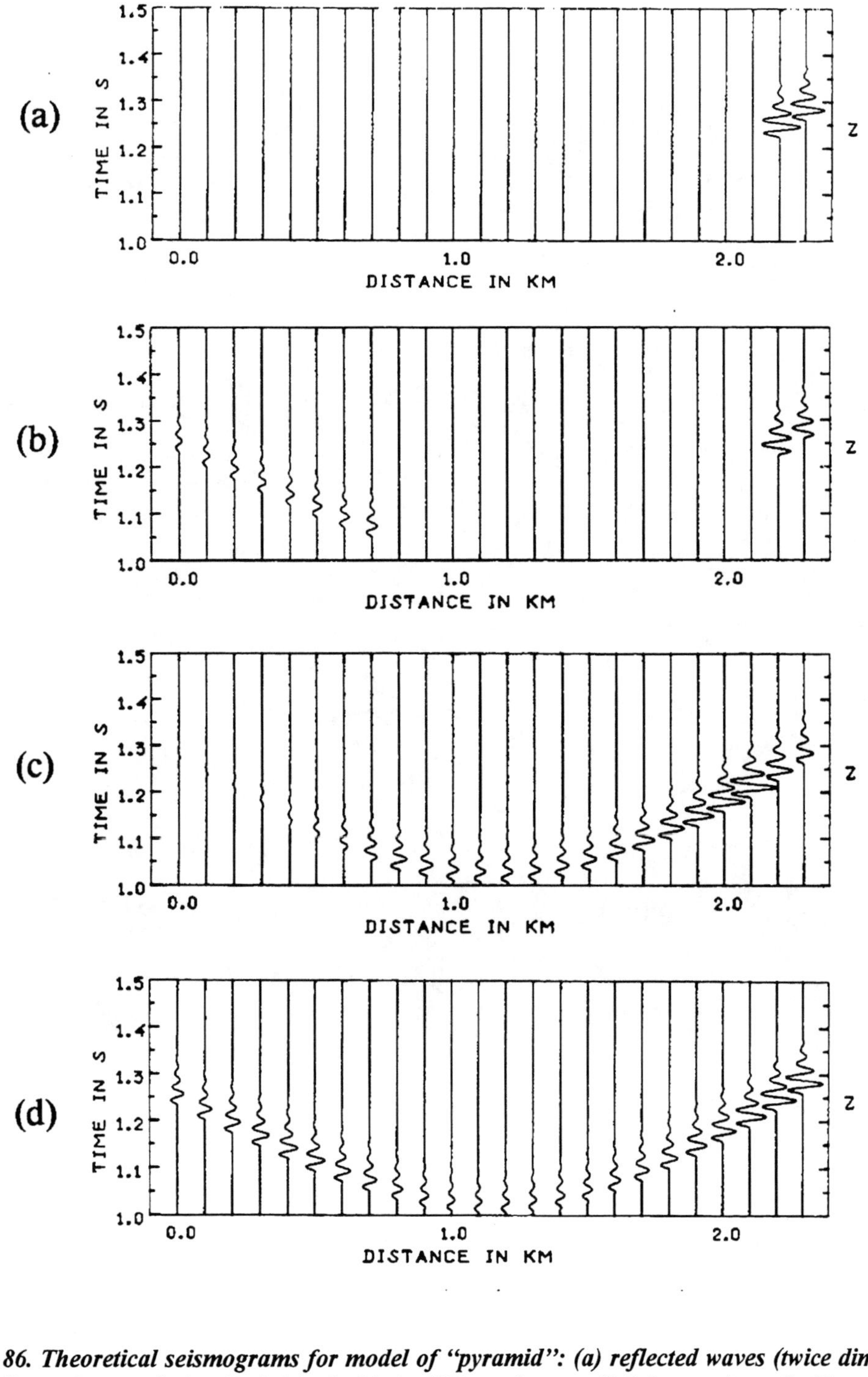

Figure 86. Theoretical seismograms for model of "pyramid": (a) reflected waves (twice diminished), (b) edge-diffracted waves (twice diminished), (c) tip-diffracted waves (1.5 times enlarged), (d) total field.

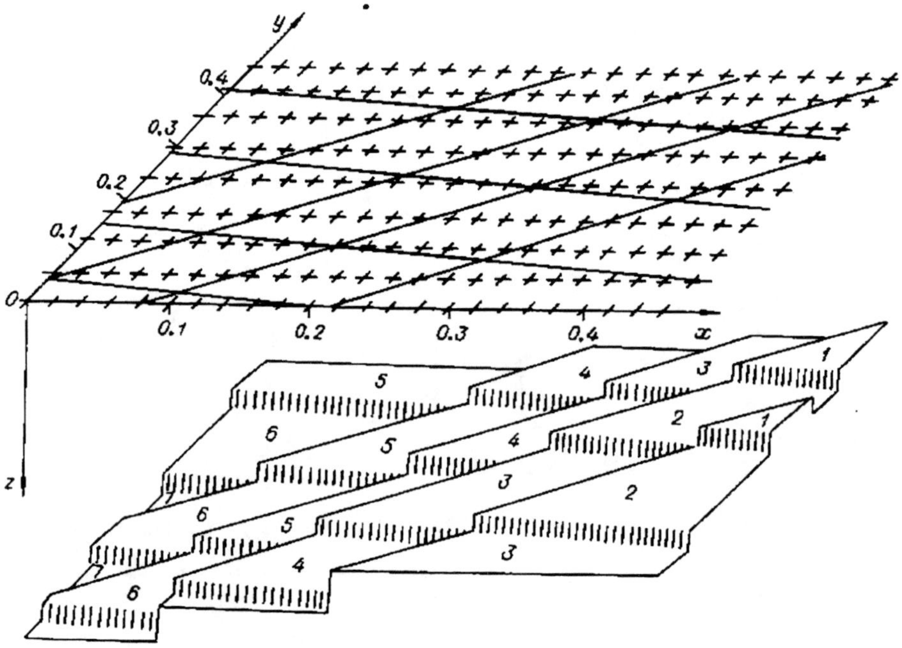

Figure 87. Model of "faults." Projection of faults is given on the plane of observation. Points of observation are shown with crosses.

For notations see Subsection 2. The depth of each block of the interface (in kilometers) is given by the formula

$$z = 0.5 + 0.015\ k, \tag{16}$$

where k is given in Figure 87. The shape of the radiated pulse is described by equation VIII.4(2) with $\beta = 20\,\pi$ Hz, $\overline{\omega} = 40\,\pi$ rd/s. The observation line of NIP in Figure 87 is determined by expression $y = 0.29$ km. Figure 90 shows the vertical component of the displacement vector of *PP* waves, computed by the ray method (a) and with the consideration of diffractions (b). Figure 91 shows a three-component seismogram of the displacement vector of converted waves of the *PS*–type (the *Z*–component is vertical, the *X*–component is oriented along the profile of observation).

The wavefields in Figure 91 have a pure diffraction character. They are formed by the transverse diffusion from the primary and secondary shadow boundaries of the reflected *PS* waves (the reflected waves themselves are absent on the seismograms). The relative scales of amplification of the seismograms show that the intensity of *PS* wavefields is about 5 times less compared with *PP* wavefields. Taking into consideration the weakening of intensity because of the diffraction (not less than 2 times) and relatively low values of the reflection coefficient of the *PS*–waves, we see that the intensity of the wavefields in Figure 91 is about the same as in the boundary layers (10) which implies that the information on the diffracted converted waves of the *PS*–type can be useful for geophysical applications. Additional details on this topic can be found in Obolentseva and Klem-Musatova, 1986 (a) and (b).

CONCLUSION

The first version of this book (in Russian) was published in 1980. Since then a number of studies have been carried out on the development and application of the ideas considered in this book. The successive approximations method was implemented for the wave propagation modeling in Malyshkin [1990 (a) and (b)]. The explicit analytical expressions were derived to evaluate the elements of multiple matrix product in the process of successive approximations. These formulas allow the computation of series V.3(2) and V.3(10) of the reflected/transmitted and edge-diffracted waves. The convergence of successive approximations has been studied numerically.

The theory for the diffraction of waves in an elastic medium, based on this book, was developed by R. Chan and F. Hron and incorporated into existing program packages (Hron et al., 1985, 1987). The accuracy, speed, and range of this method has been compared with the results produced by programs based on the Alekseev-Mikhailenko method (Mikhailenko, 1979) and the Gaussian beam method (Cerveny, 1985) with a remarkably good agreement of the results. The authors claim that the high-frequency approximation for the

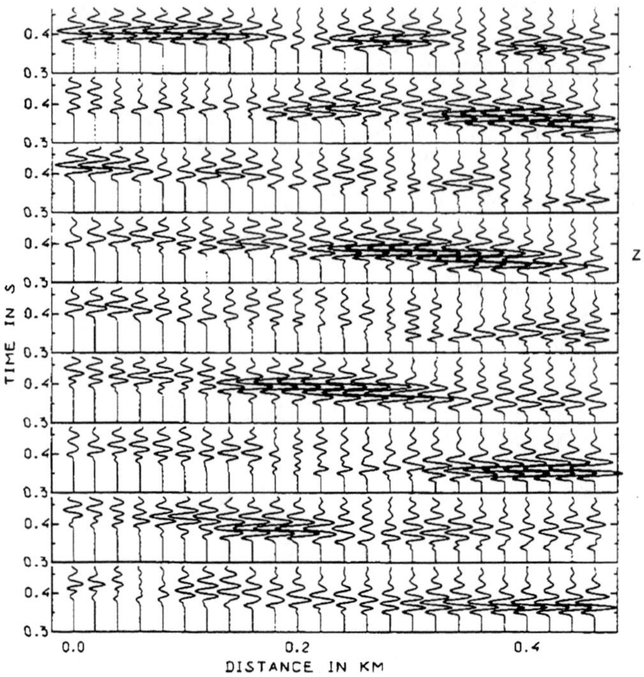

Figure 88. Theoretical seismograms for model of "faults" ($h = 5\lambda_p$).

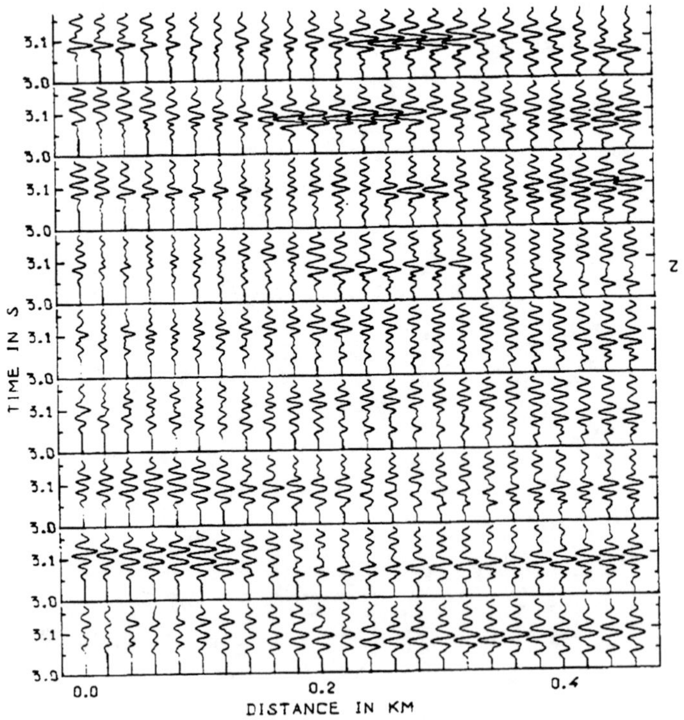

Figure 89. Theoretical seismograms for model of "faults" ($h = 50\lambda_p$).

the diffracted wavefield in an elastic medium is more than adequate in the computation of synthetic seismograms based on asymptotic ray theory and its modifications.

In (Bakker, 1990) the edge wave is described in terms of the dynamic ray tracing by deriving the parabolic equation for the dominant term of the wavefield in the boundary layer. By factorization of the geometrical spreading in the directions perpendicular and tangential to the shadow boundary, the transverse diffusion equation is derived. Its solution gives formulas VIII.2(37), VIII.2(43) - VIII.2(44) in a paraxial ray approximation. The description of the edge and vertex waves for the case of diffraction of the spherical wave on a sector of the plane interface was obtained by a high-frequency asymptotic analysis of the Kirchhoff integral [Aizenberg (1982]. It is shown that the results obtained are equivalent to the description of the corresponding waves in Chapters VIII and IX of this book.

Of special interest for seismology is the generalization of the theory of the edge-diffracted waves to anisotropic media. The derivation of uniform formulas, valid throughout the entire domain of the edge-diffracted waves, is not yet possible because of the absence of the solution of the correspondent canonical problem. However, such generalization is possible in the boundary layer approximation. Indeed, there is no need to consider the equation of motion and corresponding mathematical problems for the derivation of diffraction integrals VIII.1(17) and IX.2(19). These integrals are valid for the wave motions of any physical nature, if these motions allow the concept of wave fronts and rays (such motions in the nonstationary case are described by the differential equations of the hyperbolic type). Therefore, the generalization of the theory in the boundary layer approximation to the anisotropic media can be reduced to a high-frequency analysis of the mentioned integrals in the properly chosen ray coordinates. It is shown in Druzhinin (1988, 1990) that equations VIII.2(37), VIII.2(43), and VIII.2(44) are valid in the anisotropic media. In a 2-D case the same formulas can be obtained as one of two linearly independent asymptotic solutions of equations of motion of anisotropic media (Druzhinin and Aizenberg, 1990).

In the classical theory of diffraction (Born and Wolf, 1968) and in its contemporary modifications (Trorey, 1970, 1977; Berryhill, 1977; Hilterman, 1982; Frazer and Sen, 1985; Frazer, 1987; Zhu, 1988) the concept of the edge-diffracted waves can be introduced by a high-frequency asymptotic analysis of the Kirchhoff integral. The first version of this book (in Russian) contains a section demonstrating such an analysis. We have omitted the section from this book because it is related to a separate aspect of the development of the theory of edge-diffracted waves. This aspect appears because of the following. The modification of the ray method in Section IX.4 results in adding the corresponding diffractions to every primary and secondary shadow boundaries. However, such an approach fails within regions where the ray theory field changes rapidly, i.e., in the caustic zones. The possibility to overcome this limitation is connected with the following discussion.

If an interface is approximated by a piecewise-plane surface with sufficiently small plane elements, the arising reflected/transmitted wavefields have no caustics. In a 2-D case such wavefields with $\omega \rightarrow \infty$ can be represented by the superposition of the edge-diffracted waves spreading from the corner points of the piecewise interface (Aizenberg and Klem-Musatov, 1980). It is essential that the same form of description can be obtained by the high-frequency asymptotic analysis of the Kirchhoff integral. The corresponding analytic technique is based on the approximation of the surface of integration by the piecewise-plane surface with sufficiently small elements and analysis of each individual integral over each plane element. The method of superposition of the edge-diffracted waves with the consideration of multiple diffraction on intermediate interfaces is described in Klem-Musatov and Aizenberg (1989). Such a description is equivalent to the representation of wavefields in the form of the multiple integrals along the set of arbitrary contours. It can be shown that these integrals coincide with the high-frequency asymptotics of the known integral solutions (Frazer, 1987). In a 3-D case the piecewise-plane approximation of the interface leads to the representation of wavefields in the form of the superposition of the tip-diffracted waves (Klem-Musatov, et al., 1982; Klem-Musatov and Aizenberg, 1985). Such a description also allows a representation in the form of the surface integral coinciding asymptotically with the Kirchhoff integral when $\omega \rightarrow \infty$. There are examples of application of the edge-diffracted wave superposition method for seismic modeling of waves refracting through interfaces of complicated forms (Lunyova, 1984; Lunyova and Kharlamov, 1990).

The possibility of applying the theory being considered to seismology has been studied by different authors. One aspect of application had been considered by the late G. L. Kovalevsky in connection with his works on the detection of the small-throw faults (Kovalevsky, 1971, 1973). This aspect of application is considered in Klem-Musatov, et al., (1976), Landa and Maksimov, (1980), Landa and Mitrophanov, (1979). The method of superposition of tip-diffracted waves had been applied to the study of polarization of the converted *PS* waves reflected from the boundaries disturbed by the systems of small-throw faults (Obolentseva and Klem-Musatova, 1986). A more general seismic problem is connected with the detection of scattering objects, e.g., various reflector discontinuities, such as faults, pinchouts, sharp changes in reflective properties, etc. In Landa et al., (1987) formula VIII.2(37) is used in the method for the detection of diffracted waves scattered by such objects.

The study of applicability of the theory of the edge-diffracted waves in practical exploration problems is described in Frøyland et al., (1988) and Pajchel et al., (1988, 1989).

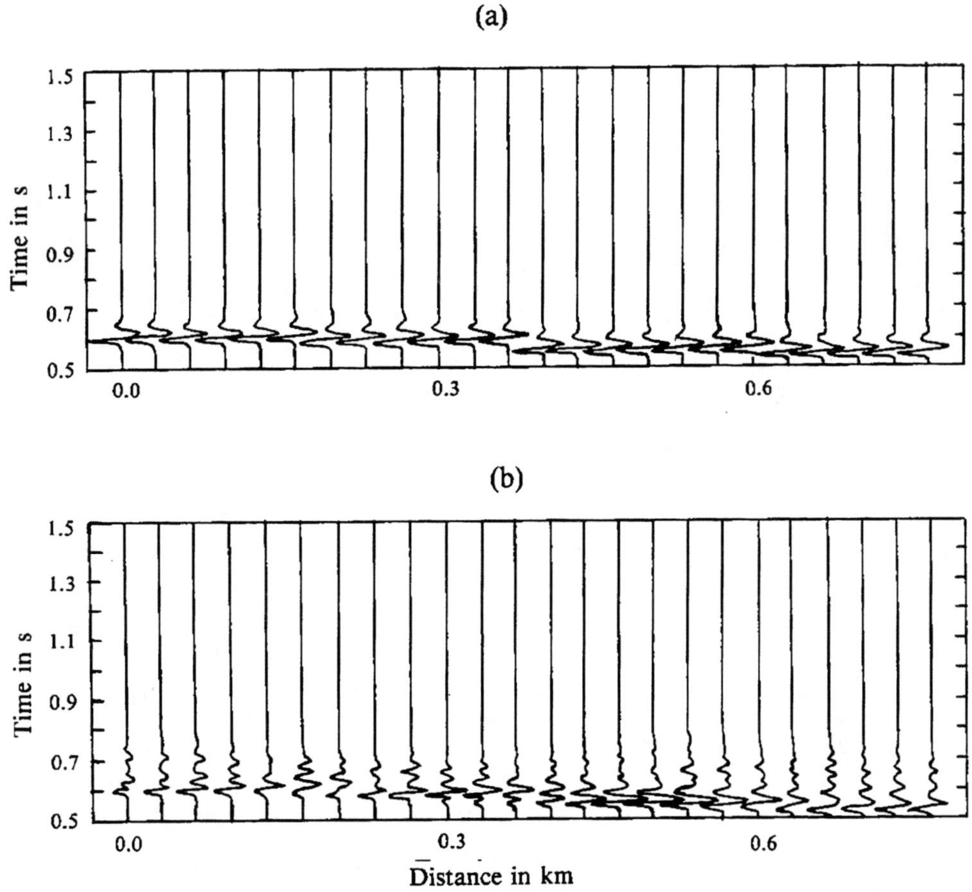

Figure 90. Theoretical seismograms for model of "faults" (vertical component of PP-waves): (a) ray method (1.3 times enlarged), (b) ray method with consideration of diffractions.

The effects of edge diffraction for different types of seismic surveys (vertical seismic profiling, normal seismic profiling, etc.) was studied by seismic modeling in different types of geological models. The migration procedures of synthetic seismic data with the consideration of diffractions were tested for the detection and resolution of some realistic geological models (see Figure 67). The study has shown that the diffraction computations by the edge-diffracted wave theory are sufficiently accurate for the applications in practical exploration problems.

We have to refer here only to the published examples of applications of the theory of the edge-diffracted waves. In fact, the experience of using this theory is much greater, because a number of enterprises have implemented diffraction formulas of Chapter IX into their seismic modeling packages. We hope that this book will encourage future studies in this field of theory of diffraction.

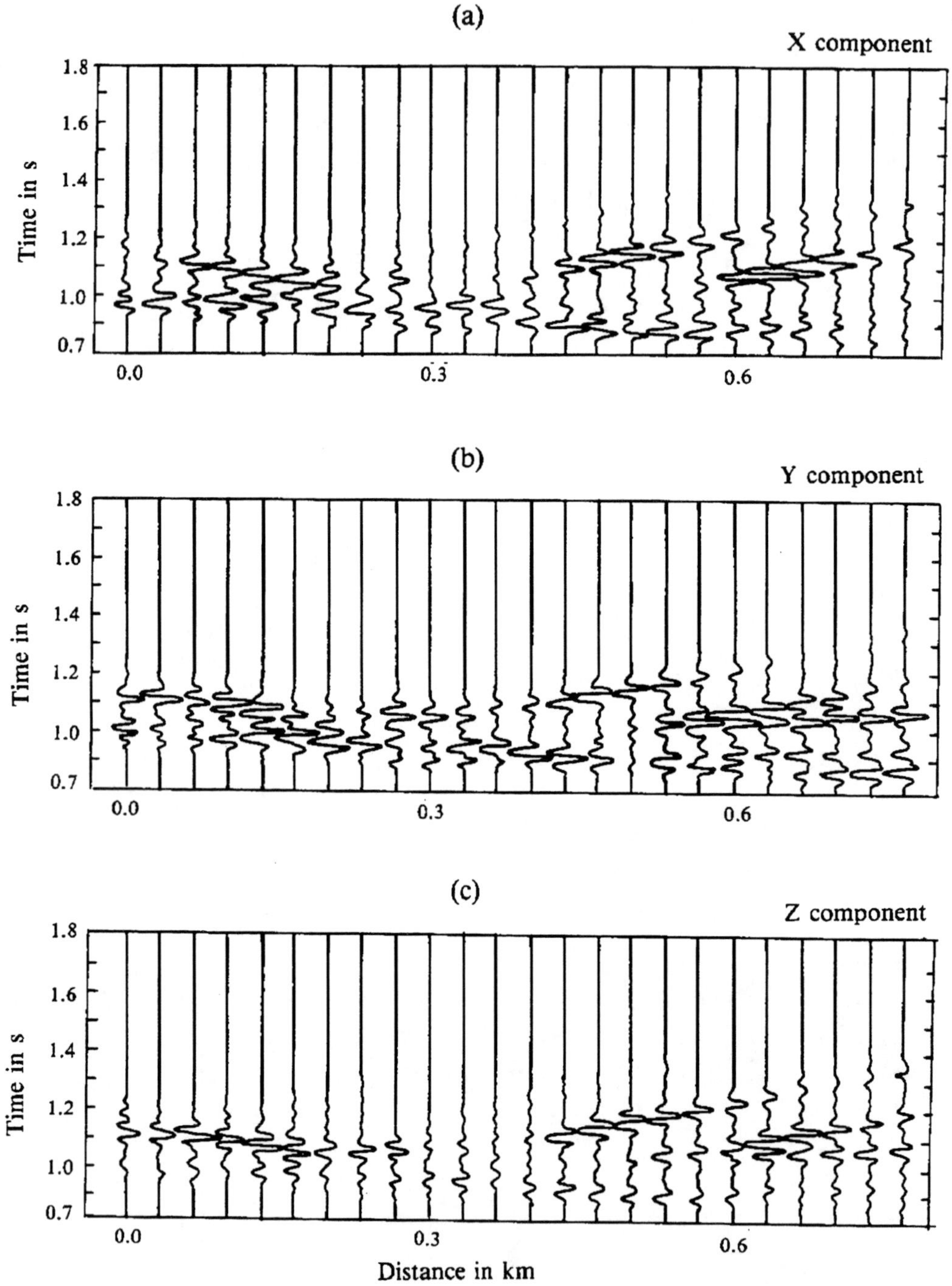

Figure 91. Theoretical three-component seismogram of converted waves of PS-type for model of "faults": (a) X-component (7.3 times enlarged), (b) Y-component (6 times enlarged), (c) Z-component (6.7 times enlarged).

APPENDIX A

PROOF OF AUXILIARY ASSERTIONS

Proof of Assertion 1

Suppose $X_{m(p)} < 0$. Then, according to inequalities III.2(9) product $K_{m(p)}$ in equations III.2(3) contains the odd number of factors K_{22}. This means that in the product III.1(5) the operator κ_{22} appears an odd number of times. According to the order of indices, equation III.1(6), in the product III.1(5) the factor κ_{22} together with the neighboring right-hand factor can appear in the form of the two following combinations only: $\kappa_{22}\ \kappa_{12}$ and $\kappa_{22}\ \kappa_{22}$. There are no combinations $\kappa_{22}\ \kappa_{11}$ and $\kappa_{22}\ \kappa_{21}$. In the product III.1(5) the first right-hand factor is κ_{12}. Therefore, by singling out in the product III.1(5), containing the odd number of factors κ_{22}, any combination $\kappa_{22}\ \kappa_{12}$ we get the representation $\kappa_{m(p)} = A\ \kappa_{22}\ \kappa_{12}\ B$, where the total number of factors in products A and B is even. By substituting this representation into expression $X_{m(p)} = \kappa_{m(p)}\ D_{m(p)}$ we get assertion III.2(11).

Proof of Assertion 2

The presence of operator κ_{12} in equation III.2(11) tells that term $B\ D_{m(p)}$ is an item of the sum, forming the first or second top row of matrix $T^j\ D$, where j is the total number of factors in the operator product B. We demonstrate the assertion under consideration in the case of $B\ D_{m(p)}$, belonging to the first top row (in the second case the demonstration is analogous).

Let us introduce the notation

$$T^j\ D = \begin{Bmatrix} B_1^+ + B\ D_{m(p)} \\ B_1^- \\ B_2^+ \\ B_2^- \end{Bmatrix}, \quad Y = \begin{Bmatrix} B\ D_{m(p)} \\ 0 \\ 0 \\ 0 \end{Bmatrix}, \quad Z = \begin{Bmatrix} B_1^+ \\ B_1^- \\ B_2^+ \\ B_2^- \end{Bmatrix},$$

where $B_\nu^\pm$ does not contain the quantities $B\ D_{m(p)}$ as terms or factors.

Let us represent matrix $T^p D$ in the form

$$T^p D = T^{p-j-2}\,(T^{j+2} D)\,.$$

By developing the matrix

$$T^{j+2} D = T^2 (T^j D) = T^2 Y + T^2 Z$$

we have

$$T^2 Y = \begin{Bmatrix} \Lambda_1 \\ 0 \\ 0 \\ \Lambda_2 \end{Bmatrix}, \qquad \begin{aligned} \Lambda_1 &= \kappa_{11}\,\kappa_{11}\,B D_{m(p)} + \kappa_{21}\,\kappa_{12}\,B D_{m(p)} \\ \Lambda_2 &= \kappa_{12}\,\kappa_{11}\,B D_{m(p)} + \kappa_{22}\,\kappa_{12}\,B D_{m(p)} \end{aligned} .$$

By developing the matrix

$$T^p D = T^{p-j-2}\,(T^2\,Y) + T^{p-j} Z$$

we got the sums III.1(4). The elements of matrix $T^{p-j}\,Z$ do not include quantities $BD_{m(p)}$.

Quantities $\kappa_{22}\,\kappa_{12}\,BD_{m(p)}$ and $\kappa_{12}\,\kappa_{11}\,BD_{m(p)}$, included in equations III.2(11) - III.2(12), are represented in the elements of matrix $T^{p-j-2}\,(T^2\,Y)$ through the term Λ_2. The latter is included in the sum III.1(4) in the form of the product

$$A_{m(p)}\,\Lambda_2 = A_{m(p)}\,\kappa_{12}\,\kappa_{11}\,B D_{m(p)} + A_{m(p)}\,\kappa_{22}\,\kappa_{21}\,B D_{m(p)} \tag{A.1}$$

where $A_{m(p)}$ denotes the products similar to equation III.1(5), containing $(p-j-2)$ factors. Because under conditions of Assertion 1 the total number of factors κ_{22} in the operator products $A_{m(p)} = A$ and B is even, we have in equation (A.1) the sum of the positive III.2(12) and the negative III.2(11) terms.

Thus, the correspondence between the quantities III.2(11) and III.2(12) reflects the correspondence between the terms of the sums (A.1). The assertion is proved.

Proof of Assertion 3

Let us introduce notation for the results of the following operations with $c_1 = c_2$:

$$B\,D_{m(p)} = \psi(\alpha) = Q_1(\alpha + a^{\pm}_{m(p)} + q_1)^{-1} \exp[-\zeta_o(\alpha + q_1)], \tag{A.2}$$

$$A f(\alpha) = Q_2 f(\alpha + q_2),$$

where Q_i and q_i are the products of terms K_{uv} and the sum of the terms ε_u, respectively, appearing in the operator products A or B. Then the sum under consideration can be written in the form

$$X_{m(p)} + X_{q(p)} = A\,\kappa_{22}\,\kappa_{12}\,\psi(\alpha) + A\,\kappa_{12}\,\kappa_{11}\,\psi(\alpha) =$$

$$= A\,[\kappa_{22}\,\kappa_{12}\,\psi(\alpha) + \kappa_{12}\,\kappa_{11}\,\psi(\alpha)] = A\,[K_{22}\,K_{12}\,\psi(\alpha + \varepsilon_1 + \varepsilon_2) +$$

$$+ K_{12}\,K_{11}\,\psi(\alpha + 2\varepsilon_1)] = Q_2[K_{22}\,K_{12}\,\psi(\alpha + \varepsilon_1 + \varepsilon_2 + q_2) +$$

$$+ K_{12}\,K_{11}\,\psi(\alpha + 2\varepsilon_1 + q_2)].$$

By denoting $z = \alpha + \varepsilon_1 + q_2$ and taking into account relation $K_{22} = -K_{11}$ we have

$$X_{m(p)} + X_{q(p)} = C\,[-\psi(z + \varepsilon_2) + \psi(z + \varepsilon_1)],\ C = Q_1\,K_{11}\,K_{12}.$$

This sum is positive, if

$$\psi(z_1 + \varepsilon_1) > \psi(z + \varepsilon_2). \tag{A.3}$$

By substituting the expression for $\psi(\alpha)$ from equation (A.2) into (A.3) we have

$$(z + a^{\pm}_{m(p)} + q_1 + \varepsilon_1)^{-1} \exp[-\zeta_0(z + q_1 + \varepsilon_1)] >$$

$$> (z + a^{\pm}_{m(p)} + q_1 + \varepsilon_2)^{-1} \exp[-\zeta_0(z + q_1 + \varepsilon_2)].$$

By denoting $x = z + a^{\pm}_{m(p)} + q_1$ we can rewrite this inequality in the form

$$(x + \varepsilon_2) \exp[\zeta_0(x + \varepsilon_2)] > (x + \varepsilon_1) \exp[\zeta_0(x + \varepsilon_1)].$$

It holds true, if $x + \varepsilon_2 > x + \varepsilon_1$, i.e., when $\varepsilon_2 > \varepsilon_1$. The assertion is proved.

Proof of Assertion 4

1. According to the known theorem of algebra, the system of linear equations has the only solution, if its determinant is not zero. By substituting expressions for R_{uv} into equation III.3(11) we can transform the latter to the form

$$\delta = \left\{ 2\,[\,(1-n)^2 \operatorname{ch}\zeta(\varepsilon_1-\varepsilon_2)+4n\,]/(1+n)^2 - \exp[-\zeta(\varepsilon_1+\varepsilon_2)]\right\} \exp[-\zeta(\varepsilon_1+\varepsilon_2)]\,. \tag{A.4}$$

According to equation III.3(1) we have $\zeta > \zeta_0$. So it is enough to prove that $\delta < 1$, when $\zeta > 0$.

2. Let us substitute equation (A.4) into the inequality $\delta < 1$ and write the result in the form

$$[\,(1+n)^2/4n\,]\operatorname{ch}\zeta(\varepsilon_1+\varepsilon_2) - [\,(1-n)^2/4n\,]\operatorname{ch}\zeta(\varepsilon_1-\varepsilon_2) > 1\,.$$

By using the relation

$$\operatorname{ch}\zeta\,(\varepsilon_1 \pm \varepsilon_2) = \operatorname{ch}\zeta\varepsilon_1 \operatorname{ch}\zeta\varepsilon_2 \pm \operatorname{sh}\zeta\varepsilon_1 \operatorname{sh}\zeta\varepsilon_2$$

and collecting the terms, connected with the products of the hyperbolic sines and cosines, in separate groups we can write the inequality under consideration in the form

$$\operatorname{ch}\zeta\varepsilon_1 \operatorname{ch}\zeta\varepsilon_2 + [\,(1+n^2)/2n\,]\operatorname{sh}\zeta\varepsilon_1 \operatorname{sh}\zeta\varepsilon_2 > 1\,. \tag{A.5}$$

On the strength of the evident inequalities

$$\operatorname{ch}\zeta\varepsilon_1 \operatorname{ch}\zeta\varepsilon_2 > 1\,,\quad [\,(1+n^2)\,/2n\,]\operatorname{sh}\zeta\varepsilon_1 \operatorname{sh}\zeta\varepsilon_2 > 0 \ \text{ with } \zeta > 0$$

condition (A.5) holds true for any $\zeta > 0$. The assertion is proved.

Proof of Assertion 5

1. Let us begin with the function $\Delta(\zeta)$. In the neighborhood of the point $\zeta = 0$ we can expand this function into a power series taking into account the first non-zero term. This yields

$$\Delta \approx B\zeta^2\,,\quad B = 4\pi^2 - (\varepsilon_1 - \varepsilon_2)^2(1-n)^2/(1+n)^2\,. \tag{A.6}$$

2. Let us take function $\Delta_\nu^\pm(\zeta)$ with $\zeta \to 0$. On the strength of the relations

$$(R_{uv})_{\zeta=0} = K_{uv}, \quad K_{uv}^2 + K_{uv}K_{vu} = 1, \quad K_{11} = -K_{22} \tag{A.7}$$

all expressions in the round brackets in formulas for A_ν and B_ν in equations III.3(12) turn to zero when $\zeta = 0$. Therefore, $\Delta_\nu^\pm = 0$ when $\zeta = 0$. The power expansion of function $\Delta_\nu^\pm(\zeta)$ in the neighborhood of point $\zeta = 0$ begins with the term depending linearly on ζ. Let us find a coefficient at this term.

3. By approximating the exponents in expressions for R_{uv} by a linear part of the power expansion

$$R_{uv} = K_{uv} \exp(-\zeta\varepsilon_u) \approx K_{uv}(1 - \zeta\varepsilon_u) \tag{A.8}$$

we have

$$R_{ab}^m R_{cd}^n R_{ef}^p \ldots \approx K_{ab}^m (1 - \zeta\varepsilon_a)^m K_{cd}^n (1 - \zeta\varepsilon_c)^n K_{ef}^p (1 - \zeta\varepsilon_e)^p \ldots \tag{A.9}$$

We can single out from these products that part which contains the first power of ζ only. To do this we can use the following approach (we drop an elementary substantiation).

Let us take a function of x, given by the product of factors (A.9),

$$f(x) = \prod_{k=1}^{K} [M_k(1 + x m_k)]^{\mu_k}.$$

The part of this product, containing only first powers of x, is defined by expressions

$$\psi(x) = x\left(\sum_{k=1}^{K} \mu_k m_k\right) \prod_{k=1}^{K} M_k^{\mu_k} = x \sum_{k=1}^{K} m_k E_k, \quad E_k = \mu_k \prod_{p=1}^{K} M_p^{\mu_p}.$$

By replacing here M_k, m_k, μ_k, x with the corresponding quantities from equation (A.9) we get the sought approximation

$$R_{ab}^m R_{cd}^n R_{ef}^p \ldots \approx -\zeta(\varepsilon_a E_a + \varepsilon_c E_c + \varepsilon_e E_e + \ldots), \tag{A.10}$$

$$E_a = mL, \quad E_c = nL, \quad E_e = pL, \quad L = K_{ab}^m K_{cd}^n K_{ef}^p \ldots$$

By using equation (A.10) we get approximate formulas for terms from equation III.3(12)

$$A_v = -\zeta(\varepsilon_1 k_v + \varepsilon_2 \ell_v), \; B_v = -\zeta(\varepsilon_1 m_v + \varepsilon_2 n_v) \text{ with } \zeta \to 0 \tag{A.11}$$

where k_v, ℓ_v, m_v, n_v are given in equations III.3(15).

4. It is sufficient to approximate factors $U^{\pm}(\zeta)$ in equation III.3(12) by the first term of the power expansion $U^{\pm}(\zeta) \approx \exp(-\alpha_1^{\mp}\zeta_0)$, because in view of approximations for A_v and B_v the linear approximation in equation III.3(12) leads only to a precise description of the quadratic part of the power expansion of function $\Delta_v^{\pm}(\zeta)$.

5. By substituting equation (A.11) and $U^{\pm}(\zeta) \approx U^{\pm}(0)$ into III.3(12) and assembling the terms at ε_1 and ε_2 in the separate groups we obtain the sought representation for $\Delta_v^{\pm}$ in the neighborhood of the point $\zeta = 0$

$$\Delta_v^{\pm} \approx \zeta A(\zeta_0) \tag{A.12}$$

where $A(\zeta_0)$ is defined in equation III.3(15). By using equation (A.12) and (A.6) we obtain equation III.3(15).

Proof of Assertion 7

Let us define norm $\| \boldsymbol{R} \|$ of matrix $\boldsymbol{R}$ as the maximum value of the moduli of elements in a row

$$\| \boldsymbol{R} \| = \max(|R_{11}| + |R_{21}|, \; |R_{12}| + |R_{22}|) \tag{A.13}$$

If

$$|R_{11}| + |R_{21}| > |R_{12}| + |R_{22}|,$$

then

$$\| \boldsymbol{R} \| = |R_{11}| + |R_{21}|.$$

In the opposite case

$$\| \boldsymbol{R} \| = | R_{12} | + | R_{22} | .$$

Then, according to the known theorem, the system III.3(7) has the only solution and the method of simple interaction III.3(17) converges to it with a speed of geometrical progression, if $\| \boldsymbol{R} \| < 1$.

Let us consider the limitations on the parameters of the problem, imposed by the condition $\| \boldsymbol{R} \| < 1$. Suppose

$$n = \rho_1 / \rho_2 < 1 , \quad \varepsilon_2 > \varepsilon_1 . \tag{A.14}$$

Then

$$| R_{11} | + | R_{21} | = | K_{11} | \exp (- \zeta \varepsilon_1) + | K_{21} | \exp (- \zeta \varepsilon_2) \le$$

$$\le (| K_{11} | + K_{21}) \exp (- \zeta \varepsilon_1) = \exp (- \zeta \varepsilon_1) ,$$

$$| R_{12} | + | R_{22} | = | K_{12} | \exp (- \zeta \varepsilon_1) + | K_{22} | \exp (- \zeta \varepsilon_2) \le$$

$$(K_{12} + | K_{22} |) \exp (- \zeta \varepsilon_1) = (3 - n) (1 + n)^{-1} \exp (- \zeta \varepsilon_1)$$

and the norm of matrix $\boldsymbol{R}$ can be defined as

$$\| \boldsymbol{R} \| = | R_{12} | + | R_{22} | \le [(3 - n) / (1 + n)] \exp (- \zeta \varepsilon_1) .$$

In this case condition $\| \boldsymbol{R} \| < 1$ is satisfied, if

$$[(3 - n) / (1 + n)] \exp (- \zeta \varepsilon_1) < 1 .$$

This inequality can be rewritten in the form

$$\exp (\zeta \varepsilon_1) > \exp \ln [(3 - n) / (1 + n)] .$$

or in the form

$$\zeta > M , \ M = (1 / \varepsilon_1) \ln [(3 - n) / (1 + n)] . \tag{A.15}$$

Let us replace the first inequality in equation (A.14) by $n > 1$. Then

$$|R_{11}| + |R_{21}| \le [(3n-1)/(1+n)] \exp(-\zeta\varepsilon_1),$$

$$|R_{12}| + |R_{22}| \le \exp(-\zeta\varepsilon_1),$$

and the norm of matrix $\boldsymbol{R}$ has to be defined as

$$\|\boldsymbol{R}\| = |R_{11}| + |R_{21}| \le [(3n-1)/(1+n)] \exp(-\zeta\varepsilon_1)$$

Then instead of condition (A.15) we have the following sufficient condition for the uniqueness of the solution of the system III.3(4) and the convergence of successive approximations:

$$\zeta > M, \; M = (1/\varepsilon_1) \ln[(3n-1)/(1+n)], \; n > 1. \tag{A.16}$$

Finally, by replacing the second inequality in condition (A.14) with $\varepsilon_2 < \varepsilon_1$ we replace the quantity ε_1 by ε_2 in equations (A.15) and (A.16). Then by introducing notation III.3(19) the sufficient condition for the uniqueness of the solution of system III.3(4) and the convergence can be written in the form III.3(20).

Proof of Assertion 8

According to the sufficient condition III.3(20) there is always such a number M that the series III.3(30) and therefore both series III.3(32) converge when $M < \zeta$. We will show first that the interval of convergence of these series is always open at the left side, because their items are positive and monotonous functions of ζ_0.

1. Let us show first that if the series

$$z_k(\zeta) = \sum_{n=1}^{\infty} f_n^{(k)}(\zeta) \tag{A.17}$$

converges at the point $\zeta = A$, it converges within the interval $A \le \zeta < \infty$, and its sum $z_k(\zeta)$ is positive and increases monotonously in this interval with ζ_0 decreasing.

To do so, we consider two numerical series $z_k(A)$ and $z_k(B)$ with $A < B$. Because all items of series (A.17) are positive monotonous functions and increase with ζ decreasing, we have $f_n^{(k)}(A) > f_n^{(k)}(B)$. Then the numerical series $z_k(B)$ has the majorizing series $z_k(A)$. Because the items of both series are positive, we have $z_k(A) > z_k(B)$. This guarantees the convergence of the series (A.17) in the interval $A \le \zeta < \infty$.

By repeating this approach in regard to numerical series $z_k(B)$ and $z_k(C)$ with $B < C$ we get $z_k(B) > z_k(C)$, which shows that the sum of the series (A.17) increases monotonously when ζ decreases.

2. Let us show that the interval of convergence of the functional series (A.17) is open at the left side $A_k < \zeta < \infty$, where A_k is some number (unknown so far).

Because all terms of the series (A.17) are positive and increase monotonously with ζ decreasing, there has to be such a number $A_k < A$ that the sum of the series $z_k(A)$ increases infinitely, when A approaches A_k from the right side (the existence of such a number is evident, because every term of the series increases exponentially with $\zeta \to -\infty$). It is a known fact of mathematical analysis that a positive monotonous function $z_k(\zeta)$, defined in the interval $A_k \le \zeta < \infty$ and infinitely increasing with ζ approaching A_k from the right side, has the infinite limit

$$\lim_{\zeta \to A_k} z_k(\zeta) = \infty, \tag{A.18}$$

i.e., for any given $N > 0$ there is such a number $\varepsilon > 0$ that

$$z_k(\zeta) > N \quad \text{with } \zeta - A_k < \varepsilon. \tag{A.19}$$

However, at the same time for any $\varepsilon > 0$ the value of the function $z_k(A_k + \varepsilon)$ is finite.

Because $z_k(A_k + \varepsilon)$ with $\varepsilon > 0$ is finite, it follows from the previous section that the series (A.17) converges in the interval $A_k + \varepsilon \le \zeta < \infty$ with any $\varepsilon > 0$. On the other hand, the series (A.17) diverges at the point $\zeta = A_k$ because of the existence of the limit (A.18). This shows that the interval of the convergence of the series under consideration is open from the left side $A_k < \zeta < \infty$.

3. Let us try to find the interval of convergence. To do this, we first demonstrate the following auxiliary assertion. Let quantity $\zeta > 0$ comply with the inequalities $A_k < \zeta < \infty$ with $k = 1, 2$, defining the intervals of convergence of the series III.3(32). Then the sum of the infinite series III.3(30) equals $\Delta_v^{\pm}(\zeta)/\Delta(\zeta)$.

Indeed, if the series III.3(32) converge for some value $\zeta > 0$ then their sum III.3(30) with the same value of ζ complies with the system III.3(7). According to Assertion 4, system III.3(7) has the only solution $\Delta_\nu^\pm(\zeta)/\Delta(\zeta)$. Hence, the sum III.3(30) can be equal to $\Delta_\nu^\pm(\zeta)/\Delta(\zeta)$ only.

4. Let us show now that the series III.3(30) converges in the open interval $\zeta > 0$. To do this, it is sufficient to show that the quantity A_k, defining the intervals of convergence $A_k < \zeta$ of the series III.3(32), complies with inequality $A_k \leq 0$.

Suppose first that $A_1 > 0$. Then on the strength of equations (A.19) term z_1 in equation III.3(30) increases infinitely, when ζ tends to A_1 from the right side. Then, according to subsection 3 of Proof of Assertion 8, the function $\Delta_\nu^\pm/\Delta$ may be unlimited in the open interval $A_1 < \zeta$. However, function $\Delta_\nu^\pm/\Delta$ is limited at any point of the open interval $\zeta > 0$. The arising contradiction shows that the quantity A_1 cannot be positive.

Because the factor at z_2 in equation III.3(30) is not zero with $\zeta > 0$, the previous consideration holds true in regard to the quantity A_2. Thus, inequalities $A_k \leq 0$ hold true on the strength of the uniqueness of the solution of system III.3(7) and series III.3(30) converges to the solution of this system, when $\zeta > 0$.

5. Let us show that the series III.3(30) converges uniformly with regard to ζ with $\zeta > C$ for any $C > 0$. Because the terms of each series in equations III.3(32) increase monotonously with ζ decreasing, in the interval $\zeta > C$ for any $C > 0$ we have inequalities $f_n^{(k)}(C) > f_n^{(k)}(\zeta)$. Because $f_n^{(k)}(C) > 0$, the convergent series with the positive items $f_n^{(k)}(C)$ is the majorizing series for the series $z_k(\zeta)$ with $\zeta > C$. This is sufficient for the series $z_k(\zeta)$ to converge uniformly in the mentioned interval. Because the multiplication by the finite function does not change the uniform convergence, the second term in equation III.3(30) also is a uniformly convergent series. Because the sum of two uniformly convergent series converges uniformly, we get the assertion under consideration.

Proof of Assertion 10

By using definition II.1(10) of function $\varphi_{uv}(\alpha)$ we have

$$\cos\varphi_{uv}(\alpha) = [\exp(\ln\eta_{uv})]\cos\alpha, \quad \eta_{uv} = c_u/c_v.$$

By expressing cosines by the formula

$$\cos \alpha = \{(1/2) \exp [-(\mathrm{sign}\ \mathrm{Im}\ \alpha)\, i\alpha]\}\,(1 + c), \tag{A.20}$$

$$c = \exp[(\mathrm{sign}\ \mathrm{Im}\ \alpha)\, 2 i\alpha],$$

where c is considered as a correction we get the representation III.7(4), where

$$\varphi(\alpha) = (\mathrm{sign}\ \mathrm{Im}\ \alpha)\, i \ln \psi(\alpha), \quad \psi(\alpha) = (1 + c)/(1 + c_\varphi), \tag{A.21}$$

$$c_\varphi = \exp[(\mathrm{sign}\ \mathrm{Im}\ \alpha)\, 2 i \varphi_{uv}(\alpha)].$$

2. First we show that function $\varphi(\alpha)$ is finite, when $|\mathrm{Im}\ \alpha| > 0$. This is true, if function $\psi(\alpha)$ is finite and has no zero values. The numerator of $\psi(\alpha)$ never turns to zero with $|\mathrm{Im}\ \alpha| > 0$, because the modulus of the exponent term is always less than unit. The numerator does not increase with $|\mathrm{Im}\ \alpha| \to \infty$, because the real part of the exponent is negative. So it is sufficient to show that the denominator of $\psi(\alpha)$ has no roots when $|\mathrm{Im}\ \alpha| > 0$.

Let us show that the equation,

$$1 + \exp[(\mathrm{sign}\ \mathrm{Im}\ \alpha)\, 2 i \varphi_{uv}(\alpha)] = 0, \tag{A.22}$$

has no roots, when $|\mathrm{Im}\ \alpha| > 0$. To do this, we introduce notation

$$x = (\mathrm{sign}\ \mathrm{Im}\ \alpha)\, 2\ \mathrm{Re}\ \varphi_{uv}(\alpha), \quad y = (\mathrm{sign}\ \mathrm{Im}\ \alpha)\ 2\ \mathrm{Im}\ \varphi_{uv}(\alpha) \tag{A.23}$$

and rewrite this equation in the form

$$1 + \exp(ix - y) = 0. \tag{A.24}$$

This equation can be satisfied for $y = 0$ only, because in the opposite case the modulus of the exponent is not unity. By taking $y = 0$ we get equation $1 + \exp(ix) = 0$. Its solution is $x = k\pi$, where k is the positive or negative whole odd integer. So equation (A.24) can be written as a pair of equations $x = k\pi$, $y = 0$. By using notation, (A.23) they can be written as

$$\mathrm{Re}\ \varphi_{uv}(\alpha) = m\pi/2, \quad \mathrm{Im}\ \varphi_{uv}(\alpha) = 0, \tag{A.25}$$

where $m = (\mathrm{sign}\ \mathrm{Im}\ \alpha)\, k$. On the strength of equations III.7(1) it is sufficient to show that the system (A.25) has no solution in the band $0 \le \mathrm{Re}\ \alpha < \pi/2$. By substituting equation III.7(2) into (A.25) we get

$$[Q - (Q^2 - R^2)^{1/2}]^{1/2} = \cos m\pi/2 = 0,$$

$$[Q - 1 + (Q^2 - R^2)^{1/2}]^{1/2} = 0. \tag{A.26}$$

These equations cannot be satisfied simultaneously. Indeed, to satisfy the first equation, we have to take $R = 0$. But then the second equation is not satisfied. Thus, the system (A.25) and, therefore, equation (A.22) have no solutions relative to α. We have demonstrated that the function $\varphi(\alpha)$ with $|\operatorname{Im}\alpha| > 0$ is finite.

3. Let us find an asymptotic formula for $\operatorname{Im}\varphi_{uv}(\alpha)$ with $|\operatorname{Im}\alpha| \to \infty$, which is necessary in the following to simplify the expression for $\psi(\alpha)$. To do so, we neglect in the expressions

$$\operatorname{sh}\operatorname{Im}\alpha = [\exp(\operatorname{Im}\alpha) - \exp(-\operatorname{Im}\alpha)]/2,$$

$$\operatorname{ch}\operatorname{Im}\alpha = [\exp(\operatorname{Im}\alpha) + \exp(-\operatorname{Im}\alpha)]/2$$

with $|\operatorname{Im}\alpha| \to \infty$ the exponentially small quantities, i.e.,

$$\operatorname{sh}\operatorname{Im}\alpha \sim (\operatorname{sign}\operatorname{Im}\alpha)[\exp|\operatorname{Im}\alpha|]/2,$$

$$\operatorname{ch}\operatorname{Im}\alpha \sim [\exp|\operatorname{Im}\alpha|]/2.$$

By substituting these expressions into formulas III.7(2) we get

$$R \sim (\eta_{uv}/2)[\exp|\operatorname{Im}\alpha|]\cos\operatorname{Re}\alpha,$$

$$M \sim (\operatorname{sign}\operatorname{Im}\alpha)(\eta_{uv}/2)[\exp|\operatorname{Im}\alpha|]\sin\operatorname{Re}\alpha,$$

$$R^2 + M^2 \sim (\eta_{uv}/2)^2 \exp(2|\operatorname{Im}\alpha|),$$

$$Q \sim (\eta_{uv}/2)^2 [\exp(2|\operatorname{Im}\alpha|)]/2,$$

$$(Q^2 - R^2)^{1/2} \sim (\eta_{uv}/2)[\exp|\operatorname{Im}\alpha|]$$

$$\times [(\eta_{uv}/8)\exp(2|\operatorname{Im}\alpha|) - \cos^2\operatorname{Re}\alpha]^{1/2} \sim (\eta_{uv}/2)^2[\exp(2|\operatorname{Im}\alpha|)]/2,$$

$$[\,Q-1+(Q^2-R^2)^{1/2}\,]^{1/2} \sim [\,(\eta_{uv}/2)^2 \exp\,(2\,|\,\mathrm{Im}\;\alpha\,|)-1\,]^{1/2}$$

$$\sim (\eta_{uv}/2) \exp\,|\,\mathrm{Im}\;\alpha\,|\,,$$

where all approximations hold true for any Re α .

By substituting the last expression into equation III.7(2) we have for $|\,\mathrm{Im}\;\alpha\,| \to \infty$

$$\mathrm{Im}\;\varphi_{uv}\,(\alpha) \sim (\mathrm{sign}\;\mathrm{Im}\;\alpha)\;\mathrm{arsh}\;[\,(\eta_{uv}/2)\exp\,|\,\mathrm{Im}\;\alpha\,|\,]$$

or

$$\mathrm{sh}\;|\,\mathrm{Im}\;\varphi_{uv}(\alpha)\,| \sim (\eta_{uv}/2)\exp\,|\,\mathrm{Im}\;\alpha\,|\,,$$

or expressing the hyperbolic sine by the Euler formula

$$\exp\,|\,\mathrm{Im}\;\varphi_{uv}\,(\alpha)\,|-\exp\left\{-|\,\mathrm{Im}\;\varphi_{uv}(\alpha)\,|\right\} \sim \eta_{uv}\exp\,|\,\mathrm{Im}\;\alpha\,|\,.$$

Because the right part exponentially increases with $|\,\mathrm{Im}\;\alpha\,| \to \infty$, we can neglect in the left part the second term

$$\exp\,|\,\mathrm{Im}\;\varphi_{uv}\,(\alpha)\,| \sim \eta_{uv}\exp\,|\,\mathrm{Im}\;\alpha\,|\,.$$

Then

$$|\,\mathrm{Im}\;\varphi_{uv}\,(\alpha)\,| \sim |\,\mathrm{Im}\;\alpha\,| + \ln\,\eta_{uv}\,.$$

By multiplying both parts by sign Im α we get the desired asymptotic formula

$$\mathrm{Im}\;\varphi_{uv}(\alpha) \sim \mathrm{Im}\;\alpha + (\mathrm{sign}\;\mathrm{Im}\;\alpha)\;\ln\,\eta_{uv}\,. \tag{A.27}$$

4. Let us find an asymptotic formula for $\psi(\alpha)$ with $|\,\mathrm{Im}\;\alpha\,| \to \infty$ by using formula (A.27). By taking into account the relation sign $\mathrm{Im}\;\varphi_{uv}(\alpha) = \mathrm{sign}\;\mathrm{Im}\;\alpha$ and substituting $\mathrm{Im}\;\varphi_{uv}(\alpha)$ with $|\,\mathrm{Im}\;\alpha\,| \to \infty$ by expression (A.27) we can write the quantities c and c_φ in the form

$$c = a_1 \exp\,(-p)\,,\quad c_\varphi = a_2 \exp(-p) \quad \text{with } p \to \infty\,, \tag{A.28}$$

where

$$a_1 = \exp\;[\,(\mathrm{sign}\;\mathrm{Im}\;\alpha)\,2\,i\;\mathrm{Re}\;\alpha\,]\,,$$

$$a_2 = \exp\left[(\text{sign Im }\alpha)2i \text{ Re } \varphi_{uv}(\alpha) - 2\ln\eta_{uv}\right],\quad p = 2|\text{Im }\alpha|\,.$$

Then function $\psi(\alpha)$ can be written as

$$\psi(\alpha) = \frac{1 + a_1 \exp(-p)}{1 + a_2 \exp(-p)} = 1 + \frac{(a_1 - a_2)\exp(-p)}{1 + a_2\exp(-p)}\,. \tag{A.29}$$

When $p \to \infty$, we can neglect in the denominator the second term for any Re α. Then we get the desired asymptotic formula

$$\psi(\alpha) \sim 1 + (a_1 - a_2)\exp(-p) \quad \text{with } p \to \infty\,. \tag{A.30}$$

Let us write a couple of inequalities that follow from the obtained expression. The cofactor at the exponent complies with the obvious inequality

$$|a_1 - a_2| \le a,\quad a = 1 + \exp(-2\ln\eta_{uv}) = 1 + \eta_{uv}^{-2}\,. \tag{A.31}$$

Then from equation (A.30) we have

$$1 - a\exp(-p) \le |\Psi(a)| \le 1 + a\exp(-p) \quad \text{with } p \to \infty\,. \tag{A.32}$$

5. Let us show that the function $\varphi(\alpha)$ with $p \to \infty$ tends to zero uniformly with regard to Re α. Let $\varepsilon > 0$ be any given number. Then the criterion for a uniform approach to the limit translates into the existence of such a number $N(\varepsilon)$, independent of Re α, that

$$|\varphi(\alpha)| < \varepsilon \quad \text{with } p > N(\varepsilon). \tag{A.33}$$

By using relation $|\varphi(\alpha)| = |\ln\psi(\alpha)|$, where $\psi(\alpha)$ is defined by equation (A.30), we can write the inequality (A.33) in the form

$$|\ln[1 + a^* \exp(-p)]| < \varepsilon \quad \text{with } p > N(\varepsilon), \tag{A.34}$$

where $a^* = a_1 - a_2$. Let us choose $N(\varepsilon)$ as follows:

$$N(\varepsilon) = \ln\left\{a^*[\exp(-\varepsilon) - 1]^{-1}\right\}. \tag{A-35}$$

Then

$$|\ln\left\{1 + a^*\exp[-N(\varepsilon)]\right\}| = \varepsilon\,. \tag{A.36}$$

Now we can see that condition (A.33) is satisfied for any Re α . The assertion is proved.

Proof of Assertion 11

1. By using definition II.1(11) we can write function $\tau_{uv}(\alpha)$ in the form

$$\tau_{uv}(\alpha) = (\eta_{uv} \sin\alpha)/\sin\varphi_{uv}(\alpha), \quad \eta_{uv} = c_u/c_v . \tag{A.37}$$

By expressing the sines by the formula

$$\sin\alpha = -\left\{ [(\text{sign Im}\,\alpha)/2i] \exp[-(\text{sign Im}\,\alpha) i\alpha] \right\} (1 - c),$$

where c is defined in equation (A.20), and taking into account relation

$$\text{sign Im}\,\varphi_{uv}(\alpha) = \text{sign Im}\,\alpha ,$$

we have

$$\tau_{uv}(\alpha) = (\text{sign Im}\,\alpha)[\text{sign Im}\,\varphi_{uv}(\alpha)]\,\eta_{uv} \left\{ \exp\{-(\text{sign Im}\,\alpha) i\alpha + \right. \tag{A.38}$$

$$\left. + [\text{sign Im}\,\varphi_{uv}(\alpha)]\, i\varphi_{uv}(\alpha)\} \right\} \theta(\alpha) =$$

$$= \eta_{uv} \left\{ \exp\{ (\text{sign Im}\,\alpha)\, i\, [\varphi_{uv}(\alpha) - \alpha]\} \right\} \theta(\alpha),$$

$$\theta(\alpha) = (1 - c)/(1 - c_\varphi),$$

$$c_\varphi = \exp\{[\text{sign Im}\,\varphi_{uv}(\alpha)]\, 2i\, \varphi_{uv}(\alpha)\} =$$

$$= \exp[(\text{sign Im}\,\alpha)\, 2i\, \varphi_{uv}(\alpha)].$$

By expressing $[\varphi_{uv}(\alpha) - \alpha]$ by equation III.7(4) and taking into account the relation

$$\eta_{uv} \exp[(\text{sign Im}\,\alpha)\, i\, e_{uv}] = 1$$

we have

$$\tau_{uv}(\alpha) = \eta_{uv} \left\{ \exp\{(\text{sign Im}\,\alpha)\, i [e_{uv} + \varphi(\alpha)]\} \right\} \theta(\alpha) =$$

$$= \theta(\alpha) \exp[(\text{sign Im}\,\alpha)\, i\, \varphi(\alpha)]. \tag{A.39}$$

By substituting the expression for $\varphi(\alpha)$ from equation (A.21) into (A.39) we have

$$\tau_{uv}(\alpha) = \theta(\alpha)/\psi(\alpha) = \frac{1 - c}{1 - c_\varphi} \times \frac{1 + c_\varphi}{1 + c} . \tag{A.40}$$

This expression can be transformed to the form III.7(5) where function $\tau(\alpha)$ can be written in the form

$$\tau(\alpha) = (c_\varphi - c)\left[\frac{1}{1 - c_\varphi} + \frac{1}{1 + c} + \frac{c_\varphi - c}{(1 - c_\varphi)(1 + c)}\right] . \tag{A.41}$$

2. Let us show that function $\tau(\alpha)$ is finite under the condition III.7(6). Because real parts of the exponents in c and c_φ are negative, function $\tau(\alpha)$ does not increase, when $|\operatorname{Im}\alpha| \to \infty$. So it is sufficient to show that denominators in equation (A.41) have no roots under the condition III.7(6). The equation $1 + c = 0$ has no roots with $|\operatorname{Im}\alpha| > 0$, because the modulus of the exponent item is less than unity. So it is sufficient to show that the equation $1 - c_\varphi = 0$ also has no roots under condition III.7(6). By substituting the expression for c_φ into the mentioned equation we have

$$1 - \exp[(\operatorname{sign}\operatorname{Im}\alpha)\, 2 i \varphi_{uv}(\alpha)] = 0 . \tag{A.42}$$

This equation differs from equation (A.22) only by the sign at the exponent. By using the approaches, applied for studying equation (A.22), it is easy to show that equation (A.42) can be written as a pair of equations

$$\operatorname{Re}\varphi_{uv}(\alpha) = n\pi, \quad \operatorname{Im}\varphi_{uv}(\alpha) = 0, \tag{A.43}$$

where n is an integer. Like with equation (A.25), it is sufficient to solve this system in the band $0 \le \operatorname{Re}\alpha < \pi/2$. Therefore, by taking $n = 0$ and substituting equations III.7(2) into (A.43) we get the following system of equations:

$$[Q - (Q^2 - R^2)^{1/2}]^{1/2} = 1, \quad [Q - 1 + (Q^2 - R^2)^{1/2}]^{1/2} = 0$$

or upon raising them to a power

$$Q - 1 = (Q^2 - R^2)^{1/2}, \quad 1 - Q = (Q^2 - R^2)^{1/2} . \tag{A.44}$$

Because the right parts of these equations coincide, the system has a solution, if their left parts coincide $Q - 1 = 1 - Q$, i.e., with $Q = 1$. Then from equation (A.44) we have $R = 1$. By substituting $Q = 1$ and $R = 1$ into the expression for Q from equation

III.7(2) we obtain $M = 0$. By substituting R and M from equation III.7(2) into expressions $R = 1$, $M = 0$, we learn that the system (A.44) has a solution, if the equations

$$\eta_{uv} \cos \operatorname{Re} \alpha \operatorname{ch} \operatorname{Im} \alpha = 1, \quad \sin \operatorname{Re} \alpha \operatorname{sh} \operatorname{Im} \alpha = 0 \tag{A.45}$$

hold true simultaneously.

To satisfy the second equation, it is necessary to suppose $\sin \operatorname{Re} \alpha = 0$ or $\operatorname{sh} \operatorname{Im} \alpha = 0$ (the case of $\alpha = 0$ does not allow satisfaction of the first equation). Suppose $\sin \operatorname{Re} \alpha = 0$. Then in the band under consideration $0 \le \operatorname{Re} \alpha < \pi/2$ we have $\operatorname{Re} \alpha = 0$. The first equation turns into

$$\eta_{uv} \operatorname{ch} \operatorname{Im} \alpha = 1 \quad \text{or} \quad \operatorname{ch} \operatorname{Im} \alpha = c_v/c_u,$$

and only has a solution with $c_v \ge c_u$. Therefore, the solution of system (A.45) is

$$\operatorname{Re} \alpha = 0, \quad \operatorname{Im} \alpha = \operatorname{arch} (c_v/c_u) \quad \text{with } c_v \ge c_u. \tag{A.46}$$

Suppose now $\operatorname{sh} \operatorname{Im} \alpha = 0$, i.e., $\operatorname{Im} \alpha = 0$. Then the first relation in equations (A.45) turns into

$$\eta_{uv} \cos \operatorname{Re} \alpha = 1 \quad \text{or} \quad \cos \operatorname{Re} \alpha = c_v/c_u$$

and only has a solution with $c_v \le c_u$. Therefore, we get the following solution of system (A.45):

$$\operatorname{Re} \alpha = \arccos (c_v/c_u), \quad \operatorname{Im} \alpha = 0 \quad \text{with } c_v \le c_u. \tag{A.47}$$

One can see from equations (A.46) and (A.47) that system (A.45) has no solution and equation (A.42) has no roots under condition III.7(6). Hence, the function $\tau(\alpha)$ is finite under condition III.7(6).

3. Let us introduce an asymptotic representation of function $\tau(\alpha)$, when $|\operatorname{Im} \alpha| \to \infty$. By substituting expressions (A.28) into (A.41) and neglecting small quantities with $p \to \infty$ we obtain

$$\tau(\alpha) \sim 2(c_\varphi - c) = 2(a_2 - a_1) \exp(-p). \tag{A.48}$$

From this formula we have a useful inequality

$$|\tau(\alpha)| \le 2\, a \exp(-p), \tag{A.49}$$

where a is defined in equation (A.31).

4. The function $\tau(\alpha)$ with $p \to \infty$ tends to zero uniformly with regard to Re α, if for any $\varepsilon > 0$ there is such a number $N(\varepsilon)$, independent of Re α, that

$$|\tau(\alpha)| < \varepsilon \quad \text{with } p > N(\varepsilon). \tag{A.50}$$

Let us show that such a number does exist.

On the strength of inequality (A.49), the inequality (A.50) holds true, if the following inequality holds true:

$$2\, a \exp(-p) < \varepsilon \quad \text{or} \quad \exp(p) > 2a/\varepsilon \quad \text{or} \quad p > \ln(2a/\varepsilon).$$

If we take

$$N(\varepsilon) = \ln(2a/\varepsilon),$$

where on the strength of inequality (A.31) the quantity a does not depend on Re α, the condition (A.50) is satisfied. The assertion is proved.

Proof of Assertion 12

1. Let us represent the functions under consideration in the form

$$K_{vv}(\alpha) = \frac{\tau_{uv}(\alpha) - \rho_{vu}}{\tau_{uv}(\alpha) + \rho_{vu}}, \quad K_{uv}(\alpha) = \frac{2\rho_{vu}}{\tau_{uv}(\alpha) + \rho_{vu}}, \tag{A.51}$$

$$\rho_{vu} = \rho_v/\rho_u, \quad u = v \mp 1,$$

where $\tau_{uv}(\alpha)$ is defined by equation II.1(11). These expressions can be rewritten in the form

$$K_{vv}(\alpha) = \widetilde{K}_{vv} + K^*(\alpha), \quad K_{uv}(\alpha) = \widetilde{K}_{uv} - K^*(\alpha) \tag{A.52}$$

$$\widetilde{K}_{vv} = (1 - \rho_{vu})/(1 + \rho_{vu}), \quad \widetilde{K}_{uv} = 2\rho_{vu}/(1 + \rho_{vu}),$$

$$K^*(\alpha) = 2\rho_{vu}\,[\tau_{uv}(\alpha) - 1](1 + \rho_{vu})^{-1}\,[\tau_{uv}(\alpha) + \rho_{vu}]^{-1}, \tag{A.53}$$

where $\widetilde{K}_{vv}$ and $\widetilde{K}_{uv}$ correspond to a particular case of $c_u = c_v$ in equations (A.51). Formulas (A.52) lead to a formal representation III.7(7), where $K(\alpha) = K^*(\alpha)$ or $K(\alpha) = -K^*(\alpha)$. Therefore, it is sufficient to show that the function $K^*(\alpha)$ with $|\text{Im } \alpha| \to \infty$ tends to zero uniformly with regard to Re α.

2. Let us substitute the function $\tau_{uv}(\alpha)$ in equation (A.53) by its representation III.7(5)

$$K^*(\alpha) = 2\,\rho_{vu}\,\tau(\alpha)(1 + \rho_{vu})^{-1}\,[\rho_{vu} + 1 + \tau(\alpha)]^{-1}. \tag{A.54}$$

On the strength of Assertion 11, function $\tau(\alpha)$ with $|\text{Im } \alpha| \to \infty$ tends to zero uniformly with regard to Re α, and its decrease has an exponential character (A.49). Therefore, it is always possible to choose such $|\text{Im } \alpha|^*$, independent of Re α, that the quantity $\tau(\alpha)$ will be any small value compared with $(\rho_{vu} + 1)$. By neglecting in expression $[\rho_{vu} + 1 + \tau(\alpha)]^{-1}$ with $|\text{Im } \alpha| \to \infty$ the small term $\tau(\alpha)$ we have

$$K^*(\alpha) = b\,\tau(\alpha),\; b = 2\,\rho_{vu}\,(1 + \rho_{vu})^{-2}. \tag{A.55}$$

One can see from expression (A.55) that function $K^*(\alpha)$ with $|\text{Im } \alpha| \to \infty$ differs from $\tau(\alpha)$ only by a constant factor. Hence, on the strength of Assertion 11, this function with $|\text{Im } \alpha| \to \infty$ tends to zero uniformly with regard to Re α. The assertion is proved.

Proof of Assertion 13

1. The form of the argument of an arbitrary function $f(\alpha)$ in the right part of equation III.7(8) follows from the definition of the operator II.2(31) and the representation of the function $\varphi_{uv}(\alpha)$, following from Assertion 10. Therefore, it is necessary only to prove the representation

$$\tau_{uv}(\alpha)\,K_{uv}(\alpha) = [1 + \lambda(\alpha)]\,\widetilde{K}_{uv}. \tag{A.56}$$

2. Let us substitute representations of functions $\tau_{uv}(\alpha)$ and $K_{uv}(\alpha)$ from equations III.7(5) and III.7(7) into (A.56). Then by resolving the result of the substitution with regard to $\lambda(\alpha)$ we get

$$\lambda(\alpha) = [1 + K(\alpha)/\widetilde{K}_{uv}\,\tau(\alpha) + K(\alpha)/\widetilde{K}_{uv}]\,\tau(\alpha).$$

Let us substitute $K(\alpha)$ by $\pm K^*(\alpha)$ from equation (A.55) with $|\operatorname{Im}\alpha| \to \infty$. Then

$$\lambda(\alpha) = [\,1 + b^*/\widetilde{K}_{uv} + b^*\,\tau(\alpha)/\widetilde{K}_{uv}]\,\tau(\alpha),$$

where $b^* = b$ or $b^* = -\,b$ from equation (A.55).

According to inequality (A.49) function $\tau(\alpha)$ decreases exponentially, when $|\operatorname{Im}\alpha| \to \infty$. Therefore, by neglecting the small quantity with $|\operatorname{Im}\alpha| \to \infty$ we get

$$\lambda(\alpha) = n\,\tau(\alpha),\ \ n = 1 + b^*/\widetilde{K}_{uv}. \tag{A.57}$$

The function $\lambda(\alpha)$ with $|\operatorname{Im}\alpha| \to \infty$ differs from $\tau(\alpha)$ by a constant factor only. Then on the strength of Assertion 11 function $\lambda(\alpha)$ with $|\operatorname{Im}\alpha| \to \infty$ tends to zero uniformly with regard to Re α. The assertion is proved.

Proof of Assertion 14

1. Let us consider expression

$$f_{ku}(f_{uv}) = \varphi_{ku}(f_{uv}) + \varepsilon_k \tag{A.58}$$

as the function of a complex variable f_{uv}. Let us take

$$f_{uv} = \bar{f}_{uv} + p\,\pi,\ \ |\operatorname{Re}\bar{f}_{uv}| \le \pi, \tag{A.59}$$

where p is an integer. Then according to equations II.1(12) we have

$$\varphi_{ku}\,(f_{uv}) = \varphi_{ku}\,\bar{f}_{uv}) + p\,\pi\,. \tag{A.60}$$

We use this relation to calculate the difference

$$f_{ku}(f_{uv}) - f_{uv} = \varphi_{ku}(f_{uv}) + \varepsilon_k - f_{uv} = [\,\varphi_{ku}\,(\bar{f}_{uv}) + p\,\pi\,] +$$

$$+ \varepsilon_k - [\,\bar{f}_{uv} + p\,\pi\,] = \varphi_{ku}\,(\bar{f}_{uv}) - \bar{f}_{uv} + \varepsilon_k\,. \tag{A.61}$$

2. Because $|\ \mathrm{Re}\ \bar{f}_{uv}| \leq \pi$, we have $|\ \mathrm{Re}\ \varphi_{ku}(\bar{f}_{uv})| < \infty$. Hence, the real part of equation (A.61) is finite

$$|\mathrm{Re}\,[f_{ku}(f_{uv}) - f_{uv}]| < \infty. \tag{A.62}$$

If $|\ \mathrm{Im}\ f_{uv}\ | < \infty$, then $|\ \mathrm{Im}\ \varphi_{ku}(f_{uv})| < \infty$. Hence, the imaginary part of equation (A.61) is finite

$$|\ \mathrm{Im}\ [f_{ku}(f_{uv}) - f_{uv}]| < \infty. \tag{A.63}$$

If $|\ \mathrm{Im}\ f_{uv}| \to \infty$, then according to equation III.7(4) there is a uniform approach to the limit

$$\varphi_{ku}(f_{uv}) \to f_{uv} + e_{ku},\ \ e_{ku} = (\,\mathrm{sign}\ \mathrm{Im}\ f_{uv})\ i\ \ln\ (c_k/c_u),$$

with regard to Re f_{uv} for $-\infty < \mathrm{Re}\ f_{uv} < \infty$. Then we have the expression

$$f_{ku}(f_{uv}) - f_{uv} \to \varepsilon_k + e_{ku}\quad \text{with}\ |\ \mathrm{Im}\ f_{uv}\ | \to \infty, \tag{A.64}$$

which is uniform with regard to Re f_{uv}.

On the strength of relations (A.62) - (A.64) for any f_{uv} we obtain the representation

$$f_{ku}(f_{uv}) = f_{uv} + \varepsilon_k + \psi_{ku}(f_{uv}), \tag{A.65}$$

where

$$\psi_{ku}(f_{uv}) \to e_{ku}\quad \text{with}\ |\ \mathrm{Im}\ f_{uv}| \to \infty \tag{A.66}$$

uniformly with regard to Re f_{uv} for $-\infty < \mathrm{Re}\ f_{uv} < \infty$.

3. By representing function f_{uv} from equation (A.65) in the form

$$f_{uv}(f_{vn}) = \varphi_{uv}(f_{vn}) + \varepsilon_u$$

and repeating all considerations (A.59) - (A.65), we get the representation

$$f_{uv}(f_{vn}) = f_{vn} + \varepsilon_u + \psi_{uv}(f_{vn}), \tag{A.67}$$

where function $\psi_{uv}(f_{vn})$ with $|\operatorname{Im} f_{vn}| \to \infty$ tends to its limit e_{uv} uniformly with regard to Re f_{vn}. By substituting equation (A.67) into (A.65) we obtain

$$f_{ku}\,[f_{uv}(f_{vn})] = f_{vn} + \varepsilon_k + \varepsilon_u + \psi_{ku}(f_{uv}) + \psi_{uv}(f_{vn}) \tag{A.68}$$

By repeating the above considerations subsequently for all inner substitutions in equation III.7(10), we obtain the representation III.7(11). The assertion is proved.

Proof of Assertion 15

Let us consider α_{kv} as a new complex variable. Then according to equation (A.56) we have

$$\tau_{uv}(\alpha_{kv})\, K_{uv}(\alpha_{kv}) = [\,1 + \lambda(\alpha_{kv})\,]\, \widetilde{K}_{uv}, \tag{A.69}$$

where $\lambda(\alpha_{kv})$ with $|\operatorname{Im} \alpha_{kv}| \to \infty$ tends to zero uniformly with regard to Re α_{kv} for $-\infty < \operatorname{Re} \alpha_{kv} < \infty$. According to equation III.7(12), function $|\operatorname{Im} \alpha_{kv}(\alpha)| \to \infty$ with $|\operatorname{Im} \alpha| \to \infty$ tends to its limit uniformly with regard to Re α for $-\infty < \operatorname{Re} \alpha < \infty$. Because the limit $\lambda(\alpha_{kv}) = 0$ with $|\operatorname{Im} \alpha_{kv}| \to \infty$ does not depend on Re α_{kv}, it follows from the previous relation that there is a passage to the limit $\lambda[\alpha_{kv}(\alpha)] \to 0$ with $|\operatorname{Im} \alpha| \to \infty$, uniform with regard to Re α. By denoting $\lambda_{uv}(\alpha) = \lambda\,[\alpha_{kv}(\alpha)]$ we get Assertion 15.

Proof of Assertion 16

The representation III.7(14) can be obtained directly from equation III.1(13) if the quantities $\alpha_{uv}(\alpha)$ and $U_{uv}(\alpha_{kv})$ are represented in the forms III.7(11) and III.7(13), respectively.

Proof of Assertion 17

1. By substituting expressions for $X_{m(p)}$ from equations III.7(14) and III.2(3) into inequality III.8(3) we have

$$|\, Q_{m(p)} \widetilde{K}_{m(p)} (\alpha + a^{\pm}_{m(p)} + \varepsilon_{m(p)} + \psi_{m(p)})^{-1} \exp[-(\zeta_0 + \delta)(\alpha - \alpha^{\pm}_{1} + \varepsilon_{m(p)} + \psi_{m(p)})]\,| \leq$$

$$\leq \mu\, |\, \widetilde{K}_{m(p)}(\operatorname{Re} \alpha + a^{\pm}_{m(p)} + \varepsilon_{m(p)})^{-1} \exp[-\zeta_0 (\operatorname{Re} \alpha - \alpha^{\pm}_{1} + \varepsilon_{m(p)}]\,|\,. \tag{A.70}$$

By taking into account relation $|\exp(x+iy)| = \exp(x)$, reducing common factors and multiplying both parts of this inequality by the positive quantity $\varepsilon_{m(p)}$, we can represent the result in the form

$$|Q_{m(p)} L_\delta \exp[-\zeta_0 \operatorname{Re}\psi_{m(p)} - \delta(\operatorname{Re}\alpha - \alpha_1^{\mp} + \varepsilon_{m(p)} + \operatorname{Re}\psi_{m(p)})]| \le \mu |L|, \tag{A.71}$$

$$L_\delta = \varepsilon_{m(p)}(\alpha + a_{m(p)}^{\pm} + \varepsilon_{m(p)} + \psi_{m(p)})^{-1},$$

$$L = \varepsilon_{m(p)}(\operatorname{Re}\alpha + a_{m(p)}^{\pm} + \varepsilon_{m(p)})^{-1}.$$

2. Let us introduce notations convenient for the proof. We represent the quantities $\varepsilon_{m(p)}$, $Q_{m(p)}$, $\psi_{m(p)}$ from equation III.7(14) in the form

$$\varepsilon_{m(p)} = \sum_{q=1}^{p} e_q, \quad Q_{m(p)} = \prod_{q=1}^{p}(1+\lambda_q), \quad \psi_{m(p)} = \sum_{q=1}^{p}\psi_q, \tag{A.72}$$

where

$$e_1 = \varepsilon_1,\ e_2 = \varepsilon_a,\ \ldots\ e_{p-1} = \varepsilon_e,\ e_p = \varepsilon_f,$$

$$\lambda_1 = \lambda_{1a},\ \lambda_2 = \lambda_{ab},\ \ldots\ \lambda_{p-1} = \lambda_{ef},\ \lambda_p = \lambda_{fv},$$

$$\psi_1 = \psi_{1a},\ \psi_2 = \psi_{ab},\ldots\ \psi_{p-1} = \psi_{ef},\ \psi_p = \psi_{fv}.$$

Note that the quantities ε_u in equation III.7(14) could have one of two values, $\varepsilon_u = \varepsilon_1$ or $\varepsilon_u = \varepsilon_2$. Suppose, for example, $\varepsilon_2 > \varepsilon_1$ and introduce any positive number ε_0 satisfying inequality $\varepsilon_0 < \varepsilon_1$. Let us introduce quantities $\bar\varepsilon_1 = \varepsilon_1 - \varepsilon_0$, $\bar\varepsilon_2 = \varepsilon_2 - \varepsilon_0$. Then any quantity ε_u from equation III.7(14) can be represented in the form

$$\varepsilon_u = \bar\varepsilon_u + \varepsilon_0,\ \bar\varepsilon_u = \varepsilon_u - \varepsilon_0 > 0,\ \ \varepsilon_0 > 0,$$

and, therefore, any quantity e_q from equations (A.72) can be written as

$$e_q = \bar e_q + \varepsilon_0,\ \bar e_q = e_q - \varepsilon_0 > 0,\ \ \varepsilon_0 > 0.$$

Then the first expression in equation (A.72) can be written

$$\varepsilon_{m(p)} = p\,\varepsilon_0 + \sum_{q=1}^{p} \overline{e}_q \,. \tag{A.73}$$

We represent quantity $Q_{m(p)}$ from equations (A.72) in the form

$$Q_{m(p)} = \exp\left(\sum_{q=1}^{p} q_q^* \right), \quad q_q^* = \ln\,(1 + \lambda_q)\,. \tag{A.74}$$

3. By substituting equations (A.73) - (A.74) and the expression for $\psi_{m(p)}$ from equations (A.72) into inequality (A.71) we get

$$|L_\delta|\,\exp\,(-p\,D) \le \mu\,|\,L\,|, \tag{A.75}$$

$$L_\delta = \varepsilon_{m(p)}\,[\,p\,\varepsilon_0 + \alpha + a^{\pm}_{m(p)} + \sum_{q=1}^{p} (\,\overline{e}_q + \psi_q\,)\,]^{-1},$$

$$L = \varepsilon_{m(p)}\,(\,p\,\varepsilon_0 + \mathrm{Re}\,\alpha + a^{\pm}_{m(p)} + \sum_{q=1}^{p} \overline{e}_q\,)^{-1},$$

$$D = \delta\,\varepsilon_0 + \delta\,(\,\mathrm{Re}\,\alpha - \alpha_1^{\pm})/p + (\,1/p\,) \sum_{q=1}^{p} [\,\delta\,\overline{e}_q + (\,\zeta_0 + \delta\,)\,\mathrm{Re}\;\psi_q - q_q^*\,]\,.$$

4. Let B_1 be such a number that for any $-\infty < \mathrm{Re}\;\alpha < \infty$, $|\;\mathrm{Im}\;\alpha\,| > B_1$ the inequality $\overline{e}_q > \mathrm{Re}\;\psi_q$ is satisfied. Because $\overline{e}_q > 0$, number B_1 exists on the strength of Assertion 16. Then in the expression for L_δ with $|\;\mathrm{Im}\;\alpha\,| > B_1$ the real part of the sum with the index q is positive.

Let p be such a number that for any $-\,C < \mathrm{Re}\;\alpha < C$, $p > p_1$ the inequality $p\,\varepsilon_0 + \mathrm{Re}\;\alpha + a^{\pm}_{m(p)} > 0$ holds true. Because $a^{\pm}_{m(p)}$ is constant and $\varepsilon_0 > 0$, number p_1 exists for any C. Then for any $-\,C < \mathrm{Re}\;\alpha < C$ with $|\;\mathrm{Im}\;\alpha\;| > B_1$ and $p > p_1$ quantities $|\;L_\delta\,|$ and $|\;L\;|$ are finite and $|\;L\;| \neq 0$.

Let us first prove the finite value of $|L|$. Because under the mentioned conditions the real parts of the denominators in L_δ and L do not turn into zero (they are always positive), it is necessary to consider the behavior of L_δ and L with $p \to \infty$ only.

Let us write L_δ in the form

$$L_\delta = (1 + R/\varepsilon_{m(p)} + iI/\varepsilon_{m(p)})^{-1}, \tag{A.76}$$

$$R = \mathrm{Re}\,\alpha + a^{\pm}_{m(p)} + \sum_{q=1}^{p} \mathrm{Re}\,\psi_q, \quad I = \mathrm{Im}\,\alpha + \sum_{q=1}^{p} \mathrm{Im}\,\psi_q,$$

where $\varepsilon_{m(p)}$ has representation (A.73). Because $\bar{e}_q > \mathrm{Re}\,\psi_q$, we have $\lim_{p\to\infty} R/\varepsilon_{m(p)} = 0$. The quantity $L_\delta = (1 + i\,\ell)^{-1}$, where $\ell = \lim_{p\to\infty} I/\varepsilon_{m(p)}$ is always finite, even if the limit does not exist. By taking $\mathrm{Im}\,\alpha = 0$, $\psi_q = 0$ in equation (A.76) we get the proof of the finite value of $|L|$.

The assertion of $|L| \neq 0$ under the mentioned conditions follows from the limit $\lim_{p\to\infty} L = 1$.

5. Let $B_m > B_1$ be such a number, depending on δ, that for any $\delta > 0$, $\mathrm{Im}\,\alpha > B_m$ the inequality

$$\delta\,\bar{e}_q > -\left[(\zeta_0 + \delta)\,\mathrm{Re}\,\psi_q - q_q^*\right] \tag{A.77}$$

holds true. Because $\delta\,\bar{e}_q > 0$ and it is independent of α, number B_m exists for any $-\infty < \mathrm{Re}\,\alpha < \infty$ on the strength of Assertion 16.

Let $p_2 > p_1$ be such a number that for any $-C < \mathrm{Re}\,\alpha < C$ and $p > p_2$ the inequality

$$\varepsilon_0 > (\mathrm{Re}\,\alpha - \alpha_1^{\pm})/p \tag{A.78}$$

holds true. The existence of number p_2 is evident.

Then with $|\,\mathrm{Im}\ \alpha\,| > B_m$ and $p > p_2$ the inequality $D > 0$, where D is defined in equations (A.75), holds true. One can check this assertion by estimating the signs of the terms in the expression for D with inequalities (A.77) and (A.78).

6. Under conditions $|\,\mathrm{Im}\ \alpha\,| > B_m$, $p > p_2$ we can write the inequality (A.75) in the form

$$M/\mu \le \exp\ (p\,D),\quad M = \max\,(\,|\,L_\delta\,|\ /\ |\,L\,|\,), \tag{A.79}$$

where $M < \infty$ on the strength of the proven inequalities $|\,L_d\,| < \infty$, $|\,L\,| \neq 0$. On the strength of the proven inequality $D > 0$, the inequality (A.79) holds true for $p > [\,\ln\,(\,M/\mu\,)\,]/D$. Hence, it holds true for $p > p_m$, where p_m complies with the inequalities $p_m > p_2$, $p_2 > [\,\ln\,(\,M/\mu\,)\,]/D$. The assertion is proved.

Proof of Assertion 18

1. On the strength of the inequality $|\,a + b\,| \le |\,a\,| + |\,b\,|$ it is sufficient to prove the more general inequality

$$|\,X_{m(p)}\,(\,\alpha\,,\eta\,,\zeta_0 + \delta\,)\,| + |\,X_{q(p)}\,(\,\alpha\,,\eta\,,\zeta_0 + \delta\,)\,| \le$$

$$\le |\,X_{m(p)}\,(\,\mathrm{Re}\,\alpha\,,1\,,\zeta_0\,) + X_{q(p)}\,(\,\mathrm{Re}\,\alpha\,,1\,,\zeta_0\,)\,| \tag{A.80}$$

instead of inequality III.8(4).

2. Let $\mu_m > 0$, $\mu_q > 0$, and p_μ be such numbers that for any $-\,C < \mathrm{Re}\ \alpha < C$ with $p > p_\mu$ inequalities

$$\mu_m\,|\,X_{m(p)}\,(\,\mathrm{Re}\,\alpha\,,1\,,\zeta_0\,)\,| + \mu_q\,|\,X_{q(p)}\,(\,\mathrm{Re}\,\alpha\,,1\,,\zeta_o\,)\,| \le$$

$$\le |\,X_{m(p)}\,(\,\mathrm{Re}\ \alpha\,,1\,,\zeta_0\,) + X_{q(p)}\,(\,\mathrm{Re}\ \alpha\,,1\,,\zeta_0\,)\,| \tag{A.81}$$

hold true. If the numbers μ_m and μ_q exist, it is sufficient to prove the more general inequalities

$$|\,X_{m(p)}\,(\,\alpha\,,\eta\,,\zeta_0 + \delta\,)\,| \le \mu_m\,|\,X_{m(p)}\,(\,\mathrm{Re}\ \alpha\,,1\,,\zeta_0\,)\,|\,,$$

$$|\,X_{q(p)}\,(\,\alpha\,,\eta\,,\zeta_0 + \delta\,)\,| \le \mu_q\,|\,X_{q(p)}\,(\,\mathrm{Re}\ \alpha\,,1\,,\zeta_0\,)\,| \tag{A.82}$$

instead of the inequality (A.80).

3. Let us show the existence of the numbers μ_m and μ_q. We use representation III.2(3) for $X_{m(p)}$ and $X_{q(p)}$, where on the strength of relations III.2(11) and III.2(12) there are the following relations:

$$a^{\pm}_{m(p)} = a^{\pm}_{q(p)}, \ \varepsilon_{m(p)} - \varepsilon_2 = \varepsilon_{q(p)} - \varepsilon_1, \ K_{m(p)} = -K_{q(p)}. \tag{A.83}$$

By substituting the mentioned representations into inequality (A.81), taking into account relations (A.83), and reducing common factors, we get

$$\begin{aligned} &\mu_m |(z+\varepsilon_2)^{-1} \exp(-\zeta_0 \varepsilon_2)| + \mu_q |(z+\varepsilon_1)^{-1} \exp(-\zeta_0 \varepsilon_1)| \le \\ &\le |(z+\varepsilon_2)^{-1} \exp(-\zeta_0 \varepsilon_2) - (z+\varepsilon_1)^{-1} \exp(-\zeta_0 \varepsilon_1)|, \\ &z = \mathrm{Re}\,\alpha + a^{\pm}_{m(p)} + E, \ E = \varepsilon_{m(p)} - \varepsilon_2 = \varepsilon_{q(p)} - \varepsilon_1. \end{aligned} \tag{A.84}$$

Let p_μ be such a number that for any $-C < \mathrm{Re}\,\alpha < C$ with $p > p_\mu$ the following inequalities hold true:

$$z > 0, \ z + \varepsilon_1 > 0, \ z + \varepsilon_2 > 0. \tag{A.85}$$

The existence of the number p_μ follows from equation (A.73). Suppose $p > p_\mu$. Then by multiplying both sides of inequality (A.84) by z, we can write the result in the form

$$\mu_m |L_2| + \mu_q |L_1| \le |L_2 - L_1|, \ L_q = \exp(-\zeta_0 \varepsilon_q) \times z/(z+\varepsilon_q). \tag{A.86}$$

On the strength of inequalities (A.85) quantities L_1 and L_2 with $p > p_\mu$ are finite and cofactors $z/(z+\varepsilon_q)$ with $p \to \infty$ tend to unity for any $-C < \mathrm{Re}\,\alpha < C$. If $\varepsilon_1 \ne \varepsilon_2$, the right part of inequality (A.86) with $p > p_\mu$ does not turn to zero for any $-C < \mathrm{Re}\,\alpha < C$. But then for any $|L_1| < \infty$, $|L_2| < \infty$, $|L_2 - L_1| > 0$ there are such small positive numbers μ_m and μ_q that the inequality (A.86) is satisfied.

4. Because with $p > p_\mu$ the numbers μ_m and μ_q exist, it is enough to prove the inequalities (A.82). According to Assertion 17 there are such numbers B_m, B_q, p_m, p_q that for any δ, μ_m, μ_q with $|\mathrm{Im}\,\alpha| > B_m$, $|\mathrm{Im}\,\alpha| > B_q$, $p > p_m$, $p > p_q$ both inequalities (A.82) are satisfied for $-C < \mathrm{Re}\,\alpha < C$.

Let B_{mq} be the maximum of numbers B_m and B_q, and p_{mq} maximum of numbers p_m and p_q. Then with $|\,\mathrm{Im}\ \alpha\,| > B_{mq}$, $p > p_{mq}$ both inequalities (A.82) are satisfied and, therefore, the inequalities III.8(4) are as well. The assertion is proved.

Proof of Assertion 19

1. Let us consider the series $\boldsymbol{R}\ (\alpha\,,\eta\,,\zeta_0\,+\,\delta\,)$. Each item of this series is represented by a finite sum Σ_m of the terms $X_{m(p)}\,(\alpha\,,\eta\,,\zeta_0\,+\,\delta\,)$. Under conditions III.8(1) with $\mathrm{Im}\ \alpha\,=\,0\,,\ \eta\,=\,1\,,$ each item of the finite sums Σ_m is positive. If in addition the conditions of Assertion 17 are satisfied, we have

$$|\,X_{m(p)}\,(\alpha\,,\eta\,,\zeta_0\,+\,\delta\,)\,|\,\leq\,X_{m(p)}\,(\mathrm{Re}\ \alpha\,,1\,,\zeta_0\,)\,.$$

By adding these inequalities for all m in the finite sum Σ_m we have

$$\Sigma_m\,|\,X_{m(p)}\,(\alpha\,,\eta\,,\zeta_0\,+\,\delta\,)\,|\,\leq\,\Sigma_m\ X_{m(p)}\,(\mathrm{Re}\ \alpha\,,1\,,\zeta_0\,)\,. \qquad \text{(A.87)}$$

Because the modulus of the sum is equal to or less than the sum of the moduli of the terms

$$|\,\Sigma_m\ X_{m(p)}\,(\alpha\,,\eta\,,\zeta_0\,+\,\delta\,)\,|\,\leq\,\Sigma_m\,|\,X_{m(p)}\,(\alpha\,,\eta\,,\zeta_0\,+\,\delta\,)\,.$$

we have from the inequality (A.87)

$$|\,\Sigma_m\ X_{m(p)}\,(\alpha\,,\eta\,,\zeta_0\,+\,\delta\,)\,|\,\leq\,\Sigma_m X_{m(p)}\,(\mathrm{Re}\ \alpha\,,1\,,\zeta_0\,)\,. \qquad \text{(A.88)}$$

2. By applying the same approach to the series $\boldsymbol{M}\ (\alpha\,,\eta\,,\zeta_0\,+\,\delta\,)$, we get the inequality

$$|\,\Sigma_0\,[\,X_{m(p)}\,(\alpha\,,\eta\,,\zeta_0\,+\,\delta\,)\,+\,X_{q(p)}\,(\alpha\,,\eta\,,\zeta_0\,+\,\delta\,)\,]\,|\,\leq$$

$$\leq\,\Sigma_0\ [\,X_{m(p)}\,(\mathrm{Re}\ \alpha\,,1\,,\zeta_0\,)\,+\,X_{q(p)}\,(\mathrm{Re}\ \alpha\,,1\,,\zeta_0\,)\,]\,, \qquad \text{(A.89)}$$

which holds true under conditions of Assertion 18.

3. On the strength of Assertions 17 and 18 there always is such a positive number B that with $|\,\mathrm{Im}\ \alpha\,| > B$ inequalities (A.88) and (A.89) are satisfied simultaneously. Then by summing them and taking into consideration that the modulus of the sum is equal to or less than the sum of the moduli of the terms, we get

$$|\,\Sigma_m\ X_{m(p)}\ (\alpha\,,\eta\,,\zeta_0\,+\,\delta\,)\,+\,\Sigma_0\ [\,X_{m(p)}\ (\alpha\,,\eta\,,\zeta_0\,+\,\delta\,)\,+$$

$$X_{q(p)}\,(\alpha\,,\eta\,,\zeta_0\,+\,\delta\,)\,]\,|\,\le$$

$$\le\,\Sigma_m\,X_{m(p)}\,(\,\mathrm{Re}\,\,\alpha\,,1\,,\zeta_0\,)\,+\,\Sigma_0\,[\,X_{m(p)}\,(\,\mathrm{Re}\,\,\alpha\,,1\,,\zeta_0\,)\,+\,X_{q(p)}\,(\,\mathrm{Re}\,\,\alpha\,,1\,,\zeta_0\,)\,]\,,$$

or in the other notation

$$\Big|\sum_{m(p)\,=\,1}^{N(p)} X_{m(p)}\,(\,\alpha\,,\eta\,,\zeta_0\,+\,\delta\,)\,\Big|\;\le\;\sum_{m(p)\,=\,1}^{N(p)} X_{m(p)}\,(\,\mathrm{Re}\,\,\alpha\,,1\,,\zeta_0\,)\,. \tag{A.90}$$

4. On the left side of the last inequality there is a modulus of the pth term of the series III.8(7) with $\mathrm{Im}\ \alpha\,\ne\,0\,,\ \eta\,\ne\,1$, while on the right side a corresponding positive term of the same series with $\mathrm{Im}\ \alpha\,=\,0\,,\ \eta\,=\,1$ is found. Hence, the series $S_\nu^\pm\,(\,\mathrm{Re}\ \alpha\,,1\,,\zeta_0\,)$ can serve as a majorizing series of the series $S_\nu^\pm\,(\,\alpha\,,\eta\,,\zeta_0\,+\,\delta\,)$. But then the convergence of series III.8(6) and III.8(7) follows from the convergence of the series $S_\nu^\pm\,(\,\mathrm{Re}\ \alpha\,,1\,,\zeta_0\,)$ or, what is the same, from the absolute convergence of the series $\tilde{S}_\nu^\pm\,(\,\mathrm{Re}\ \alpha\,,1\,,\zeta_0\,)$. The assertion is proved.

Proof of Assertion 20

According to Assertion 19 the series $S_\nu^\pm\,(\,\alpha\,,\eta\,,\zeta_0\,+\,\delta\,)$ converges absolutely with any $\delta\,>\,0$ and $|\ \mathrm{Im}\ \alpha\ |\,>\,B$, if the series $S_\nu^\pm\,(\,\mathrm{Re}\ \alpha\,,1\,,\zeta_0\,)$ converges absolutely. According to Assertion 9 the latter converges absolutely with any $\zeta_0\,>\,0$, i.e., the condition of Assertion 19 is satisfied. Then the series $S_\nu^\pm\,(\,\alpha\,,\eta\,,\zeta_0\,)$ converges absolutely with any $\zeta_0\,>\,0$. Indeed, for any small $\zeta_0\,>\,0$ there are such small $\lambda\,>\,0$ and $\delta\,>\,0$ that the inequality $\lambda\,+\,\delta\,\le\,\zeta_0$ is satisfied. Then the convergence of the series $S_\nu^\pm\,(\,\mathrm{Re}\ \alpha,1\,,\lambda\,)$ follows from the convergence of the series $S_\nu^\pm\,(\,\alpha,\eta\,,\lambda\,+\,\delta\,)$ with $\lambda\,+\,\delta\,\le\,\zeta_0$. The assertion is proved.

Proof of Assertion 21

1. Let us consider the result of operation κ_{uv} on an arbitrary function $f(\,\alpha\,)$, defined by equation III.7(8). According to Assertion 13 for any given small number $\mu_1\,>\,0$ there always is such a finite number $B_1\,>\,0$ that for any $-\,\infty\,<\,\mathrm{Re}\ \alpha\,<\,\infty$ the following inequalities hold true:

$$|\,\lambda\,(\,\alpha\,)\,|\,<\,\mu_1\,,\ |\,\varphi\,(\,\alpha\,)\,|\,<\,\mu_1\quad\text{with}\ \ |\ \mathrm{Im}\ \alpha\ |\,>\,B_m\,. \tag{A.91}$$

Because the imaginary quantity e_{uv} with $0 < c_1/c_2 < \infty$ is limited, for any given large number $\mu_2 > 0$ there always is such a number $B_2 > 0$ that

$$|\, i \operatorname{Im} \alpha - e_{uv}| > \mu_2 \quad \text{with } |\operatorname{Im} \alpha| > B_2 . \tag{A.92}$$

But then for any given small number μ there is such a number $B > 0$ that for any $-\infty < \operatorname{Re} \alpha < \infty$ the following inequality holds true:

$$|\, \kappa_{uv} f(\alpha) - \tilde{\kappa}_{uv} f(\alpha)| < \mu \quad \text{with } |\operatorname{Im} \alpha| > B , \tag{A.93}$$

where

$$\tilde{\kappa}_{uv} f(\alpha) = \tilde{K}_{uv} f(\alpha + \varepsilon_u) \tag{A.94}$$

is the result of the operation III.7(8) with $c_1 = c_2$.

2. We denote $\tilde{\boldsymbol{T}}$ and $\tilde{\boldsymbol{X}}$ the operator $\boldsymbol{T}$ and the matrix $\boldsymbol{X}$, respectively, in the case of $c_1 = c_2$. We denote $\boldsymbol{Y} = \boldsymbol{X} - \tilde{\boldsymbol{X}}$. By subtracting the equation $\tilde{\boldsymbol{X}} = \tilde{\boldsymbol{T}}\tilde{\boldsymbol{X}} + \tilde{\boldsymbol{T}}\boldsymbol{D}$ from $\boldsymbol{X} = \boldsymbol{TX} - \boldsymbol{TD}$ we get

$$\boldsymbol{Y} = \boldsymbol{TX} - \tilde{\boldsymbol{T}}\tilde{\boldsymbol{X}} + \boldsymbol{TD} - \tilde{\boldsymbol{T}}\boldsymbol{D} . \tag{A.95}$$

Let us write the operation $\tilde{\boldsymbol{T}}\tilde{\boldsymbol{X}}$ in the form

$$\tilde{\boldsymbol{T}}\tilde{\boldsymbol{X}} = \tilde{\boldsymbol{T}}(\boldsymbol{X} - \boldsymbol{Y}) = \widetilde{\boldsymbol{TX}} - \tilde{\boldsymbol{T}}\boldsymbol{Y} .$$

By substituting the $\tilde{\boldsymbol{T}}\tilde{\boldsymbol{X}}$ operation equation into equation (A.95) we get

$$\boldsymbol{Y} = \tilde{\boldsymbol{T}}\boldsymbol{Y} + \boldsymbol{Q} \tag{A.96}$$

$$\boldsymbol{Q} = \boldsymbol{TX} - \tilde{\boldsymbol{T}}\boldsymbol{X} + \boldsymbol{TD} - \tilde{\boldsymbol{T}}\boldsymbol{D} .$$

According to equation (A.93), each element of matrix $\boldsymbol{Q}$ tends to zero, when $|\ \mathrm{Im}\ \alpha\ | \to \infty$. Therefore, equation (A.96) with Im $\alpha \to \pm\infty$ turns into the homogeneous equation $\boldsymbol{Y} = \boldsymbol{TY}$. According to Assertion 6 the homogeneous equation with $c_1 = c_2$ has a trivial solution $\boldsymbol{Y} = \boldsymbol{O}$ only, where $\boldsymbol{O}$ is zero matrix. Hence, $\boldsymbol{X} = \widetilde{\boldsymbol{X}}$ with Im $\alpha \to \pm\infty$. The assertion is proved.

Proof of Assertion 22

1. According to Assertions 19 and 20, both series III.8(6) and III.8(7) converge in the domain $|\ \mathrm{Im}\ \alpha\ | > \mathrm{const}$. Because the modulus of a complex number is equal or larger than the moduli of its real and imaginary parts, the absolute convergence of the series,

$$A^{\pm} = \sum_{p=1}^{\infty} |\,\mathrm{Re}\ \widetilde{V}_p^{\pm}\ (\pm\alpha \mp \theta_\nu^{\pm})\,|,\quad B^{\pm} = \sum_{p=1}^{\infty} |\,\mathrm{Im}\ \widetilde{V}_p^{\pm}\ (\pm\alpha \mp \theta_\nu^{\pm})\,|, \tag{A.97}$$

follows from the convergence of the series III.8(7), which is the majorizing series.

2. Let us write the series III.8(8) in the form

$$\mathrm{Re}\ S_\nu = \sum_{p=1}^{\infty} R_p,\quad \mathrm{Im}\ S_\nu = \sum_{p=1}^{\infty} I_p, \tag{A.98}$$

$$R_p = \mathrm{Re}\ \widetilde{V}_p^{+}(\alpha - \theta_\nu^{+}) - \mathrm{Re}\ \widetilde{V}_p^{-}(-\alpha + \theta_\nu^{-}),$$

$$I_p = \mathrm{Im}\ \widetilde{V}_p^{+}(\alpha - \theta_\nu^{+}) - \mathrm{Im}\ \widetilde{V}_p^{-}(-\alpha + \theta_\nu^{-}).$$

The sum (or a difference) of two absolutely convergent series is an absolutely convergent series. Hence, it follows from the convergence of the series (A.97) that the series (A.98), i.e., the series with the positive terms

$$\sum_{p=1}^{\infty} |\ R_p\ |,\ \sum_{p=1}^{\infty} |\ I_p\ |$$

converge absolutely. Then the series

$$\sum_{p=1}^{\infty} (|\ R_p\ | + |\ I_p\ |)$$

converges. The convergence of the series III.8(9) follows from the triangular inequality

$$|U_{vp}| = (|R_p|^2 + |I_p|^2)^{1/2} \le |R_p| + |I_p| \,.$$

The assertion is proved.

APPENDIX B

SPECIAL FUNCTIONS OF THE PLANE WAVE THEORY

Function $\varphi_{vk}(\alpha)$

1. Definition—We consider a branch of the multivalued function

$$\varphi_{vk}(\alpha) = \arccos \eta_{vk} \cos \alpha \tag{B.1}$$

of the complex variable α with a given real positive parameter η_{vk}. The branch under consideration is determined by the following conditions:

$$\varphi_{vk}(\alpha) = \alpha \quad \text{with} \quad \eta_{vk} = 1, \tag{B.2}$$

$$\varphi_{vk}(\alpha \pm \pi) = \varphi_{vk}(\alpha) \pm \pi, \quad \varphi_{vk}(-\alpha) = -\varphi_{vk}(\alpha)$$

Let us find functions $u(x, y)$ and $v(x, y)$ in the expression

$$u + iv = \arccos \eta_{vk} \cos(x + iy). \tag{B.3}$$

By representing this expression in the form $\cos(u + iv) = \eta_{vk} \cos(x + iy)$ and equating its real and imaginary parts we get

$$\cos u \operatorname{ch} v = A; \quad \sin u \operatorname{sh} v = B; \tag{B.4}$$

$$A = \eta_{vk} \cos x \operatorname{ch} y; \quad B = \eta_{vk} \sin x \operatorname{sh} y.$$

Now it is easy to get the relations

$$A^2/\cos^2 u - B^2/\sin^2 u = 1; \quad A^2/\operatorname{ch}^2 v + B^2/\operatorname{sh}^2 v = 1,$$

which we consider as the equations for determining u and v. They can be written in the same form

$$A^2/z + B^2/(z - 1) = 1,$$

where $z = \cos^2 u$ or $z = \mathrm{ch}^2 v$. This equation has two roots

$$z = Q \pm (Q^2 - A^2)^{1/2};\ Q = (1 + A^2 + B^2)/2, \tag{B.5}$$

where the arithmetic value of the square root has to be taken.

Let us study the properties of these roots. By adding up the quantity $(1 + A^2 - Q^{2})$ to both parts of the obvious inequality $B^2 \geq 0$ we get

$$(Q - 1)^2 \leq Q^2 - A^2. \tag{B.6}$$

Because the left part is positive, we have the inequality $Q^2 \geq A^2$. The latter shows that the roots (B.5) are real.

Let us prove the inequalities

$$0 \leq Q - (Q^2 - A^2)^{1/2} \leq 1, \tag{B.7}$$

$$1 \leq Q + (Q^2 - A^2)^{1/2} \tag{B.8}$$

Because the values of roots (B.5) are arithmetical, on the strength of inequality (B.6) we have

$$(Q - 1)(Q^2 - A^2)^{-1/2} \leq (Q^2 - A^2)^{1/2} (Q - 1)^{-1} \text{ with } Q > 1,$$

$$(Q - 1)(Q^2 - A^2)^{-1/2} \geq (Q^2 - A^2)^{1/2} (Q - 1)^{-1} \text{ with } Q < 1.$$

These inequalities hold true only under the conditions

$$(Q - 1)(Q^2 - A^2)^{-1/2} \leq 1 \qquad \text{with } Q > 1,$$

$$(Q - 1)(Q^2 - A^2)^{-1/2} \geq -1 \quad \text{with } Q < 1,$$

The first inequality is guaranteed even more if $Q < 1$, and the second one if $Q > 1$. This proves the right inequality in (B.7) and inequality (B.8).

By adding Q^2 to both parts of the obvious inequality $A^2 \geq 0$ we get $Q^2 \geq Q^2 - A^2$. Because $Q > 0$, we have

$$Q\,(Q^2 - A^2)^{-1/2} \geq (Q^2 - A^2)^{1/2}\,Q^{-1}.$$

This inequality holds true, if $Q \geq (Q^2 - A^2)^{1/2}$. This proves the left inequality in (B.7)

It is easy to see from equations (B.7) - (B-8) that in equation (B.5) we have to take $\cos^2 u = H_1^2$ and $\mathrm{ch}^2\, v = H_2^2$ with

$$H_1 = [\,Q - (Q^2 - A^2)^{1/2}\,]^{1/2},\quad H_2 = [\,Q + (Q^2 - A^2)^{1/2}\,]^{1/2}, \tag{B.9}$$

where the arithmetic values of square roots have to be taken. By resolving the mentioned expressions with regard to u and v we get

$$u = \arccos\,(\pm H_1),\quad v = \pm\,\mathrm{arsh}\,(H_2^2 - 1)^{1/2}.$$

Let us choose the sign to satisfy the corresponding condition (B.2) with $\eta_{vk} = 1$. If $\eta_{vk} = 1$, we have $H_1 = |\cos x|$, $(H_2^2 - 1)^{1/2} = |\,\mathrm{sh}\, y|$. Now we can see that in the band $0 \leq x \leq \pi$ the mentioned condition is satisfied, if we choose the branches as follows:

$$u(x,y) = \begin{cases} \arccos H_1 & \text{with } 0 < x \leq \pi/2, \\ \arccos(-H_1) = \arcsin H_1 + \pi/2 & \text{with } \pi/2 \leq x \leq \pi, \end{cases} \tag{B.10}$$

$$v(x,y) = \pm\,\mathrm{arsh}\,(H_2^2 - 1)^{1/2} \qquad \text{with } \pm y > 0, \tag{B.11}$$

where $y \neq 0$.

If $y = 0$, we have

$$A = \eta_{vk}\cos x,\ B = 0,\ Q = (1 + A^2)/2,\ Q^2 - A^2 = (1 - A^2)^2/4.$$

Because we have to take an arithmetic value of the square root $(Q^2 - A^2)^{1/2}$, we have

$$(Q^2 - A^2)^{1/2} = (1 - A^2)/2 \text{ with } A < 1,\ (Q^2 - A^2)^{1/2} = (A^2 - 1)/2 \text{ with } A > 1.$$

Then

$$\begin{aligned} H_2^2 &= 1 \quad \text{with } A < 1, \\ H_2^2 &= A^2 \quad \text{with } A > 1. \end{aligned} \tag{B.12}$$

2. *Properties*—Qualitative properties of the transformation of the complex plane of α by the unifying function (B.1) are illustrated in Figure 92. In Figure 92 a points B and D correspond to the branch point with $\eta_{vk} < 1$ and $\eta_{vk} > 1$, respectively, and lines BCB and CD to the branch cuts with $\eta_{vk} < 1$ and $\eta_{vk} > 1$, respectively.

Let us mention some properties of this transformation.

The imaginary parts of the unifying function possess the property

$$\text{sign } v = \text{sign } y \quad \text{with } y \neq 0 . \tag{B.13}$$

The real axis $y = 0$ of the plane of α is transformed according to the following rules: If

$$\eta_{vk} \cos x < 1 , \tag{B.14}$$

there are relations (Figure 92b)

$$u = \text{arc cos } A , \; v = 0 , \; A = \eta_{vk} \cos x . \tag{B.15}$$

If

$$\eta_{vk} \cos x > 1 , \tag{B.16}$$

the transformation is two-valued: the different sides of the branch cuts CD in Figure 92a are transformed into different parts CD of the boundaries of the band under consideration in Figure 92c, according to the rule

$$u = 0 , \; v = \pm \text{ arsh } (A^2 - 1) , \; A = \eta_{vk} \cos x , \tag{B.17}$$

where the top (bottom) signs have to be taken for the transformations of the top (bottom) sides of the branch cut CD.

Thus, when $y = 0$ and $\eta_{vk} \cos x > 1$, it is necessary to have some additional condition to choose the branch of the unifying function uniquely.

There is a relation

$$\varphi_{vk} (\overline{\alpha}) = \overline{\varphi_{vk} (\alpha)} , \tag{B.18}$$

where the dash above denotes a complex conjugate value. This follows from equation (B.11).

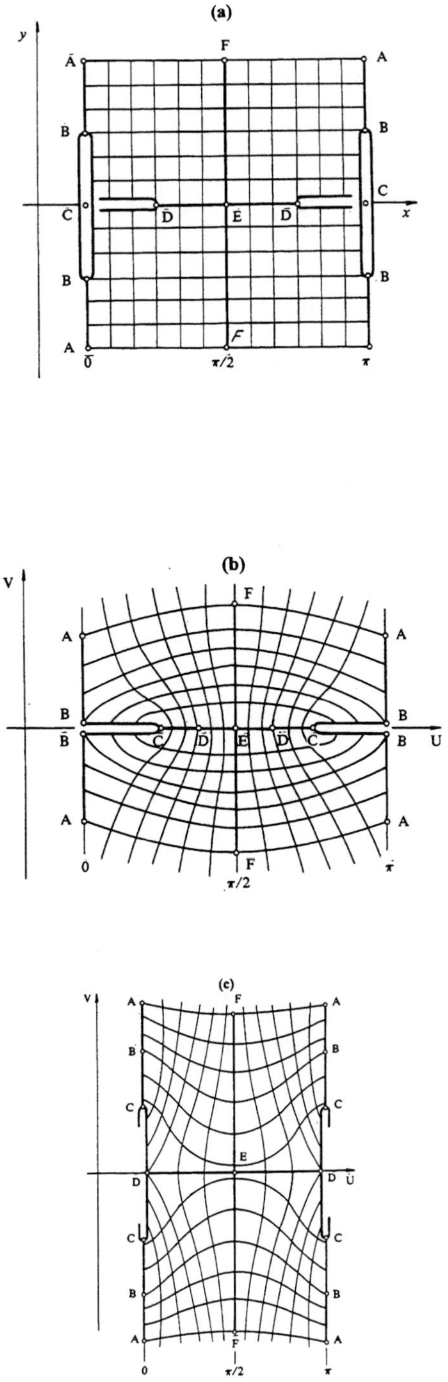

Figure 92. Mapping the rectangular mesh of the complex plane $\alpha = x + iy$ (a) on the complex plane $\varphi_{vk} = u + iv$ by means of the unifying function B(1) with $\eta_{vk} < 1$ (b) and $\eta_{vk} > 1$ (c).

By using equations (B.2) we can express the unifying function of an arbitrary argument through its principle value

$$\varphi_{vk}(\alpha) = b\ \varphi_{vk}\ [b\ (\alpha - d)] + d, \tag{B.19}$$

$$\left.\begin{aligned} b &= 1,\ d = \pi E(\mathrm{Re}\ \alpha/\pi) \text{ with } \mathrm{Re}\ \alpha/\pi - E(\mathrm{Re}\ \alpha/\pi) < 1/2, \\ b &= -1,\ d = \pi E(\mathrm{Re}\ \alpha/\pi) + \pi \text{ with } \mathrm{Re}\ \alpha/\pi - E(\mathrm{Re}\ \alpha/\pi) \geq 1/2 \end{aligned}\right\}, \tag{B.20}$$

where $0 \leq b\ (\mathrm{Re}\ \alpha - d) < \pi/2$ and $E(x)$ is the whole part of x.

3. *Inverse function*—Suppose

$$\varphi_{vk}\ (\alpha) = \beta. \tag{B.21}$$

By writing equation (B.21) in the form $\eta_{vk}\ \cos\ \alpha = \cos\ \beta$ and resolving the latter with regard to α we get the inverse function

$$\alpha = \varphi_{kv}\ (\beta) = \mathrm{arc\,cos}\ [(1/\eta_{vk})\ \cos\ \beta]. \tag{B.22}$$

Function $\tau_{vk}\ (\alpha)$

1. *Definition*—This function is defined by the expression

$$\tau_{vk}(\alpha) = d\ \varphi_{vk}(\alpha)/d\alpha = (\sin\ \alpha)/\ [(1/\eta_{vk})^2 - \cos^2\ \alpha]^{1/2}, \tag{B.23}$$

and $\varphi_{vk}\ (\alpha)$ was defined previously.

2. *Transformation formulas*---Let us write functions $u(x,y)$, $v(x,y)$, $U(x,y)$, $V(x,y)$ from the following expressions:

$$\tau_{vk}(x+iy) = u(x,y) + i\,v(x,y),\ 1/\tau_{vk}(x+iy) = U(x,y) + i\,V(x,y) \tag{B.24}$$

By substituting equation (B.23) into (B.24) and separating real and imaginary parts we get

$$u(x,y) = A/N,\ v(x,y) = B/N, \tag{B.25}$$

$$U(x,y) = NA/D,\ V(x,y) = -\ NB/D, \tag{B.26}$$

$$N = (X^2 + Y^2)^{1/4},\ D = \sin^2\ x + \mathrm{sh}^2\ y,$$

$$A = \cos\ (\varphi/2)\ \sin\ x\ \mathrm{ch}\ y + \sin\ (\varphi/2)\ \cos\ x\ \mathrm{sh}\ y,$$

$$B = \cos(\varphi/2)\cos x \operatorname{sh} y - \sin(\varphi/2)\sin x \operatorname{ch} y,$$

$$X = (1/\eta_{vk})^2 - (\cos x \operatorname{ch} y)^2 + (\sin x \operatorname{sh} y)^2, \; Y = (\sin 2x \operatorname{sh} 2y)/2,$$

$$\varphi = (\operatorname{sign} Y) \operatorname{arctg} |Y/X| \qquad \text{with } X \geq 0,$$

$$\varphi = (\operatorname{sign} Y)(\pi - \operatorname{arctg}|Y/X|) \quad \text{with } X < 0,$$

3. Properties—The real axis $y = 0$ of the plane of α under condition (B.14) is transformed by function $\tau_{vk}(\alpha)$, according to the rule

$$u = \eta_{vk}^{-1}\, 2 \sin x \times (1 - \eta_{vk}^2 \cos^2 x)^{-1/2}, \quad v = 0. \tag{B.27}$$

Under condition (B.16) the transformation is two-valued

$$u = 0, \quad v = \mp \eta_{vk}^{-1}\, 2 \sin x \times (\eta_{vk}^2 \cos^2 x - 1)^{-1/2}, \tag{B.28}$$

where the top (bottom) signs have to be taken for the transformations of the top (bottom) sides of the branch cuts CD (Figure 92).

By using standard analysis one can see that $u(x, y)$ does not turn to zero in the band $0 \leq x \leq \pi$, except for the points on the branch cuts. This means that the real part of the unifying function is a monotonous function of x.

The function under consideration possesses the properties

$$\tau_{vk}(\alpha) = 1 \text{ with } \eta_{vk} = 1, \; \tau_{vk}(\alpha \pm \pi) = \tau_{vk}(\alpha), \; \tau_{vk}(-\alpha) = \tau_{vk}(\alpha),$$

$$\tau_{vk}(\overline{\alpha}) = \overline{\tau_{vk}(\alpha)}\,. \tag{B.29}$$

The three first properties can be proved by the substitution into the left parts of equation (B.23) and (B.18). The last one follows directly from equations (B.25). By using these properties we can express the function of an arbitrary argument through its principle value

$$\tau_{vk}(\alpha) = \tau_{vk}[b(\alpha - d)], \tag{B.30}$$

where b and d are defined by equations (B.20).

APPENDIX C

RECURRENT FUNCTIONS

To develop computing algorithms, it is necessary to use more information on the recurrent functions, introduced in Chapter IV. Here we consider these functions

$$P_{m(p)}(\alpha) = P_{m(0,p-1)}(\alpha), \tag{C.1}$$

$$P'_{m(p)}(\alpha) = T_{m(0,p-1)}(\alpha), \tag{C.2}$$

$$H_{m(p)}(\alpha) = H_{m(0,p-1)}(\alpha), \tag{C.3}$$

as particular cases of the more general functions$P_{m(u,v)}(\alpha)$, $T_{m(u,v)}(\alpha)$, and $H_{m(u,v)}(\alpha)$.

1. Wave sequences

1. Reflection/transmission operator—Let us clarify the meaning of the operator II.4(23). To do this, we will consider a well-known problem of the reflection/transmission of a plane wave at the plane interface.

Let

$$y = x \tan \varepsilon_k \tag{C.4}$$

be the equation of an interface between two elastic media with wave velocities c_1, c_2 and c_3, c_4, respectively (Figure 93). The incident harmonic wave

$$f_k = A_k(\bar{\theta}_k) \exp(-i\eta_k), \quad \eta_k = k_k\, r \cos(\theta - \bar{\theta}_k) \tag{C.5}$$

is given in the lower region. Here r, θ are the polar coordinates; $\bar{\theta}_k$) is the direction of incidence; k_k is the wave number; $A_k(\bar{\theta}_k)$ is the wave amplitude, depending on the

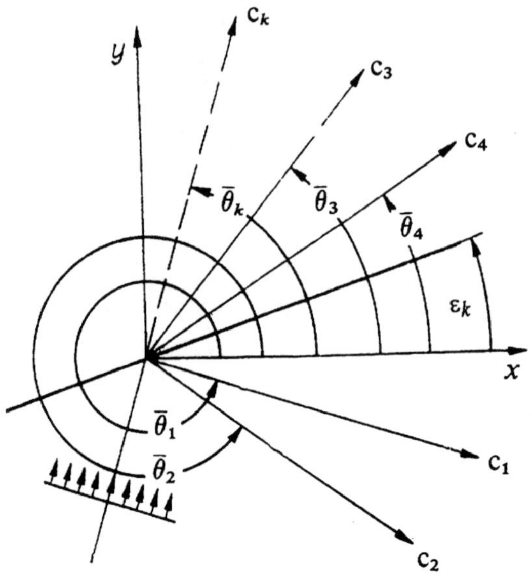

Figure 93. Ray scheme of reflection/transmission.

direction of incidence. The problem is to find the expressions for the reflected/transmitted waves under some given boundary conditions at the interface (C.4).

We look for the reflected/transmitted waves in the form of

$$f_j = K_{kj} \, (\bar{\theta}_k - \varepsilon_k) \, A_k \, (\bar{\theta}_k) \, \exp \, (-i \, \eta_j) \, , \quad \eta_j = k_j \, r \, \cos \, (\theta - \bar{\theta}_j) \, ,$$
$$j = 1 \, , \, 2 \, , \, 3 \, , \, 4 \, , \tag{C.6}$$

where $\bar{\theta}_j$ is the direction of propagation; $K_{kj} \, (\bar{\theta}_k - \varepsilon_k)$ is the sought reflection/transmission coefficient, considered as a function of the angle $\bar{\theta}_k - \varepsilon_k$ between the incident ray and the interface.

We write eikonals of all waves as

$$\eta_j = k_j (x \, \cos \, \bar{\theta}_j + y \, \sin \, \bar{\theta}_j) \, , \quad x = r \, \cos \, \theta \, , \quad y = r \, \sin \, \theta \, . \tag{C.7}$$

At the interface (C.4) this expression turns into

$$\eta_j = k_j\, x\, (\cos \bar{\theta}_j + \tan \varepsilon_k \sin \bar{\theta}_j) = (k_j\, x / \cos \varepsilon_k) \cos (\bar{\theta}_j - \varepsilon_k). \tag{C.8}$$

By substituting equations (C.5) - (C.8) into conditions II.4(3) we can find the reflection/transmission coefficients, if Snell's law,

$$k_k \cos (\bar{\theta}_k - \varepsilon_k) = k_j \cos (\bar{\theta}_j - \varepsilon_k), \tag{C.9}$$

is taken into consideration. Let all the relevant computations be performed and functions $K_{kj}(\bar{\theta}_k - \varepsilon_k)$ and directions $\bar{\theta}_j$ from equation (C.6) be found.

Let us introduce in equation (C.6) a new reference system of directions, related to the interface,

$$\alpha_j = \bar{\theta}_j - \varepsilon_k. \tag{C.10}$$

From equation (C.9) we have

$$\alpha_j = \varphi_{jk}(\alpha_k), \quad \alpha_k = \varphi_{kj}(\alpha_j), \tag{C.11}$$

$$\bar{\theta}_j = \varphi_{jk}(\alpha_k) + \varepsilon_k, \quad \bar{\theta}_k = \varphi_{kj}(\alpha_j) + \varepsilon_k,$$

where $\varphi_{kv}(\alpha)$ is the unifying function II.1(10). By substituting $\bar{\theta}_j$ from equation (C.10) and $\bar{\theta}_k$ from equation (C.11) into equation (C.6) we get

$$f_j = K_{kj}[\varphi_{kj}(\alpha_j)]\, A_k[\varphi_{kj}(\alpha_j) + \varepsilon_k] \exp[-i\, k_j\, r \cos(\gamma - \alpha_j)], \tag{C.12}$$

where

$$\gamma = \theta - \varepsilon_k. \tag{C.13}$$

Let us represent the incident wave amplitude in the form

$$A_k(\bar{\theta}_k) = S_k(\bar{\theta}_k)\, d\bar{\theta}_k, \tag{C.14}$$

where $S_k(\bar{\theta}_k)$ is the directional characteristic and $d\bar{\theta}_k$ is the differential of the independent variable $\bar{\theta}_k$. When substituting variable $\bar{\theta}_k$ by α_j, the differential $d\bar{\theta}_k$ has to be transformed according to

$$d\bar{\theta}_k = d\,[\,\varphi_{kj}(\alpha_j) + \varepsilon_k\,] = d\,\varphi_{kj}(\alpha_j) = [\,d\,\varphi_{kj}(\alpha_j)/d\,\alpha_j\,]\,d\,\alpha_j\ . \tag{C.15}$$

According to definition II.1(11) we have

$$d\,\varphi_{kj}(\alpha_j)/d\,\alpha_j = \tau_{kj}(\alpha_j)\,,$$

and equation (C.15) turns into

$$d\bar{\theta}_k = \tau_{kj}(\alpha_j)\,d\,\alpha_j\ . \tag{C.16}$$

The result of substitution of equations (C.14) and (C.16) into (C.12) can be written

$$f_j = \tau_{kj}(\alpha_j)\,K_{kj}[\,\varphi_{kj}(\alpha_j)\,]\,S_k[\,\varphi_{kj}(\alpha_j) + \varepsilon_k\,]\exp[\,-i\,k_j\,r\cos(\alpha_j - \gamma)\,]\,d\,\alpha_j\,, \tag{C.17}$$

where γ is determined by equation (C.13).

The reflection/transmission laws allow a generalization to the case of complex directions of propagation. If α_j is complex, equation (C.17) describes an inhomogeneous reflected/transmitted plane wave. Comparing this expression with equation II.4(23), we see that the operator $\sigma^{\pm}_{u(m)v(n)}$ transforms function $f(\alpha)$ according to the ordinary reflection/transmission law. The quantities from equation II.4(23) can be interpreted as follows:

α is the complement of the reflection/transmission angle, $\varphi_{u(m)v(n)}(\alpha)$ is the complement of the angle of incidence;

$K^{\pm}_{u(m)v(n)}(\alpha_k)$ is the reflection/transmission coefficient, considered as a function of the angle of incidence α_k;

$\tau_{u(m)v(n)}(\alpha)$ is the coefficient, accounting for the variation of the directional characteristic, caused by the change of the reference system of direction $\alpha \rightarrow \varphi_{v(n)u(m)}(\alpha)$.

This is the representation of the sought wavefields in the form of the Sommerfeld-Malyuzhinetz integral [II.2(2)] that gives the very possibility of such a simple interpretation. The sought wavefield is represented by a superposition of inhomogeneous plane waves. Their directions of propagation depend on the complex variable of integration α. Their unknown directional characteristic $S_\nu^{\pm}(\alpha)$ depends on α as well. As a result of this representation finding the elements of matrix $\boldsymbol{X}$ in equation II.4(29) can be reduced to a reflection/transmission problem of inhomogeneous plane waves.

Thus, the generation of individual components of matrix $\boldsymbol{X}$ in a successive approximations process can be described in the framework of an ordinary concept of the multiple reflection/transmission on a set of non-parallel interfaces. The solution of the operator equation II.4(29) by the successive approximations method II.3(38) can be reduced to the calculation of inhomogeneous plane waves, arising in the process of an infinite sequence of the reflections/transmissions on a set of non-parallel interfaces. According to this interpretation, an individual term of the p^{-th} power of operator $\boldsymbol{T}$ in equation II.3(35) corresponds to the set of p–fold reflected/transmitted inhomogeneous plane waves.

Let us take as an example the calculation of three successive approximations in the acoustic case of three wedge-shaped regions ($N = 3$). According to equation II.3(35) we have

$$\begin{Bmatrix} X_1^+ \\ X_1^- \\ X_2^+ \\ X_2^- \\ X_3^+ \\ X_3^- \end{Bmatrix} \approx \sum_{p=1}^{3} \begin{bmatrix} 0 & \kappa_{11}^+ & 0 & 0 & \kappa_{31}^+ & 0 \\ \kappa_{11}^- & 0 & 0 & \kappa_{21}^- & 0 & 0 \\ \kappa_{12}^+ & 0 & 0 & \kappa_{22}^+ & 0 & 0 \\ 0 & 0 & \kappa_{22}^- & 0 & 0 & \kappa_{32}^- \\ 0 & 0 & \kappa_{23}^+ & 0 & 0 & \kappa_{33}^+ \\ 0 & \kappa_{13}^- & 0 & 0 & \kappa_{33}^- & 0 \end{bmatrix}^p \times \begin{Bmatrix} D_1^+ \\ 0 \\ 0 \\ 0 \\ 0 \\ 0 \end{Bmatrix}, \tag{C.18}$$

where in matrix $\boldsymbol{D}$ the only nonzero element D_1^+ is taken for simplicity. The matrices $\boldsymbol{T}^p\ \boldsymbol{D}$ with $p = 1, 2, 3$, corresponding to successive approximations, look like

$$\begin{Bmatrix} 0 \\ \kappa_{11}^{-}\ D_1^{+} \\ \kappa_{12}^{+}\ D_1^{+} \\ 0 \\ 0 \\ 0 \end{Bmatrix} \quad \begin{Bmatrix} \kappa_{11}^{+}\ \kappa_{11}^{-}\ D_1^{+} \\ 0 \\ 0 \\ \kappa_{22}^{-}\ \kappa_{12}^{+}\ D_1^{+} \\ \kappa_{23}^{+}\ \kappa_{12}^{+}\ D_1^{+} \\ \kappa_{13}^{-}\ \kappa_{11}^{-}\ D_1^{+} \end{Bmatrix} \quad \begin{Bmatrix} \kappa_{31}^{+}\ \kappa_{23}^{+}\ \kappa_{12}^{+}\ D_1^{+} \\ \kappa_{11}^{-}\ \kappa_{11}^{+}\ \kappa_{11}^{-}\ D_1^{+} + \kappa_{21}^{-}\ \kappa_{22}^{-}\ \kappa_{12}^{+}\ D_1^{+} \\ \kappa_{12}^{+}\ \kappa_{11}^{+}\ \kappa_{11}^{-}\ D_1^{+} + \kappa_{22}^{+}\ \kappa_{22}^{-}\ \kappa_{12}^{+}\ D_1^{+} \\ \kappa_{32}^{-}\ \kappa_{13}^{-}\ \kappa_{11}^{-}\ D_1^{+} \\ \kappa_{33}^{+}\ \kappa_{13}^{-}\ \kappa_{11}^{-}\ D_1^{+} \\ \kappa_{33}^{-}\ \kappa_{23}^{+}\ \kappa_{12}^{+}\ D_1^{+} \end{Bmatrix}.$$

The matrix, obtained as a result of three successive approximations, looks like

$$X = \begin{Bmatrix} \kappa_{11}^{+}\ \kappa_{11}^{-}\ D_1^{+} + \kappa_{31}^{+}\ \kappa_{23}^{+}\ \kappa_{12}^{+}\ D_1^{+} \\ \kappa_{11}^{-}\ D_1^{+} + \kappa_{11}^{-}\ \kappa_{11}^{+}\ \kappa_{11}^{-}\ D_1^{+} + \kappa_{21}^{-}\ \kappa_{22}^{-}\ \kappa_{12}^{+}\ D_1^{+} \\ \kappa_{12}^{+}\ D_1^{+} + \kappa_{12}^{+}\ \kappa_{11}^{+}\ \kappa_{11}^{-}\ D_1^{+} + \kappa_{22}^{+}\ \kappa_{22}^{-}\ \kappa_{12}^{+}\ D_1^{+} \\ \kappa_{22}^{-}\ \kappa_{12}^{+}\ D_1^{+} + \kappa_{32}^{-}\ \kappa_{13}^{-}\ \kappa_{11}^{-}\ D_1^{+} \\ \kappa_{23}^{+}\ \kappa_{12}^{+}\ D_1^{+} + \kappa_{33}^{+}\ \kappa_{13}^{-}\ \kappa_{11}^{-}\ D_1^{+} \\ \kappa_{13}^{-}\ \kappa_{11}^{-}\ D_1^{+} + \kappa_{33}^{-}\ \kappa_{23}^{+}\ \kappa_{12}^{+}\ D_1^{+} \end{Bmatrix}. \tag{C.19}$$

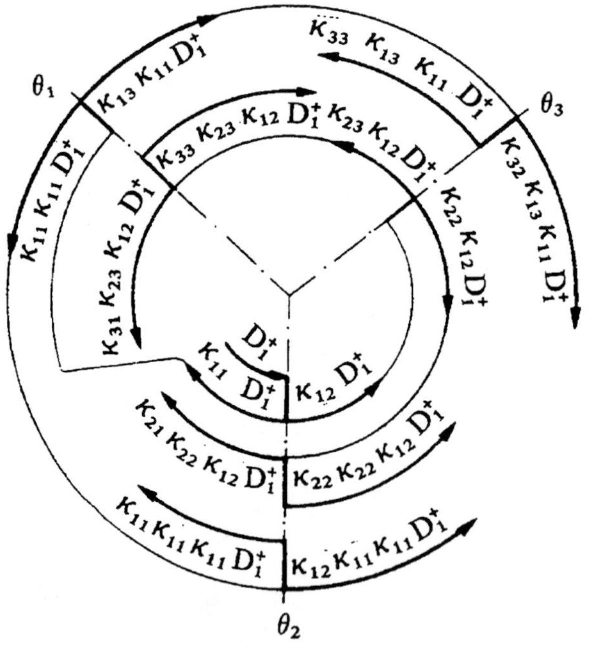

Figure 94. Scheme of formation of the elements of matrix X (acoustics).

Figure 94 shows the scheme of generation of the elements of this matrix in the process of successive approximations.

2. *Generalized waves*—We can introduce a concept of *a generalized wave* by the following definitions:

1. The generalized wave is the solution of Helholmtz's equation, represented in the form of the Sommerfeld-Malyuzhinetz integral $F_{\nu\ell}^{+}$ or $F_{\nu\ell}^{-}$ from equations II.4(4) with $\ell = 1$ or $\ell = 2$;

2. The function $S_{\nu\ell}^{\pm}(\alpha)$ in the integral, representing a generalized wave, contains only products (not the sums) of the reflection/transmission operators $\sigma_{u(m)v(n)}^{\pm}$;

3. The quantities $F_{okg}^{\pm}$ in equations II.4(4) are *the primary generalized waves.*

For example, in the acoustic case each term of each row in matrix (C.19) is a transformant of the corresponding generalized wave.

Now we can interpret the successive approximation process in terms of multiple reflections/transmissions of generalized waves.

3. *Reflection/transmission graph*—If the primary generalized waves are given, we can consider reflections/transmissions on interfaces and represent the solution as an infinite sum of generalized waves. A set of such waves can be put in order by the *reflection/transmission graph,* showing all possible reflections/transmissions (see Chapter IV). The problem of enumerating the branches of the graph is the problem of developing the matrix product. It also can be interpreted as a problem of encoding all possible transitions from one interface to another that can be solved in many different ways.

Let us introduce the boundary indices ν^{+} and ν^{-} of a νth wedge-shaped region as was done in Section IV.2.5 (an example of such notations for $N = 3$ is shown in Figure 95). Then all possible transitions from one interface to another in conformity with the reflection/transmission graph can be encoded with some sequences of these indices. It is clear that index $\nu^{\pm}$ can be put in correspondence with that element (line) of the reflection/transmission graph which depicts the transition from boundary $\theta = \theta_{\nu}^{\pm}$ to

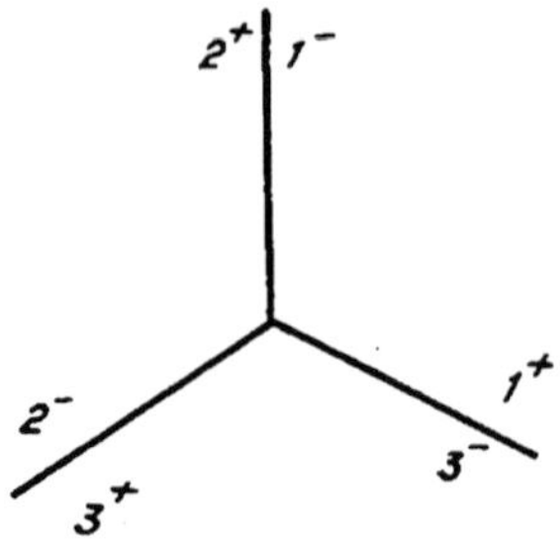

Figure 95. Boundary indices of the wedge-shaped regions.

boundary $\theta = \theta_\nu^\mp$. Hence, any branch of the reflection/transmission graph can be encoded with a sequence of boundary indices, if any of its neighboring indices form the following combinations:

$$u^\pm u^\mp \text{ or } u^\pm v^\pm , \tag{C.20}$$

where $u^\mp$ corresponds to the reflection from boundary $\theta = \theta_u^\mp$, and $v^\pm$ to the transmission through boundary $\theta = \theta_\nu^\pm$. Let $p + 1$ be the total number of boundary indices in such a sequence. Then the case of $p = 0$ corresponds to encoding the primary generalized waves, $p = 1$ to the single reflections/transmissions, $p = 2$ to the double reflections/transmissions, etc. An individual sequence of $p + 1$ indices also can be encoded with the double index $m(p)$ where m is the number of this sequence.

For example, in the case of $N = 3$ (Figure 95) there are the following boundary indices only: 1^+, 1^-, 2^+, 2^-, 3^+, 3^-. If a couple of the primary generalized waves is given in the region with $\nu = 1$, the initial index of any sequence is 1^+ or 1^-. This is the case of $p = 0$. The single reflections and transmissions ($p = 1$) are encoded with the following sequences: 1^+1^-, 1^-1^+ and 1^+2^+, 1^-3^-, respectively. The double reflections/transmissions ($p = 2$) are encoded as follows: $1^+1^-1^+$, $1^+1^-3^-$, $1^-1^+1^-$, $1^-1^+2^+$, $1^+2^+2^-$, $1^+2^+3^+$, $1^-3^-3^+$, $1^-3^-2^-$. The three-fold reflections/transmissions ($p = 3$) are encoded as follows: $1^+1^-1^+1^-$, $1^+1^-1^+2^+$, etc. Thus, an effective algorithm of finding the reflection/transmission graph can be based on generating the boundary index sequences in conformity with equations (C.20).

In the following we assign the index $m(p)$ to each individual generalized wave, where m is the number of the branch of the graph and p is the number of reflections/transmissions, corresponding to the power of operator $\boldsymbol{T}^p$ in the successive approximation series.

We assign the index $m\,(\,0\,)$ to the primary generalized waves and all relevant parameters. We use $(\,p\,,p\,+\,1\,)$ to denote an interface between the $m\,(\,p\,)^{th}$ and the $m\,(\,p\,+\,1\,)^{th}$ generalized wave domains. The symbol $\varepsilon_{m(p)}$ denotes the angular dimension of the pth generalized wave domain. Note that the same parameter (or interface) can be encoded differently, depending on the graph branch to which it belongs. An example of the graph is shown in Figure 96.

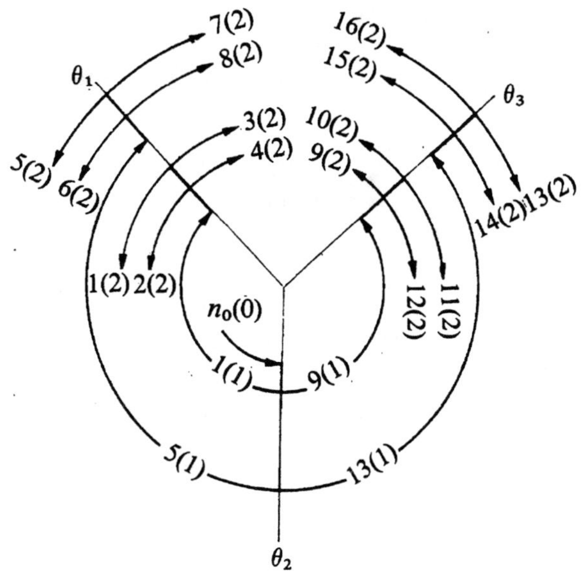

Figure 96. Example of the reflection/transmission graph for three contacting media (elastodynamics).

4. *Multifold operations*—By using the previously selected symbols we can write equation II.4(4) as the sum of generalized waves

$$F^{\pm}_{\nu\ell} = \sum_{p=1}^{\infty} \sum_{m(p)}^{\pm\nu\ell} F^{\pm}_{m(p)}\,,\ F^{\pm}_{m(p)} = (\,1/2\,\pi\,i\,) \int_{\Gamma_o} S_{m(p)}\,(\,\alpha\,)\ \exp\,[\,-\,i\,k_{\nu\ell}\,r$$

$$\cos\,(\,\alpha\,-\,\gamma^{\pm}_{\nu}\,)\,]\,d\,\alpha\,, \tag{C.21}$$

$$\gamma^{\pm}_{\nu} = \pm\,(\,\theta\,-\,\theta^{\pm}_{\nu}\,)\,,$$

where the summation with $1 \le p < \infty$ is carried out over the indices $m(p)$ of the reflection/transmission graph. The sum $F^{\pm}_{\nu\ell}$ includes only those generalized waves, which are formed by reflections/transmissions at the boundary $\theta = \theta_\nu^\pm$ and characterized by the wave number $k_{\nu\ell}$.

Let us introduce a new notation connected with the reflection/transmission graph,

$$\left.\begin{aligned} \varphi_{m(p-1)m(p)}(\alpha) &= \varphi_{k\nu}(\alpha) \\ \tau_{m(p-1)m(p)}(\alpha) &= \tau_{k\nu}(\alpha) \\ K_{m(p-1)m(p)}(\alpha) &= K_{k\nu}^{\pm}(\alpha) \end{aligned}\right\} \quad \text{with } k = m(p-1),\ \nu = m(p)\ . \tag{C.22}$$

Let us denote the reflection/transmission operator $\sigma_{u(m)v(n)}^{\pm}$ by $d_{m(p)}$ and represent it as a product of the operations

$$d_{m(p)} = \tau_{m(p-1)m(p)}(\alpha)\, K_{m(p-1)m(p)}\,[\,\varphi_{m(p-1)m(p)}(\alpha)\,]\,\zeta_{m(p)}\ , \tag{C.23}$$

where

$$\zeta_{m(p)}\, f(\alpha) = f\,[\,\varphi_{m(p-1)m(p)}(\alpha) + \varepsilon_{m(p-1)}\,]\ . \tag{C.24}$$

Then the function $S_{m(p)}(\alpha)$ in equation (C.21) can be determined by the recursion relation

$$S_{m(p)}(\alpha) = d_{m(p)}\, S_{m(p-1)}(\alpha)\ . \tag{C.25}$$

Let us fix the index m of some branch of the graph and consider a sequence of recursions (C.25) at some part $u \le p \le v$ of this branch. By using equation (C.25) repeatedly we have

$$S_{m(v)}(\alpha) = d_{m(v)}\, d_{m(v-1)} \cdots d_{m(u+1)}\, d_{m(u)}\, S_{m(u-1)}(\alpha)\ . \tag{C.26}$$

The result of the multiple use of operator $d_{m(p)}$ can be written as

$$S_{m(v)}(\alpha) = G_{m(u,v)}(\alpha)\, S_{m(u-1)}\,[\,P_{m(u,v)}(\alpha)\,]\ , \tag{C.27}$$

where function $P_{m(u,v)}(\alpha)$ describes the result of multiple substitutions $\zeta_{m(p)}$ according to equations (C.23) - (C.24) and $G_{m(u,v)}(\alpha)$ is the result of multiplications and substitutions. We are going to consider these functions.

2. Function $P_{m(u,v)}(\alpha)$

1. Complex rays—First let us take the function $P_{m(u,v)}(\alpha)$. We must study this function both with $u < v$ and $u > v$. To distinguish between these situations, we introduce a special symbol

$$\sigma = \sigma(u,v) = \text{sign}\,(v - u) = \begin{cases} 1, & \text{when } v > u \\ -1, & \text{when } v < u. \end{cases} \tag{C.28}$$

and write the sequence of indices p from $p = u$ till $p = v$ in the form

$$p = u,\ u + \sigma,\ u + 2\sigma,\ \ldots,\ v - 2\sigma,\ v - \sigma,\ v\,.$$

By introducing function

$$q_{m(p)m(p+\sigma)}(\alpha) = \varphi_{m(p)m(p+\sigma)}(\alpha) + \varepsilon_{m(p)} \tag{C.29}$$

we can rewrite the definition of the operator (C.24) as

$$\zeta_{m(p)} f(\alpha) = f\,[\,q_{m(p-\sigma)m(p)}(\alpha)\,]\,. \tag{C.30}$$

The function $P_{m(u+v)}(\alpha)$ describes the result of the multiple using this operator

$$\zeta_{m(v+\sigma)}\,\zeta_{m(v)}\,\zeta_{m(v-\sigma)}\cdots\zeta_{m(u+\sigma)}\,\zeta_{m(u)}\,f(\alpha) = f\,[\,P_{m(u,v)}(\alpha)\,]\,. \tag{C.31}$$

By using equation (C.30) we can represent function $P_{m(u,v)}(\alpha)$ from equation (C.31) as

$$P_{m(u,v)}(\alpha) = q_{m(u)m(u+\sigma)}(\,q_{m(u+\sigma)m(u+2\sigma)}(\,\ldots$$
$$q_{m(v-\sigma)m(v)}(\,q_{m(v)m(v+\sigma)}(\alpha))\ldots)) \tag{C.32}$$

Let us show that this function describes a complex direction of the reflected/transmitted ray. The total number of reflections/transmission, in a generalized wave, can be called *the order of a generalized wave.* Let us consider first the formation of a plane wave of the $(v - u + 1)^{th}$ order (Figure 97). Let α_u be the direction of the incident ray in some arbitrary reference system. Let α'_{v+1} be the direction of the $(v - u + 1)^{th}$ reflected/transmitted ray in the other arbitrary reference system. Let $(\pi/2 - \alpha'_p)$ and $(\pi/2 - \alpha_p)$ be the angles of incidence and reflection/transmission, respectively, in the pth region and $\varepsilon_{m(p)}$ the angle between the boundaries of this region.

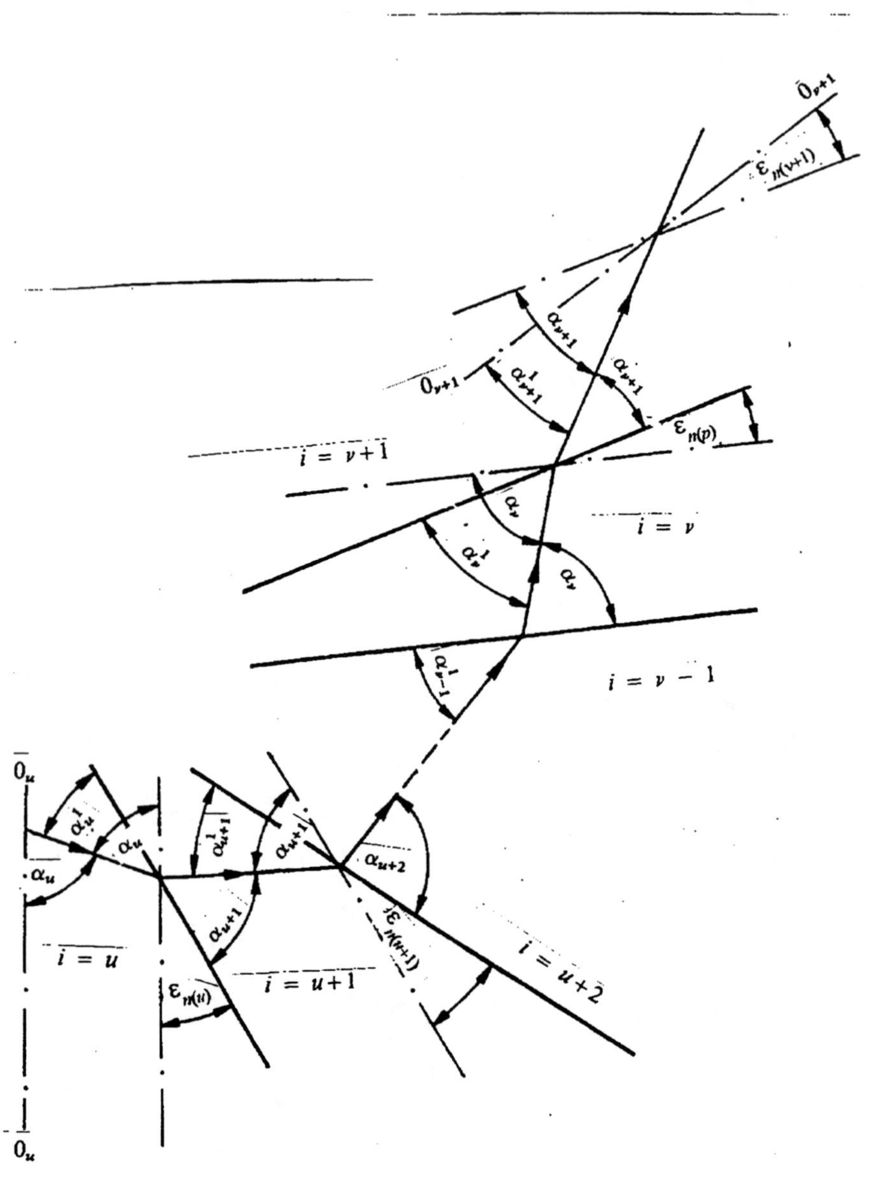

Figure 97. Ray scheme of formation of the multifold generalized wave.

Angles α_p and $\alpha_p^{'}$ are connected by an obvious relationship

$$\alpha_p = \alpha '_p + \varepsilon_{m(p)} . \tag{C.33}$$

The angles $\alpha '_p$ and α_{p+1} are connected under Snell's law

$$\alpha '_p = \varphi_{m(p)m(p+1)} (\alpha_{p+1}) . \tag{C.34}$$

From these relations we have

$$\alpha_p = q_{m(p)m(p+1)} (\alpha_{p+1}) , \tag{C.35}$$

where $q_{m(p)m(p+1)}$ is determined by equation (C.29). Equation (C.35) relates directions of the incident and reflected/transmitted rays in a single reflection/transmission act in a reference system, pertinent to the interface.

Let us take by definition

$$P_{m(u,u)} (\alpha) = \lim_{u \leftarrow v} P_{m(u,v)} (\alpha) = q_{m(u)m(u+\sigma)} (\alpha) . \tag{C.36}$$

Then by letting $p = u$ in equation (C.35) we have

$$\alpha_u = P_{m(u,u)} (\alpha_{u+1}) .$$

By substituting α_{u+1} from equation (C.35) into the right part of this equation and taking into consideration definition (C.32) we have

$$\alpha_u = p_{m(u,\, u)} \left[q_{m(u+1)m(u+2)} (\alpha_{u+2}) \right] = P_{m(u,u+1)} (\alpha_{u+2}) .$$

By expressing in the right part α_{u+2} through α_{u+3} by means of equations (C.35) and (C.32) we have

$$\alpha_u = P_{m(u,u+2)} (\alpha_{u+3}) .$$

By multiple use of the described approach we get

$$\alpha_u = P_{m(u,v)} (\alpha_{v+1}) . \tag{C.37}$$

The previous considerations allow us to understand the geometrical sense of function $P_{m(u,v)}$. This function connects the directions of the incident and the reflected/transmitted ray of the $(v - u + 1)^{th}$ order, i.e., it describes the change in the ray direction caused by $(v-u+1)$ reflections/transmissions. If the angle α_{v+1} is given, this function allows us to find the direction of the incident ray α_u in some given reference system $0_u\,0_u$ (see Figure 97).

Let us find now an inverse function, which would allow us to express the direction of the $(v-u+1)^{th}$ order ray through the direction of the incident ray. From equation (C.34) we have

$$\alpha'_u = \varphi_{m(u)m(u+1)}(\alpha_{u+1}) = \varphi_{m(u)m(u+1)}(\alpha'_{u+1} + \varepsilon_{m(u+1)}) .$$

By solving this expression relative to α'_{u+1} we have

$$\alpha'_{u+1} = \varphi_{m(u+1)m(u)}(\alpha'_u) - \varepsilon_{m(u+1)} = -\varphi_{m(u+1)m(u)}(-\alpha'_u) - \varepsilon_{m(u+1)} = \tag{C.38}$$

$$= -q_{m(u+1)m(u)}(-\alpha'_u) .$$

From equation (C.34) we have

$$\alpha'_{u+1} = \varphi_{m(u+1)m(u+2)}(\alpha_{u+2}) = \varphi_{m(u+1)m(u+2)}(\alpha'_{u+2} + \varepsilon_{m(u+2)}) .$$

By solving this expression relative to α'_{u+2} we have

$$\alpha'_{u+2} = \varphi_{m(u+2)m(u+1)}(\alpha'_{u+1}) - \varepsilon_{m(u+2)} = -\varphi_{m(u+2)m(u+1)}(-\alpha'_{u+1}) - \varepsilon_{m(u+2)} =$$

$$= -q_{m(u+2)m(u+1)}(-\alpha'_{u+1}) .$$

By substituting α'_{u+1} from equation (C.38) into the previous equation we have

$$\alpha'_{u+2} = -q_{m(u+2)m(u+1)}\left[q_{m(u+1)m(u)}(-\alpha'_u)\right] = -P_{m(u+2\,,u+1)}(-\alpha'_u) .$$

By multiple use of this approach we get

$$\alpha'_{v+1} = -P_{m(v+1,\,u+1)}(-\alpha'_u) . \tag{C.39}$$

Equation (C.39) allows us to find the direction of the $(v-u+1)^{th}$ order ray in some given reference system $0_{v+1}\ 0_{v+1}$ (See Figure 97), if the incident angle $\pi/2 - \alpha'_u$ at the first interface is given.

2. *Formal definition*—Let us take two sets of real positive parameters, put in order by means of an integer,

$$\eta_{m(p)m(p+\sigma)} \text{ and } \varepsilon_{m(p)} \text{ with } p = u\,,\ u+\sigma\,,\ u+2\sigma\,,\ \dots\,,\ v-\sigma\,,\ v\,, \tag{C.40}$$

where σ is determined by equation (C.28). Although the symbol m has no special meaning, do not drop it for the sake of notation. Let the functions

$$\varphi_{m(p)m(p+\sigma)}(\alpha) = \arccos \eta_{m(p)m(p+\sigma)} \cos\alpha\,, \tag{C.41}$$

$$\tau_{m(p)m(p+\sigma)}(\alpha) = d\,\varphi_{m(p)m(p+\sigma)}(\alpha)/d\alpha$$

be determined by equations (B.1), (B.2) and (B.23) of Appendix B for each $\eta_{m(p)m(p+\sigma)}$.

Let us define the function of the complex variable $P_{m(u,v)}(\alpha)$, depending on parameters (C.40), by the following recursion relations:

$$\left.\begin{aligned} &\alpha_{v+\sigma} = \alpha \\ &\alpha_p = \varphi_{m(p)m(p+\sigma)}(\alpha_{p+\sigma}), + \varepsilon_{m(p)} \text{ with } p = v\,,\ v-\sigma\,,\ \dots\,, u+\sigma\,,\ u \\ &P_{m(u,v)}(\alpha) = \alpha_u \end{aligned}\right\} \tag{C.42}$$

We can use another convenient definition of the same function. To do this, we consider index u in equations (C.42) as a current one, i.e.,

$$P_{m(p,v)}(\alpha) = \alpha_p = \varphi_{m(p)m(p+\sigma)}(\alpha_{p+\sigma}) + \varepsilon_{m(p)}\,, \tag{C.43}$$

$$P_{m(p+\sigma,v)}(\alpha) = \alpha_{p+\sigma} = \varphi_{m(p+\sigma)m(p+2\sigma)}(\alpha_{p+2\sigma}) + \varepsilon_{m(p+\sigma)}\,. \tag{C.44}$$

From these formulas we get a recurrent relation

$$P_{m(p,v)}(\alpha) = \varphi_{m(p)m(p+\sigma)}\,[P_{m(p+\sigma,v)}(\alpha)] + \varepsilon_{m(p)}\,. \tag{C.45}$$

By taking $p = v$ in equation (C.44) and taking into account the first relation from equations (C.41) we have

$$P_{m(v+\sigma,v)}(\alpha) = \alpha\,. \tag{C.46}$$

The successive of substitutions (C.45) with $p = v, v - \sigma, \dots, u + \sigma, u$ under condition (C.46) also determines function $P_{m(u,v)}(\alpha)$ with $u \neq v$. When $u = v$ we can by definition take

$$P_{m(v,v)}(\alpha) = \lim_{u \to v} P_{m(u,v)}(\alpha) = q_{m(v)m(v+\sigma)}(\alpha),$$
$$P_{m(u,u)}(\alpha) = \lim_{u \leftarrow v} P_{m(u,v)}(\alpha) = q_{m(u)m(u+\sigma)}(\alpha), \tag{C.47}$$

where $q_{m(p)m(p+\sigma)}(\alpha)$ is determined by equation (C.29).

A uniquely defined branch of function $P_{m(u,v)}(\alpha)$ in a complex plane of α can be singled out by cuts, connecting its branch points pairwise (a discussion of the branch points follows). When $\mathrm{Im}\,\alpha = 0$, the function can be double valued (see Section 1.2 of Appendix B). To make the function single valued, it is necessary to use some condition of the physical kind (see Section II.3.7).

3. *Properties*—1. The result of substitutions (C.42) with $p = k, k - \sigma, \dots, u + \sigma, u$ where $k < v$ with $u < v$ and $k > v$ with $u > v$, gives the function $P_{m(u,k)}(\alpha_{k+\sigma})$. The function $\alpha_{k+\sigma}(\alpha)$ is formed by substitutions $p = v, v - \sigma, \dots, k + \sigma$ and, according to equation (C.44), can be written in the form $\alpha_{k+\sigma} = P_{m(k+\sigma,v)}(\alpha)$. Therefore, the result of substitutions with $p = v, v - \sigma, \dots, u + \sigma, u$ yields

$$P_{m(u,v)}(\alpha) = P_{m(u,k)}\,[P_{m(k+\sigma,v)}(\alpha)] \tag{C.48}$$

2. From definitions (C.42) and equations (B.2) of Appendix B we have

$$P_{m(u,v)}(\alpha \pm \pi) = P_{m(u,v)}(\alpha) \pm \pi. \tag{C.49}$$

3. By using notation (C.29) we can write equations (C.42) as

$$P_{m(u,v)}(\alpha) = q_{m(u)m(u+\sigma)}\left\{q_{m(u+\sigma)m(u+2\sigma)}\left[\dots q_{m(v)m(v+\sigma)}(\alpha)\dots\right]\right\}. \tag{C.50}$$

By differentiating expression (C.50) as a composite function we have

$$d\,P_{m(u,v)}(\alpha)/d\alpha = (d\,q_{m(u)m(u+\sigma)}/d\,q_{m(u+\sigma)m(u+2\sigma)} \times$$
$$\times\,(d\,q_{m(u+\sigma)m(u+2\sigma)}/d\,q_{m(u+2\sigma)m(u+3\sigma)})\,\dots\,(d\,q_{m(v)m(v+\sigma)}/d\alpha), \tag{C.51}$$

where according to the second expression from equations (C.41)

$$d\,q_{m(p)m(p+\sigma)}\,/\,d\,q_{m(p+\sigma)m(p+2\sigma)} = \tau_{m(p)m(p+\sigma)}\,(\,q_{m(p+\sigma)m(p+2\sigma)}\,(\,\ldots$$

$$\ldots\; q_{m(v)m(v+\sigma)}\,(\alpha)\;\ldots\;) = \tau_{m(p)m(p+\sigma)}\;[P_{m(p+\sigma,\,v)}\,(\,\alpha\,)\,]\,.$$

This expression can be rewritten as

$$d\,P_{m(u,\,v)}\,(\,\alpha\,)\,/\,d\,\alpha = \tau_{m(v)m(v+\sigma)}\,(\,\alpha\,)\prod_{n=v-\sigma}^{u}\tau_{m(n)m(n+\sigma)}\,[\,P_{m(n+\sigma,\,v)}\,(\,\alpha\,)\,]\,. \tag{C.52}$$

4. On the strength of equation (B.18) of Appendix B we have in equations (C.42),

$$\alpha_p\,(\,\bar{\alpha}_{p\pm1}\,) = \overline{\alpha_p\,(\,\alpha_{p\pm1})}\;.$$

Then from equations (C.42) we get

$$P_{m(u,\,v)}\,(\,\bar{\alpha}\,) = \overline{P_{m(u,\,v)}\,(\,\alpha\,)}\;. \tag{C.53}$$

4. *Inverse function*—Suppose $P_{m(u,\,v)}\,(\,\alpha\,) = z$. Let us solve this equation relative to α . By using equation (C.45) we have

$$P_{m(u,\,v)}\,(\,\alpha\,) = \varphi_{m(u)m(u+\sigma)}\,[\,P_{m(u+\sigma,\,v)}\,(\,\alpha)\,] + \varepsilon_{m(u)}\;. \tag{C.54}$$

By solving the right part relative to $P_{m(u+\sigma,\,v)}\,(\,\alpha)$ with the help of equations (B.21) - (B.22) of Appendix B we have

$$P_{m(u+\sigma,\,v)}\,(\,\alpha\,) = \varphi_{m(u+\sigma)m(u)}\,(\,z_u\,)\,, \tag{C.55}$$

$$z_u = P_{m(u,\,v)}\,(\,\alpha\,) - \varepsilon_{m(u)} = \varphi_{m(u)m(u+\sigma)}\,[\,P_{m(u+\sigma,\,v)}\,(\,\alpha\,)\,]\;. \tag{C.56}$$

Let us use in the left part of equation (C.55) representation

$$P_{m(u+\sigma,\,v)}\,(\,\alpha\,) = \varphi_{m(u+\sigma)m(u+2\sigma)}\,[\,P_{m(u+2\sigma,\,v)}\,(\,\alpha\,)\,] + \varepsilon_{m(u+\sigma)} = z_{u+\sigma} + \varepsilon_{m(u+\sigma)}\;,$$

relation $\varphi_{kv}\,(\,\alpha\,) = -\;\varphi_{kv}\,(\,-\,\alpha\,)$, and equation (C.29). Then we get a recurrent formula

$$z_{u+\sigma} = -\;q_{m(u+\sigma)m(u)}\,(\,-\,z_u\,)\,. \tag{C.57}$$

By substituting u by $u + k\sigma$ subsequently with $k = 1, 2, \ldots$ and expressing the quantity $z_{u+k\sigma}$ for every k in the right part through the same quantity from the left part with $k - 1$, we get

$$z_{u+(k+1)\sigma} = -q_{m[u+(k+1)\sigma]m(u+k\sigma)}(q_{m(u+k\sigma)m[u+(k-1)\sigma]}(\cdots q_{m(u+\sigma)m(u)}(-z_u)\ldots).$$

By taking $v = u + (k+2)\sigma$ we can rewrite this expression as

$$z_{v-\sigma} = -q_{m(v-\sigma)m(v-2\sigma)}(q_{m(v-2\sigma)m(v-3\sigma)}(\cdots q_{m(u+\sigma)m(u)}(-z_u)\ldots).$$

By taking into consideration equation (C.50) we have

$$z_{v-\sigma} = -P_{m(v-\sigma,\, u+\sigma)}(-z_u). \tag{C.58}$$

According to equations (C.56) and (C.47) we have

$$z_{v-\sigma} = \varphi_{m(v-\sigma)m(v)}[P_{m(v,\, v)}(\alpha)] = \varphi_{m(v-\sigma)m(v)}[q_{m(v)m(v+\sigma)}(\alpha)].$$

By substituting the derived expression into equation (C.58) and solving the result relative to α we get

$$\alpha = -\varphi_{m(v+\sigma)m(v)}\left\{q_{m(v)m(v-\sigma)}[P_{m(v-\sigma,\, u+\sigma)}(-z_u)]\right\}. \tag{C.59}$$

According to equation (C.50) we have

$$q_{m(v)m(v-\sigma)}[P_{m(v-\sigma,\, u+\sigma)}(-z_u)] = P_{m(v,\, u+\sigma)}(-z_u). \tag{C.60}$$

By substituting the initial condition $P_{m(u,\, v)}(\alpha) = z$ into equation (C.56) we have

$$z_u = z - \varepsilon_{m(u)}. \tag{C.61}$$

By substituting equations (C.60) and (C.61) into (C.59) we get the sought formula

$$\alpha = -\varphi_{m(v+\sigma)m(v)}[P_{m(v,\, u+\sigma)}(\varepsilon_{m(u)} - z)]. \tag{C.62}$$

While deriving this formula, we used the representation $v = u + (k+2)\sigma$ with $k \geq 0$. This representation fails, if $v = u + \sigma$. In this case it is easy to obtain the desired expression directly by solving equation $P_{m(u,\, u+\sigma)}(\alpha) = z$ relative to α, i.e.,

$$\alpha = -\varphi_{m(u+2\sigma)m(u+\sigma)}[q_{m(u+\sigma)m(u)}(\varepsilon_{m(u)} - z)]. \tag{C.63}$$

Equation $P_{m(u,u)}(\alpha) = z$ can be easily solved relative to α as well

$$\alpha = -\varphi_{m(u+\sigma)m(u)}(\varepsilon_{m(u)} - z) . \tag{C.64}$$

Thus, we have obtained the relation, connecting the straight and inverse functions, in the form

$$\left.\begin{aligned} &P_{m(u,u)}(\alpha) = z, && \alpha = -\varphi_{m(u+\sigma)m(u)}(\varepsilon_{m(u)} - z), \\ &P_{m(u,u+\sigma)}(\alpha) = z, && \alpha = -\varphi_{m(u+2\sigma)m(u+\sigma)}[q_{m(u+\sigma)m(u)}(\varepsilon_{m(u)} - z)], \\ &P_{m(u,v)}(\alpha) = z, && \alpha = -\varphi_{m(v+\sigma)m(v)}[P_{m(v,u+\sigma)}(\varepsilon_{m(u)} - z)] . \end{aligned}\right\} \tag{C.65}$$

5. Forms of equations (C.38) and (C.39). By taking $\alpha_u = z$, $\alpha_{u+1} = \alpha$ equation (C.38) can be written as the first line of equations (C.65). By taking $\alpha_u = z$, $\alpha_{v+1} = \alpha$, equation (C.39) can be written as the second or third line of equations (C.65).

5. Branch points—Function $\varphi_{m(p)m(p+\sigma)}(\alpha_{p+\sigma})$ in equation (C.42) has the branch points

$$\alpha_{p+\sigma} = \pm \arccos(1/\eta_{m(p)m(p+\sigma)}) + n\pi, \quad n = 0, \pm 1, \pm 2, \ldots \tag{C.66}$$

By expressing $\alpha_{p+\sigma}$ through $P_{m(p+\sigma,v)}(\alpha)$ in equation (C.44) we get an equation for the branch points of function (C.44),

$$P_{m(p+\sigma,v)}(\alpha) = \pm \arccos(1/\eta_{m(p)m(p+\sigma)}) + n\pi . \tag{C.67}$$

By solving this equation relative to α for every $p = v, v-\sigma, \ldots, u+\sigma, u$ it is possible to find all the branch points of function $P_{m(u,v)}(\alpha)$.

Let us first take $p = v$. Then taking into consideration equation (C.46) we get

$$\alpha = \pm \arccos(1/\eta_{m(v)m(v+\sigma)}) + n\pi, \quad n = 0, \pm 1, \pm 2, \ldots \tag{C.68}$$

Now let us take $p = v - \sigma$. Then taking into account equations (C.45) and (C.46) we have

$$\begin{aligned} P_{m(p+\sigma,v)}(\alpha) &= P_{m(v,v)}(\alpha) = \varphi_{m(v)m(v+\sigma)}[P_{m(v+\sigma,v)}(\alpha)] + \varepsilon_{m(v)} = \\ &= \varphi_{m(v)m(v+\sigma)}(\alpha) + \varepsilon_{m(v)} . \end{aligned} \tag{C.69}$$

By substituting equation (C.69) into (C.67) with $p = v - \sigma$ and solving the left part relative to α by means of equations (B.21) - (B.22) of Appendix B we get

$$\alpha = \varphi_{m(v+\sigma)m(v)} \, [\, \pm \arccos(1/\eta_{m(v-\sigma)m(v)}) - \varepsilon_{m(v)} + n\pi \,], \; n = 0, \pm 1, \pm 2, \ldots \tag{C.70}$$

Let us take $p = v - 2\sigma$. Then according to equations (C.45) and (C.69) we derive

$$P_{m(p+\sigma,\, v)}(\alpha) = P_{m(v-\sigma,\, v)}(\alpha) = \varphi_{m(v-\sigma)m(v)} \, [P_{m(v,\, v)}(\alpha)] + \varepsilon_{m(v-\sigma)} =$$

$$= \varphi_{m(v-\sigma)m(v)} \, [\, \varphi_{m(v)m(v+\sigma)}(\alpha) + \varepsilon_{m(v)} \,] + \varepsilon_{m(v-\sigma)} \, .$$

By substituting the derived expression into equation (C.67) with $p = v - 2\sigma$ and solving the left part relative to α we get

$$\alpha = \varphi_{m(v+\sigma)m(v)} \left\{ \varphi_{m(v)m(v-\sigma)} \, [\pm \arccos(1/\eta_{m(v-2\sigma)m(v-\sigma)}) + n\pi - \varepsilon_{m(v-\sigma)}] - \varepsilon_{m(v)} \right\},$$
$$n = 0, \pm 1, \pm 2, \ldots \tag{C.71}$$

When $p = v - k\sigma$ with $k > 2$, equation (C.67) can be solved by using the third formula from equations (C.65). To do this, we have to substitute index u by $p + \sigma$ in the mentioned formula, and z by the right part of equation (C.67). In addition, from equation (C. 28) we have

$$\sigma(u, v) = \sigma(p + \sigma, v) = \sigma(v - k\sigma, v) = \mathrm{sign}\,[v - (v - k\sigma)] = \mathrm{sign}\,(k\sigma) = \sigma \, .$$

By taking into account the previous expression and making the mentioned substitutions in equation (C.65) we obtain

$$\alpha = -\varphi_{m(v+\sigma)m(v)} \left\{ P_{m(v, p+2\sigma)} \, [\, \varepsilon_{m(p+\sigma)} \mp \arccos(1/\eta_{m(p)m(p+\sigma)}) + n\pi \,] \right\},$$
$$n = 0, \pm 1, \pm 2, \ldots \quad \text{with } p = v - 3\sigma, \, v - 4\sigma, \, \ldots, \, u + \sigma, \, u \, . \tag{C.72}$$

Formulas (C.68), (C.70), (C.71), and (C.72) give all the branch points of function $P_{m(u,\, v)}(\alpha)$.

3. Function $T_{m(u,\, v)}\,(\,\alpha\,)$

1. Definition—This function is determined by the expression

$$T_{m(u,\, v)}\,(\,\alpha\,) \;=\; d\,P_{m(u,\, v)}\,(\,\alpha\,)/d\,\alpha \;. \tag{C.73}$$

By using equation (C.52) we can rewrite equation (C.73) in the form

$$T_{m(u,\, v)}\,(\,\alpha\,) \;=\; \tau_{m(v)m(v+\sigma)}\,(\alpha)\, \prod_{n=v-\sigma}^{u} \, \tau_{m(n)m(n+v)} \,[\; P_{m(n+\sigma,\, v)}\,(\,\alpha\,)\,] \;. \tag{C.74}$$

The branch points of this function are determined by equations (C.68), (C.70), (C.71), and (C.72). The function under consideration turns to infinity at these points.

2. Properties—1. From the second relation in equations (B.29) of Appendix B, equation (C.49) and representation (C.74) we have

$$T_{m(u,\, v)}\,(\,\alpha\, \pm\, \pi\,) \;=\; T_{m(u,\, v)}\,(\,\alpha\,)\,. \tag{C.75}$$

2. From the last relation in equations (B.29) of Appendix B, equation (C.53), and representation (C.74) we have

$$T_{m(u,\, v)}\,(\,\overline{\alpha}\,) \;=\; \overline{\tau_{m(v)m(v+\sigma)}\,(\alpha)}\, \prod_{n=v-\sigma}^{u} \, \tau_{m(n)m(n+\sigma)} \,[\; \overline{P_{m(n+\sigma,\, v)}\,(\,\alpha\,)}\,] \;=$$

$$=\; \overline{\tau_{m(v)m(v+\sigma)}\,(\alpha)}\, \prod_{n=v-\sigma}^{u} \, \overline{\tau_{m(n)m(n+\sigma)} \,[\; P_{m(n+\sigma,\, v)}\,(\,\alpha\,)\,]} \;.$$

By using an obvious formula for a product of complex conjugate quantities $= \overline{z_p}\; \overline{z_{p+1}} \;=\; \overline{z_p\; z_{p+1}}$ we get

$$T_{m(u,\, v)}\,(\,\overline{\alpha}\,) \;=\; \overline{T_{m(u,\, v)}\,(\,\alpha\,)} \;. \tag{C.76}$$

4. Function $H_{m(u,\, v)}\,(\,\alpha\,)$

The cofactor $G_{m(u,\, v)}\,(\,\alpha\,)$ in equation (C.27) can be found by multiplying operators (C.26) and dividing the result by $S_{m(u-1)}\;[\,P_{m(u,\, v)}\,(\,\alpha\,)\,]$. This yields

$$G_{m(u,\,v)}(\alpha)\ \mathfrak{M}_{m(v)m(v+1)}(\alpha)\prod_{p=u}^{p=v-1}\mathfrak{M}_{m(p)m(p+1)}\,[\,P_{m(p+1,\,v)}(\alpha)\,]\,, \tag{C.77}$$

$$\mathfrak{M}_{m(p)m(p+1)}(\alpha) = \tau_{m(p)m(p+1)}(\alpha)\ K_{m(p)m(p+1)}\,[\,\varphi_{m(p)m(p+1)}(\alpha)\,]\ . \tag{C.78}$$

Let us write this expression in a more convenient form. To do this, we introduce function

$$H_{m(u,\,v)}(\alpha) = K_{m(v)m(v+1)}\,[\,\varphi_{m(v)m(v+1)}(\alpha)\,] \times$$

$$\times \prod_{p=u}^{p=v-1} K_{m(p)m(p+1)}\left\{\,\varphi_{m(p)m(p+1)}\,[\,P_{m(p+1,\,v)}(\alpha)\,]\right\}\,. \tag{C.79}$$

Then taking into consideration equation (C.52) we can write equation (C.77) as

$$G_{m(u,\,v)}(\alpha) = T_{m(u,\,v)}(\alpha)\ H_{m(u,\,v)}(\alpha)\ . \tag{C.80}$$

Let us show how equations (C.27) and (C.80) can be obtained within the framework of the plane waves reflection/transmission concept. We can write the amplitude of an incident wave in the form

$$A_u(\alpha_u) = S(\alpha_u)\,d\alpha_u\,, \tag{C.81}$$

where $S(\alpha_u)$ is its directional characteristic. The amplitude of the $(v-u+1)^{th}$ order wave can be written as

$$A_{v+1}(\alpha_{v+1}) = H_{m(u,\,v)}(\alpha_{v+1})\ A_u\,[\,\alpha_u(\alpha_{v+1})\,]\,, \tag{C.82}$$

where functions $H_{m(u,\,v)}(\alpha_{v+1})$ and $A_u\,[\,\alpha_u(\alpha_{v+1})\,]$ are to be found.

Let us first find function $A_u\,[\,\alpha_u(\alpha_{v+1})\,]$ by substituting subsequently variable α_p by α_{p+1} according to equations (C.35) and (C.16)

$$\alpha_p = q_{m(p)m(p+1)}(\alpha_{p+1})\,,\ \ d\alpha_p = \tau_{m(p)m(p+1)}(\alpha_{p+1})\,d\alpha_{p+1}\ . \tag{C.83}$$

By substituting α_u with α_{u+1} in equation (C.81) we have

$$A_u = S\,[\,q_{m(u)m(u+1)}(\alpha_{u+1})\,]\ \tau_{m(u)m(u+1)}(\alpha_{u+1})\,d\alpha_{u+1} =$$

$$= S\,[\,P_{m(u,\,u)}\,(\,\alpha_{u+1}\,)\,]\quad \tau_{m(u)m(u+1)}\,(\,\alpha_{u+1}\,)\,d\,\alpha_{u+1}\ .$$

By substituting α_{u+1} with α_{u+2} we have

$$A_u = S\left\{\,P_{m(u,\,u)}\,[\,q_{m(u+1)m(u+2)}\,(\,\alpha_{u+2}\,)\,]\right\}\,\tau_{m(u)m(u+1)}\,[\,q_{m(u+1)m(u+2)}\,(\,\alpha_{u+2}\,)\,]\ \times$$

$$\times\quad \tau_{m(u+1)m(u+2)}\,(\,\alpha_{u+2}\,)\,d\,\alpha_{u+2} = S\,[\,P_{m(u,\,u+1)}\,(\,\alpha_{u+2}\,)\,]\ \times$$

$$\times\quad \tau_{m(u)m(u+1)}\ [\,P_{m(u+1,\,u+1)}\,(\,\alpha_{u+2}\,)\,]\ \tau_{m(u+1)m(u+2)}\,(\,\alpha_{u+2})\ d\,\alpha_{u+2}\ .$$

By substituting α_{u+2} with α_{u+3} we have

$$A_u = S\left\{\,P_{m(u,\,u+1)}\,[\,q_{m(u+2)m(u+3)}\,(\,\alpha_{u+3}\,)\,]\right\}\,\tau_{m(u)m(u+1)}\times$$

$$\times\left\{P_{m(u+1,\,u+1)}\,[\,q_{m(u+2)m(u+3)}\,(\,\alpha_{u+3}\,)\,]\right\}\,\tau_{m(u+1)m(u+2)}\,[\,q_{m(u+2)m(u+3)}\,(\,\alpha_{u+3}\,)\,]\times$$

$$\times\,\tau_{m(u+2)m(u+3)}\,(\,\alpha_{u+3}\,)\,d\,\alpha_{u+3} = S\,[\,P_{m(u,\,u+2)}\,(\,\alpha_{u+3}\,)\,]\ \ \tau_{m(u)m(u+1)}\,[\,P_{m(u+1,\,u+2)}$$

$$(\alpha_{u+3}\,)\,]\ \times\ \tau_{m(u+1)m(u+2)}\,[\,P_{m(u+2,\,u+2)}\,(\,\alpha_{u+3}\,)\,]\,\tau_{m(u+2)m(u+3)}\,(\,\alpha_{u+3}\,)\,d\,\alpha_{u+3}\ .$$

By using this technique repeatedly we obtain as a result of substituting α_v by α_{v+1} the sought function in the form

$$A_u\,[\,\alpha_u\,(\,\alpha_{v+1}\,)\,] = S\,[\,P_{m(u,\,v)}\,(\,\alpha_{v+1}\,)\,]\ T_{m(u,\,v)}\,(\,\alpha_{v+1}\,)\,d\,\alpha_{v+1}\ , \tag{C.84}$$

where

$$T_{m(u,\,v)}\,(\,\alpha_{v+1}\,) = \tau_{m(v)m(v+1)}\,(\,\alpha_{v+1}\,)\ \prod_{p=u}^{v-1}\ \tau_{m(p)m(p+1)}\ [\,P_{m(p+1,\,v)}\,(\,\alpha_{v+1}\,)\,]\ . \tag{C.85}$$

Let us now find the function $H_{m(u,\,v)}$, which corresponds to the product of $(\,v-u+1\,)$ reflection/transmission coefficients. We can represent such a product in the form

$$H_{m(u,\,v)} = K_{m(u)m(u+1)}\,(\,\alpha'_u\,)\ K_{m(u+1)m(u+2)}\,(\,\alpha'_{u+1}\,)\ \ldots$$

$$\ldots\ K_{m(v-1)m(v)}(\alpha'_{v-1})\ K_{m(v)m(v+1)}(\alpha'_v)\ ,$$

where we consider reflection/transmission coefficients as functions of the corresponding angles of incidence. By expressing α'_p through α_{p+1} according to equation (C.34) we have

$$H_{m(u,v)} = K_{m(u)m(u+1)}\,[\,\varphi_{m(u)m(u+1)}(\alpha_{u+1})\,] \times$$

$$\times\ K_{m(u+1)m(u+2)}\,[\,\varphi_{m(u+1)m(u+2)}(\alpha_{u+2})\,]\ \ldots\ K_{m(v-1)m(v)}\,[\,\varphi_{m(v-1)m(v)}(\alpha_v)\,] \times$$

$$\times\ K_{m(v)m(v+1)}\,[\,\varphi_{m(v)m(v+1)}(\alpha_{v+1})\,]\ .$$

By expressing α_p through α_{v+1} according to equation (C.37) we obtain the desired formula

$$H_{m(u,v)}(\alpha_{v+1}) = K_{m(v)m(v+1)}\,[\,\varphi_{m(v)m(v+1)}(\alpha_{v+1})\,] \times$$

$$\times \prod_{p=u}^{v-1} K_{m(p)m(p+1)}\left\{\,\varphi_{m(p)m(p+1)}\,[\,P_{m(p+1,v)}(\alpha_{v+1})\,]\right\}\ . \qquad \text{(C.86)}$$

Now by using equations (C.84) and (C.86) we can write equation (C.82) in the form

$$A_{v+1}(\alpha_{v+1}) = G_{m(u,v)}(\alpha_{v+1})\ S\,[\,P_{m(u,v)}(\alpha_{v+1})\,]\,d\,\alpha_{v+1}\ , \qquad \text{(C.87)}$$

where

$$G_{m(u,v)}(\alpha_{v+1}) = T_{m(u,v)}(\alpha_{v+1})\ H_{m(u,v)}(\alpha_{v+1})\ . \qquad \text{(C.88)}$$

The function $S_{m(p)}(\alpha)$ from equation (C.21) can be written as

$$\begin{aligned} S_{m(p)}(\alpha) &= G_{m(0,p-1)}(\alpha)\,[\,P_{m(0,p-1)}(\alpha) - \alpha_{m(0)}\,]^{-1} = \\ &= T_{m(0,p-1)}(\alpha)\ H_{m(0,p-1)}(\alpha)\,[\,P_{m(0,p-1)}(\alpha) - \alpha_{m(0)}\,]^{-1} = \\ &= [\,d\,P_{m(0,p-1)}(\alpha)/d\alpha\,]\ H_{m(0,p-1)}(\alpha)\,[\,P_{m(0,p-1)}(\alpha) - \alpha_{m(0)}\,]^{-1}\ , \end{aligned} \qquad \text{(C.89)}$$

where $\alpha_{m(0)}$ is determined by equation IV.1(22).

APPENDIX D

SPECIAL FUNCTIONS OF BOUNDARY LAYERS

1. Function $W(w)$

1. From equations V.2(16), V.2(21), and V.2(22) we have

$$W(w) = (1/2\pi)\int_0^\infty t^{-1/2}\,(1+t)^{-1}\,\exp\,(i\pi w^2 t/2)\,dt. \tag{D.1}$$

When Im $w = 0$ and using the representation

$$\exp\,(i\pi w^2 t/2) = \cos(\pi w^2 t/2) + i\,\sin\,(\pi w^2 t/2) \tag{D.2}$$

we derive

$$\mathrm{Re}\;W(w) = (1/2\pi)\int_0^\infty t^{-1/2}(1+t)^{-1}\,\cos\,(\pi w^2 t/2)\,dt, \tag{D.3}$$

$$\mathrm{Im}\;W(w) = (1/2\pi)\int_0^\infty t^{-1/2}(1+t)^{-1}\,\sin\,(\pi w^2 t/2)\,dt. \tag{D.4}$$

Suppose $w = iv$ with Im $v = 0$. Then equation (D.2) can be written

$$\exp\,(i\pi w^2 t/2) = \exp(-i\pi v^2 t/2)\,\cos\,(\pi v^2 t/2) - i\,\sin\,(\pi v^2 t/2), \tag{D.5}$$

and from equation (D.3) - (D.4) we have

$$\mathrm{Re}\;W(iv) = \mathrm{Re}\;W(w),\quad \mathrm{Im}\;W(iv) = -\,\mathrm{Im}\;W(w)\,. \tag{D.6}$$

So we get the following property of the function under consideration:

$$W(iw) = \overline{W(w)}\,, \tag{D.7}$$

where the dash above the term denotes a complex conjugate value.

2. By substituting a known asymptotic representation of the incomplete gamma function (Abramowitz and Stegun, 1972),

$$\Gamma(1/2, z) \sim z^{-1/2} \exp(-z) \times [1 + O(|z|^{-1})] \text{ with } |z| \to \infty \tag{D.8}$$

into equation V.2(23), we get an asymptotic representation of the function under consideration

$$W(w) \sim (\pi w \sqrt{2})^{-1} \exp(i\pi/4) \times [1 + O(|w|^{-1})] \text{ with } |w| \to \infty. \tag{D.9}$$

3. By substituting a known value of the incomplete gamma function

$$\Gamma(1/2, 0) = \sqrt{\pi} \tag{D.10}$$

into equation V.2(23), we get

$$W(0) = 1/2. \tag{D.11}$$

4. By using a known formula

$$d\,\Gamma(1/2, z)/dz = -z^{-1/2} \exp(-z), \tag{D.12}$$

and differentiating equation V.2(23), we get

$$d\,W(w)/dw = 2^{-1/2} \exp(-i\pi/4) - i\pi w W(w), \tag{D.13}$$

$$d^2\,W(w)/dw^2 = -i\pi\,[W(w) + w\,dW(w)/dw]. \tag{D.14}$$

5. By expressing the incomplete gamma function through the Fresnel integral

$$(2\sqrt{\pi})^{-1}\,\Gamma(1/2, z) = F(-\sqrt{iz}) = 1 - F(+\sqrt{iz}), \tag{D.15}$$

$$F(z) = \pi^{-1/2} \exp(-i\pi/4) \int_{-\infty}^{z} \exp(it^2)\,dt, \tag{D.16}$$

we get

$$W(w) = F(-\sqrt{iz}) \exp z = [1 - F(+\sqrt{iz})] \exp z, \; z = -i\pi w^2/2 \tag{D.17}$$

or

$$W(w)\exp(i\pi w^2/2) = F(-w\sqrt{\pi/2}) = 1 - F(+w\sqrt{\pi/2}). \tag{D.18}$$

2. Function $\Psi(\rho, \zeta)$

1. Integral representation—When

$$0 \le \rho < \infty,\ 0 \le \zeta \le \pi/2, \tag{D.19}$$

the function under consideration is determined by the formulas

$$\Psi(\rho,\zeta) = J\cos\zeta, \tag{D.20}$$

$$J = (2\pi i)^{-1} \int_{\Gamma} (\sin\alpha - \sin\zeta)^{-1} \exp[-(i\pi\rho^2/2)\sin^2\alpha]\, d\alpha. \tag{D.21}$$

The ends of contour Γ go to infinity in the semibands $-\pi/2 < \mathrm{Re}\,\alpha < 0$ when $\mathrm{Im}\,\alpha > 0$ and $0 < \mathrm{Re}\,\alpha < \pi/2$ when $\mathrm{Im}\,\alpha < 0$.

By using equations IX.3(22), IX.3(24), and IX.3(30) in the intervals (D.19) we can also determine the same functions by the expressions:

$$\Psi(\rho,\zeta) = \Psi^+ - \Psi^-, \tag{D.22}$$

$$\Psi^\pm = (4\pi i)^{-1} \int_{\Gamma} \cot[(\alpha - \psi^\pm)/2] \exp[-(i\pi\rho^2/2)\sin^2\alpha]\, d\alpha, \text{ and} \tag{D.23}$$

$$\psi^+ = \zeta,\ \psi^- = \pi - \zeta. \tag{D.24}$$

A pair of more useful expressions for this function can be writtin using equation (D.21) in the form $J = I^+ + I^-$ where I^+ and I^- are the integrals due to the semi-infinite parts Γ^+ and Γ^- of the contour Γ, respectively, where $\mathrm{Im}\,\alpha > 0$ and $\mathrm{Im}\,\alpha < 0$. In the integrals $I^\pm$ we introduce a new variable $z = \mp 2\alpha$. Then Γ^+ changes to Γ^-, and after elementary transformations we obtain

$$J = -(i\pi)^{-1}\exp(-2i\nu) \int_{\Gamma_1} (\cos z - \cos 2\zeta)^{-1} \sin\zeta \times \exp(2i\nu\cos z)\, dz,$$
$$\nu = \pi\rho^2/8, \tag{D.25}$$

where contour Γ_1 goes from point $z = 0$ to infinity in the semiband $0 < \text{Re } z < \pi$, $\text{Im } z < 0$. Introducing a new variable $s = \exp(-iz)$ and considering the relationships

$$(\cos z - \cos 2\zeta)^{-1} dz = 2i(s^2 - 2s\cos 2\zeta + 1)^{-1} ds$$

$$= \sin^{-1} 2\zeta \times \left\{[s - \exp(2i\zeta)]^{-1} - [s - \exp(-2i\zeta)]^{-1}\right\} ds,$$

we obtain

$$\Psi(\rho, \zeta) = \sin 2\zeta \times \exp(-2i\nu) J^*/\pi, \tag{D.26}$$

$$J^* = \int_L (s^2 - 2s\cos 2\zeta + 1)^{-1} \exp[i\nu(s + s^{-1})] ds, \tag{D.27}$$

or

$$\Psi(\rho, \zeta) = (2\pi i)^{-1} (I^+ - I^-) \exp(-2i\nu), \tag{D.28}$$

$$I^\pm = \int_L (s - \mu^\pm)^{-1} \exp[i\nu(s + s^{-1})] ds, \quad \mu^\pm = \exp(\pm 2i\zeta), \tag{D.29}$$

where L is any contour going from $s = 0$ to $s = 1$ in the semicircle $|s| < 1$, $-\pi < \arg s < 0$.

2. *Values at the shadow boundaries*—If $\zeta = 0$, the observation point belongs to a secondary shadow boundary. Let us calculate the value of the function being considered in this case, using expressions (D.20) and (D.21).

The integrand in equation (D.21) has a simple pole at the point $\alpha = \zeta \geq 0$. For $\zeta \to 0$, this pole moves toward the point $\alpha = 0$ along the real axis from the right. Let us superpose the line of integration Γ onto the imaginary axis, surrounding the point $\alpha = 0$ with a semicircle of a small radius R. Here, because of the symmetry of the integrand, the integrals in the positive and negative semi-infinite parts of the imaginery axis cancel each other. Then only the integral over the semicircle surrounding the point $\alpha = 0$ remains. Introducing a new variable of integration ψ, based on the formula $\alpha = R \exp(i\psi)$, we obtain

$$J = (R/2\pi) \int_{-3\pi/2}^{-\pi/2} \{\sin[R\exp(i\psi)] - \sin\zeta\}^{-1} \times$$

$$\exp\{i\psi - i(\pi\rho^2/2)\sin^2[R\exp(i\psi)]\}\, d\psi .$$

It is possible for $R \to 0$ to neglect the second component in the exponent, as well as to use the approximation $\sin[R\exp(i\psi)] \approx R\exp(i\psi)$. In the limit for $\zeta \to 0$, we find $J = 1/2$ at $\zeta = 0$. Substituting this value in equation (D.20), we obtain

$$\Psi(\rho, 0) = 1/2 . \tag{D.30}$$

If $\zeta = \pi/2$, the observation point belongs to a primary shadow boundary. The integral (D.21) is modulo limited at $\zeta = \pi/2$. Therefore, from equation (D.20), it immediately follows that

$$\Psi(\rho, \pi/2) = 0 . \tag{D.31}$$

We note that for the integral (D.27), the inequality $0 < |J^*(\rho, \pi/2)| < \infty$ is correct for $\rho < \infty$. Therefore, from equation (D.26), we obtain

$$\arg\Psi(\rho, \pi/2) = \arctan[(S\cos 2\nu - R\sin 2\nu)(R\cos 2\nu + S\sin 2\nu)^{-1}], \tag{D.32}$$

$$R = \mathrm{Re}\, J^*(\rho, \pi/2), \quad S = \mathrm{Im}\, J^*(\rho, \pi/2).$$

3. *Asymptotic formula for* $\rho \to 0$—The function under consideration at $\rho \to 0$ is expressed by means of elementary functions. We use expressions (D.28) and (D.29) to obtain the corresponding formulas.

Let us expand the exponential factor of formula (D.29) in the series

$$\exp(i\nu s) = 1 + \delta, \quad \delta = \sum_{k=1}^{\infty} (i\nu s)^k / k! . \tag{D.33}$$

Since $|\nu s| \le \nu$, for $\nu \ll 1$ at the line of integration, the asymptotic estimate $\delta \sim O(\nu)$ is correct. Therefore, for $\nu \ll 1$, the component δ can be neglected in equation (D.33), which permits the following approximation to be used: $\exp[i\nu(s + s^{-1})] \approx \exp(i\nu s^{-1})$. Substituting this representation in equation (D.29) and converting to a new variable $x = s^{-1}$, we obtain an approximate expression of the integral for $\nu \ll 1$

$$I^{\pm} = \mu^{\mp} \int_1^{\infty} x^{-1} (x - \mu^{\mp})^{-1} \exp(i\nu x)\, dx. \tag{D.34}$$

Using the identity

$$a x^{-1} (x + a)^{-1} = -(x + a)^{-1} + x^{-1},$$

we transform the last integral to the form

$$I^{\pm} = -\int_1^{\infty} (x - \mu^{\mp})^{-1} \exp(i\nu x)\, dx + \int_1^{\infty} x^{-1} \exp(i\nu x)\, dx \tag{D.35}$$

Substituting equation (D.35) into (D.28) and converting to a new variable $z = -i\nu(x - \mu^{\mp})$, we obtain

$$\Psi = S \exp(-i\nu), \tag{D.36}$$

$$S = (2\pi i)^{-1} [E^{+} \exp(-z^{+}) - E^{-} \exp(-z^{-})],$$

$$E^{\pm} = \int_{-z^{\pm}}^{\infty} z^{-1} \exp(-z)\, dz = -Ei(z^{\pm}),\ z^{\pm} = i\nu\,[1 - \exp(\pm 2i\zeta)], \tag{D.37}$$

where the path of integration is located in the region Re $z > -$ Im $\nu\mu^{\pm}$, from which the semicircle with radius ν and the center at the point $z = i\nu\mu^{\pm}$ is excluded. Here $Ei(z)$ is the exponential integral function in the plane z, which is cut along the positive imaginary axis.

For $|z^{\pm}| \ll 1$, it is possible to approximate the integral exponential function by the first terms of its known power expansion $Ei(z) \approx \ln \gamma z - i\pi$, where $\gamma = 1.781072418$ is the Euler constant, and the exponential factors by the first terms of the Taylor series $\exp(-z^{\pm}) \approx 1 - z^{\pm}$. Then

$$S \approx (2\pi i)^{-1} [\ln(z^{-}/z^{+}) + (z^{+} - z^{-})(\ln\gamma - i\pi) + z^{+}\ln z^{+} - z^{-}\ln z^{-}].$$

Substituting the value $z^{\pm}$ here, after elementary transformations, we obtain

$$S \approx 1/2 - \zeta/\pi - \nu[A + i(\sin 2\zeta \times \ln\nu)/\pi], \tag{D.38}$$

$$A = 2^{-1} \sin 2\zeta + i(1 - 2\zeta/\pi)\sin^2\zeta + i\pi^{-1} \sin 2\zeta \times \ln(2\gamma \sin\zeta).$$

For $\nu \to 0$, it is possible to neglect the quantity A, since it is always modulo limited, while $|\ln \nu|$ increases without limit. On the strength of the same considerations, in the power expansion of the exponential factor from equation (D.36) all the powers of ν can be neglected. Then substituting equation (D.38) into (D.36) we obtain

$$\Psi \approx 1/2 - \zeta/\pi - i(\nu/\pi)\sin 2\zeta \times \ln \nu \quad \text{when } \rho \to 0. \tag{D.39}$$

It follows from equation (D.39) that for $\rho \to 0$, the modulus of the function being considered is practically constant

$$|\Psi| \approx 1/2 - \zeta/\pi, \quad \rho \to 0. \tag{D.40}$$

while the argument is changed in the following manner:

$$arg\ \Psi = -\arctan[(\nu \ln \nu)(\pi/2 - \zeta)^{-1} \sin 2\zeta], \quad \rho \to 0. \tag{D.41}$$

In equation (D.41) for $\zeta = \pi/2$, the limit of an indeterminate $0/0$ occurs, which is readily removed on the basis of l'Hopital's rule:

$$\arg \Psi = -\arctan(2\nu \ln \nu) \quad \text{when } \zeta = \pi/2, \quad \rho \to 0. \tag{D.42}$$

4. Asymptotic formula at $\rho \to \infty$—For large values of ρ, the integral (D.21) can be calculated by the saddle-point method. The integrand has saddle points $\alpha = \pm k\pi/2$ $(k = 0, 1, 2, \ldots)$, determined from the equation $d(\sin^2 \alpha)/d\alpha = 0$. We shall consider the case in which contour Γ passes through the point $\alpha = 0$ along the steepest descent path $\mathrm{Re}\ i \sin^2 \alpha > 0$, $\mathrm{Im}\ i \sin^2 \alpha = 0$. For $|\alpha| \ll 1$ the equation of this path takes the form $\arg \alpha = 3\pi/4$, $\arg \alpha = -\pi/4$. In this case, using the saddle-point method yields

$$\Psi(\rho, \zeta) \sim (\pi \rho \sqrt{2})^{-1} \cot \zeta \times \exp(5\pi i/4) + O(\rho^{-2}). \tag{D.43}$$

This formula is not suitable for $\zeta \to 0$. In order to get a more general formula, we turn to the representation (D.22). Using the expansion in the partial fractions

$$\cot(x/2) = 2\sum_{n=-\infty}^{\infty} (x - 2\pi n)^{-1}, \tag{D.44}$$

we represent equation (D.23) in the form

$$\Psi^{\pm} = \sum_{n=-\infty}^{\infty} \Psi_n^{\pm}, \tag{D.45}$$

$$\Psi_n^{\pm} = (2\pi i)^{-1} \int_{\Gamma} (\alpha - \psi^{\pm} - 2\pi n)^{-1} \exp\left[-(i\pi\rho^2/2) \sin^2 \alpha \right] d\alpha$$

Replacing $\sin^2 \alpha$ with a power-series expansion in the neighborhood of the saddle-point $\alpha = 0$, and ommitting the third and higher degrees gives $\sin^2 \alpha \approx \alpha^2$. The integral obtained has been previously studied [see equations VIII.2(29) - VII.2(34)] and is expressed by the function (D.1)

$$\Psi_n^{\pm} = s_n^{\pm} W(w_n^{\pm}), \quad w_n^{\pm} = |\psi^{\pm} + 2\pi n| \, \rho, \tag{D.46}$$

except for the sign ($s_n^{\pm} = 1$ or $s_n^{\pm} = -1$). In order for this expression to remain continuous at $n \neq 0$ for the transition across the shadow boundary $\zeta = 0$, it is necessary to take $s_n^{\pm} = \text{sign}(\psi^{\pm} + 2\pi n)$. Substituting equations (D.45) and (D.46) into (D.22), we obtain another asymptotic formula

$$\Psi(\rho, \zeta) \sim \sum_{n=-\infty}^{\infty} \left[s_n^{+} W(w_n^{+}) - s_n^{-} W(w_n^{-}) \right] + O(\rho^{-2}), \tag{D.47}$$

which, in contrast to equation (D.43), is suitable for neighborhoods of the secondary shadow boundaries of $\zeta = 0$ as well. Outside these neighborhoods, the asymptotic representation of equation (D.9),

$$W(w_n^{\pm}) \sim (\pi w_n^{\pm} \sqrt{2})^{-1} \exp(i\pi/4), \tag{D.48}$$

is correct, and with its help formula (D.47) can be reduced to the form of equation (D.43).

5. *Complex-conjugate values*—Let us write an individual term in the sum (D.45) in the form

$$\Psi_n^{\pm} = (2\pi i)^{-1} \int_{\Gamma} (\ell + \alpha)^{-1} \exp(\pm iq \sin^2 \alpha) \, d\alpha, \tag{D.49}$$

where

$$q = |\pi\rho^2/2|, \quad \ell = -(\psi^{\pm} + 2\pi n). \tag{D.50}$$

Here it is necessary to take plus for $\rho^2 < 0$ and minus for $\rho^2 > 0$.

Let us superpose the contour of integration on the imaginary axis $\alpha = iy$.

Then

$$\Psi_n^{\pm} = (2\pi)^{-1} \int_{-\infty}^{\infty} (\ell + iy)^{-1} \exp(\pm ia)\, dy, \quad a = -q \,\mathrm{sh}^2 y. \tag{D.51}$$

By multiplying the numerator and denominator of the integrand by $(\ell - iy)$ and using the representation

$$\exp(\pm ia) = \cos a \pm i \sin a, \tag{D.52}$$

we can write equation (D.51) in the form

$$\Psi_n^{\pm} = \ell (2\pi)^{-1} \int_{-\infty}^{\infty} (\ell^2 + y^2)^{-1} (\cos a \pm i \sin a)\, dy +$$

$$+ (2\pi)^{-1} \int_{-\infty}^{\infty} y (\ell^2 + y^2)^{-1} (\pm \sin a - i \cos a)\, dy . \tag{D.53}$$

It is easy to see that the second integral is zero, because the contributions over the intervals $-\infty < y < 0$ and $0 < y < \infty$ cancel each other. Therefore, we have

$$\Psi_n^{\pm} = M \pm i N, \tag{D.54}$$

$$M = (\ell / 2\pi) \int_{-\infty}^{\infty} (\ell^2 + y^2)^{-1} \cos a \, dy,$$

$$N = (\ell / 2\pi) \int_{-\infty}^{\infty} (\ell^2 + y^2)^{-1} \sin a \, dy, \tag{D.55}$$

where it is necessary to take plus for $\rho^2 < 0$ and minus for $\rho^2 > 0$.

Let us consider expression (D.54) as a function of parameter ρ. Then it follows from equation (D.54) that on the strength of the relationships

$$\rho = |\rho| \text{ when } \rho^2 > 0, \quad \rho = i|\rho| \text{ when } \rho^2 < 0, \tag{D.56}$$

$$\Psi_n^{\pm}(i|\rho|, \zeta) = \overline{\Psi_n^{\pm}(|\rho|, \zeta)}, \tag{D.57}$$

where the complex conjugate value is marked by the dash.

Because expression (D.57) represents the property of each individual term in the sum (D.45), the sum itself possesses the same property

$$\Psi\,(\,i|\rho|,\zeta) = \overline{\Psi\,(|\rho|,\,\zeta)}\;. \tag{D.58}$$

APPENDIX E

GEOMETRIC CHARACTERISTICS OF EDGE WAVES IN HOMOGENEOUS MEDIA

1. Ray coordinates

Let $x_i\,(i = 1, 2, 3)$ be an orthogonal coordinate system with the origin at an arbitrary point of space and with an arbitrary orientation of the axes in which the equation of the diffracting edge has the parametric representation

$$x_i = x_i(M_0) \quad \text{for } i = 1, 2, 3, \tag{E.1}$$

where the $x_i(M_0)$ are functions of the point M_0 of the edge.

We introduce a local orthogonal coordinate system $\bar{x}_i\,(i = 1, 2, 3)$ with the origin at arbitrary point M_0 of the edge. We select the directions of axes $\bar{x}_1$, $\bar{x}_2$ arbitrarily, and match axis $\bar{x}_3$ with the tangent to the edge. The initial and local coordinates are related by the relationship

$$x_i = \sum_{j=1}^{3} a_{ij}(M_0)\bar{x}_j + b_i(M_0), \quad \bar{x}_i = \sum_{j=1}^{3} a_{ji}(M_0)x_j - b_i(M_0), \tag{E.2}$$

where $a_{ij}(M_0)$ is the directional cosine of axis $\bar{x}_j$ relative to axis x_i, and $b_i(M_0)$ are coordinates of the origin of the system $\bar{x}_i$ in the initial coordinate system x_i, the indicated quantities being functions of the point of the edge. We note that the matrix of transformation of orthogonal coordinates to orthogonal coordinates has well-known properties

$$\det\,[a_{ij}] = 1, \sum_{i=1}^{3} a_{ij}^2 = \sum_{j=1}^{3} a_{ij}^2 = 1, \sum_{i=1}^{3} a_{ij}\,a_{ik} = \sum_{j=1}^{3} a_{kj}\,a_{ij} = 0, \tag{E.3}$$

which will be used subsequently.

Each point on the diffracting edge radiates a cone of diffracted rays with an axis on the tangent to the edge, i.e., the axis $\bar{x}_3$ in the local rectangular coordinate system. We relate the orthogonal system of ray coordinates x_D^i $(i = 1, 2, 3)$ with the point on the edge. As the coordinate x_D^1 we take the distance along the diffracted ray to the edge. As x_D^2 we take the magnitude of a dihedral angle between the planes intersecting along the tangent to the edge at the vertex of the cone of diffracted rays (the selection of plane $x_D^2 = 0$ is arbitrary). We will consider as the coordinate x_D^3 the semivertex angle of the cone of the diffracted rays, determined by the law of edge diffraction (see Section I.6)

$$x_D^3 = \arccos\,[(c/c_0)\cos\varepsilon], \tag{E.4}$$

where ε is an acute angle between the incident ray and the tangent to the edge at M_0, c_0 and c are the velocities of the incident and diffracted waves respectively. The initial orthogonal coordinates are expressed in terms of the ray coordinates according to the first equation from (E.2), in which it is necessary to substitute:

$$\bar{x}_1 = x_D^1 \cos x_D^2 \sin x_D^3,\ \bar{x}_2 = x_D^1 \sin x_D^2 \sin x_D^3,\ \bar{x}_3 = x_D^1 \cos x_D^3, \tag{E.5}$$

where a_{ij} and b_i do not depend on x_D^1 and x_D^2 .

In Section VI.1.3 we introduced a metric coefficient VI.1(29), which can be written now as

$$g_{22} = \sum_{n=1}^{3} (\partial x_n/\partial x_D^2)^2 . \tag{E.6}$$

Substituting equations (E.2) and (E.5) into (E.6) and taking into consideration equation (E.3), we get

$$g_{22} = (x_D^1 \sin x_D^3)^2 . \tag{E.7}$$

2. Jacobian

Let us derive an explicit expression for the Jacobian of transformation from the orthogonal coordinates to the ray coordinates

$$J_D = D\,(x_1, x_2, x_3)/D\,(x_D^1, x_D^2, x_D^3) . \tag{E.8}$$

Knowing the formulas for relating the orthogonal x_i and the ray x_D^i coordinates, we can write the right side of expression (E.8) in an explicit and very simple form. We will proceed with the derivation of the corresponding formula. Differentiating the first expression from equation (E.2) and the expression (E.5) with respect to the ray coordinates x_D^i, taking into account the second and third properties from (E.3) of the matrix of transformation of coordinates x_i to $\bar{x}_i$, and using the rules of calculations of determinants, we transform the functional determinant (E.8) to the form

$$J_D = D x_D^1 \, (x_D^1 + r_D), \quad r_D = E/D, \tag{E.9}$$

where the following notations are used:

$$D(x_D^2, x_d^3) = \begin{vmatrix} A_{11} & A_{12} & A_{13} \\ A_{21} & A_{22} & A_{23} \\ A_{31} & A_{32} & A_{33} \end{vmatrix}, \quad E(x_D^2, x_D^3) = \begin{vmatrix} A_{11} & A_{12} & T_1 \\ A_{21} & A_{22} & T_2 \\ A_{31} & A_{32} & T_3 \end{vmatrix}, \tag{E.10}$$

$$A_{i1} = (a_{i1} \cos x_D^2 + a_{i2} \sin x_D^2) \sin x_D^3 + a_{i3} \cos x_D^3,$$

$$A_{i2} = (-a_{i1} \sin x_D^2 + a_{i2} \cos x_D^2) \sin x_D^3,$$

$$A_{i3} = \partial\,(a_{i1} \cos x_D^2 \sin x_D^3 + a_{i2} \sin x_D^2 \sin x_D^3 + a_{i3} \cos x_D^3)/\partial x_D^3, \text{ and}$$

$$T_i = \partial b_i / \partial x_D^3 .$$

Later we see that the quantity r_D is the radius of curvature of the normal section of the front of the diffracted wave made by plane $x_D^2 = \text{const}$ at the edge point. The cofactor D in equation (E.9) can be expressed in terms of r_D by means of the following considerations of localizability. Since D and r_D do not depend on x_D^1, we can determine D on the basis of equation (E.9) by means of the finite relationship

$$D = (1/r_D) \lim_{x_D^1 \to 0} (J_D / x_D^1) . \tag{E.11}$$

In the neighborhood of an isolated point on the edge, a local plane approximation is valid for describing the geometry of the fronts, rays, and interfaces (see I.3). Therefore, when $x_D^1 \to 0$ we can consider

$$\lim_{x_D^1 \to 0} (J_D / x_D^1) = \lim_{x_D^1 \to 0} (J^* / x_D^1) , \tag{E.12}$$

where J^* is the Jacobian of the transformation from the orthogonal coordinates x_i to the ray coordinates x_D^i in the case of diffraction of the plane wave on a rectilinear edge (it is assumed that at point M_0 the geometry of the rays and edge in this case coincide with the given geometry). In the case of diffraction of the plane wave on a rectilinear edge, the quantity x_D^3 is not a coordinate, it is the constant for each diffracted ray, and has the role of a parameter. Therefore, the space of the orthogonal coordinates becomes two-dimensional, and the coordinate x_3 can be expressed by x_1, x_2 and the space parameter x_D^3. In calculating $J^*(x_1, x_2)$ we can match system (x_1, x_2) with $(\bar{x}_1, \bar{x}_2)$ — this does not affect the value of the Jacobian. The ray and orthogonal coordinates are related by

$$x_1 = x_D^1 \cos x_D^2 \sin x_D^3 , \quad x_2 = x_D^1 \sin x_D^2 \sin x_D^3 ,$$

$$x_D^1 = (x_1^2 + x_2^2)^{1/2} / \sin x_D^3 , \quad x_D^2 = \mathrm{arctg}\,(x_2/x_1), \tag{E.13}$$

and the Jacobian has the form:

$$J^* = D(x_1, x_2)/D(x_D^1, x_D^2) = x_D^1 \sin^2 x_D^3 . \tag{E.14}$$

Substituting expression (E.14) into (E.11) and then into (E.9), we obtain

$$J_D(x_D^1, x_D^2, x_D^3) = [x_D^1 (x_D^1 + r_D) \sin^2 x_D^3]/r_D . \tag{E.15}$$

As the first ray coordinate we also can take the time of propagation from the edge along the diffracted ray $\tau = x_D^1 / c$, where c is the wave velocity. Because the Jacobian of the transformation from orthogonal coordinates to the new ray coordinates

$$J = D(x_1, x_2, x_3)/D(\tau, x_D^2, x_D^3) \tag{E.16}$$

is related with the Jacobian (E.8) by the relationship

$$J = c J_D , \tag{E.17}$$

from equation (E.15) we obtain

$$J/c^2 = [\tau (c\tau + r_D) \sin^2 x_D^3]/r_D . \tag{E.18}$$

3. Focal properties

An isolated diffracted wave can be regarded kinematically as the result of radiation from certain focal surfaces (caustics). The focal surfaces are formed by those space points (foci) at which the distance between adjacent rays is characterized by an infinitesimally small quantity of the second or higher order (Born and Wolf, 1968). At these surfaces the Jacobian (E.15) turns to zero. But then it follows from (E.15) that the field of diffracted rays has two focal surfaces, determined by the equations

$$x_D^1(x_1, x_2, x_3) = 0, \quad x_D^1(x_1, x_2, x_3) = -r_D(x_1, x_2, x_3). \tag{E.19}$$

The first expression in equation (E.19) is the equation of the edge. This result is obvious – it follows directly from the law of the edge diffraction (see Section I.6).

The geometric sense of the second expression in equation (E.19) is also easy to understand in the terms of paraxial optics (Born and Wolf, 1968). A set of rays, close in direction, forms a "thin pencil." The thin pencil can be characterized by its central ray and two focal lines – two mutually orthogonal rectilinear line segments. The set of rays of such a thin pencil can be obtained by joining all pairs of points on the mentioned line segments. The planes, containing the central ray and a focal line, are the principal planes. The radii of the sections of the wave front by such planes are the principal radii of curvature.

In the case under consideration one of the focal lines is the edge, and the other is determined by the second expression in equation (E.19). The model of a thin pencil of four rays (the ray tube) is shown in Figure 98. Now the sense of the quantity r_D is clear – it is the distance from the edge to the focal line, i.e., the principal radius of curvature of the edge wave front at the edge. Because the corresponding principal plane touches the surface $x_D^2 = \text{const}$ at the edge, the quantity r_D can also be determined as the radius of curvature of the section of the edge wave front by surface $x_D^2 = \text{const}$ at the edge.

It follows from equation (E.9) that in the general case the quantity r_D is a function of two ray coordinates, i.e., $r_D = r_D(x_D^2, x_D^3)$. Let us show that it depends on x_D^2 in the case of curvilinear edges only. Let the edge be rectilinear. Then the orthogonal coordinate system x_i in equation (E.2) can be chosen in such a way that its axes coincide with the axes of the local rectangular system $\bar{x}_i$. Then

$$a_{ij}(M_0) \equiv 0 \text{ when } i \neq j, \; a_{ii}(M_0) \equiv 1, \; \partial a_{ij}/\partial x_D^3 \equiv 0, \; b_1 \equiv b_2 \equiv 0, \tag{E.20}$$

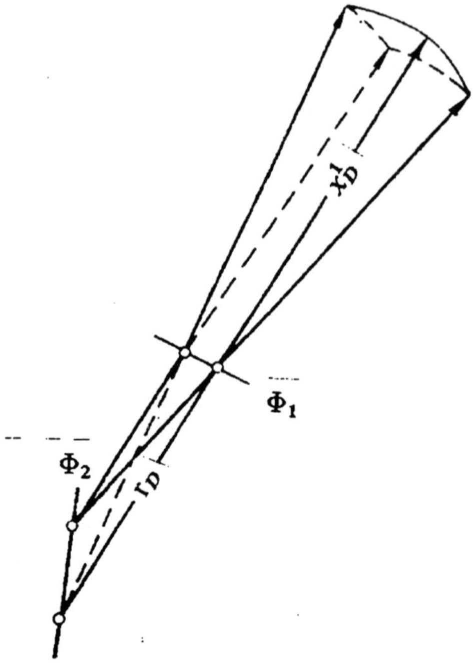

Figure 98. Model of the thin pencil with focal lines Φ_1 (edge) and Φ_2.

and from equation (E.9) we have

$$r_D = -(\partial b_3 / \partial x_D^3) \sin x_D^3, \tag{E.21}$$

where $b_3\ (x_D^3)$ is the distance from some fixed point on the edge to the current point on the edge. Now it is clear that in the case of a rectilinear edge the focal line of each thin pencil is a circle with its center at the edge. An example of focal lines for the case of diffraction of the spherical wave on a rectilinear edge is shown in Figure 99.

Let us show now what additional geometric meaning has the quantity r_D at the shadow boundary, given by the following equation:

$$x_D^2 = T\ (x_D^3)\ , \tag{E.22}$$

where the form of function T depends on the geometry of the edge and the directions of incident rays. The quantity under consideration at this surface can be written as

$$r_D = r_D\ [\ T(x_D^3),\ x_D^3\ ]\ . \tag{E.23}$$

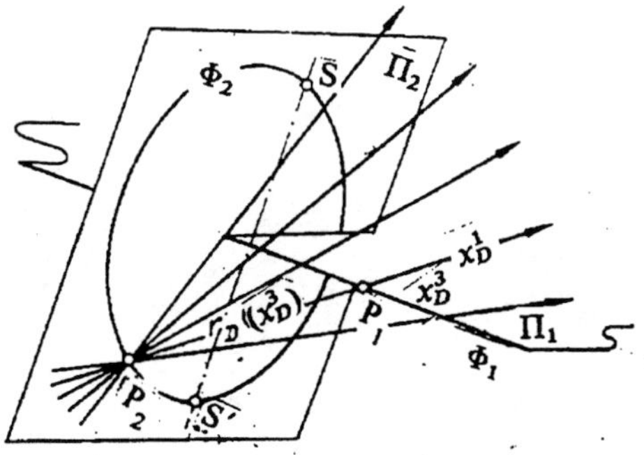

Figure 99. Focal lines Φ_1 (edge) and Φ_2 in the case of diffraction of the spherical wave on the half-plane Π_1. Π_2 ***– plane perpendicular to the edge.*** P_1 ***and*** P_2 ***– running points of lines*** Φ_1 ***and*** Φ_2, ***respectively.***

In the neighborhood of each point of the edge $x_D^1 = 0$, $x_D^3 = \mathrm{const}$ the shadow boundary can be approximated by its tangent plane, containing the ray $x_D^2 = T(x_D^3)$, $x_d^3 = \mathrm{const}$ and the tangent to the edge. Because at the shadow boundary any ray is simultaneously reflected/transmitted and diffracted, the lines of sections of the reflected/transmitted wave front and the diffracted wave front by the mentioned tangent plane coincide in a sufficiently small neighborhood of the edge. Therefore, the radii of curvature of the sections of these wave fronts by the mentioned tangent plane coincide at the edge as well. In this way the quantity (E.23) can be regarded as a radius of curvature of the section of the reflected/transmitted wave front by the shadow boundary at the edge.

APPENDIX F

EDGE-DIFFRACTED WAVE EIKONAL IN THE VICINITY OF THE CENTRAL RAY (DIFFRACTION OF SPHERICAL WAVE)

Here we will develop the ratio [IX.2(33)] for the simplest case of diffraction of a spherical wave on the rectilinear semi-edge in an homogeneous medium. To do this, we first derive an approximate expression of the edge-diffracted wave eikonal in a small vicinity of the central ray $\sigma = 0$ (see Sections IX.1(3) - IX.1(4).

Let Π_k and ρ_k with $k = 1, 2$ denote, respectively, the principal planes and principal radii of curvature of the normal cross sections of the edge-diffracted wave front at the central ray $\sigma = 0$. This front is a surface of rotation about the edge. It is a well-known fact of differential geometry that one of the principal planes of the surface of rotation contains the axes of rotation itself. Let it be plane Π_2. Let Π be a plane containing the central ray $\sigma = 0$ and forming angle $\psi^{\pm}$ with plane Π_1. Let ℓ denote the radius of curvature of the cross section of the edge-diffracted wave front by plane Π at the central ray. According to the formula of Euler we have

$$\ell^{-1} = \rho_1^{-1} \cos^2 \psi^{\pm} + \rho_2^{-1} \sin^2 \psi^{\pm} \tag{F.1}$$

In a small vicinity of the central ray the edge-diffracted wave front can be approximated by the surface formed by the lines of equal curvature $\ell = \ell(\psi^{\pm})$. Then the edge-diffracted wave eikonal can be approximated by the expression

$$\tau_{mn} \approx \ell / c_m + \delta \quad \text{with } \sigma \to 0, \tag{F.2}$$

where $\delta = \delta(\psi^{\pm})$ is the value of the eikonal at $\ell(\psi^{\pm}) = 0$ and c_m the propagation velocity. Note, quantity δ does not depend on σ.

By using the cosine theorem we can represent quantity ℓ in the form (Figure 100)

$$\ell = (\rho^2 + \rho_D^2 + 2\rho\rho_D \cos\sigma)^{1/2}, \tag{F.3}$$

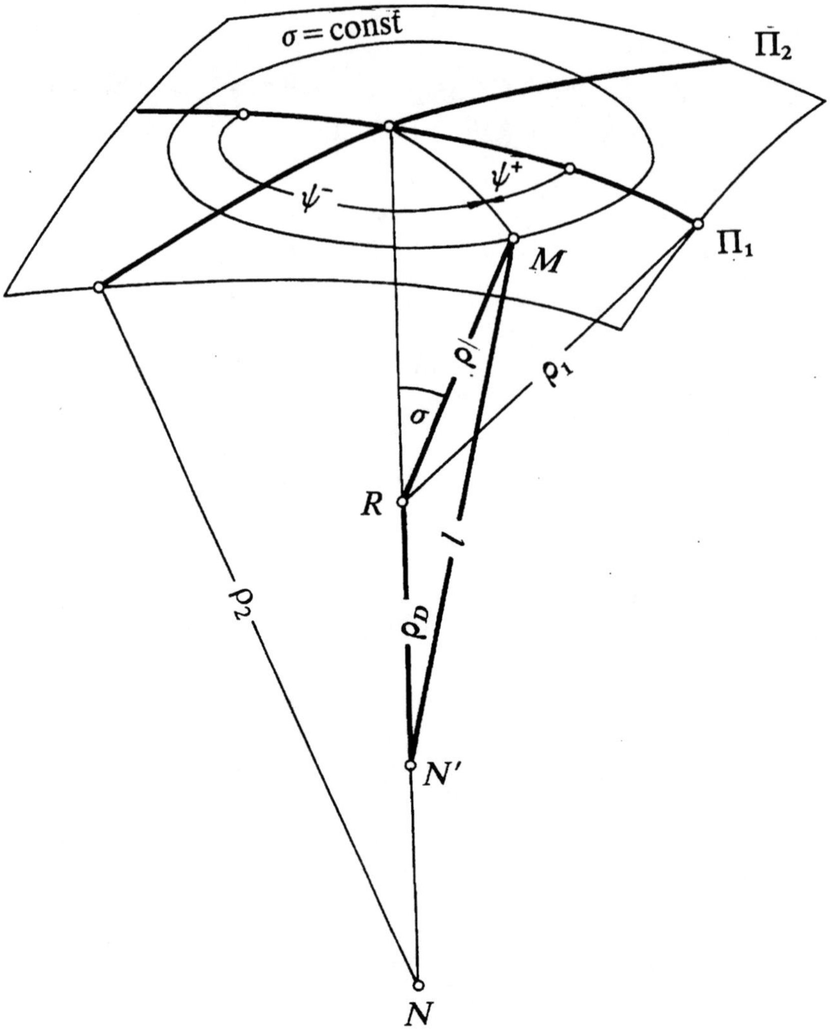

Figure 100. Edge-diffracted wavefront in the neighborhood of the central ray. *N* ***– source.*** *R* ***– tip.*** *N'* ***– center of curvature of the wavefront cross section by the plane*** $\psi^{\pm}$ = const. Π_1 ***and*** Π_2 ***– traces of the principle planes.***

where ρ is the distance from the tip, and $\rho_D = \rho_D(\psi^{\pm})$ is the distance between the tip and the center of curvature $\ell = 0$. Upon substituting equation (F.3) into (F.2) and differentiating we find

$$\left[\, \partial^2 \tau_{mn}(\tau_{mnp}, \psi^{\pm}, \sigma)/\partial\sigma^2 \,\right]_{\sigma=0} = -\, c_m^{-1}\, \rho\, \rho_D/(\rho + \rho_D)\,, \tag{F.4}$$

where τ_{mnp} is the traveltime along the trajectory "source – tip – observation point."

Let us consider this expression. When $\sigma = 0$, we have

$$\ell = \rho + \rho_D,\ \rho_1 = \rho,\ \rho_2 = \rho + \rho^*,\ \rho^* = (\rho_D)_{|\psi^{\pm}| = \pi/2}\ . \tag{F.5}$$

By substituting equations (F.5) into (F.1) and solving the result relative to ρ_D we get

$$\rho_D = \rho\,\rho^*\,\sin^2\psi^{\pm} \times (\rho + \rho^*\cos^2\psi^{\pm})^{-1}\ . \tag{F.6}$$

By substituting equation (F.6) into (F.4) we have

$$\left[\partial^2\tau_{mn}(\tau_{mnp},\psi^{\pm},\sigma)/\partial\sigma^2\right]_{\sigma=0} = -\,c_m^{-1}\,\rho\,\rho^*\,\sin^2\psi^{\pm} \times (\rho + \rho^*)^{-1} =$$
$$= \sin^2\psi^{\pm} \times \left[\partial^2\tau_{mn}(\tau_{mnp},\psi_L,\sigma)/\partial\sigma^2\right]_{\sigma=0} \text{ with } \psi_L = \pi/2$$
$$\text{or } \psi_L = -\,\pi/2\,. \tag{F.7}$$

By substituting equation (F.7) into equation IX.2(33) we obtain

$$A = \sin^2\psi^{\pm}\ . \tag{F.8}$$

Note, this expression does not depend on the curvature of the incident wave front. Therefore, it is valid in the case of diffraction of the plane wave, too.

REFERENCES

Abramowitz, M. and Stegun, I. A., 1972, Handbook of Mathematical Functions: U.S. Government Printing Office, Washington, DC.

Achenback, J. D., Gautesen, A. K., and McMaken, H., 1980, Application of ray theory to diffraction of elastic waves by cracks in acoustic, electromagnetic and elastic wave scattering – Focus on the T-matrix approach: Pergamon Press, New York, 355-371.

Aizenberg, A. M., 1982, Scattering of seismic waves by broken edge of a flat boundary: Soviet Geol. Geophys., **23**, 5, 74-82.

Aizenberg, A. M. and Klem-Musatov, K. D., 1980, Calculation of wave fields by the method of superposition of the edge waves: Soviet Geol. Geophys., **21**, 6, 79-94.

Babich, V. M. and Alekseyev, A. S., 1958, A ray method of computing wave front intensities: Bull. Acad. Sci. USSR, Geophys. Ser., **1**, 9-15.

Babich, V. M. and Buldyrev, V. S., 1972, Asymptotic methods in problems of diffraction of short waves: Nauka, Moscow (in Russian).

Bakker, P. M., 1990, Theory of edge diffraction in terms of dynamic ray tracing: Geophys. J. Int., **102**, 177-189.

Ben-Menahem, A. and Beydoun, W. B., 1985, Range of validity of seismic ray and beam methods in general inhomogeneous media – I. General theory: Geophys. J. Roy. Astr. Soc., **82**, 207-234.

Berryhill, J. F., 1977, Diffraction response for non-zero separation of source and receiver: Geophysics, **42**, 1158-1176.

Born, M. and Wolf, E., 1968, Principles of optics: Pergamon Press, Oxford.

Borovikov, V. A. and Kinber, B. E., 1978, Geometrical theory of diffraction: Svjaz (in Russian).

Červený, V., 1985a, Gaussian beam synthetic seismograms: J. Geophys., **58**, 44-72.

———, 1985b, The application of ray tracing to the propagation of shear waves in complex media *in* Handbook of geophysical exploration: 15a, Geophysical Press, London-Amsterdam.

Červený, V., Molotkov, I. A., and Pšenčik, I., 1977, Ray method in seismology: Universita Karlova, Praha.

Druzhinin, A. B., 1988, Kinematic law of diffraction on the ridge in anisotropic medium: Soviet Geol. Geophys., **29**, 12, 119-122 (in Russian).

Druzhinin, A. B., 1990, Edge waves in anisotropic medium: Soviet Geol. Geophys., **31**, 3, 118-128 (in Russian).

Druzhinin, A. B. and Aizenberg, A. M., 1990, Paraxial asymptotics of elastodynamical equations for axially symmetric inhomogeneous anisotropic medium: Soviet Geol. Geophys., **6**, 129-138.

Felsen, L. B. and Marcuvitz, N., 1973, Radiation and scattering of waves: New Jersey, Prentice-Hall, Englewood Cliffs.

Fertig, J. and Muller, G., 1979, Approximate diffraction theory for transparant half-planes with application to seismic-wave diffraction at coal seams: J. Geophys., **46**, 349-367.

Fock, V. A., 1965, Electromagnetic diffraction and propagation problems: New York, Pergamon Press.

Frank, Ph. and Mises, R., 1935, Die Differential -und Integralgleihungen der Mechanik und Physic: 2 Aufl., Braunschweig.

Frazer, L. N., 1987, Synthetic seismograms using multifold path integrals – I. Theory: Geoph. J. Roy. Astr. Soc., **88**, 621-646.

Frazer, L. N. and Sen, M. K., 1985, Kirchhoff-Helmholtz reflection seismograms in a latterally inhomogeneous multi-layered elastic medium – I. Theory: Geoph. J. Roy. Astr. Soc., **80**, 121-147.

Frøyland, L. A., Helle, H. B., Riste, P. and Sandø, I., 1988, A study of detectability and resolution of a complex structure by seismic survey modelling and synthetic data processing: Norsk Hydro A/S, Bergen (Norway).

Grad, M., 1979, Dynamic properties of diffracted waves in the Earth's crust models: Acta Geophysica Polonica, **27**, 4, 355-367.

Hanyga, A., 1989, Boundary effects in asymptotic diffraction theory: Seismol, Obsv., Univ. Bergen, Seismo-Ser., 35, 36, 37.

Hilterman, F., 1970, Three-dimensional seismic modeling: Geophysics, **35**, 1020-1037.

———, 1982, Interpretative lessons from three-dimensional modeling: Geophysics, **47**, 784-808.

Hönl, H., Maue, A. W., and Westpfahl, K., 1961, Theorie der Beugung: Springer-Verlag, Berlin-Göttingen-Heidelberg.

Hron, F., Daley, P. F., Berkes, Z., Chan, R., and Zheng, B. S., 1985, Annual Report of the Institute of Earth and Planetary Physics of the University of Alberta: Edmonton, Alberta, Canada, 20-21.

Hron, F., Chan, R., and Zheng, B. S., 1987, Annual Report of the University of Earth and Planetary Physics of the University of Alberta: Edmonton, Alberta, Canada, 20-21.

Janke, E., and Emde, F., 1945, Tables of functions: Dover Publ.

Karal, F. C., and Keller, J. B., 1959, Elastic wave propagation in homogeneous and inhomogeneous media: J. Acoust. Soc. Am., **31**, 694-705.

Keller, J. B., 1962, A geometrical theory of diffraction: J. Opt. Soc. Am. **52**, 116-130.

Klem-Musatov, K. D., Kovalevsky, G. L., and Tokmulina, L. R., 1972, On intensity of waves diffracted on the edge: Geologiya i Geopfizika, **5**, 82-92 (in Russian).

Klem-Musatov, K. D., Kovalevsky, G. L., and Chernyakov, V. G., 1975, On the spectrum and shape of diffracted waves: Soviet Geol. Geophys., **16**, No. 9, 86-94.

Klem-Musatov, K. D., Kovalevsky, G. L., and Chernyakov, V. G., and Maksimov, L. G., 1975, Mathematical modeling of diffraction of seismic waves in angular regions: Soviet Geol. Geophys., **16**, No. 11, 88-97.

Klem-Musatov, K. D., and Tatarnikov, M. A., 1976, On intensity of diffracted waves in inhomogeneous medium: Soviet Geol. Geophys., **17**, No. 8, 78-82.

Klem-Musatov, K. D., Kovalevsky, G. L., and Chernyakov, V. G., 1976, Seismic anomalies associated with local disturbances: Soviet Geol. Geophys., **17**, No. 12, 103-121.

Klem-Musatov, K. D., Aizenberg, A. M., and Klem-Musatova, G. A., 1982, An algorithm for mathematical modeling of three-dimensional diffraction fields: Soviet Geol. Geophys., **23**, No. 6, 116-121.

Klem-Musatov, K. D., and Aizenberg, A. M., 1985, Seismic modeling by methods of the theory of edge waves: J. Geophys., **57**, 90-105.

———, 1989, the edge wave superposition method (2-D scalar problem): Geophys. J. Int., **99**, 351-367.

Kouyoumjian, R. G., Pathak, P. H., and Burnside, W. D., 1980, The uniform geometrical theory of diffraction and its application to electromagnetic radiation and scattering *in* Acoustic, electromagnetic and elastic wave scattering – Focus on the T-matrix approach: Pergamon Press, 373-397.

Kovalevsky, G. L., 1971, Kinematic and some dynamic features of diffracted seismic waves: Geologiya i Geopfizika, **7**, 101-110 (in Russian).

———, 1973, Kinematic and dynamic features of head-diffracted seismic waves on faults in real media: Geologiya i Geopfizika, **3**, 71-85 (in Russian).

Kovalevsky, G. L., Lokzik, V. V., and Averko, E. M., 1971, On dynamic features of diffracted seismic waves: Geologiya i Geopfizika, **5**, 89-99 (in Russian).

Kozak, J., and Wanieck, L., 1975, Wave phenomena on blocks a-schlieren model study: Studia geoph. et geod., **19**.

Landa, E. I., and Mitrophanov, G. M., 1979, Estimation of parameters of small throw faults by seismograms of CDP: Bull. Acd. Sci. USSR, Earth's Physics Ser., **7**, 34-41.

Landa, E. I., and Maksimov, L. A., 1980, Sampling of algorithm of distinguishing the low-amplitude faults: Soviet Geol. Geophys., **21**, No. 12, 108-113.

Landa, E., Shtivelman, V., and Gelchinsky, B., 1987, A method for detection of diffracted waves on common-offset sections: Geophys. Prosp., **35**, 359-373.

Lunyova, M. N., 1984, Mathematical modeling of wave fields by method of superposition of the edge waves in the method of alternating waves of earthquakes: Pacific Geology, **4**, 103-114 (in Russian).

———, 1988, Specific features of waves passing through a curvilinear interface in the method of alternating waves of earthquakes: Pacific Geology, **4**, 114-121 (in Russian).

Lunyova, M. N., and Kharlamov, S. M., 1990, Parallel physical and mathematical modeling of waves passing through the complex interface: Soviet Geol. Geophys., **31**, No. 2, 103-109 (in Russian).

Malyshkin, O. V., 1990a, Algorithm of mathematical modeling of diffraction wave fields in sectorial media (two-dimensional acoustic case): Geologiya i Geopfizika, **10**, 72-81.

Malyshkin, O. V., 1990b, A method of encoding reflected transmitted waves in the wedging-out bed structures: All-Union Institute of Scientific and Technical Information BNHNTN, number 5478-B90, Deposited 24.10.90 (in Russian).

Malyuzhinetz, G. D., 1951, Some generalizations of method of reflections in theory of diffraction of sinusoidal waves, Doctorate thesis, Acd. Sci. USSR, Physical Institut (in Russian).

———, 1955, Radiation of sound by oscillating faces of an arbitrary wedge: Akustich. zh. **1**, 2, 144-164 and **3**, 226-234 (in Russian).

———, 1958, The formula of inversion for the Sommerfeld integral: Dokl. Akad. Nauk USSR, **118**, No. 6, 1099-1102 (in Russian).

———, 1959, Development in our concepts of diffraction phenomena: Sov. Phys. Uspekhi, **69**, 749-758 (in Russian).

Mikhailenko, B. G., 1979, Method of solution of dynamic problems of seismology for two-dimensional inhomogeneous models of media: Dokl. Akad. Nauk USSR, **246**, No. 1, 47-51 (in Russian).

———, 1988, Seismic fields in complex media (Atlas of snap-shots and synthetic seismograms): Acad. Sci. USSR, Siberian Division, Computing Center, Novosibirsk (in Russian).

Muskhelishwily, N. I., 1968, Singular integral equations: Nauka, Moscow (in Russian).

Obolentseva, I. R., and Klem-Musatova, G. A., 1986, Polarization characteristics of *PS* alternating waves reflected from the boundaries disturbed by the series of parallel faults: Soviet Geol. Geophys., **27**, 2, (in Russian).

———, 1986, Polarization of reflected alternating waves of *PS*-type in the case of the boundary breaked by intersecting faults: Soviet Geol. Geophys., **27**, 4, 89-97 (in Russian).

Pajchel, J., Helle, H. B., and Frøyland, L. A., 1988, Computation of seismic edge diffractions by the theory of edge waves: Norsk Hydro A/S, Research Centre, Bergen (Norway).

Pajchel, J., Helle, H. B., and Frøyland, L. A., 1989, The theory of edge waves applied to the modeling of seismic diffraction in VSP: EAEG 1989, Paper No. C-39, Berlin.

Starobinetz, A. E., 1988, Detection and interpretation of diffracted and quasi-diffracted waves: Nedra, Moscow (in Russian).

Trorey, A. W., 1970, A simple theory for seismic diffraction: Geophysics, **35**, 762-784.

———, 1977, Diffractions for arbitrary source-receiver locations: Geophysics, **42**, 1177-1182.

Tuzhilin, A. A., 1963, New representation of diffraction fields in wedge-shaped regions with ideal boundaries: Akustich, zh., **9**, No. 2,209-214 (in Russian).

Ufimtsev, P. J., 1965, Transverse diffusion in diffraction on a wedge: Radiotekhnika i elektronika: **10**, No. 6, 1013-1022 (in Russian).

Young, Th, 1802, On the theory of light and colors: Philos. Trans. Roy. Soc. London, **91**, No. 1, 12-48.

Zhu, T., 1988, A ray-Kirchhoff method for body-wave calculations in inhomogeneous media: Theory: Geophys. J., **92**, 181-193.